£2-50

AP

G000273006

ADVANCED LEVEL
APPLIED
MATHEMATICS

C. G. LAMBE B.A., Ph.D.

*Formerly Associate Professor of Mathematics,
Royal Military College of Science, Shrivenham*

HODDER AND STOUGHTON
LONDON   SYDNEY   AUCKLAND   TORONTO

ISBN 0 340 04509 4

First printed 1953
Reprinted 1955, 1957, 1959, 1960, 1962 (with corrections)
1964 (with corrections), 1966 (with corrections)
Second edition 1969
Third edition 1970
Reprinted 1971 (with corrections)
Reprinted 1973 (with corrections)
Reprinted 1977, 1978, 1980

Filmset by Keyspools Ltd, Golborne, Lancs.
Printed in Great Britain for
Hodder and Stoughton Educational,
a division of Hodder and Stoughton Ltd,
Mill Road, Dunton Green, Sevenoaks, Kent, by
Biddles Ltd, Guildford, Surrey

GENERAL EDITOR'S FOREWORD

SIR GRAHAM SUTTON, C.B.E., D.Sc., LL.D., F.R.S.

THE present volume is one of a series on physics and mathematics, for the upper forms at school and the first year at the university. The books have been written by a team of experienced teachers at the Royal Military College of Science, where, among other things, students are prepared for London (External) Degrees in Natural Science and Engineering. The series therefore forms an integrated course of study based on many years experience in the teaching of physics and mathematics.

In preparing their manuscripts the writers have been mainly guided by the examination syllabuses of London University, the Joint Board of Oxford and Cambridge and the Joint Matriculation Board, but they have also taken a broad view of their tasks and have endeavoured to produce works which aim to give a student that solid foundation without which it is impossible to proceed to higher studies. The books are suitable either for class teaching or self-study; there are many illustrative examples and large collections of problems for solution taken, in the main, from recent examination papers.

It is a truism too often forgotten in teaching that knowledge is acquired by a student only when his interest is aroused and maintained. The student must not only be shown how a class of problems in mathematics is solved but, within limits, why a particular method works and, in physics, why a technique is especially well adapted for some particular measurement. Throughout the series special emphasis has been laid on illustrations which may be expected to appeal to the experience of the student in matters of daily life, so that his studies are related to what he sees, feels and knows of the world around him. Treated in this way, science ceases to be an arid abstraction and becomes vivid and real to the inquiring mind.

The books have therefore been written, not only to ensure the passing of examinations, but as a preparation for the exciting world which lies ahead of the reader. They incorporate many of the suggestions which have been made in recent years by other teachers and, it is hoped, will bring some new points of view into the classroom and the study. Last, but by no means least, they have been written by a team working together, so that the exchange of ideas has been constant and vigorous. It is to be hoped that the result is a series which is adequate for all examinations at this level and yet broad enough to satisfy the intellectual needs of teachers and students alike.

O. G. SUTTON

PREFACE TO THE FIRST EDITION

THIS book includes under the heading of Applied Mathematics the subjects of Statics, Dynamics, Hydrostatics and Statistics. It covers the requirements in these subjects for the General Certificate of Education at the Advanced level of the various examining boards, the London University Intermediate examination and the Cambridge Qualifying examination.

I have assumed that the student reading this book will have had some instruction, possibly in a practical way, in elementary mechanics, so that the ideas of force, energy, etc., will not be completely unfamiliar to him. I have also assumed a working knowledge of the elements of the calculus.

It is customary nowadays to teach Statics and Dynamics as one subject, but in a book of this nature I felt that it would be more convenient for reference if the subjects were grouped separately, and this is not to be taken as advocating the teaching of the subjects in isolation.

An elementary treatment of vectors is given in an appendix. The increasing use of vectors in more advanced work makes it desirable that the student at the Intermediate level should have some acquaintance with their chief characteristics. Vectors are, however, an abstraction from such quantities as forces, velocities, etc., and it would be a psychological mistake to consider the abstraction before one is familiar with the reality from which it comes. A teacher may, however, find it convenient to introduce the subject of vectors gradually when he feels that the student is ready for it.

It is hoped that the section on Statistics will not be considered out of place in this book, and an attempt has been made to link up the treatment of sets of numbers with ideas of centres of gravity and moments of inertia.

I wish to express my thanks to colleagues and friends at the Royal Military College of Science for many helpful suggestions made during the preparation of this book. I am also indebted to Dr. E. T. Davies, Professor of Mathematics, University of Southampton, Dr. D. R. Dickinson, Senior Mathematics Master, Bristol Grammar School, Mr. H. K. Prout, Head of the Department of Mathematics, Royal Naval College, Dartmouth, and Mr. G. R. Sisson, Head of the Department of Mathematics, Royal Military Academy, Sandhurst, who have read parts of the manuscript and offered constructive criticisms.

For permission to use questions set in various examinations I wish to thank the Syndics of the Cambridge University Press, the Senate of the University of London, the Oxford and Cambridge Schools Examination Board, and the Joint Matriculation Board.

I also thank the Controller of H.M. Stationery Office for permission to use questions set in Civil Service examinations.

C. G. LAMBE

PREFACE TO THE SECOND EDITION

IN this edition some changes have been made to keep in line with modern trends in Applied Mathematics and with actual or pending changes in the A-level syllabus.

The new opening chapter deals with Vectors, at first in an elementary way but going on to vectors in three-dimensional space, scalar and vector products and vector equations of straight lines, planes, curves and surfaces.

A new chapter (Chapter 21) on Mathematical Methods has been inserted which deals with the formation and solution of algebraic and differential equations applicable to simple physical situations and also discusses some further topics in Statics and Dynamics.

In view of the national change to metric units the Système International (SI) has been introduced, and a conversion table from other units has been included. Many exercises have been changed and added so that the student can gain experience of working with metric units.

To save space, the short chapter on compressible fluids has been omitted.

PREFACE TO THE THIRD EDITION

IN this edition there has been a complete change-over to SI units, which are now mandatory for all A-level examinations, and all the exercises and examples in this book have been reworked in these units.

C. G. LAMBE

The source of examples and exercises is indicated by the following symbols:

CS.   Civil Service Examinations.

L.U.   London University Intermediate and Certificate Examinations.

N.U.   Northern Universities' Certificate Examinations.

O.C.   Oxford and Cambridge Joint Board Certificate Examinations.

Q.E.   Mechanical Sciences Tripos Qualifying Examination.

CONTENTS

I VECTOR ANALYSIS
CHAPTER 1

II STATICS
CHAPTER 2

CHAPTER 3

CHAPTER 4

CHAPTER 5

CHAPTER 6

CHAPTER 7

CHAPTER 8

PART I—VECTOR ANALYSIS

CHAPTER 1

VECTORS

1.1 Introductory

In Statics and Dynamics it is necessary to establish theorems concerning the compounding and resolution of forces, velocities, accelerations and other quantities. Much repetition is avoided by showing that these are all vector quantities which can be represented by a straight line segment or vector, and proving some general theorems for vectors as such. The use of vector symbols also leads to compactness which is of great value in more advanced parts of applied mathematics.

The theorems on vectors constitute a sort of algebra with rules similar to those of ordinary algebra and in the first part of this chapter we shall describe the notation used for vectors and establish the basic theorems of vector algebra. This should be a sufficient introduction to the subject for a student meeting vectors for the first time.

Study of the second part of the chapter on vectors may well be delayed until the student has become familiar with their use in Statics and Dynamics. In this part the three-dimensional components of a vector are considered and used in scalar and vector products. Here also vectors are differentiated and integrated and straight lines, planes and curves are represented by vectors containing one or more scalar parameters.

1.2 Definition of a Vector

A *vector* is a straight line of a given magnitude drawn in a given direction in a given sense.

If I walk 5 kilometres due East and then 4 kilometres due North-East, my displacement can be shown diagrammatically. A line AB of length 5 cm drawn parallel to the top of the page represents the displacement to the East, and a line BC of length 4 cm inclined at 45° to AB produced represents the second displacement (Fig. 1).

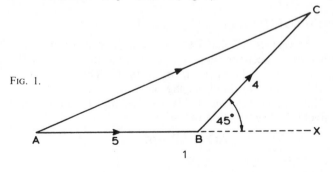

Fig. 1.

Here the lines AB and BC are vectors. They are marked with arrows in the diagram to show their sense, that is that they are drawn from A to B and from B to C rather than the reverse. The sense of a vector is usually indicated by the order of the letters and this is sometimes confirmed by an arrow. Thus we may write the above vectors as

$$\overrightarrow{AB} \text{ and } \overrightarrow{BC}.$$

Times bold type is used to denote a vector. Thus we may write a vector as **AB**, or it may be referred to by a single letter such as **a**. In written work it is convenient to underline the letters, writing $\underline{AB}$ or $\underline{a}$.

The magnitude of a vector is called its *modulus*. Thus the modulus of the vector **AB** is the length AB, which is 5. The modulus of a vector **a** is denoted by the letter a (in italics) or by $|a|$. The *direction* of a vector may be given (in two-dimensional work) as its inclination to a fixed direction. Thus the direction of the vector **BC** (Fig. 1) is 45° measured in a counter-clockwise direction from AX. In three dimensional work (see §1.10) the *direction cosines* of the line are used to specify its direction. The vector whose direction is that of a given vector **a** and whose modulus is unity is called the *unit vector* in the direction of **a** and is denoted by the symbol **â**.

A vector as such is not considered as having any definite location and equal and parallel vectors are equivalent. Thus the statement **a** = **b** means that the vectors **a** and **b** are equal in magnitude, are parallel, and are in the same sense. A vector **AB** may, however, be drawn from a fixed point A and obviously gives the displacement of the point B from the point A. Such a vector is called a *position vector* with respect to A, this being an example of a localised vector.

When dealing with vectors one refers to ordinary numbers, that is numbers not associated with a direction, as *scalars*. The effect of multiplying a vector by a scalar is to alter its magnitude while leaving its direction unaltered; the sense is altered if the scalar is negative. Thus 2**AB** is a vector whose direction is the same as that of **AB** but whose modulus is twice that of **AB**. Hence, since **â** has unit modulus, a**â** is, in fact, merely an alternative way of writing **a**. Thus **a** = a**â**.

1.3 Addition of Vectors

In Fig. 1 the vectors **AB** and **BC** represent displacements to the East and North-East respectively and it is clear that the result of the two displacements is a displacement from A to C. Thus the vector **AC** represents the total or resultant displacement.

AC is called the *vector sum* of **AB** and **BC** and by an analogy with ordinary algebraical summation we write

$$AC = AB + BC. \tag{1.1}$$

The vector sum of two vectors is thus defined as the third side of a triangle of which the given vectors are two sides. By measurement on an accurate diagram it will be found that $AC = 8{\cdot}32$ cm and angle $CAB = 19° 52'$. This gives the magnitude, direction and sense of **AC** and shows that the resultant displacement is $8{\cdot}32$ kilometres in a direction E $19° 52'$ N.

If an additional vector **CD** is drawn from C (Fig. 2) it is easily seen that

$$\begin{aligned} \mathbf{AD} &= \mathbf{AC} + \mathbf{CD} \\ &= \mathbf{AB} + \mathbf{BC} + \mathbf{CD}. \end{aligned} \tag{1.2}$$

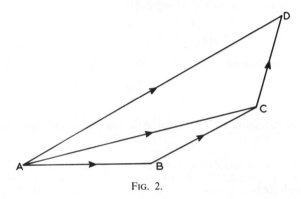

Fig. 2.

Thus any number of vectors can be summed by placing them end to end and their sum is the vector drawn from A to close the polygon that they form.

1.4 Calculation of the Sum of Two Vectors

Let **AB** be a vector whose modulus is AB and whose direction makes an angle α with a fixed direction AX; let **BC** have modulus BC and be inclined at an angle β to AX (Fig. 3). Then the angle between the positive

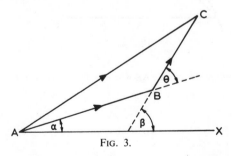

Fig. 3.

directions of the vectors is θ, where $\theta = \beta - \alpha$, and θ is an external angle of the triangle ABC.

Applying the cosine rule to the triangle ABC, we have

$$AC^2 = AB^2 + BC^2 - 2AB \cdot BC \cdot \cos ABC,$$

and, since $\cos ABC = \cos(180° - \theta) = -\cos\theta$,

$$AC^2 = AB^2 + BC^2 + 2AB \cdot BC \cdot \cos\theta. \tag{1.3}$$

This gives the modulus AC of the vector $\mathbf{AC}$. The positive sign of the term containing $\cos\theta$ should be noted.

Applying the sine rule to the triangle ABC we have

$$\frac{BC}{\sin CAB} = \frac{AC}{\sin ABC}$$

and hence, since $\sin ABC = \sin(180° - \theta) = \sin\theta$,

$$\sin CAB = \frac{BC \sin\theta}{AC}. \tag{1.4}$$

This gives the direction of the vector $\mathbf{AC}$, since its inclination to AX is $\alpha + CAB$.

Example 1. *ABC is an equilateral triangle. A vector of modulus 3 has the direction of the side AB and a vector of modulus 2 has the direction of BC. Find the sum of these vectors.*
Let the side AB have length 3 units (Fig. 4); mark off D on BC so that $BD = 2$ units.

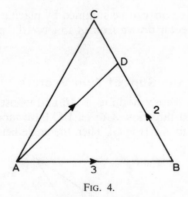

FIG. 4.

Then $\mathbf{AD}$ is the sum of the vectors $\mathbf{AB}$ and $\mathbf{BD}$. By the cosine rule

$$AD^2 = 3^2 + 2^2 - 2 \cdot 3 \cdot 2 \cdot \cos 60° = 7,$$

giving

$$AD = 2·646 \text{ units}.$$

By the sine rule

$$\frac{\sin DAB}{2} = \frac{\sin 60°}{2·646}.$$

Hence

$$\sin DAB = \frac{1 \cdot 732}{2 \cdot 646} = 0 \cdot 6545,$$

and

$$DAB = 40° 53'.$$

Thus the sum has modulus 2·646 and is inclined at an angle 40° 53' to *AB*.

1.5 Vector Algebra

We have used the summation sign of algebra to indicate the vector sum of vectors. This usage can be justified by showing that this kind of summation obeys the laws of ordinary algebraical summation.

The *commutative law* of algebra states that the order in which two quantities are summed is irrelevant, that is $a+b = b+a$. This law holds

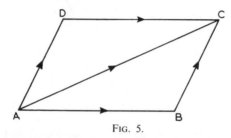

FIG. 5.

for vector summation. Let **AB** and **BC** be two vectors and **AC** their vector sum (Fig. 5). Complete the parallelogram *ABCD*. Then since opposite sides of a parallelogram are equal and parallel the vectors **AD** and **BC** have the same modulus and direction, and so have the vectors **AB** and **DC**. That is **AD** = **BC**, **DC** = **AB**. Now by vector addition

$$\mathbf{AC} = \mathbf{AB} + \mathbf{BC} \quad \text{and} \quad \mathbf{AC} = \mathbf{AD} + \mathbf{DC}.$$

Hence, replacing **AD** and **DC** in the second equation, we have

$$\mathbf{AB} + \mathbf{BC} = \mathbf{BC} + \mathbf{AB}.$$

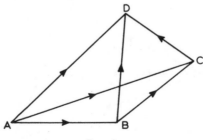

FIG. 6.

The *associative law* of algebra states that $a + (b + c) = (a + b) + c$, where the quantities in brackets are added first. This also holds for vector summation. From Fig. 6 it is easily seen that

$$\mathbf{AD} = \mathbf{AB} + (\mathbf{BC} + \mathbf{CD}) = (\mathbf{AB} + \mathbf{BC}) + \mathbf{CD}.$$

Subtraction is included in vector algebra by defining the vector $-\mathbf{b}$ as a vector whose modulus and direction is the same as that of $\mathbf{b}$ but which is drawn in the opposite sense to $\mathbf{b}$. Then

$$\mathbf{a} - \mathbf{b} = \mathbf{a} + (-\mathbf{b}).$$

The vectors $\mathbf{a} + \mathbf{b}$ and $\mathbf{a} - \mathbf{b}$ are shown in Fig. 7.

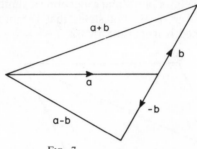

FIG. 7.

The student may also wish to verify that the associative and distributive laws of algebraical multiplication apply to the multiplication of vectors by scalar quantities. Thus if m and n are scalars,

$$m(n\mathbf{a}) = n(m\mathbf{a}) = mn\mathbf{a},$$
$$(m + n)\mathbf{a} = m\mathbf{a} + n\mathbf{a},$$
$$n(\mathbf{a} + \mathbf{b}) = n\mathbf{a} + n\mathbf{b}.$$

Example 2. *Prove that, if λ and μ are positive scalar quantities, $\lambda\mathbf{AB} + \mu\mathbf{AC} = (\lambda + \mu)\mathbf{AD}$ where $\lambda\mathbf{DB} + \mu\mathbf{DC} = 0$.*

Since $\lambda\mathbf{DB} + \mu\mathbf{DC} = 0$ the directions of $\mathbf{DB}$ and $\mathbf{DC}$ must be the same but in opposite sense. Therefore D (Fig. 8) is a point on BC which divides BC in the ratio

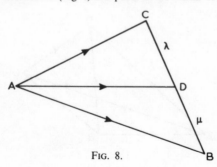

FIG. 8.

of λ to μ. Now $\mathbf{AB} = \mathbf{AD} + \mathbf{DB}$ and $\mathbf{AC} = \mathbf{AD} + \mathbf{DC}$, therefore

$$\lambda\mathbf{AB} = \lambda\mathbf{AD} + \lambda\mathbf{DB}, \quad \mu\mathbf{AC} = \mu\mathbf{AD} + \mu\mathbf{DC}.$$

Adding we have

$$\lambda\mathbf{AB} + \mu\mathbf{AC} = (\lambda+\mu)\mathbf{AD} + \lambda\mathbf{DB} + \mu\mathbf{DC}$$
$$= (\lambda+\mu)\mathbf{AD}.$$

1.6 Components of a Vector

Let $r = OP$ join the origin of coordinates to a point P whose coordinates are (x, y) (Fig. 9). The vector $\mathbf{r}$ is called the *position vector* of the point P. The angle POX is θ, where $\tan\theta = y/x$, and (r, θ) are the polar coordinates of P so that $x = r\cos\theta$, $y = r\sin\theta$ and $r^2 = x^2 + y^2$. Then

$$\mathbf{OP} = \mathbf{ON} + \mathbf{NP}, \tag{1.5}$$

where $\mathbf{ON}$ has modulus $x(=r\cos\theta)$ and direction OX and $\mathbf{NP}$ has modulus $y(=r\sin\theta)$ and direction OY. The vectors $\mathbf{ON}$ and $\mathbf{NP}$ are

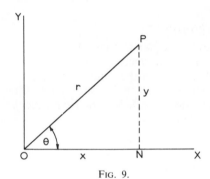

FIG. 9.

called the *components* of the vector $\mathbf{OP}$ in the directions OX and OY respectively and $\mathbf{OP}$ is the vector sum of its components.

A unit vector in the positive direction of the x-axis is denoted by the symbol i (italics) and a unit vector in the positive direction of the y-axis by j (italics). With this notation $\mathbf{ON} = xi$, $\mathbf{NP} = yj$, and the equation (1.5) becomes

$$\mathbf{r} = \mathbf{OP} = xi + yj. \tag{1.6}$$

Alternatively we may write

$$\mathbf{r} = r\cos\theta . i + r\sin\theta . j,$$

and, since the modulus r is a scalar quantity,

$$\mathbf{r} = r(i\cos\theta + j\sin\theta). \tag{1.7}$$

In this form the modulus r is shown as multiplying the unit vector $i \cos \theta + j \sin \theta$ which is $\hat{r}$. Thus, for example, a vector $\mathbf{r}$ whose modulus is 4 units and whose direction makes an angle of $30°$ with OX has components

$$4 \cos 30° = 3{\cdot}464, \ 4 \sin 30° = 2$$

and we may write

$$\mathbf{r} = 3{\cdot}464i + 2j.$$

If a vector is given in terms of its components, its modulus and direction are easily found. For example, let $\mathbf{r} = 3i + 4j$. Then

$$r^2 = 3^2 + 4^2 = 25,$$
$$r = 5,$$
$$\tan \theta = 4/3 = 1{\cdot}333$$
$$\theta = 53° \ 8'.$$

Thus $\mathbf{r}$ has modulus 5 units and its direction is inclined at $53° \ 8'$ to OX.

1.7 Addition by Components

When the sum of several coplanar vectors has to be found this is most easily done by expressing each vector as a sum of its components and adding the components. Since all the components parallel to a direction OX have the same direction their sum is obtained by simple addition, and similarly for the components parallel to the perpendicular direction OY.

Let the vectors to be summed be

$$\mathbf{r}_n = x_n i + y_n j$$

where $n = 1, 2, 3, \ldots$ Then

$$\mathbf{r}_1 + \mathbf{r}_2 + \mathbf{r}_3 + \ldots = (x_1 + x_2 + x_3 + \ldots)i + (y_1 + y_2 + y_3 + \ldots)j.$$

Thus if R is the modulus of the sum and θ its inclination to OX, we have

$$R = \sqrt{\{(x_1 + x_2 + x_3 + \ldots)^2 + (y_1 + y_2 + y_3 + \ldots)^2\}} \tag{1.8}$$

and

$$\tan \theta = \frac{y_1 + y_2 + y_3 + \ldots}{x_1 + x_2 + x_3 + \ldots} \tag{1.9}$$

Example 3. *Vectors whose moduli are 3, 4, 6 and 7 act in directions making angles $30°$, $90°$, $135°$ and $240°$ respectively with a direction OX. Find their sum.*

The vectors in terms of their components parallel to and perpendicular to OX are

$$3(i \cos 30° + j \sin 30°) = 2{\cdot}598i + 1{\cdot}5j,$$
$$4(i \cos 90° + j \sin 90°) = \qquad \ 4j,$$
$$6(i \cos 135° + j \sin 135°) = -4{\cdot}243i + 4{\cdot}243j,$$
$$7(i \cos 240° + j \sin 240°) = -3{\cdot}5i - 6{\cdot}062j.$$

Adding the components we find for the sum

$$\mathbf{R} = -5 \cdot 145 i + 3 \cdot 681 j.$$

Hence

$$R = \sqrt{\{5 \cdot 145^2 + 3 \cdot 681^2\}} = 6 \cdot 326,$$

and

$$\tan \theta = -\frac{3 \cdot 681}{5 \cdot 145} = -0 \cdot 7153,$$

$$\theta = 180° - 35° \ 34' = 144° \ 26'.$$

Thus the sum has modulus 6·33 and its direction makes an angle of 144° 26' with OX.

1.8 The Scalar Product of Two Vectors

The *scalar product* of two vectors $\mathbf{a}$ and $\mathbf{b}$ is defined as the *number* $ab \cos \theta$, where a and b are the moduli of the vectors and θ the angle between their direction. The scalar product is denoted by $\mathbf{a} \cdot \mathbf{b}$.

Since $\cos 0° = 1$ and $\cos 90° = 0$, it follows that the scalar product of parallel vectors is the product of their moduli and the scalar product of perpendicular vectors is zero. Perpendicularity of two vectors $\mathbf{a}$ and $\mathbf{b}$ is often proved by showing that their scalar product $\mathbf{a} \cdot \mathbf{b} = 0$ and this is probably the principal use of scalar products. For the unit vectors i and j

$$i.i = j.j = 1, \quad i.j = j.i = 0. \tag{1.10}$$

The square of a vector $\mathbf{a}$ is defined as $\mathbf{a} \cdot \mathbf{a}$ and written as $\mathbf{a}^2$, and we have $\mathbf{a}^2 = a^2$.

Since $b \cos \theta$ is the magnitude of the projection of the vector $\mathbf{b}$ on the direction of $\mathbf{a}$, the scalar product of two vectors is the product of the modulus of one and the projection of the modulus of the other on its line. Since the projection of the modulus of $\mathbf{b} + \mathbf{c}$ on any direction is sum of the projections of $\mathbf{b}$ and $\mathbf{c}$ on that direction, it follows that

$$\mathbf{a} \cdot (\mathbf{b} + \mathbf{c}) = \mathbf{a} \cdot \mathbf{b} + \mathbf{a} \cdot \mathbf{c},$$

and hence the distributive law of multiplication holds for scalar products. Hence

$$(x_1 i + y_1 j) \cdot (x_2 i + y_2 j)$$
$$= x_1 x_2 i^2 + y_1 y_2 j^2 + x_1 y_2 i.j + y_1 x_2 j.i$$
$$= x_1 x_2 + y_1 y_2,$$

when we use the relations (1.10). Therefore if θ is the angle between the directions of these two vectors, we have

$$\sqrt{(x_1^2 + y_1^2)} \sqrt{(x_2^2 + y_2^2)} \cos \theta = x_1 x_2 + y_1 y_2. \tag{1.11}$$

Example 4. *Find the angle between the directions of the vectors* $3i + 4j$ *and* $5i - 12j$.

Here

$$x_1{}^2 + y_1{}^2 = 25, \ x_2{}^2 + y_2{}^2 = 169,$$
$$x_1 x_2 + y_1 y_2 = -33,$$

so that, from (1.11)

$$5 \times 13 \times \cos \theta = -33,$$

giving

$$\cos \theta = -33/65 = -0.5077$$

and

$$\theta = 120° \ 31'.$$

1.9 Vector Quantities

A *vector quantity* is one that can be represented in magnitude and direction by a vector, and which is such that two or more such quantities can be added by vector summation. We have seen that displacement can be represented by a vector and the effect of two displacements is obtained by vector addition. Therefore displacement is a vector quantity.

Now velocity is defined (see §13.1) as displacement in unit time and the sum of two velocities is the sum of two displacements in unit time. Therefore velocity is a vector quantity.

Similarly, acceleration is defined (see §13.4) as change of velocity in unit time and the sum of two velocity changes can be obtained by vector addition. Therefore acceleration is a vector quantity.

The basic law of Dynamics is Newton's second law (see §15.3) $F = ma$ which states that force is the product of mass and acceleration. Since the mass is a scalar quantity this implies that the force has the same direction as the acceleration. Hence, since acceleration is a vector quantity so is force, and Newton's law can be written in vector form as

$$\mathbf{F} = m\mathbf{a}. \tag{1.12}$$

Strictly, this applies to forces acting on a particle of negligible dimensions and further consideration is necessary before applying this equation to a rigid body.

The implications of this important principle will be considered later. For the moment it is sufficient to note that the vectors we have been considering in this chapter may represent displacements, velocities, accelerations or forces acting on particles.

Example 5. *A bomb which is falling vertically with velocity* 200 *m/s explodes and breaks into fragments. Each fragment is given an additional velocity of* 100 *m/s in some direction by the explosion. Prove that the fragments continue to move downwards within a cone of semi-vertical angle* 30°.

Let a fragment be thrown in a direction inclined at θ to the downward vertical.

Let v be its new velocity inclined at an angle α to the downward vertical (Fig. 10); v is obtained by vector addition of the velocities of 200 m/s and 100 m/s. Then

$$v^2 = 200^2 + 100^2 + 2.200.100 \cos \theta,$$

giving

$$v = 100\sqrt{(5 + 4 \cos \theta)},$$

and

$$\sin \alpha = \frac{100}{v} \sin \theta = \frac{\sin \theta}{\sqrt{(5 + 4 \cos \theta)}}.$$

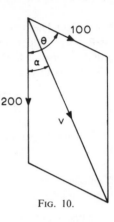

The maximum value of $\sin \alpha$ occurs when

$\cos \theta = -1/2$, $\theta = 120°$, and then

$$\sin \alpha = \frac{\sin 120°}{\sqrt{(5 - 2)}} = \frac{1}{2}.$$

Fig. 10.

Therefore, the maximum value of α is 30° and no fragment will deviate by more than 30° from the vertical.

EXERCISES 1 (a)

1. The medians of a triangle ABC meet at G. Prove that

$$\mathbf{AG} = \tfrac{1}{3}(\mathbf{AB} + \mathbf{AC}).$$

Hence show that $AG = \tfrac{1}{3}\sqrt{(2b^2 + 2c^2 - a^2)}$.

2. Express as a product of its modulus and a unit vector the sum of the vectors $i - 3j$, $3i + 3j$, $-3i + 4j$, $4(i + 2j)$.

3. If $\mathbf{OP} = i - 3j$ and $\mathbf{OQ} = 4i - 5j$, find the vector $\mathbf{PQ}$ and calculate its modulus. If $\mathbf{OR} = 4i + 5j$ and $\mathbf{OS} = 2i + 2j$ prove that $\mathbf{PQ}$ and $\mathbf{RS}$ are perpendicular.

4. If $\mathbf{OA} = ai + bj$, $\mathbf{OB} = ci + dj$, prove that the area of the triangle OAB is $\pm 0.5 (ad - bc)$.

5. Find the area of a triangle formed by the vectors $2i + 3j$, $3i + 4j$.

6. D, E, F are the mid-points of the sides BC, CA, AB of a triangle. Prove that $\mathbf{AD} + \mathbf{BE} + \mathbf{CF} = 0$.

7. Show that the triangle ABC, where A is the point $(5, 7)$, B is $(7, 4)$, C is $(8, 9)$, is right-angled at A and find its area.

8. If $\mathbf{a} + \mathbf{b} = a\hat{\mathbf{c}}$ and $\hat{\mathbf{a}}.\hat{\mathbf{c}} = 0$, show that $b = a\sqrt{2}$.

9. E and F are the mid-points of the diagonals AC and BD of a quadrilateral $ABCD$. Prove that $\mathbf{AB} + \mathbf{AD} + \mathbf{CB} + \mathbf{CD} = 4\mathbf{EF}$.

10. P is a point in the side BC of a triangle ABC and Q is another point. Prove that, if $\mathbf{AP} + \mathbf{PB} + \mathbf{PC} = \mathbf{PQ}$, $\mathbf{AB} = \mathbf{CQ}$.

11. In any triangle ABC, $\mathbf{CB} = \mathbf{AB} + \mathbf{CA}$. By squaring both sides of this equation prove that $BC^2 = CA^2 + AB^2 - 2CA.AB \cos A$.

12. $ABCD$ is a square. Prove that

$$3\mathbf{AB} + 4\mathbf{BC} + 5\mathbf{CD} + 8\mathbf{DA} + 3\mathbf{AC} = \mathbf{DB}.$$

13. The resultant of two intersecting forces P and $2P$ is $P\sqrt{3}$. Find the angle between the forces and the angle made by the resultant with the force of magnitude P.
(L.U.)

14. Forces 3,2,1,4 newton act at a point along the lines OA, OB, OC, OD respectively. $AOB = 60°$, $AOC = 150°$, $AOD = 270°$. Find the magnitude of the resultant and its inclination to OA.

15. $ABCDEF$ is a regular hexagon. Find the sum

$$4\mathbf{AB} + 5\mathbf{BD} + 2\mathbf{CD} + 3\mathbf{DE} + 6\mathbf{EF} + 3\mathbf{FA}.$$

16. $OABC$ is a square of side $2a$. i, j are unit vectors along OA, OC. The mid-point of AB is L; the mid-point of BC is M; OL, AM meet at P; BP meets OA at N. Show that the segment OP can be measured by the vector $\lambda(2ai + aj)$ and also by the vector $2ai + \mu(2aj - ai)$. Hence determine λ and μ. Prove that $ON = \frac{2}{3} OA$.
(O.C.)

17. Two unit vectors $\hat{\mathbf{a}}$ and $\hat{\mathbf{b}}$ are such that the line of action of $\hat{\mathbf{b}}$ makes an angle $+60°$ with the line of action of $\hat{\mathbf{a}}$. If $\mathbf{v}_1 = 2\hat{\mathbf{a}} - \hat{\mathbf{b}}$, $\mathbf{v}_2 = -\hat{\mathbf{a}} + 3\hat{\mathbf{b}}$ and $\mathbf{v}_3 = 3\hat{\mathbf{a}} + \hat{\mathbf{b}}$.

(i) find $\mathbf{v}_3$ in terms of $\mathbf{v}_1$ and $\mathbf{v}_2$,

(ii) prove that $2\mathbf{v}_1 + 2\mathbf{v}_2 + \mathbf{v}_3$ is of magnitude $5\sqrt{3}$.   (O.C.)

1.10 Directions in Three Dimensional Space

The position of a point P is given relative to three mutually perpendicular axes and origin O as (x, y, z) where x, y and z are the projections of OP on the axes, OX, OY and OZ respectively (Fig. 11).

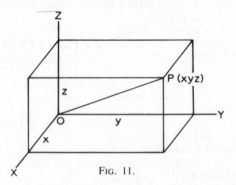

Fig. 11.

Let the inclinations of OP to the axes be α, β and γ, so that

$$P\hat{O}X = \alpha, \ P\hat{O}Y = \beta, \ P\hat{O}Z = \gamma.$$

Then

$$x = OP \cos\alpha, \ y = OP \cos\beta, \ z = OP \cos\gamma. \tag{1.13}$$

The quantities $\cos \alpha$, $\cos \beta$, $\cos \gamma$ are called the *direction-cosines* of the line OP and are usually denoted by the symbols l, m, n respectively, so that

$$l = \cos \alpha, \; m = \cos \beta, \; n = \cos \gamma. \tag{1.14}$$

and

$$x = OP \times l, \; y = OP \times m, \; z = OP \times n. \tag{1.15}$$

Now since OP is the diagonal of a rectangle with edges of lengths x, y and z,

$$OP^2 = x^2 + y^2 + z^2$$

and from (1.15)

$$x^2 + y^2 + z^2 = OP^2 (l^2 + m^2 + n^2)$$

it follows that

$$l^2 + m^2 + n^2 = 1. \tag{1.16}$$

This is an important property of direction-cosines that the sum of their squares is unity and when two of them are known the magnitude of the third can be found from (1.16). Frequently only the ratios of the direction-cosines are given and not their actual values; these are called *direction ratios* and if the direction ratios of a line are known its direction-cosines are easily deduced from (1.16).

Thus if the direction ratios of a line are $2:4:6$, we write $2^2 + 4^2 + 6^2 = 56$ and dividing each of the ratios by $\sqrt{(56)}$ we have the direction-cosines

$$\frac{2}{\sqrt{(56)}}, \frac{4}{\sqrt{(56)}}, \frac{6}{\sqrt{(56)}},$$

the sum of whose squares is obviously unity.

A negative value of a direction-cosine merely shows that the angle made by the line with the positive direction of the appropriate axis is greater than $90°$.

In the above the line OP has been taken, for simplicity, as passing through the origin. The direction-cosines of a line joining any two points $Q(x_1, y_1, z_1)$ and $R(x_2, y_2, z_2)$ are easily found. The projection of QR on the axes OX, OY, OZ are clearly $x_2 - x_1$, $y_2 - y_1$, $z_2 - z_1$ respectively and hence the direction ratios of QR are

$$x_2 - x_1 : y_2 - y_1 : z_2 - z_1.$$

Since

$$QR^2 = (x_2 - x_1)^2 + (y_2 - y_1)^2 + (z_2 - z_1)^2$$

the direction-cosines of the line QR are

$$\frac{x_2 - x_1}{QR}, \frac{y_2 - y_1}{QR}, \frac{z_2 - z_1}{QR}.$$

Notice that if a line lies wholly in the xy-plane its inclination to OZ is 90° and hence its direction-cosines can be taken as l, m, o, where $l^2 + m^2 = 1$.

1.11 Components of a Vector in Three Dimensions

The direction of a vector $\mathbf{r}$ of modulus r can be specified with respect to axes $OXYZ$ by its direction-cosines l, m, n. Then the components of the vector, which are its projections on the coordinate axes are

$$rl, rm, rn.$$

A unit vector in the positive direction of the z-axis is denoted by the symbol k (italics) so that in terms of the unit vectors i, j, k, the vector $\mathbf{r}$ can be written as the sum of its component vectors, that is

$$\mathbf{r} = rli + rmj + rnk, \tag{1.17}$$

or we may write

$$\mathbf{r} = r(li + mj + nk). \tag{1.18}$$

In this form the modulus r is shown as multiplying the unit vector $li + mj + nk$; this is clearly a unit vector since $l^2 + m^2 + n^2 = 1$.

If a vector is given in terms of its components its modulus and direction are easily found. For example let $\mathbf{r} = 2i - 3j + 6k$. Then $2 : -3 : 6$ are direction ratios of the vector and since $2^2 + 3^2 + 6^2 = 49 = 7^2$, the direction-cosines are $2/7, -3/7, 6/7$, and

$$\mathbf{r} = 7(\tfrac{2}{7}i - \tfrac{3}{7}j + \tfrac{6}{7}k)$$

Thus the vector has modulus 7 and direction-cosines as found.

1.12 Addition by Components

As in §1.7, the sum of several vectors is most easily found by summing their components.

Example 6. *Three forces acting on a particle are represented by the vectors $2i - 3j + 6k$, $i - 5j + k$, $i + 3j - 4k$, the units of force being newtons. Find the magnitude and direction of the resultant force.*

The sum of the three vectors is easily seen to be

$$4i - 5j + 3k$$

and since $4^2 + 5^2 + 3^2 = 50 = (5\sqrt{2})^2$, this may be written

$$5\sqrt{2}\left(\frac{4\sqrt{2}}{10}i - \frac{5\sqrt{2}}{10}j + \frac{3\sqrt{2}}{10}k\right)$$

so that the resultant has magnitude $5\sqrt{2}$ newtons and direction cosines $0{\cdot}4\sqrt{2}$, $-0{\cdot}5\sqrt{2}$, $0{\cdot}3\sqrt{2}$.

1.13 Scalar Products

The scalar product $\mathbf{a}.\mathbf{b}$ being defined as in §1.8 as the scalar quantity $ab\cos\theta$ we have in three-dimensions in addition to the relations (1.10)

$$k.k = 1, \quad i.k = j.k = 0 \tag{1.19}$$

so that

$$\begin{aligned}
(x_1i+y_1j&+z_1k).(x_2i+y_2j+z_2k) \\
&= x_1x_2i^2 + y_1y_2j^2 + z_1z_2k^2 \\
&= x_1x_2 + y_1y_2 + z_1z_2.
\end{aligned} \tag{1.20}$$

Hence, since the moduli of the two vectors are $(x_1{}^2+y_1{}^2+z_1{}^2)^{\frac{1}{2}}$ and $(x_2{}^2+y_2{}^2+z_2{}^2)^{\frac{1}{2}}$ the angle θ between the directions of the vectors is given by the equation

$$(x_1{}^2+y_1{}^2+z_1{}^2)^{\frac{1}{2}}(x_2{}^2+y_2{}^2+z_2{}^2)^{\frac{1}{2}}\cos\theta = x_1x_2+y_1y_2+z_1z_2.$$

In particular, the vectors $x_1i+y_1j+z_1k$ and $x_2i+y_2j+z_2k$ are perpendicular if

$$x_1x_2+y_1y_2+z_1z_2 = 0. \tag{1.21}$$

1.14 Vector Products

The *vector product* of two vectors $\mathbf{a}$ and $\mathbf{b}$ including an angle θ is denoted by the symbol $\mathbf{a} \times \mathbf{b}$ and is defined as
(1) a vector,
(2) whose modulus is $ab\sin\theta$,
(3) whose direction is perpendicular to the directions of both $\mathbf{a}$ and $\mathbf{b}$,
(4) whose sense is that in which a rotation of the vector $\mathbf{a}$ towards the vector $\mathbf{b}$ would drive a right-handed screw along the direction $\mathbf{a} \times \mathbf{b}$.
Suppose the time shown on a clock face is four o'clock and the minute hand is a vector $\mathbf{a}$ of modulus 7 in its direction while the hour hand is a vector $\mathbf{b}$ of modulus 6 in its direction. Then $ab\sin\theta = 7 \times 6 \times \sin 120°$ $= 21\sqrt{3}$.

A rotation of the minute hand towards the hour hand would drive a right-handed screw *into* the clock face. Hence $\mathbf{a} \times \mathbf{b}$ is a vector of modulus $21\sqrt{3}$ perpendicular to and into the clock face. It follows that $\mathbf{b} \times \mathbf{a}$ is a vector of the same modulus but in the opposite sense, so that

$$\mathbf{a} \times \mathbf{b} = -\mathbf{b} \times \mathbf{a}. \tag{1.22}$$

In particular we have

$$\begin{aligned}
i \times i &= j \times j = k \times k = 0, \\
i \times j &= k, \quad j \times k = i, \quad k \times i = j, \\
j \times i &= -k, \quad k \times j = -i, \quad i \times k = -j.
\end{aligned} \tag{1.23}$$

It can be seen that vector multiplication of two vectors obeys the associative and distributive laws of algebraic multiplication provided the order of letters in the products is not changed. Assuming this we have

$$
\begin{aligned}
(x_1 i + & y_1 j + z_1 k) \times (x_2 i + y_2 j + z_2 k) \\
= & x_1 x_2 i \times i + y_1 y_2 j \times j + z_1 z_2 k \times k \\
& + (x_1 y_2 i \times j + y_1 x_2 j \times i) + (y_1 z_2 j \times k + z_1 y_2 k \times j) \\
& + (z_1 x_2 k \times i + x_1 z_2 i \times k) \\
= & i(y_1 z_2 - z_1 y_2) + j(z_1 x_2 - x_1 z_2) + k(x_1 y_2 - y_1 x_2).
\end{aligned} \tag{1.24}
$$

This important formula can be written as a determinant:

$$
\begin{vmatrix}
i & j & k \\
x_1 & y_1 & z_1 \\
x_2 & y_2 & z_2
\end{vmatrix} \tag{1.25}
$$

Example 7. *Find the modulus and unit vector of the vector product of the vectors* $\mathbf{a} = 2i - 3j + 6k$ *and* $\mathbf{b} = i - 5j + 4k$.

The vector product is

$$
\mathbf{a} \times \mathbf{b} = \begin{vmatrix}
i & j & k \\
2 & -3 & 6 \\
1 & -5 & 4
\end{vmatrix}
$$

$$
\begin{aligned}
&= i\{(-3 \times 4) - (-5 \times 6)\} + j\{6 \times 1 - 2 \times 4\} + k\{2 \times (-5) - 1 \times (-3)\} \\
&= 18i - 2j - 7k \\
&= \sqrt{(377)}\left\{\frac{18}{\sqrt{(377)}}i - \frac{2}{\sqrt{(377)}}j - \frac{7}{\sqrt{(377)}}k\right\}
\end{aligned}
$$

Hence the modulus is $\sqrt{(377)}$ and the quantity in brackets is the unit vector.

In more advanced work certain quantities used in Dynamics, such as the moment of a force about an axis and the velocity due to a rotation can be expressed as vector products.

1.15 Derivative of a Vector

A vector may be a function of a scalar quantity such as the time t. Thus the vector

$$
\mathbf{a} = it^2 + jt
$$

will vary both in magnitude and direction with t. We can obtain the differential coefficient of such a vector with respect to the time and this differential coefficient, itself a vector, will give the rate of change of both magnitude and direction of the original vector.

Let $\mathbf{r} = \mathbf{OP}$ be a vector drawn from a fixed point O (Fig. 12) and varying with the time so that at time t OP is its magnitude and the direction of OP its direction. Let $\mathbf{OP}'$ be the magnitude and direction of the vector at time $t + \delta t$.

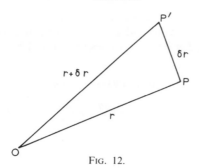

FIG. 12.

If we denote the vector $\mathbf{OP'}$ by $\mathbf{r} + \delta\mathbf{r}$ then by vector subtraction $\delta\mathbf{r} = \mathbf{PP'}$ is the change of $\mathbf{r}$ in time δt. The vector $\delta\mathbf{r}$ has both magnitude and direction and is not to be confused with the increase in the modulus of $\mathbf{r}$.

Then $\dfrac{\delta\mathbf{r}}{\delta t}$ is a vector, and the differential coefficient of $\mathbf{r}$ is defined as

$$\frac{d\mathbf{r}}{dt} = \lim_{\delta t \to 0} \frac{\delta\mathbf{r}}{\delta t}.$$

Since in the limit the direction of $\delta\mathbf{r}$ is that of a tangent at P to the locus of P, the direction of the derivative vector is along this tangent. The differential coefficient or derivative of a vector $\mathbf{r}$ with respect to the time is denoted by $\dot{\mathbf{r}}$ and its second derivative by $\ddot{\mathbf{r}}$. Thus

$$\dot{\mathbf{r}} = \frac{d\mathbf{r}}{dt}, \quad \ddot{\mathbf{r}} = \frac{d\dot{\mathbf{r}}}{dt} = \frac{d^2\mathbf{r}}{dt^2}.$$

It should be emphasised that $\dot{\mathbf{r}}$ is not the same as $\dot{r}$, which is the rate of change of the modulus of the vector and takes no account of the change in its direction.

The derivative of the sum of two vectors.
If

$$\mathbf{r} = \mathbf{r}_1 + \mathbf{r}_2$$
$$\delta\mathbf{r} = \delta\mathbf{r}_1 + \delta\mathbf{r}_2$$

so that

$$\frac{\delta\mathbf{r}}{\delta t} = \frac{\delta\mathbf{r}_1}{\delta t} + \frac{\delta\mathbf{r}_2}{\delta t}$$

and

$$\dot{\mathbf{r}} = \lim_{\delta t \to 0} \frac{\delta\mathbf{r}}{\delta t} = \dot{\mathbf{r}}_1 + \dot{\mathbf{r}}_2 \qquad (1.26)$$

The derivative of the product of a scalar and a vector.

Let $\mathbf{r} = a\mathbf{s}$ where a is a scalar and $\mathbf{s}$ a vector, both varying with the time. At time $t + \delta t$ let a and $\mathbf{s}$ has the values $a + \delta a$ and $\mathbf{s} + \delta \mathbf{s}$ respectively. Then

$$\delta\mathbf{r} = (a + \delta a)(\mathbf{s} + \delta\mathbf{s}) - a\mathbf{s}$$

$$\frac{\delta\mathbf{r}}{\delta t} = a\frac{\delta\mathbf{s}}{\delta t} + \mathbf{s}\frac{\delta a}{\delta t} + \delta a\frac{\delta\mathbf{s}}{\delta t}.$$

Since in the limit δa tends to zero we have

$$\frac{d\mathbf{r}}{dt} = a\frac{d\mathbf{s}}{dt} + \mathbf{s}\frac{da}{dt}. \qquad (1.27)$$

Derivatives of a vector in terms of its components.

Let

$$\mathbf{r} = i x + j y + k z.$$

The unit vectors i, j, k are constant both in magnitude and direction and their derivatives are therefore zero. Hence, using (1.26) and (1.27) we have

$$\dot{\mathbf{r}} = i\dot{x} + j\dot{y} + k\dot{z}. \qquad (1.28)$$

It follows that if $\mathbf{r}$ is the displacement of a particle from a fixed point O, $\dot{\mathbf{r}}$ is the rate of change of this displacement, that is the velocity, and hence the components of velocity parallel to fixed axes of coordinates are

$$\frac{dx}{dt}, \quad \frac{dy}{dt}, \quad \frac{dz}{dt}.$$

Similarly the acceleration of the particle is the rate of change of velocity, that is $\ddot{\mathbf{r}}$, and

$$\ddot{\mathbf{r}} = i\ddot{x} + j\ddot{y} + k\ddot{z} \qquad (1.29)$$

so that the components of acceleration parallel to the axes are

$$\frac{d^2x}{dt^2}, \quad \frac{d^2y}{dt^2}, \quad \frac{d^2z}{dt^2}.$$

1.16 Derivative of a Unit Vector

The derivative of a unit vector in a variable direction which at time t makes an angle θ with a fixed direction OX has modulus $\dfrac{d\theta}{dt}$ and direction making an angle $\theta + \frac{1}{2}\pi$ with OX.

Let

$$\hat{\mathbf{r}} = i\cos\theta + j\sin\theta.$$

Then

$$\frac{d}{dt}\hat{\mathbf{r}} = i\left(-\sin\theta\,\frac{d\theta}{dt}\right)+j\left(\cos\theta\,\frac{d\theta}{dt}\right)$$

$$= \left(\frac{d\theta}{dt}\right)\{i\cos(\theta+\tfrac{1}{2}\pi)+j\sin(\theta+\tfrac{1}{2}\pi)\} \qquad (1.30)$$

Now $i\cos(\theta+\tfrac{1}{2}\pi)+j\sin(\theta+\tfrac{1}{2}\pi)$ is a vector of unit modulus in a direction making an angle $\theta+\tfrac{1}{2}\pi$ with OX; this is therefore the direction of $\dfrac{d\hat{\mathbf{r}}}{dt}$ and its modulus is $\dot{\theta}\left(=\dfrac{d\theta}{dt}\right)$.

Velocity and acceleration in polar coordinates.

Let $\mathbf{r}$ denote the displacement of a particle from a fixed point O (Fig. 13) in a direction making an angle θ with OX. $\hat{\mathbf{r}}$ is a unit vector in this direction; let $\hat{\mathbf{s}}$ be a unit vector in the perpendicular direction inclined at angle $\theta+\tfrac{1}{2}\pi$ to OX.

Then
$$\mathbf{r} = r\hat{\mathbf{r}}$$
$$\dot{\mathbf{r}} = \dot{r}\hat{\mathbf{r}}+r\frac{d}{dt}\hat{\mathbf{r}}$$
$$= \dot{r}\hat{\mathbf{r}}+r\dot{\theta}\hat{\mathbf{s}}.$$

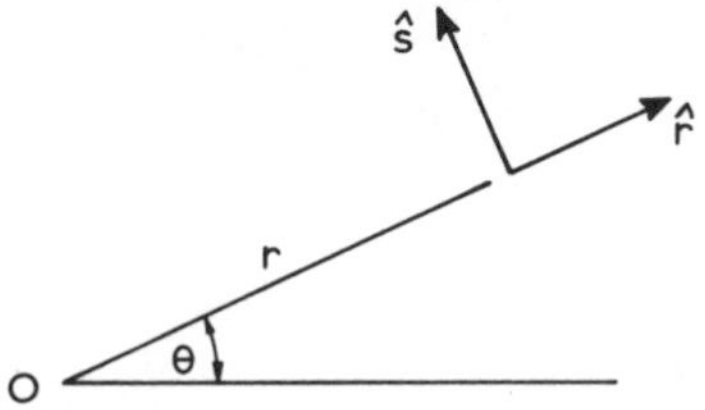

Fig. 13.

Thus the velocity has components $\dot{r}$ and $r\dot{\theta}$ along and perpendicular to the radius vector.

Similarly

$$\ddot{\mathbf{r}} = \ddot{r}\hat{\mathbf{r}}+\dot{r}(\dot{\theta}\hat{\mathbf{s}})+(\dot{r}\dot{\theta}+r\ddot{\theta})\hat{\mathbf{s}}+r\dot{\theta}\frac{d}{dt}\hat{\mathbf{s}}.$$

and, since the derivative of $\hat{\mathbf{s}}$ is $\dot{\theta}(-\hat{\mathbf{r}})$

$$\ddot{\mathbf{r}} = (\ddot{r}-r\dot{\theta}^2)\hat{\mathbf{r}}+(r\ddot{\theta}+2\dot{r}\dot{\theta})\hat{\mathbf{s}}. \qquad (1.32)$$

Hence the components of acceleration are $(\ddot{r}-r\dot{\theta}^2)$ along the radius vectors and $(r\ddot{\theta}+2\dot{r}\dot{\theta})$ perpendicular to the radius vector. The latter expression is more easily remembered as $\dfrac{1}{r}\dfrac{d}{dt}(r^2\dot{\theta})$.

Tangential and normal components.

The intrinsic equation of a curve is given in terms of the distance s measured along the curve from a fixed point and the angle ψ made by the tangent with a fixed direction. We shall find the components of velocity and acceleration along the tangent to the curve and along the normal for a particle moving along the curve.

If **r** be the displacement from a fixed point O of a particle moving on a plane curve at time t and $\mathbf{r} + \delta\mathbf{r}$ the displacement at time $t + \delta t$, $\delta\mathbf{r}$ is the chord joining the two points on the curve and the modulus of $\delta\mathbf{r}$ is to the first order of small quantities equal to the distance δs moved along the curve. Hence $\dot{\mathbf{r}}$, which is the velocity, has modulus $v = \dfrac{ds}{dt}$ and direction which is the limiting direction of the chord, that is of the tangent to the curve.

Let $\hat{\mathbf{t}}$ be a unit vector along the tangent and $\hat{\mathbf{n}}$ a unit vector along the normal (Fig. 14).

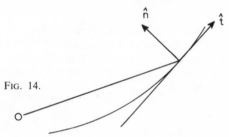

FIG. 14.

We have

$$\dot{\mathbf{r}} = \mathbf{v} = v\hat{\mathbf{t}} \tag{1.33}$$

and hence

$$\ddot{\mathbf{r}} = \dot{\mathbf{v}} = \dot{v}\hat{\mathbf{t}} + v\dot{\psi}\hat{\mathbf{n}}. \tag{1.34}$$

Now $\dot{\psi} = \dfrac{d\psi}{ds} \cdot \dfrac{ds}{dt} = \dfrac{v}{\rho}$, where ρ is the radius of curvature, and hence the components of acceleration along the tangent and the normal are

$$\dot{v}\left(= \frac{d^2 s}{dt^2}\right) \quad \text{and} \quad v\dot{\psi}\left(= \frac{v^2}{\rho}\right). \tag{1.35}$$

1.17 Integration of Vectors

If **b** is the derivative of a vector **a** so that $\dfrac{d\mathbf{a}}{dt} = \mathbf{b}$ then integration being defined as the reverse process to differentiation we write

$$\int \mathbf{b}\, dt = \mathbf{a} \tag{1.36}$$

and **a** is called the indefinite integral of **b**. More generally, the integral of **b** is $\mathbf{a} + \mathbf{c}$ where **c** is an arbitrary constant vector. Also the definite integral of **b** between values t_1 and t_2 of t is

$$\int_{t_1}^{t_2} \mathbf{b}\, dt = \mathbf{a}_2 - \mathbf{a}_1 \tag{1.37}$$

where $\mathbf{a}_1$ and $\mathbf{a}_2$ are the values of $\mathbf{a}$ corresponding to t_1 and t_2.

Example 8. *Parabolic motion.*

If a particle moves freely under gravity the acceleration is vertically downwards. The x-axis being horizontal and the y-axis vertically upwards we may write the acceleration vector as $-gj$. If $\mathbf{r}$ is the position vector of a particle with respect to an origin O, the velocity is $\dot{\mathbf{r}}$ and the acceleration $\ddot{\mathbf{r}}$ and we have

$$\ddot{\mathbf{r}} = -gj \tag{1.39}$$

Integrating with respect to t and remembering that j is constant in magnitude and direction we have

$$\dot{\mathbf{r}} = -gtj + \mathbf{v}_0 \tag{1.40}$$

The added constant vector $\mathbf{v}_0$ is the velocity when $t = 0$ and if this velocity is in a direction inclined at angle α to the x-axis, $\mathbf{v}_0 = (v_0\cos\alpha)i + (v_0\sin\alpha)j$.

Integrating once more

$$\mathbf{r} = -\tfrac{1}{2}gt^2 j + \mathbf{v}_0 t$$

there being no added constant since $\mathbf{r} = 0$ when $t = 0$.

Hence

$$\mathbf{r} = (v_0 t\cos\alpha)i + (v_0 t\sin\alpha - \tfrac{1}{2}gt^2)j \tag{1.41}$$

and this gives the x and y coordinates of a point on the parabola at time t.

1.18 Vector Equation of a Straight Line

Let $\mathbf{a}$ and $\mathbf{b}$ be the position vectors of two points A and B and let $\mathbf{r}$ be the position vector of a point C on the straight line. Then (see Example 2)

$$\lambda\mathbf{a} + \mu\mathbf{b} = (\lambda + \mu)\mathbf{r}$$

where $\lambda:\mu$ is the ratio AC to BC. Hence the position vector of *any* point C on AB is given by the equation

$$\mathbf{r} = \lambda\mathbf{a} + \mu\mathbf{b}, \text{ where } \lambda + \mu = 1. \tag{1.42}$$

This is a parametric form of equation with λ as a variable parameter. The Cartesian form of the equation is found by writing $\mathbf{r} = xi + yj + zk$, $\mathbf{a} = x_1 i + y_1 j + z_1 k$, $\mathbf{b} = x_2 i + y_2 j + z_2 k$, so that

$$xi + yj + zk = (\lambda x_1 + \mu x_2)i + (\lambda y_1 + \mu y_2)j + (\lambda z_1 + \mu z_2)k$$

giving, since $\mu = 1 - \lambda$,

$$\begin{aligned}
x &= \lambda x_1 + \mu x_2 = \lambda(x_1 - x_2) + x_2 \\
y &= \lambda y_1 + \mu y_2 = \lambda(y_1 - y_2) + y_2 \\
z &= \lambda z_1 + \mu z_2 = \lambda(z_1 - z_2) + z_2.
\end{aligned}$$

Equating the three values of λ given by these equations we have

$$\frac{x-x_2}{x_1-x_2} = \frac{y-y_2}{y_1-y_2} = \frac{z-z_2}{z_1-z_2}. \tag{1.43}$$

This is the Cartesian form of the equation of the straight line in three dimensions. If the straight line lies in the xy-plane, $z = z_1 = z_2 = 0$ and the quantity $(z-z_2)/(z_1-z_2)$ is omitted.

Alternatively, if l, m, n are the direction cosines of a straight line passing through A the position vector of a point on this line is easily seen to be

$$\mathbf{r} = \mathbf{a} + \rho(li + mj + nk)$$

where ρ is the distance of the point from A. Hence the equation of the line can be written in the form

$$\mathbf{r} = \mathbf{a} + \rho\hat{\mathbf{c}} \tag{1.44}$$

where $\hat{\mathbf{c}}$ is a unit vector in the direction of the line and ρ is a parameter. Substituting $\mathbf{r} = xi + yj + zk$ and eliminating ρ we have the Cartesian form

$$\frac{x-x_1}{l} = \frac{y-y_1}{m} = \frac{z-z_1}{n}.$$

Example 9. $A(3, -2, 7)$, $B(-1, 4, -5)$, $C(2, -1, 0)$, $D(-1, 5, 3)$ *are four points. Prove that the lines AB and CD intersect.*

The vector equations of AB and CD are respectively $\mathbf{r}_1$ and $\mathbf{r}_2$ where

$$\begin{aligned}
\mathbf{r}_1 &= \lambda(3i - 2j + 7k) + (1 - \lambda)(-i + 4j - 5k) \\
&= (4\lambda - 1)i + (4 - 6\lambda)j + (-5 + 12\lambda)k \\
\mathbf{r}_2 &= \rho(2i - j) + (1 - \rho)(-i + 5j + 3k) \\
&= (3\rho - 1)i + (5 - 6\rho)j + (3 - 3\rho)k.
\end{aligned}$$

At a common point we must have

$$\begin{aligned}
4\lambda - 1 &= 3\rho - 1 \\
4 - 6\lambda &= 5 - 6\rho \\
-5 + 12\lambda &= 3 - 3\rho
\end{aligned}$$

The first two of these equations give $\lambda = \frac{1}{2}$, $\rho = \frac{2}{3}$ and these values satisfy the third equation; the consistency of the equations shows that the lines do in fact intersect. Substituting for λ we find

$$\mathbf{r}_1 = i + j + k$$

giving the point of intersection $(1, 1, 1)$.

1.19 Vector Equation of a Plane

Let $\mathbf{a}$, $\mathbf{b}$, $\mathbf{c}$ be the position vectors of points $A(x_1, y_1, z_1)$, $B(x_2, y_2, z_2)$, $C(x_3, y_3, z_3)$. Then the vector equation of a plane through the points A, B and C is

$$\mathbf{r} = \lambda\mathbf{a} + \mu\mathbf{b} + v\mathbf{c} \tag{1.45}$$

where $\lambda + \mu + v = 1$, λ and μ being parameters.

This is easily seen since, if (Fig. 15)
$\mathbf{r}_1$ be the position vector of a point
D on AB (see Example 2)

$$(\lambda+\mu)\mathbf{r}_1 = \lambda\mathbf{a}+\mu\mathbf{b}$$

Hence, if $\mathbf{r}$ is the position vector of
a point on DC it follows (see Example
2) that

$$(\lambda+\mu+\nu)\mathbf{r} = (\lambda+\mu)\mathbf{r}_1 + \nu\mathbf{c}$$
$$= \lambda\mathbf{a}+\mu\mathbf{b}+\nu\mathbf{c}$$

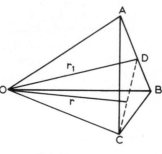

Fig. 15.

and this gives the value of $\mathbf{r}$ when
$\lambda+\mu+\nu = 1$. Substituting $\mathbf{r} = xi+$
$yj+zk$ in the equation and equating the vector components in the direction
of each axis gives

$$x = \lambda x_1 + \mu x_2 + \nu x_3 = x_1 + \mu(x_2 - x_1) + \nu(x_3 - x_1)$$
$$y = \lambda y_1 + \mu y_2 + \nu y_3 = y_1 + \mu(y_2 - y_1) + \nu(y_3 - y_1)$$
$$z = \lambda z_1 + \mu z_2 + \nu z_3 = z_1 + \mu(z_2 - z_1) + \nu(z_3 - z_1).$$

Elimination of the parameters μ and ν leads to the Cartesian form of the
equation of a plane which is most simply expressed in the form of the
determinant

$$\begin{vmatrix} x-x_1 & y-y_1 & z-z_1 \\ x_2-x_1 & y_2-y_1 & z_2-z_1 \\ x_3-x_1 & y_3-y_1 & z_3-z_1 \end{vmatrix} = 0 \qquad (1.46)$$

Alternatively, let $\mathbf{a} = x_1 i + y_1 j + z_1 k$ be the position vector of a point
A, $\mathbf{r} = xi+yj+zk$ the position vector of *any* point P on a plane through
A and $\hat{\mathbf{c}} = li+mj+nk$ a unit vector whose direction is normal to the
plane. Then the vector $\mathbf{r}-\mathbf{a}$ being in the plane is perpendicular to the
normal so that

$$(\mathbf{r}-\mathbf{a}).\hat{\mathbf{c}} = 0 \qquad (1.47)$$

and this is a vector equation of the plane.

In Cartesian coordinates this gives

$$\{(x-x_1)i+(y-y_1)j+(z-z_1)k\}.(li+mj+nk) = 0$$

so that

$$l(x-x_1)+m(y-y_1)+n(z-z_1) = 0 \qquad (1.48)$$

which is the Cartesian form of the equation.

Example 10. *A plane passes through the points* $(1, 1, 1)$, $(1, -2, 2)$, $(-1, -3, 1)$. *Write down the vector equation of the plane and deduce the scalar product form of the equation and the Cartesian equation.*

The vector form is, with $\lambda + \mu + \nu = 1$,

$$\begin{aligned}\mathbf{r} &= \lambda(i+j+k) + \mu(i-2j+2k) + \nu(-i-3j+k)\\ &= (i+j+k) + \mu(-3j+k) + \nu(-2i-4j)\end{aligned}$$

Let $\mathbf{c} = li + mj + nk$ be a vector perpendicular to $\mathbf{r} - (i+j+k)$ for all values of μ and ν, then

$$\begin{aligned}(li+mj+nk).(-3j+k) &= 0\\ (li+mj+nk).(-2i-4j) &= 0\end{aligned}$$

giving

$$-3m+n = 0 \quad \text{and} \quad -2l-4m = 0.$$

This leads to the solution $l:m:n = 2:-1:-3$ and $\mathbf{c} = 2i-j-3k$.

Hence we have the alternative form of vector equation

$$\{\mathbf{r} - (i+j+k)\}.(2i-j-3k) = 0.$$

The Cartesian form follows by putting $\mathbf{r} = xi + yj + zk$ giving

$$\begin{aligned}2(x-1)-(y-1)-3(z-1) &= 0\\ 2x-y-3z+2 &= 0.\end{aligned}$$

1.20 Vector Equations of Curves and Surfaces

Any plane curve whose equation can be written in parametric form can be specified by a vector equation. Thus for a plane curve given by

$$x = f(t), \ y = \phi(t),$$

the vector equation is

$$\mathbf{r} = f(t)i + \phi(t)j. \tag{1.49}$$

Examples of conic sections given by vector equations referred to the centre as origin are:

a circle	$\mathbf{r} = (a\cos\theta)i + (a\sin\theta)j$
a parabola	$\mathbf{r} = (at^2)i + (2at)j$
an ellipse	$\mathbf{r} = (a\cos\phi)i + (b\sin\phi)j$
a hyperbola	$\mathbf{r} = (a\sec\phi)i + (b\tan\phi)j$
a rectangular hyperbola	$\mathbf{r} = (ct)i + (c/t)j$

A three-dimensional curve can also be given by a vector equation. Thus, for example, a helix is given by the equation

$$\mathbf{r} = (a\cos\theta)i + (a\sin\theta)j + (b\theta)k.$$

A change of origin to a point whose position vector is $\mathbf{r}_1$ alters each equation by the addition of $\mathbf{r}_1$ to the left-hand side. Thus the equation of a circle with centre at O referred to the point whose position vector is $\mathbf{r}_1$ is

$$\mathbf{r} + \mathbf{r}_1 = (a \cos \theta)i + (a \sin \theta)j.$$

A surface may also be given by equations in parametric form, but in this case there are two parameters. If the parametric equations are

$$x = f(s, t), \ y = \phi(s, t), \ z = \psi(s, t)$$

the vector equation is

$$\mathbf{r} = f(s, t)i + \phi(s, t)j + \psi(s, t)k \qquad (1.50)$$

Thus, for example, we have the equations of:

a sphere $\qquad \mathbf{r} = (a \cos \theta \cos \phi)i + (a \cos \theta \sin \phi)j + (a \sin \theta)k$

a cone $\qquad \mathbf{r} = (t \cos \phi)i + (t \sin \phi)j + (t \tan \alpha)k$

a paraboloid of
   revolution $\qquad \mathbf{r} = (at^2 \cos \theta)i + (at^2 \sin \theta)j + 2atk.$

EXERCISES 1 (b)

1. A is the point $(1, -2, 3)$ and B the point $(3, 4, 6)$. Express the vector **AB** as the product of its modulus and a unit vector.

2. O the origin, $A(1, -2, 3)$ and $B(3, 4, 6)$ are the vertices of a triangle and G is its centroid. A force of 5 units acts along the line AG. Express this force as a vector.

3. Show that vectors $\mathbf{a} = 4i - 2j - 4k$, $\mathbf{b} = 8i + 10j + 3k$, $\mathbf{c} = -17i + 22j - 28k$ are mutually perpendicular. If these vectors represent forces find the magnitude and direction ratios of their resultant.

4. A force of 12 N acts in a direction $1 : -2 : -2$ and a force of 21 N in a direction $-2 : 3 : 6$. Find the magnitude and direction of their resultant.

5. Calculate the modulus and unit vectors of the sum of the vectors $i - 3j + 4k$, $3i + 2j + 5k$, $-3i + 5j - k$.

6. Forces of 2, 3 and 4 N act at a corner O of a cube, one along each of the diagonals of the faces that meet at O. Find the magnitude of the resultant and its inclination to each of the edges that meet at O.

7. The position vectors of P and Q are $i - 3j + 4k$ and $4i - 5j - 2k$ respectively. Find the length of PQ and the unit vector parallel to PQ.

8. Find the cosine of the angle between the vectors $\mathbf{OA} = 2i - 6j + 3k$ and $\mathbf{OB} = -i + 4j + 8k$ and the area of the triangle OAB.

9. Three non-coplanar vectors $\mathbf{a}, \mathbf{b}, \mathbf{c}$ each has unit magnitude and the angle between $\mathbf{a}$ and $\mathbf{b}$ is γ. If the vector $\mathbf{u}$ is defined by $\mathbf{u} = \mathbf{b} - (\mathbf{a} . \mathbf{b})\mathbf{a}$, prove that $\mathbf{u}$ is perpendicular to $\mathbf{a}$ and has modulus $\sin \gamma$.

10. The opposite pairs of edges of a tetrahedron are $\mathbf{a}, \mathbf{a}'$; $\mathbf{b}, \mathbf{b}'$; $\mathbf{c}, \mathbf{c}'$ respectively and $\mathbf{a} . \mathbf{a}' = \mathbf{b} . \mathbf{b}' = 0$. Prove that $\mathbf{c} . \mathbf{c}' = 0$ and that $\mathbf{a}^2 + (\mathbf{a}')^2 = \mathbf{b}^2 + (\mathbf{b}')^2 = \mathbf{c}^2 + (\mathbf{c}')^2$.

11. **OA** and **OB** are the vectors $2i - 3j + 6k$ and $8i - 4j + k$ respectively. Find the vector product $\mathbf{OA} \times \mathbf{OB}$ and deduce the area of the triangle OAB.

12. Find the unit vector which is perpendicular to the vectors $2i - 3j + 6k$ and $-6i + 2j + 3k$.

13. If $\mathbf{a}, \mathbf{b}$ and $\mathbf{c}$ are the position vectors of points A, B and C respectively, prove that the area of the triangle ABC is the modulus of

$$\tfrac{1}{2}(\mathbf{b} \times \mathbf{c} + \mathbf{c} \times \mathbf{a} + \mathbf{a} \times \mathbf{b}).$$

14. A force $(3i-2j+2k)$ N and a force $(7i+4j-6k)$ N act on a particle during a displacement $(5i-6j-k)$ metres. Find the work done.

15. The position vector of a particle at time t with respect to fixed axes is $(t^2+1)i-2tj+(t^2-1)k$. Find the magnitude and the direction of the velocity and of the acceleration at time t and the angle between their directions.

16. The position vector of a particle describing an ellipse is $\mathbf{r} = (a\cos\theta)i+(b\sin\theta)j$. Prove that if the ellipse is described with uniform angular velocity ω, then
$$\ddot{\mathbf{r}} = -\omega^2\mathbf{r}.$$

17. A particle describes the helix $\mathbf{r} = (a\cos\theta)i+(a\sin\theta)j+(b\theta)k$ with uniform angular velocity ω. Prove that it moves with constant speed $\omega\sqrt{(a^2+b^2)}$ and that its acceleration is $a\omega^2$.

18. Find the position vector of the point of intersection of the lines whose vector equations are
$$\mathbf{r}_1 = \lambda(2j-3k)+(1-\lambda)(6i-7j+15k)$$
$$\mathbf{r}_2 = \mu(-17j+11k)+(1-\mu)(3i+7j-k).$$

19. A plane passes through the points $(1,2,3)$, $(-1,3,-2)$, $(4,-2,-3)$. Find the vector equation of the plane in the normal form.

20. Find the position vectors of the points of intersection of the line $\mathbf{r} = \lambda(i+j)+(1-\lambda)(2i-3j)$ with the rectangular hyperbola $\mathbf{r} = \mu i+(1/\mu)j$.

EXERCISES 1 (c)

1. An aeroplane flies 50 kilometres on bearing $45°$, then 80 kilometres on bearing $300°$, and finally 60 kilometres on bearing $240°$. Find its distance and bearing from its starting point.

2. In a triangle ABC let the perpendiculars from B and C to the opposite sides meet in D. Prove that $\mathbf{AC}.(\mathbf{DA}+\mathbf{AB}) = 0$, $\mathbf{AB}.(\mathbf{DA}+\mathbf{AC}) = 0$, and hence that $\mathbf{DA}.\mathbf{BC} = 0$, showing that the perpendiculars drawn from the vertices to the opposite sides are concurrent.

3. ABC is a triangle in which $AB = 7$ m, $BC = 3$ m, $CA = 5$ m. Find the sum $\mathbf{BC}+3\mathbf{AC}+2\mathbf{BA}$.

4. $ABCD$ is a quadrilateral; P, Q, R, S are the mid-points of its sides and O is any point in its plane. Show that the system of forces represented by $\mathbf{OA}, \mathbf{OB}, \mathbf{OC}, \mathbf{OD}$ has the same resultant as the system represented by $\mathbf{OP}, \mathbf{OQ}, \mathbf{OR}, \mathbf{OS}$.
(L.U.)

5. Two forces are completely represented by the sides AB, AC of a triangle ABC. Show that their resultant is completely represented by $2\mathbf{AD}$, where D is the mid-point of BC. A point O within a given triangle PQR is such that forces completely represented by OP, OQ, OR are in equilibrium. Prove that O is the centroid of the triangle.
(L.U.)

6. L, M, N are the mid-points of the sides BC, CA, AB of a triangle. The perpendiculars from M and N to CA and AB respectively meet at K. Prove that $\mathbf{AB}.(\mathbf{AK}-\tfrac{1}{2}\mathbf{AB}) = 0$, $\mathbf{AC}.(\mathbf{AK}-\tfrac{1}{2}\mathbf{AC}) = 0$, and hence that $\mathbf{BC}.(\mathbf{AK}-\mathbf{AL})=0$, and that the perpendiculars to the sides BC, CA, AB from L, M, N, respectively, are concurrent.

7. R is the resultant of forces P and $2P$ acting at O, the angle between their lines of action being $60°$. A third force S is greater than R and also acts at O. If the maximum and minimum values of the resultant of all three forces are 26 and 12 N find P in newton.
(O.C.)

8. When moving East at 10 km/h the wind seems to blow from due North. When the speed is doubled it appears to come from the North-East. Find the speed and true direction of the wind.

9. Five wires radiating from the top of a telephone pole produce the following horizontal pulls: 200 N due South, 190 N due East, 205 N due North-East, 185 N at 30° East of North and 210 N due North-West. Find the magnitude and direction of the total pull on the post.

10. The position vectors of 3 points A, B, C are $i+2j$, $4i+3j$, $3i-j$ respectively. Prove that, if D, E, F are the mid-points of BC, CA, AB respectively,

$$\mathbf{BA} + \mathbf{CA} = 2\mathbf{DA}.$$

Write down the vector equations of the lines DA, EB, CF and show that they are concurrent at G whose position vector is $(8/3)i + (4/3)j$.

11. The coordinates of A, B, C are $(1, -2, 3)$, $(4, -2, 1)$, $(5, 2, -4)$ respectively. Show that the area of the triangle ABC is the modulus of $\frac{1}{2}\mathbf{BC} \times \mathbf{CA}$ and find this area.

12. In the equations

$$\mathbf{a} \times \mathbf{x} = \mathbf{b}, \quad \mathbf{a}.\mathbf{x} = b,$$

$\mathbf{x}$ is an unknown vector, $\mathbf{a} = 3i+6j+2k$ and $\mathbf{b} = 2i-3j+6k$. Find $\mathbf{x}$.

13. If $\mathbf{a}$, $\mathbf{b}$, $\mathbf{c}$ are the position vectors of points A, B, C respectively, prove that the area of the triangle ABC is the modulus of

$$\tfrac{1}{2}(\mathbf{b} \times \mathbf{c} + \mathbf{c} \times \mathbf{a} + \mathbf{a} \times \mathbf{b})$$

Find the area of the triangle when the coordinates of A, B, C are $(-1, 4, 2)$, $(2, -3, 1)$, $(4, -1, -1)$.

14. OA, OB, OC are three edges of a tetrahedron. Show that $\frac{1}{2}\mathbf{OB} \times \mathbf{OC} = \Delta\mathbf{\hat{n}}$, where Δ is the area of the triangle OBC and $\mathbf{\hat{n}}$ is a unit vector perpendicular to the plane OBC. Show further that $\mathbf{\hat{n}}.\mathbf{OA}$ is the height of A above the plane OBC. Hence show that the volume of the tetrahedron is

$$\tfrac{1}{6}\mathbf{OA}.(\mathbf{OB} \times \mathbf{OC}).$$

Find this volume if the coordinates of A, B, C are $(1, 1, 1)$, $(2, -1, 1)$, $(3, 2, -4)$.

15. The coordinates of points A, B, C are $(1, 2, 3)$, $(2, 0, 1)$, $(-1, 3, 2)$ respectively. Verify that, if $\mathbf{a}$, $\mathbf{b}$, $\mathbf{c}$ are equal to the position vectors of A, B, C with respect to the origin

$$\mathbf{a} \times (\mathbf{b} \times \mathbf{c}) = (\mathbf{a}.\mathbf{c})\mathbf{b} - (\mathbf{a}.\mathbf{b})\mathbf{c}$$

where the quantities in brackets are evaluated first.

16. If $\mathbf{a} = 2i+3j-k$, $\mathbf{b} = i-2j+2k$, $\mathbf{c} = 3i+j+k$, show that $\mathbf{a}.(\mathbf{b} \times \mathbf{c}) = 0$ and $(\mathbf{a}-\mathbf{b}) \times \mathbf{c} = 2(\mathbf{a} \times \mathbf{b})$.

17. $\mathbf{a}$, $\mathbf{b}$, $\mathbf{c}$ are position vectors of points $(x_1, y_1, 0)$, $(x_2, y_2, 0)$, $(x_3, y_3, 0)$. Show that $\mathbf{b} \times \mathbf{c} = k(x_2 y_3 - y_2 x_3)$, and hence that

$$\mathbf{a} \times (\mathbf{b} \times \mathbf{c}) = (\mathbf{a}.\mathbf{c})\mathbf{b} - (\mathbf{a}.\mathbf{b})\mathbf{c}.$$

18. The vector equations of two lines are

$$\mathbf{r} = \mathbf{a} + \mathbf{b}t, \quad \mathbf{r} = \mathbf{c} + \mathbf{d}s.$$

Show that where the lines intersect

$$\mathbf{d} \times (\mathbf{a} - \mathbf{c}) = t\mathbf{d} \times \mathbf{b}$$

and hence, since $\mathbf{b} \cdot (\mathbf{d} \times \mathbf{b}) = 0$, that if the lines intersect

$$\mathbf{b} \cdot \{\mathbf{d} \times (\mathbf{a} - \mathbf{c})\} = 0.$$

19. Show that the vector equation of the plane containing the straight lines $\mathbf{r} = \mathbf{a} + t\mathbf{b}$ and $\mathbf{r} = \mathbf{b} + s\mathbf{a}$ is

$$\mathbf{r} \cdot (\mathbf{a} \times \mathbf{b}) = 0.$$

20. Three non-coplanar vectors $\mathbf{a}$, $\mathbf{b}$, $\mathbf{c}$ each have unit magnitude; the angles between $\mathbf{b}$ and $\mathbf{c}$, $\mathbf{c}$ and $\mathbf{a}$, $\mathbf{a}$ and $\mathbf{b}$ are respectively α, β, γ. Prove that, if $\mathbf{u} = \mathbf{b} - (\mathbf{a} \cdot \mathbf{b})\mathbf{a}$ and $\mathbf{v} = \mathbf{c} - (\mathbf{a} \cdot \mathbf{c})\mathbf{a}$ and the angle between $\mathbf{u}$ and $\mathbf{v}$ is A,

$$\cos \alpha = \cos \beta \cos \gamma + \sin \beta \sin \gamma \cos A.$$

21. A tetrahedron $OABC$ is formed by vectors $\mathbf{OA}$, $\mathbf{OB}$, $\mathbf{OC}$. Prove that if G is the centroid of the triangle ABC,

$$3\mathbf{OG} = \mathbf{OA} + \mathbf{OB} + \mathbf{OC}.$$

If the moduli of the vectors are a, b, c and the angles BOC, COA, AOB are α, β, γ respectively prove that

$$9(OG)^2 = a^2 + b^2 + c^2 + 2bc \cos \alpha + 2ca \cos \beta + 2ab \cos \gamma.$$

Show further that, if θ is the angle between $\mathbf{AB}$ and $\mathbf{OC}$,

$$\cos \theta (a^2 + b^2 - 2ab \cos \gamma)^{\frac{1}{2}} = b \cos \alpha - a \cos \beta. \qquad \text{(L.U.)}$$

22. Two helices

$$\mathbf{r}_1 = (a \cos \theta)i + (a \sin \theta)j + (a\theta)k,$$
$$\mathbf{r}_2 = (a \cos n\theta)i - (a \sin n\theta)j + (a\theta)k,$$

where $n > 0$, intersect at successive points P_1, P_2 and P_3. Prove that

$$P_1 P_2 = 2a(\sin^2\phi + \phi^2)^{\frac{1}{2}}, \text{ where } \phi = \pi/(n+1),$$

and $$P_1 P_3 = 2a(\sin^2 2\phi + 4\phi^2)^{\frac{1}{2}}. \qquad \text{(L.U.)}$$

23. Prove that, if $\mathbf{OA} = \mathbf{a}$, $\mathbf{OB} = \mathbf{b}$, $\mathbf{OC} = \mathbf{c}$, the perpendicular distance of C from the straight line AB is

$$\frac{|\mathbf{b} \times \mathbf{c} + \mathbf{c} \times \mathbf{a} + \mathbf{a} \times \mathbf{b}|}{|\mathbf{b} - \mathbf{a}|}$$

24. Show that the point of intersection of the line $\mathbf{r} = \mathbf{a} + t\mathbf{b}$ with the plane $\mathbf{r} \cdot \mathbf{n} = p$ has position vector

$$\frac{\mathbf{a} + \mathbf{b}(p - \mathbf{a} \cdot \mathbf{n})}{\mathbf{b} \cdot \mathbf{n}}.$$

PART II—STATICS

CHAPTER 2

FORCES ACTING AT A POINT

2.1 Introduction

Statics is the science which discusses the action of forces on bodies which are at rest. A body which is at rest under the action of two or more forces is said to be in *equilibrium*. *Force* is defined as that which changes or tends to change the state of rest or uniform motion of a body in a straight line.

Forces are observed through their action on particles or bodies. A particle is a portion of matter whose dimensions are negligible and whose position may therefore be given as that of a mathematical point. A body may be considered as made up of an indefinitely large number of particles, and a rigid body is one in which the relative positions of the particles are invariable.

Forces may be classified as (i) attractions, when the force is exerted on a body without any visible contact with the body, for example, the force of gravity; (ii) tensions or compressive forces, such as are exerted by strings or struts supporting a body; (iii) reactions, which are the equal and opposite forces between two bodies in contact with each other.

Force is measured in terms of the force of gravity and in the metric system the standard force is that with which the earth attracts a standard bar of platinum whose mass is called one kilogramme. This standard force is called one kilogramme weight and written as 1 kgf, the f standing for force. The British unit is one pound weight written as 1 lbf.

Other forces are measured by comparison with the standard force, possibly by suspension from a spring balance in which the extension of the spring is known to be proportional to the force. Thus we can measure forces of 1 gramme weight, 1 ton weight, etc.

These are all gravitational forces whose magnitude is the earth's attraction of a particular mass. Since the acceleration due to gravity is not the same in different latitudes, the force 1 kgf which gives this acceleration to a mass of one kilogramme is not the same in different localities and it is necessary to have an absolute measure of force. This unit is called the *newton* (abbreviation N), defined as the force which will give to a mass of 1 kilogramme an acceleration of 1 metre per second per second. It is shown (§15.4) that

$$1 \text{ kgf} = g \text{ newton,}$$

where g, the acceleration due to gravity, is 9·81 metres per second per second approximately. Absolute units of force are used almost exclusively in this book.

When the *mass* of a body is written as M or m we shall understand this quantity to be in *kilogrammes* unless otherwise stated. When the *weight* of a body is written as W we shall understand this to be the force of gravity acting on the body in *newtons*, and $W = Mg$.

In the mathematical treatment of statical problems certain assumptions are made which are not in accord with the physical world as we know it. Thus, bodies are usually assumed to be rigid and, consequently, two bodies may be assumed to have contact at a mathematical point. Similarly, a string is often taken as being inextensible, taut, and having no weight. Surfaces are taken as being perfectly smooth, and pulleys and wheels as being frictionless. The mathematical theory of statics is built on such concepts, which are close enough to the truth to enable sufficiently accurate calculations to be made in practical problems.

We may therefore define *smooth surfaces* as being such that the force of reaction between them is always perpendicular to the common tangent plane at their point of contact.

A *light string* is defined as having no weight, and if such a string is taut the force of tension must be the same throughout its length. The tension in such a string is not altered if the string changes direction by contact with a smooth surface or by passing over a frictionless pulley.

An *elastic string* is one for which the strain, that is, the ratio of extension to original length, is proportional to the tension in the string.

If l be the original length, x the extension and T the tension, the strain is x/l and we have

$$T = \lambda \frac{x}{l}$$

where λ is a constant for the particular string. This is Hooke's Law, which is approximately true both for tension and compression of all materials within certain limits. The constant λ depends on the material and is proportional to the cross-section area of the string; it is known as the Modulus of Elasticity, and its units are the same as the units of the tension T. Thus a tension λ would give unit strain, that is, it would double the length of the string if Hooke's Law were true for a tension of this magnitude.

2.2 Characteristics of Forces

Equal Forces. Two forces are said to be equal when they act on a particle in opposite directions, there being no other forces acting on the particle, and it remains in equilibrium.

Transmissibility of Forces. The effect of a force on a rigid body depends on its magnitude and on its line of action, but is independent of the position of the point of application of the force on the line of action. This principle follows from consideration of the manner in which force is transmitted from particle to particle in a body.

Specification of a Force. A force acting on a body may be described completely by stating

    (i) its magnitude,
    (ii) its line of action,
    (iii) the sense in which it acts along its line of action.

It follows from the principle of transmissibility that the point of application of a force to a body may be taken as any convenient point on its line of action. Thus in calculating the resultant of two coplanar forces it is convenient to take their points of application at the intersection of their lines of action.

Force as a Vector

It was seen in §1.9 that forces acting on a particle are vector quantities and may be adequately represented by straight lines of length proportional to the magnitude of each force and drawn in the direction in which each force acts. Thus the resultant of two or more forces acting on a particle may be obtained by vector addition. It must be remembered, however, that a vector specifies only magnitude and direction whereas a force acting on a rigid body is not fully defined unless its line of action is also given. For this reason a vector representing a force is sometimes called a *line localized vector*.

2.3 The Parallelogram of Forces

If two forces acting on a particle at a point O be represented in magnitude and direction by lines OA and OB, the effect of these two forces on the particle is the same as that of a single force represented in magnitude and direction by OC, where OC is the diagonal of the parallelogram of which OA and OB are two sides (Fig. 16).

The force represented by *OC* is called the *resultant* of the two given forces.

The theorem follows directly from the fact that forces acting on particles are vector quantities and the vector **OC** is the sum of the vectors **OA** and **AB**. We may also note that since opposite sides of a parallelogram are equal and parallel **BC** and **AC** also represent the forces and

$$\begin{aligned} \mathbf{OC} &= \mathbf{OA} + \mathbf{OB} \\ &= \mathbf{OA} + \mathbf{AC} \\ &= \mathbf{OB} + \mathbf{BC}. \end{aligned}$$

If two forces act on a rigid body, and their lines of action intersect, the forces may be taken as acting on a particle at their point of intersection, and their resultant will be a single force at this point, and hence with a line of action through the intersection of the lines of action of the given forces. The resultant may be found by drawing the vectors representing the two forces, completing the parallelogram and measuring the length and inclination of the diagonal.

Calculation of the Resultant

Let P and Q be two given forces whose directions include an angle θ and let them be represented by the vectors OA and OB respectively (Fig. 16). Let R be the resultant represented by the vector OC.

As in §1.4 we have

$$OC^2 = OA^2 + AC^2 + 2OA \cdot AC \cdot \cos \theta,$$

that is

$$R^2 = P^2 + Q^2 + 2PQ \cos \theta,$$

and also

$$\sin COA = \frac{Q \sin \theta}{R}, \qquad \sin OCA = \frac{P \sin \theta}{R}.$$

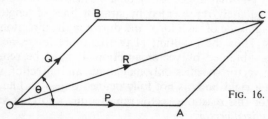

FIG. 16.

Cor. 1.

If $\theta = 0$, the forces P and Q act in the same straight line in the same sense, then $R = P + Q$. Similarly, if $\theta = 180°$, $R = P - Q$.

Cor. 2.

If two forces acting on a particle are in equilibrium, their resultant must be zero, and hence they must be equal and opposite forces with the same line of action.

Example 1. *The resultant of two forces P, Q is equal to P in magnitude; and that of two forces $2P$, Q (acting in the same direction as before) is also equal to P. Find the magnitude of Q and prove that the direction of Q makes an angle of 150° with P.* (O.C.)

Let α be the angle made by the direction of Q with P. We have for the resultant in the two cases

$$P^2 = P^2 + Q^2 + 2PQ \cos \alpha,$$

and

$$P^2 = 4P^2 + Q^2 + 4PQ \cos \alpha.$$

Hence, eliminating $\cos \alpha$

$$-P^2 = 2P^2 - Q^2$$
$$Q = P . \sqrt{3}$$
$$\cos \alpha = -\frac{Q^2}{2PQ} = -\frac{\sqrt{3}}{2}$$
$$\alpha = 150°.$$

Example 2. *ABC is a triangle: M is the point of trisection of AB nearer to A and N is the point of trisection of CA nearest to C. Prove that a force acting along MN and proportional to the length MN is equivalent to three forces parallel to the sides BC, CA, AB of the triangle and proportional to $(2/9)BC$, $(-4/9)CA$, $(-1/9)AB$ respectively.*

Here evidently (Fig. 17)

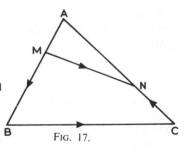

$$\mathbf{MN} = \mathbf{MB} + \mathbf{BC} + \mathbf{CN}$$
$$= \mathbf{BC} + \tfrac{1}{3}\mathbf{CA} + \tfrac{2}{3}\mathbf{AB}.$$

Also $0 = \mathbf{BC} + \mathbf{CA} + \mathbf{AB}$

Multiplying the second equation by (7/9) and subtracting it from the first we find

$$\mathbf{MN} = \tfrac{2}{9}\mathbf{BC} - \tfrac{4}{9}\mathbf{CA} - \tfrac{1}{9}\mathbf{AB}$$

and this proves the theorem.

Fig. 17.

EXERCISES 2 (a)

1. Forces of 12 N and 9 N act on a particle and their directions include an angle of 60°. Find the magnitude of the resultant and the angle made by its direction with the force of 12 N.
2. Forces of 12 N and 9 N act in directions which include an angle of 120°. Find the magnitude of the resultant.
3. Forces of 5 N and 7 N have a resultant of 10 N. Find the angles made by the 5-N force and by the resultant with the 7-N force.
4. Equal masses of 10 kg are attached to the end of a light inextensible string which passes over three smooth pegs in a wall. The pegs are the vertices of an equilateral triangle whose base is horizontal. Find the thrust on each peg.
5. A force is represented by the vector **OP**. If this force be resolved into two forces represented by vectors $\lambda\mathbf{OX}$ and $\mu\mathbf{OY}$ where X and Y are two points such that XY passes through P and $XP/PY = k$, show that $\lambda = 1/(1+k)$, $\mu = k/(1+k)$. .

(O.C.)

2.4 Resolution of Forces

If two forces P and Q act in directions which are at right angles (Fig. 18), the parallelogram of forces is a rectangle and we have for the magnitude and direction of their resultant R,

$$R = \sqrt{P^2 + Q^2},$$

$$\tan \theta = \frac{Q}{P}.$$

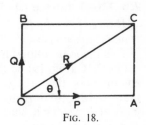

Fig. 18.

Also, $OC \cos \theta = OA$, $OC \sin \theta = OB$,

therefore $P = R \cos \theta,$

$$Q = R \sin \theta.$$

Hence, a single force R in a direction making an angle θ with a given straight line will have the same effect on a particle as forces $R \cos \theta$ along the given straight line and $R \sin \theta$ in a perpendicular direction.

$R \cos \theta$ and $R \sin \theta$ are called the *components* of the force R in the given directions, or the *resolved parts* of the force R in the given directions.

If forces P and Q act in directions which include an angle α we may resolve the force Q into components $Q \cos \alpha$ along the direction of P, and $Q \sin \alpha$ in a perpendicular direction.

Hence the resultant of P and Q will be the resultant of forces $P + Q \cos \alpha$ and $Q \sin \alpha$ in perpendicular directions.

Hence

$$R^2 = (P + Q \cos \alpha)^2 + (Q \sin \alpha)^2$$
$$= P^2 + Q^2 + 2PQ \cos \alpha,$$

and

$$\tan \theta = \frac{Q \sin \alpha}{P + Q \cos \alpha}.$$

Cor. A given force R, represented by a vector OC, may be resolved into components in any two given directions by drawing parallels to the given directions through the extremities O and C of OC and thus forming a parallelogram whose diagonal is OC and whose sides are parallel to the given directions. The sides of the parallelogram are then the components of R.

EXERCISES 2 (*b*)

1. Forces of $3P$ and $4P$ act on a particle in directions which are at right-angles. Find the magnitude of the resultant and its inclination to the larger force.
2. A force has components 10 N and 5 N in directions North and East respectively. Find the magnitude and direction of the force.
3. A force of 8 N acts in the direction North-East and a force of 5 N in the direction North 30° West. Find the sums of their components in directions North and East.
4. A force P acts in the direction North-East. Find components of this force in directions East and North-West.

2.5 The Triangle of Forces

If three forces acting on a particle can be represented by the sides of a triangle, taken in order, they will be in equilibrium.

This theorem follows from the parallelogram of forces.

Let OAC (Fig. 19) be the triangle whose sides represent in magnitude and direction the three given forces P, Q and R. Completing the parallelogram $OABC$ by drawing parallels to OA and AC through C and O to meet at B, we have, since OB also represents the force Q, that the force R is equal and opposite to the resultant of P and Q, and therefore the three forces are in equilibrium.

Conversely, if three forces P, Q and R, acting at a point be in equilibrium they can be represented by the sides of any triangle whose sides are respectively parallel to the directions of the forces.

Let OA and OB (Fig. 19) represent the forces P and Q respectively, then OC the diagonal of the parallelogram represents their resultant. But R must be equal and opposite to their resultant, hence CO

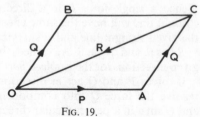

Fig. 19.

represents the force R, and since AC is equal and parallel to OB, AC represents the force Q. Hence, the triangle OAC is a triangle whose sides are proportional to the forces P, Q and R, and from the geometrical properties of similar triangles, any triangle whose sides are respectively parallel to those of OAC will be similar to the triangle OAC and therefore its sides will be proportional to the forces P, Q and R.

The triangle of forces can never represent the lines of action of the three forces, since by hypothesis their lines of action meet in a point. Hence, the sides of the triangle may be the lines of action of two of the forces and a line parallel to the line of action of the third force.

2.6 Lami's Theorem

If three forces act on a particle in equilibrium, each is proportional to the sine of the angle between the other two.

This follows from the sine rule for the triangle of forces OAC (Fig. 19), viz.

$$\frac{OA}{\sin OCA} = \frac{AC}{\sin AOC} = \frac{CO}{\sin CAO},$$

therefore,

$$\frac{P}{\sin OCA} = \frac{Q}{\sin AOC} = \frac{R}{\sin CAO}.$$

For the purposes of this theorem the angle between two forces may be taken as either of the angles made by the intersection of two vectors since these angles are supplementary and therefore their sines are equal.

Example 3. *A particle of mass 10 kg is suspended by two strings which make angles of 30° and 45° respectively with the horizontal. Find the tensions in the strings.*

Let the tensions in the strings be T_1 and T_2 respectively. We have three forces T_1, T_2 and $10g$ N acting at the point C (Fig. 20) in equilibrium. The tensions may be found by equating to zero the resolved parts of the forces in two directions or by using the triangle of forces.

(i) Resolving the forces acting at C horizontally and vertically and equating to zero we have

$$T_1 \cos 45 - T_2 \cos 30 = 0,$$
$$T_1 \sin 45 + T_2 \sin 30 - 10g = 0.$$

Hence

$$T_1(\sin 45 \cos 30 + \cos 45 \sin 30) = 10g \cos 30,$$
$$T_2(\sin 45 \cos 30 + \cos 45 \sin 30) = 10g \cos 45.$$

$$T_1 = \frac{10g \cos 30}{\sin 75} = 8 \cdot 97g \text{ N}$$

$$T_2 = \frac{10g \cos 45}{\sin 75} = 7 \cdot 32g \text{ N}$$

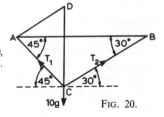

Fig. 20.

(ii) A triangle of forces may be found by drawing a parallel to the string CB through a point A on the other string to meet the vertical through C in D. Then the sides of the triangle CAD are parallel respectively to the forces T_1, T_2 and $10g$ N and hence the lengths of its sides are proportional to these forces.
Since
$$ADC = 60°$$
$$DCA = 45°$$
$$CAD = 75°$$

we have by the sine rule
$$\frac{CA}{\sin 60} = \frac{AD}{\sin 45} = \frac{DC}{\sin 75}$$

and, therefore,
$$\frac{T_1}{\sin 60} = \frac{T_2}{\sin 45} = \frac{10g}{\sin 75},$$

leading to the same results as before.

EXERCISES 2 (c)

1. A particle is in equilibrium under the action of 3 forces which act in directions South-East, North and West respectively. Find the ratio of the forces.
2. A mass of 10 kg is suspended by two strings of lengths 3 m and 4 m from two points at the same level 5 m apart. Find the tensions in the strings.
3. A mass of 30 kg hangs vertically at the end of a light string. If the mass is pulled aside by a horizontal force P so that the string makes an angle of 30° with the vertical, find the magnitude of the force P and the tension in the string.
4. A mass of 10 kg rests in equilibrium on a smooth plane inclined at 30° to the horizontal being held by a light string inclined at 15° to the line of greatest slope. Find the tension in the string and the reaction of the plane.

2.7 Polygon of Forces

The resultant of two forces P and Q is found by adding the vectors P and Q. Thus if OA (Fig. 21) represents the force P and AB represents the force Q, OB represents the resultant of P and Q. Similarly the resultant of forces P, Q and R is the resultant of R and the force represented by OB, and hence OC represents the resultant of P, Q and R, OD the resultant of forces P, Q, R and S, etc.

If the vectors representing a number of forces acting on a particle form a closed polygon when placed end to end in this way, it follows that their resultant is zero and hence that the system is in equilibrium.

The resultant of a number of forces acting on a particle may be found graphically by the above method since it is represented by the vector which closes the polygon of forces.

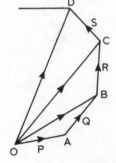

Fig. 21.

Analytically, if a number of forces P, Q, R ... make angles α, β, γ ... respectively with a given line OX, their resolved parts along and perpendicular to OX are:

along OX, $P\cos\alpha$, $Q\cos\beta$, $R\cos\gamma$, ...
perpendicular to OX. $P\sin\alpha$, $Q\sin\beta$, $R\sin\gamma$, ...

Hence, if F be the resultant of the forces and the resultant makes an angle θ with OX we have

$$F\cos\theta = P\cos\alpha + Q\cos\beta + R\cos\gamma + ...$$
$$F\sin\theta = P\sin\alpha + Q\sin\beta + R\sin\gamma + ...$$

These results may be written as

$$F\cos\theta = \Sigma P\cos\alpha$$
$$F\sin\theta = \Sigma P\sin\alpha,$$

and hence

$$F = \sqrt{(\Sigma P\cos\alpha)^2 + (\Sigma P\sin\alpha)^2}$$
$$\tan\theta = \frac{\Sigma P\sin\alpha}{\Sigma P\cos\alpha}.$$

The forces P, Q, R ... will be in equilibrium if their resultant is zero and hence necessary conditions for equilibrium are

$$\Sigma P\cos\alpha = 0,$$
$$\Sigma P\sin\alpha = 0.$$

That is, the sums of the resolved parts of the forces in two perpendicular directions must be zero.

Example 4. *Four forces acting at a point are in equilibrium. The magnitudes and directions of three of them are respectively 4 N due North, 7 N South-East, 4 N South 30° West. Find the magnitude and direction of the fourth force.*

Let the fourth force have components X and Y newtons in directions due East and due North (Fig. 22). Then resolving in these two directions we have

$$X + 7\cos 45 - 4\cos 60 = 0$$
$$Y + 4 - 7\cos 45 - 4\cos 30 = 0.$$

Therefore

$$X = 4\cos 60 - 7\cos 45 = -2.95$$
$$Y = 4\cos 30 + 7\cos 45 - 4 = 4.41.$$

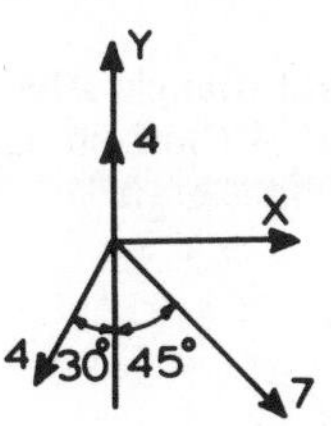

FIG. 22.

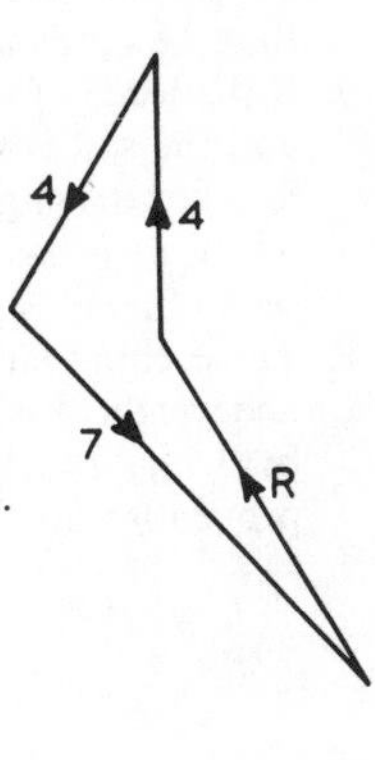

FIG. 23.

Combining these components we have a force

$$R = \sqrt{X^2 + Y^2} = 5\cdot31 \text{ N}$$

at an angle to the West of North given by

$$\tan^{-1}\frac{2\cdot95}{4\cdot41} = 33° \; 47'.$$

Graphically, the fourth force may be found by drawing the polygon of force (Fig. 23) of which the lengths and directions of three sides are known. Since the forces are in equilibrium the remaining side must represent the unknown force in magnitude and direction.

EXERCISES 2 (d)

1. Forces 3, 2, 1, 4 N act at a point along the lines OA, OB, OC, OD, respectively. $AOB = 60°$, $BOC = 90°$, $COD = 120°$. Find the magnitude of the resultant and its inclination to OA.

2. $ABCDEF$ is a regular hexagon. Forces of 4, 5, 2, 3, 6, 3 N act at a point in directions parallel respectively to the sides AB, BC, CD, DE, EF, FA. Find the magnitude of their resultant and its inclination to AB.

3. $ABCDEF$ is a regular hexagon. Forces of 10, 12, 8, 9, P, Q N act at a point in directions parallel respectively to the sides AB, BC, CD, DE, EF, FA and the forces are in equilibrium. Find the values of P and Q.

4. Two forces acting at a point are 50 N in a direction North-East and 100 N in a direction North-West. Find the magnitude and direction of a third force which will balance them. Another force of 25 N acts at the same point in some Northerly direction between due East and due West. Between what directions will the resultant of the three forces of 50, 100 and 25 N act and what will be the greatest value of this resultant?

5. ABC is a triangle in which $AB = 7$ m, $BC = 3$ m, $CA = 5$ m. Find (1) graphically, (2) analytically the resultant of the following forces acting at a point: 3 N in the direction BC, 9 N in the direction AC, 9 N in the direction BA.   (O.C.)

6. When a picture is hung by a single cord there are two ways of attaching the cord: one by fastening the ends of the cord to the picture rings; another by passing the cord through both rings and knotting the ends together. The depth of the picture below the hook being the same, which of these methods involves the greater stress on (1) the hook, (2) the rings? (Neglect friction and assume that the cords and the picture are in the same vertical plane.)   (O.C.)

7. If the force of the wind P on the sail of a ship makes an angle α with the sail and the sail is set to make an angle β with the keel of the ship, show that the forward driving force of the wind on the ship is $P \sin \alpha \sin \beta$. Hence, show that when $\alpha + \beta$ has a constant value the driving force is greatest when the sail is set so that $\alpha = \beta$.

8. Three equal strings are knotted together to form an equilateral triangle ABC and weight W is suspended from C. If the system is supported, with AB horizontal, by strings attached to A and B, each making an acute angle α with the horizontal, prove that the tension in AB is

$$\frac{W \sin (60° - \alpha)}{\sqrt{3} \sin \alpha}.$$ (L.U.)

9. The resultant of two intersecting forces P and $2P$ is $P\sqrt{3}$. Find the angle between the forces and the angle made by the resultant with the force of magnitude P.
(L.U.)

10. A uniform rod AB of length $2a$ and weight W is freely hinged to a vertical wall at A and is held by a light string of length c joining the mid-point of the rod to a point C at a distance b vertically above A. Find the tension in the string and the reaction at the hinge.

11. Three forces P, Q, R, act at the incentre I of a triangle ABC in the directions IA, IB, IC respectively. Prove that the forces are in equilibrium if

$$P^2 : Q^2 : R^2 = a(b+c-a) : b(c+a-b) : c(a+b-c).$$ (L.U.)

12. The ends of a light inextensible string of length l are fastened to two points A and B at the same horizontal level and at distance a apart. A smooth ring of weight W slides on the string and a horizontal force X is applied to the ring so that it rests in equilibrium below B. Prove that $X = aW/l$ and that the tension in the string is $W(a^2+l^2)/2l^2$. (L.U.)

13. Four horizontal wires are attached to a telephone post and exert the following tensions in newton on it: 20 North, 30 East, 40 South-West, 50 South-East. Calculate the resulting pull on the post and find its direction. (O.C.)

14. A pulley carries a mass of 30 kg and can slide freely up and down a smooth vertical groove. It is held up by a string passing round the pulley so that the two parts of the string make angles of 30° and 60° with the horizontal: show that the tension in the string is slightly under $22g$ N. (O.C.)

15. A body of mass 20 kg is suspended from a fixed point by a string, and is in equilibrium with the string inclined at 20° to the vertical under the action of a force making an angle of 60° with the downward vertical. Find graphically, or otherwise, the magnitude of the force and the tension in the string.

Assuming that the force remains constant in magnitude but varies in direction, find the greatest possible inclination of the string to the vertical. (O.C.)

16. $ABCD$ is a quadrilateral and O is the mid-point of the line joining the mid-points of AB and CD. Show that four forces acting at O represented by the lines OA, OB, OC, OD form a system in equilibrium.

17. A, B, C are collinear points, and O is a point not on the line ABC. Forces P, Q, R acting along OA, OB, OC respectively are in equilibrium. Prove that

$$\frac{P}{OA.BC} = \frac{Q}{OB.CA} = \frac{R}{OC.AB}.$$ (O.C.)

18. Prove that if O, A, B, C are concyclic points and forces P, Q, R acting along OA, OB, OC respectively are in equilibrium, then

$$\frac{P}{BC} = \frac{Q}{CA} = \frac{R}{AB}.$$ (O.C.)

CHAPTER 3

PARALLEL FORCES, MOMENTS, COUPLES

3.1 Resultant of Parallel Forces

We have seen that the resultant of two forces acting on a particle may be found by the parallelogram of forces. Also, if two forces act on two distinct particles of a rigid body, by the principle of transmissibility of force, they may be taken to act on the particle at the point where their lines of action intersect, and their resultant may also be taken as acting on this particle. The point where the lines of action intersect may be outside the body, but the magnitude and line of action of the resultant may still be found by supposing the point of intersection to be rigidly connected with the body. When two forces whose lines of action are parallel act on a body their resultant cannot be found by the parallelogram of forces. Such forces are said to be *like* when they act in the same direction, *unlike* when they act in opposite directions. The method of finding their resultant is given in the following theorems.

The resultant of two like parallel forces P and Q acting on a rigid body is a force of magnitude P+Q parallel to the forces P and Q, and if A and B be any two points on the lines of action of P and Q the resultant divides the line AB internally in the inverse ratio of the forces.

Let A and B (Fig. 24) be any two points on the lines of action of P and Q respectively, and let the forces be considered to act at these points. At A and B we may suppose two equal and opposite forces R to act along the line AB. By the principle of transmissibility, the resultant of these forces will be zero and they will not affect the equilibrium of the body.

Let AHEK be a parallelogram of forces for the forces P and R acting at A so that the diagonal AE represents the resultant of P and R.

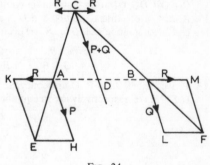

Fig. 24.

Let BLFM be a parallelogram of forces for the forces Q and R acting at B so that the diagonal BF represents the resultant of Q and R.

Produce the diagonals EA and FB to meet at C; then the resultant of P and R and the resultant of Q and R may both be considered to act at C.

40

Resolving each of these resultants into their original components, we have, acting at C two equal and opposite forces R, and forces P and Q acting along CD, which is parallel to AH and BL. The forces R are in equilibrium, hence the original forces are equivalent to a force $P+Q$ acting along AD.

Now the triangles CDA and AHE are similar by construction, therefore

$$\frac{CD}{DA} = \frac{AH}{HE} = \frac{P}{R}.$$

Also, the triangles CDB and BLF are similar by construction, therefore

$$\frac{CD}{DB} = \frac{BL}{LF} = \frac{Q}{R}.$$

Hence $$CD.R = DA.P = DB.Q,$$

therefore $$\frac{DA}{Q} = \frac{DB}{P},$$

that is, the point D divides AB *internally* in the inverse ratio of the forces P and Q.

The resultant of two unlike parallel forces P and Q of unequal magnitudes acting on a rigid body is a force of magnitude $P-Q$ acting in the direction of the force P, and if A and B be any two points on the lines of action of P and Q the resultant divides the line AB externally in the inverse ratio of the forces.

Let P be the greater of the two forces and A and B (Fig. 25) any two points on their line of action.

As before, suppose two equal and opposite forces R to act at A and B and let AE represent the resultant of P and R and BF the resultant of Q and R; let the lines FB and AE meet at C. Then the resultant of P and R and the resultant of Q and R may both be considered to act at C.

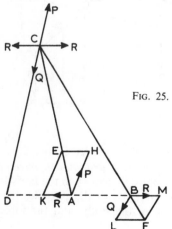

Fig. 25.

Resolving each of these resultants into its component forces, we have, acting at C, two equal and opposite forces R and forces P and Q acting along CD, which is parallel to HA and BL, in opposite senses. Hence, the resultant of these forces is a single force $P-Q$ acting along CD.

Now the triangles CDA and EKA

are similar by construction, therefore

$$\frac{CD}{DA} = \frac{EK}{KA} = \frac{P}{R}.$$

Also, the triangles CDB and BLF are similar by construction, therefore

$$\frac{CD}{DB} = \frac{BL}{LF} = \frac{Q}{R}.$$

Hence, $CD.R = DA.P = DB.Q,$

therefore $$\frac{DA}{Q} = \frac{DB}{P},$$

that is, the point D divides the line AB externally in the inverse ratio of the forces P and Q.

If $P = Q$, the above method of finding the resultant breaks down, since the diagonals AE and BF will be parallel and will not intersect. There is, therefore, no single force which is equivalent to two equal unlike parallel forces. Such a pair of forces is called a couple, and their effect on the equilibrium of a body will be considered in § 3.3.

By the methods considered above it is possible to find the resultant of any number of parallel forces acting on a body by finding resultants of two forces at a time. The final resultant will be the algebraic sum of the forces.

3.2 Centre of Parallel Forces

Let the parallel forces be $P_1, P_2, P_3 \dots$ and let them at act at the points $A_1, A_2, A_3 \dots$ (Fig. 26). Then whatever be the directions of the forces the resultant of P_1 and P_2 acts through a point C in $A_1 A_2$, where $P_1 . CA_1 = P_2 . CA_2$. Similarly, the resultant of this force and P_3 will pass through a point D in CA_3, where $P_3 . A_3 D = (P_1 + P_2)$. CD, and so on until the final resultant is reached. The point through which the final resultant acts is called the centre of the parallel forces, and its position does not depend on the common direction of the forces.

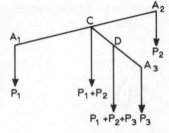

Fig. 26.

The weights of the constituent particles of a body are a system of parallel forces such as we have considered, and the centre of these forces is called the *centre of gravity* or *centre of mass* of the body. Thus, the position of the centre of gravity in the body is independent of the direction in which the weights of the particles act, that is, it is independent of the orientation of the body, and the force which is the total weight of the body may be taken to act vertically through the centre of gravity.

In considering the equilibrium of a body under the action of various forces the weight of the body acting at its centre of gravity must be included, and the position of the centre of gravity of bodies of various shapes is considered in Chapter 7.

If a body made of uniform material has a centre of symmetry G such that to any particle A of the body there corresponds an equal particle A' in the line AG on the opposite side of G and at the same distance from G, then the resultant of the weights of A and A' will pass through G. The resultant of the weights of every such pair of particles will pass through G and therefore G must be the centre of gravity of the body.

Thus the centre of gravity of a uniform thin rod is at its mid-point, the centre of gravity of a rectangle or parallelogram at the intersection of its diagonals, the centre of gravity of a circle, ellipse or sphere at the centre of symmetry.

The centre of gravity of a uniform triangular lamina is at the point of intersection of its medians (see § 7.1).

EXERCISES 3 (a)

1. Three equal parallel forces act at the vertices of a triangle ABC; find their centre (i) when the forces are like, (ii) when the force at A is in the opposite sense to those at B and C.
2. A lamina in the form of a parallelogram $ABCD$ lies on a smooth horizontal plane and is acted on by forces kAB along AB and kAD along AD. The lamina is kept in equilibrium by parallel forces acting at B and D respectively. Find the magnitudes of these forces and their lines of action.   (L.U.)
3. A uniform beam AB is 6 m long and its mass is 24 kg. It rests on two vertical supports at C and D, CD being a distance of 3 m, and the pressures on the supports at C and D are $16g$ N and $8g$ N respectively. Find the lengths of AC and DB, assuming that A is nearer to C than D.
4. A uniform beam rests in a horizontal position supported at a point distant 2 m from one end and carrying 10 kg suspended from this end. The pressure on the support is $30g$ N. Determine the weight and length of the beam.

3.3 Moment of Force

The moment of a force about a given point is the product of the force and the perpendicular distance from the point to the line of action of the force.

Consider a rigid body with one point O fixed and a force P acting on the body; then if the force P does not pass through O it will tend to turn the body about O. This turning effect increases with the distance of the point O from the line of action of P and is measured by the moment of the force about O.

If AB (Fig. 27) represents the force P in magnitude and line of action and p is the length of the perpendicular from O on AB, then the moment Pp is represented by $p.AB$, that is, twice the area of the triangle OAB.

Moments may be positive or negative, according to the sense in which the force tends to turn the body. A convenient convention is to regard moments as positive if they tend to turn the body about the point in an anti-clockwise sense and negative if in a clockwise sense. The algebraic sum of the moments of two or more forces about a point is obtained by giving to each moment its appropriate sign and adding them.

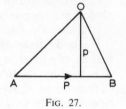

FIG. 27.

The algebraic sum of the moments of two forces about a point in their plane is equal to the moment of their resultant about the same point.

(i) Assuming that the two given forces P and Q are not parallel, let them meet at A (Fig. 28).

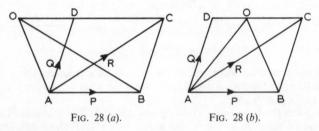

FIG. 28 (*a*).   FIG. 28 (*b*).

Let O be the given point.

Through O draw a parallel to the line of action of P to meet the line of action of Q in D. Then let AD represent the magnitude of Q and draw AB to represent the magnitude of P on the same scale. Completing the parallelogram $ABCD$, AC represents the resultant R of P and Q in magnitude and direction.

Now, the triangle OAB is half the parallelogram $ABCD$, and is therefore equal in area to the triangle ADC.

Hence, if O lies outside the angle DAB (Fig. 28 (*a*))

$$\Delta\, OAD + \Delta\, OAB = \Delta\, OAC.$$

If O lies within the angle DAB (Fig. 28 (*b*))

$$\Delta\, OAB - \Delta\, OAD = \Delta\, OAC.$$

But $2\Delta\ OAB$, $2\Delta\ OAD$, $2\Delta\ OAC$ represent the moments of the forces P, Q, R, respectively, about O. Hence, if O lies outside the angle DAB, the sum of the moments of P and Q is equal to the moment of R about O; if O lies within the angle DAB, the difference of the moments of P and Q is equal to the moment of R about O, and in this case the moments of P and Q have opposite senses.

Therefore, in either case the moment of R about O is equal to the algebraic sum of the moments of P and Q about O.

(ii) If the forces P and Q are parallel, let OAB be a line drawn from O perpendicular to the lines of action of P and Q, and let the resultant $R(=P+Q)$ act at C.

Then $P.AC = Q.CB$.

If O does not lie between A and B (Fig. 29), the moments of A and B about O have the same sense and their sum is $P.OA + Q.OB$

$$= P(OC - AC) + Q(OC + CB)$$
$$= (P+Q)OC$$
$$= R.OC.$$

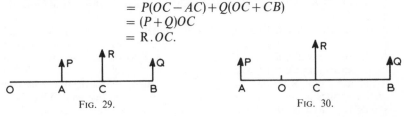

FIG. 29.   FIG. 30.

If O lies between A and B (Fig. 30) the moments of A and B about O have opposite senses and the algebraic sum of their moments is

$$Q.OB - P.OA$$
$$= Q(OC + CB) - P(AC - OC).$$
$$= (P+Q)OC$$
$$= R.OC.$$

If the forces P and Q act in opposite directions and $P > Q$ (say) the point C lies outside AB and the above proofs hold if the length AC is taken as negative. If, however, $P = Q$, the forces have no single resultant and the theorem has no meaning.

The algebraic sum of the moments of any number of forces P, Q, R, S. ... acting in one plane on a rigid body is equal to the moment of their resultant.

The theorem supposes that the forces have a single resultant, and follows immediately by applying the previous theorem to the resultant of P and Q, to the resultant of this force and R, and so on.

It follows that the algebraic sum of the moments of the forces about any point on their resultant is zero.

If the forces are in equilibrium, the resultant is zero, and hence the algebraic sum of the moments of the forces about any point will be zero, and we have the following important theorem:

When a rigid body is in equilibrium under the action of a number of coplanar forces the algebraic sum of the moments of the forces about any point in their plane will be zero.

The converse is not true, since any given point might lie on the resultant of the forces. It will be proved in the next chapter that a necessary and sufficient condition for the equilibrium of a system of coplanar forces is that the sum of the moments of the forces about each of three non-collinear points should be zero.

EXERCISES 3 (b)

1. A light triangular lamina ABC is freely suspended by the vertex C and particles of masses P and Q are attached at A and B respectively. The lamina hangs in equilibrium with the internal bisector of the angle ACB vertical. Find the ratio $P:Q$ in terms of the sides of the triangle. (L.U.)

2. A non-uniform rod AB of length 20 m rests horizontally on two supports at C and D, where $AC = BD = 4$ m. The greatest mass that can be hung from A without disturbing the equilibrium is 8 kg, and the greatest mass that can be hung from B is 10 kg. Find the mass of the rod and the distance of its centre of gravity from A. (L.U.)

3. A rod AB, 10 m in length, is supported horizontally by vertical forces at C and D, where $AC = 1$ m, $DB = 3$ m. A mass of 9 kg placed at A will just disturb equilibrium, as will a mass of 15 kg placed at B. Find the mass of the rod, and the distance of its centre of mass from A. (L.U.)

4. A uniform plank, 9 m long, of mass 80 kg, is supported horizontally by two vertical strings attached at distances 1 m and 8 m from one end. What mass should be placed on the plank at one end so that (i) the tension in one of the strings just vanishes, (ii) the tension in one string is double the tension in the other? (L.U.)

5. Three metres of a plank, 9 m long and of mass 100 kg, project over the side of a quay. What mass must be placed on the end of the plank so that a man of mass 75 kg may be able to walk to the other end without the plank tipping over? (O.C.)

3.4 Couples

We have seen that a couple is the term used to denote two equal unlike parallel forces whose lines of action are not the same. Since in any resolution of forces the constituent forces of a couple will balance, they may be neglected, but their moment about any point will not be zero and must be taken into account.

The moment of a couple about any point in the plane of the forces is equal to the product of one of the forces and the perpendicular distance between the lines of action of the forces.

Let the magnitude of each force be P. Let OAB be a line drawn from any point O perpendicular to the lines of action of the forces to meet them in A and B respectively.

If O does not lie between the lines of action (Fig. 31 (a)), the sum of the moments of the forces about O is

$$P.OB - P.OA$$
$$= P(OB - OA)$$
$$= P.AB.$$

If O lies between the lines of action of the forces (Fig. 31 (b)) or on one

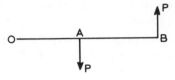

FIG. 31 (*a*).

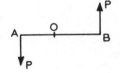

FIG. 31 (*b*).

of the lines of action, the sum of the moments of the forces about O is

$$P.OB + P.OA$$
$$= P(OB + OA)$$
$$= P.AB.$$

The perpendicular distance AB is called the *arm* of the couple. Since the moment of a couple is the same for any point in its plane, it is usual to specify a couple by its moment alone. Thus we speak of a couple of 5 N m, meaning that this is the value of its moment about any point, without any reference to the magnitude of the constituent forces, which will nevertheless be two definite forces with definite lines of action. The effect on the equilibrium of a body will be the same if the forces are of 5 N with an arm of 1 m, or of 10 N with an arm of 0·5 N.

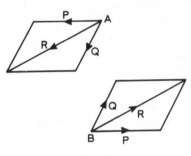

FIG. 32.

Two couples acting on a rigid body in the same plane are equivalent to a single couple whose moment is the algebraic sum of the two couples.

Let the couples be two forces P with arm p and two forces Q with arm q respectively (Fig. 32).

(i) If the lines of action of P and Q are not parallel, let one of the forces P meet one of the forces Q at A and let the other two forces meet at B.

Then at A we have forces P and Q whose resultant is R (say), and at B we have forces P and Q whose resultant is also R in a parallel direction but in the opposite sense, and the two forces R constitute a couple.

The moment of this couple is the moment about A of the force R acting at B, that is, the moment about A of the forces P and Q acting at B which are the components of R, that is

$$Pp + Qq$$

(ii) If the lines of action of P and Q are parallel we may combine them into a force $P+Q$ acting in one direction and a force $P+Q$ acting in the opposite direction which constitute a couple.

Let a perpendicular to the lines of action of the forces meet the lines of action of the forces P in A, A', the forces Q in B, B', the forces $P+Q$ in C, C' (Fig. 33).

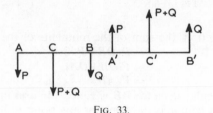

FIG. 33.

The moment of the resultant couple is the moment of the force $P+Q$ at C about C', which equals the sum of the moments of its component forces P and Q about C'.

Therefore the moment of the resultant couple

$$= P.AC' + Q.BC'$$
$$= P(AA' + A'C') + Q(BB' - C'B')$$
$$= Pp + Qq + (P.A'C' - Q.C'B').$$

$P.A'C' - Q.C'B' = 0$, since C' lies on the resultant of P and Q; therefore the moment of the resultant couple is $Pp + Qq$.

Two theorems on couples which follow from the preceding theorem are:

A number of couples in the same plane acting on a rigid body are equivalent to a single couple whose moment is the algebraic sum of their moments.

Two couples acting on a rigid body in the same plane whose moments are equal and opposite balance each other.

3.5 Some Theorems on Couples

The resultant of a single force P and a couple, acting in the same plane on a rigid body, is a single force P whose line of action is displaced from that of the given force but is parallel to it.

Let the forces of the couple be Q, and let the line of action of P meet the line of action of one of the forces Q in A (Fig. 34). Let the resultant of the forces P and Q acting at A be R, and let the line of action of R meet the other force Q in B. The force R may be taken as acting at B and may be resolved back into forces P and Q acting at B, in directions parallel to the directions of the forces P and Q acting at A. The two forces Q at B

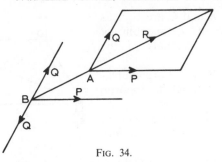

Fig. 34.

balance each other, and we are left with the single force P with a line of action through B in a direction parallel to the direction of the given force P.

If three forces acting on a rigid body be represented in magnitude, direction and line of action by the sides of a triangle taken in order, they are equivalent to a couple whose moment is represented by twice the area of the triangle.

By hypothesis the lines of action of the three forces do not pass through a point, and hence the theorem of the triangle of forces does not apply to these forces.

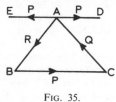

Fig. 35.

Let ABC be the triangle (Fig. 35) with forces P, Q, R acting along and proportional to the sides BC, CA, AB respectively. At A introduce two equal and opposite forces P in directions AD and AE parallel to BC. Then the force P acting in the direction AD together with the forces Q and R are three forces acting at a point parallel to and proportional to the sides of the triangle taken in order, and are therefore in equilibrium. We are left with two forces P acting along BC and AE respectively, which form a couple. The arm of this couple is the perpendicular from A on BC, and hence, since BC represents the force P, the moment of the couple is represented by twice the area of the triangle ABC.

Two equal and opposite couples acting on a rigid body in planes which are parallel will balance each other.

Since the effect of each couple depends only on its moment, we may without loss of generality take each of the couples as being composed of forces P with arm p. We may take the arms of the couples as lengths AB and CD (Fig. 36), which are opposite sides of a rectangle. We thus have to consider the effect of four forces P at the corners of a rectangle whose plane is perpendicular to the planes of the original couples. The forces at A and C are in the same sense, and likewise the forces at B and D are in the same sense.

The forces P at A and C are equivalent to a force $2P$ at O, the point of intersection of the diagonals of the rectangle.

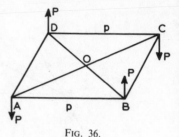

The forces P at B and D are equivalent to a force $2P$ at O in the opposite direction.

Hence, the four forces P form a system in equilibrium, and the couples therefore balance.

FIG. 36.

Cor. It follows that the effect of a couple on a rigid body in a given plane is unaltered by transferring it to any parallel plane. Hence, if a straight line be drawn perpendicular to the plane of a couple, the moment of the couple about the straight line is defined as its moment about the point in which the line cuts its plane. Thus couples of equal moment in parallel planes may be considered as having equal moments about any straight line perpendicular to their planes, that is, as having the same turning effect about any axis perpendicular to their planes.

EXERCISES 3 (c)

1. *ABCD* is a square of side 1 metre. Forces of 5, 3, 4 and 6 N act along the sides *AB*, *BC*, *CD* and *DA* respectively, and forces of $\sqrt{2}$ N and $2\sqrt{2}$ N act along the diagonals *AC* and *BD* respectively. Show that the system of forces reduces to a couple and find its moment.

2. A horizontal beam has one end built into a wall. The masonry pressures on the beam are equivalent to a force of $150g$ N acting vertically downwards at 75 cm from the point where the beam enters the wall at *A*, and a force of $225g$ N acting vertically upwards at 30 cm from *A*. Find the upward force acting at *A* and the moment of the couple which together with this force is equivalent to the given system.

3. The coupling at the front of a railway wagon is 15 cm higher than that at the rear; the axles are 2·4 m apart and the centre of gravity of the wagon is mid-way between the axles. If the pull in each of the couplings is $2\,500g$ N, find the difference between the loads on the front and rear axles.

4. The centre of gravity of a gate of mass M kg is 1 m from the vertical line containing the two hinges, which are $\frac{2}{3}$ m apart. Show that the horizontal components of the action of the hinges on the gate form a couple and find their magnitude.

EXERCISES 3 (d)

1. *ABCD* is a rectangle in which $AB = 4$ cm and $BC = 3$ cm. Forces of $2g$ N, $1g$ N, $2g$ N and $5g$ N act along *AB*, *BC*, *CD* and *AC* respectively, the direction in each case being indicated by the order of the letters. Calculate the direction and magnitudes of parallel forces through *B* and *D* which are together equivalent to the given system.   (L.U.)

2. A light horizontal rod, 40 cm long, is supported by two vertical props, each 10 cm from an end of the rod, and is loaded with 16 kg at each end. What masses hung from the ends will produce in one prop a pressure double and in the other prop a pressure half of that produced by the 16-kg masses?   (O.C.)

3. In a rectangular plate $ABCD$, $AB = 15$ cm, $BC = 30$ cm. Along the sides AB, BC, CD, DA there act forces of 10, 20, 20, 40 N respectively in the sense indicated by the order of the letters. Show that their resultant is parallel to one of the diagonals and find the resultant in magnitude and position.   (L.U.)

4. $ABCD$ is a quadrilateral in which $AB = BC$, $CD = DA$, A and C are right angles and the angle B is $60°$. Equal forces $\sqrt{3}P$ act along AD and DC; equal forces P act along CB and BA. Find the magnitude of their resultant and the point in which it cuts BC produced.   (O.C.)

5. Parallel forces $2P$, P and $-P$ (two like and one unlike) act at the vertices A, B and C of a triangle; show that their centre is G, where $BDAG$ is a parallelogram, AD being the median of the triangle through A.   (O.C.)

6. A uniform beam, 2 m long, which weighs $40g$ N, is supported in a horizontal position by two vertical strings attached to its ends. Neither string can support a tension of more than $30g$ N. Find the greatest weight that will not cause either of the strings to break, wherever it is placed on the beam, and determine the length of beam on which a weight of $16g$ N can be placed without causing either of the strings to break.   (O.C.)

7. A square piece of thin wood $ABCD$, 20 cm by 20 cm, resting on a smooth table is acted on by forces of $3g$ N along AB, $2g$ N along BC, $5g$ N along DC, and $4g$ N along DA; but the square does not move, as it is pinned to the table by a smooth pin through a point in the line joining the mid-points of AB and DC. Find the position of the pin and the magnitude of the pressure exerted on it by the board.   (O.C.)

8. A horizontal beam $ABCD$ rests on two supports at B and C, where $AB = BC = CD$. It is found that the beam will just tilt when a mass of p kg is hung from A or when a mass of q kg is hung from D. Find the weight of the beam, and prove that its centre of gravity divides AD in the ratio $2p+q:p+2q$.   (O.C.)

9. A heavy non-uniform beam AB, of length l, rests across a fixed peg P and carries equal loads W_1 hung from each end. In the equilibrium position with the beam horizontal the distance AP is x_1. For another pair of equal loads W_2 the corresponding distance AP is x_2. Prove that the weight of the beam W is given by
$$(x_1 - x_2)W = (W_1 - W_2)l - 2W_1x_1 + 2W_2x_2.   (L.U.)$$

10. A semicircular lamina rests on a smooth horizontal table. AD is the bounding diameter and B, C are the points of trisection of the semicircular arc. The lamina is acted upon by three forces, $1g$ N along AB, $3g$ N along CB and $1g$ N along CD. Find the position of a point in the perpendicular bisector of AD through which a smooth pin should be driven through the lamina and into the table so that the lamina will not rotate. Find also the magnitude and direction of the reaction on the pin.   (L.U.)

11. A uniform metal plate of mass 36 kg is in the form of an equilateral triangle. It is supported with its plane horizontal by three vertical strings, each attached to the mid-point of one of the sides of the triangle. A mass P is placed at one of the corners of the plate. Find the value of P if (i) the tension in one of the strings vanishes, (ii) the tensions in the strings are in the ratios $1:2:2$.   (L.U.)

12. A uniform bent lever with arms at right angles and of lengths in the ratio $3:4$ is freely supported from the angle, and carries masses of 20 kg and 8 kg at the ends of the shorter and longer arms respectively. In the position of equilibrium the two arms are equally inclined to the vertical. Find the weight of the lever.
(L.U.)

13. Forces of magnitudes 1, 2, 3, 6, 5, 4 units act respectively along the sides AB, CB, CD, ED, EF, AF of a regular hexagon, the sense of each force being indicated by the order of the letters. Prove that the six forces are equivalent to a couple and find its moment if the side of the hexagon is a. (L.U.)

14. $ABCD$ is a square of side 2 metres. Forces of 4, 3, 2, $1g$ N act along AB, CB, CD, DA respectively. Calculate the magnitude and direction of the force through A and the moment of the couple which are together equivalent to the given system of forces. Also calculate the distance from A of the point in which the line of action of a single force, equivalent to the system, intersects AB.
(L.U.)

15. One end of a heavy uniform bar of weight W N and length $2a$ m is attached to the end of a light inextensible string which hangs freely from a ceiling. A couple of moment Gg N m acts on the bar in a vertical plane containing the string. Show that equilibrium is possible only if $G \leqslant Wa$, and find the positions of the rod and the string and the tension in the string, when this condition is satisfied. (L.U.)

16. Forces of 3, 13 and 5 N act along OX, OA and OB respectively, where OA and OB are on the same side of the straight line $X'OX$, and rotation from OX to OA and OA to OB is anticlockwise. $\tan^{-1} AOX = 5/12$, $\tan^{-1} BOX' = 4/3$. A force P forms with the given forces a couple of clockwise moment 90 N m. Find the magnitude and direction of P and the distance from O of the point where its line of action intersects OX. (L.U.)

17. ABC is a triangle in which the angle A is a right angle, $AB = 4$ m and $AC = 3$ m. The moments of a force in the plane of the triangle, about A, B and C, are respectively 8 N m, -8 N m and 14 N m. Calculate the magnitude of the force, and the distance from A of the point where its line of action intersects AB.
(L.U.)

18. $ABCD$ is a rectangle in which $AB = 12$ cm, $AD = 5$ cm. Forces of $7g$ N and $13g$ N respectively act along AB and BD. Find the magnitude and direction of the force through C and the moment of the couple which, together with the given forces, will form a system in equilibrium. (L.U.)

19. A weighing machine is constructed as follows: A stiff beam $ABCD$ is pivoted at C, BC being less than CD. Equal rods BF, DE, are suspended from B and D, and their ends F and E are joined by a rod of length equal to BD, the rods being freely jointed at B, D, E, F; a scale-pan is attached to the middle point of FE. The counterpoise is a weight P which can slide along AC. If M is the position of P when the machine is in equilibrium without any load, show how to graduate the machine. (L.U.)

20. A uniform bar, 2 m long and of mass 34 kg, is suspended by two vertical strings. One is attached to a point 25 cm from one end and can just support a mass of 18 kg without breaking; the other is attached $\frac{1}{3}$ m from the other end and can just support 20 kg. A mass of $3 \cdot 4$ kg is now attached to the rod. Find the length of beam within which it can be attached without breaking either string.
(L.U.)

21. A telephone pole *AB*, 10 m high, has five wires radiating from the top *B*, producing the following horizontal pulls: $200g$ N due South, $190g$ N due East, $205g$ N due North-East, $185g$ N at $30°$ East of North, and $210g$ N due North-West. The pole is stayed by a wire running from the top and fixed to a point *C* on the ground 3·6 m horizontally from the foot of the pole.

Find the tension in the stay *CB* and the inclination of *AC* to the South in order that there shall be no overturning moment on the pole.   (Q.E.)

22. A rectangular plate 4 m × 3 m lies on a horizontal surface. The centre of mass of the plate is 1 m from a 4-m edge and 1·5 m from a 3-m edge. The mass of the plate is 120 kg. Determine the vertical forces which, applied to the four corners of the plate in turn, would just raise them off the ground.   (Q.E.)

CHAPTER 4

COPLANAR FORCES

4.1 Reduction of a System of Coplanar Forces

Any system of coplanar forces acting on a rigid body can be reduced to a single force or a single couple.

This theorem follows at once from the work of the previous chapter. By the parallelogram of forces, or by the theorems on the resultant of parallel forces, the resultant of any two forces may be found; this combined with a third force will determine the resultant of the first three forces, and so on until a final resultant is reached. Should the summation of forces at any stage lead to a couple, the resultant of the couple and the next force to be added may be found. Hence, the magnitude and line of action of the resultant of all the forces may be found, provided that the addition of the last force does not lead to a couple.

Any system of coplanar forces acting on a rigid body is equivalent to a force acting at a given point of the body together with a couple.

Let O be the given point (Fig. 37). Suppose the system of forces has a resultant which is a single force P. Introduce two equal and opposite forces P parallel to the resultant at O. Then one of these forces with the resultant forms a couple and we have a single force P at O and a couple. If the system of forces reduces to a couple, then the force at O will be zero.

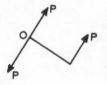

Fig. 37.

4.2 Analytical Representation

With reference to rectangular axes through a given point O (Fig. 38) let the forces of a system be P_1, P_2, P_3...and let these forces act at the points $(x_1, y_1), (x_2, y_2), (x_3, y_3)$...respectively. Further, let the components of the forces P_1, P_2, P_3 ...parallel to the axes be X_1 and Y_1, X_2 and Y_2, X_3 and Y_3... Introduce at O two equal and opposite forces X_1 parallel to OX and two equal and opposite forces Y_1 parallel to OY. Then we have forces X_1 and Y_1 acting at O and two couples whose moments are $x_1 Y_1$ and $-y_1 X_1$.

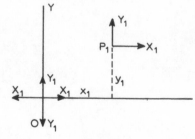

Fig. 38.

54

Thus the force P_1 acting at (x_1, y_1) is equivalent to a force with components X_1 and Y_1 parallel to the axes acting at O and a couple whose moment is $x_1Y_1 - y_1X_1$.

Similarly, the force P_2 acting at (x_2, y_2) is equivalent to a force with components X_2 and Y_2 parallel to the axes acting at O and a couple whose moment is $x_2Y_2 - y_2X_2$. In the same way, each force of the system is equivalent to two forces acting at O parallel to the axes and a couple.

If the resultant of all the forces acting at O has components X and Y parallel to the axes, we have

$$X = X_1 + X_2 + X_3 + \ldots = \Sigma X_1,$$
$$Y = Y_1 + Y_2 + Y_3 + \ldots = \Sigma Y_1.$$

Also, the couples may be compounded into a single couple G whose moment is the sum of the moments of all the couples, that is,

$$G = (x_1Y_1 - y_1X_1) + (x_2Y_2 - y_2X_2) + (x_3Y_3 - y_3X_3) + \ldots$$
$$= \Sigma(x_1Y_1 - y_1X_1).$$

The forces X and Y are equivalent to a single force P acting at O, where $P = \sqrt{(X^2 + Y^2)}$. Hence, the system reduces to a single force P at O and a couple G.

Cor. 1. The condition that the system of forces should reduce to a couple is that P should be zero, and for this X and Y should each be zero, that is,

$$\Sigma X_1 = \Sigma Y_1 = 0.$$

Cor. 2. If the system of forces reduces to a single force its line of action

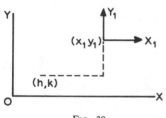

FIG. 39.

may be found. The sum of the moments of the forces of the system about any point on the line of action of the resultant will be zero.

The moment of the force P_1 at $(x_1 y_1)$ (Fig. 39) about the point (h, k) is

$$(x_1 - h)Y_1 - (y_1 - k)X_1$$
$$= (x_1Y_1 - y_1X_1) - hY_1 + kX_1.$$

Hence, the sum of the moments of all the forces about the point (h, k) is

$$\Sigma(x_1Y_1 - y_1X_1) - h\Sigma Y_1 + k\Sigma X_1$$
$$= G - hY + kX.$$

If the point (h, k) lies on the resultant, we have

$$G - hY + kX = 0.$$

This is true for any point (h, k) on the resultant, and hence the locus of such points is the line whose equation is

$$G - xY + yX = 0,$$

which is therefore the equation of the line of action of the resultant. This equation determines a definite straight line unless the coefficients of x and y are both zero, and this is the case where the system reduces to a couple.

Example 1. *ABCDEF is a regular hexagon of side a metres with centre at O. Forces of 1, 2, 3, 5, 4, 2 N act along the sides AB, BC, CD, DE, EF, FA. Reduce the forces to a force at O and a couple and find the line of action of a single force equivalent to the system.*

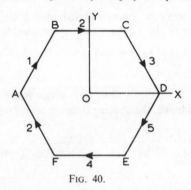

FIG. 40.

Taking OD (Fig. 40) as the x-axis, the components of the six forces parallel to the axes are

$$X_1 = \frac{1}{2}, \qquad Y_1 = \frac{\sqrt{3}}{2},$$

$$X_2 = 2, \qquad Y_2 = 0,$$

$$X_3 = \frac{3}{2}, \qquad Y_3 = -3\frac{\sqrt{3}}{2},$$

$$X_4 = -\frac{5}{2}, \qquad Y_4 = -5\frac{\sqrt{3}}{2},$$

$$X_5 = -4, \qquad Y_5 = 0,$$

$$X_6 = -1, \qquad Y_6 = 2\frac{\sqrt{3}}{2},$$

so that

$$X = -\frac{7}{2}, \qquad Y = -5\frac{\sqrt{3}}{2},$$

$$X^2 + Y^2 = \frac{49}{4} + \frac{75}{4} = 31,$$

$$P = \sqrt{(X^2 + Y^2)} = \sqrt{(31)}.$$

$$\tan^{-1}\frac{Y}{X} = \tan^{-1}\frac{5\sqrt{3}}{7}$$

The resultant force at O is therefore $\sqrt{31}$ N in a direction making an angle $\pi + \tan^{-1}\frac{5\sqrt{3}}{7}$ with OX.

The sum of the moments of the forces about O

$$= -\frac{a\sqrt{3}}{2}(1+2+3+5+4+2) = -17\frac{\sqrt{3}}{2}a \text{ mN}.$$

Let $(h, 0)$ be the coordinates of the point where the single resultant meets OX. The components of the resultant being X and Y, the moment of the resultant about O will be

$$h \times Y = -\frac{5\sqrt{3}}{2}h.$$

Putting this quantity equal to $-17\frac{\sqrt{3}}{2}a$ we have

$$h = \frac{17}{5}a \text{ metres.}$$

The single resultant therefore cuts OX at this distance from O.

Alternatively, the equation of the line of action of the single force is

$$G - xY + yX = 0,$$

that is

$$-17\frac{\sqrt{3}}{2}a + \frac{5\sqrt{3}}{2}x - \frac{7}{2}y = 0,$$

and this line meets the x-axis where $x = \frac{17}{5}a$.

4.3 Conditions for Equilibrium

We have seen that a system of coplanar forces acting on a rigid body can be reduced to a single force and a couple. Since a force and a couple cannot balance each other unless each is zero, we must have the force and couple vanishing separately for equilibrium.

With reference to rectangular axes in the plane of the forces, we have (§4.2) for the components of the resultant force through an arbitrary origin

$$X = \Sigma X_1,$$
$$Y = \Sigma Y_1,$$

and the couple is

$$G = \Sigma(x_1 Y_1 - y_1 X_1).$$

Hence, necessary and sufficient conditions for the equilibrium of the body under the action of the system of forces are

$$X = Y = G = 0.$$

The two conditions $X = Y = 0$, mean that the sum of the resolved parts of the forces in two directions at right angles, and hence in any two different directions, must be zero, and this ensures that the body as a whole shall have no motion.

The condition $G = 0$ means that the sum of the moments of the forces about any point in the plane must be zero, and this ensures that the body shall have no rotation about any point.

Hence, we have in all three conditions for equilibrium. An alternative set of three conditions which is sometimes more convenient in practice is given in the following theorem.

4.4 Moment Condition for Equilibrium

If a system of coplanar forces acts on a rigid body and the sum of the moments of the forces about each of three points which do not lie in a straight line is zero, then the body is in equilibrium.

Any system of coplanar forces can be reduced to a force or a couple, and the fact that the sum of their moments is zero about one point shows that the forces cannot reduce to a couple in this case. Hence, they must reduce to a single force.

The fact that the sum of the moments of the forces about each of two points is zero shows that either both of the points lie on the line of action of the resultant force or that the resultant force is zero.

If two of the points lie on the line of action of the resultant, the third point cannot lie on the same straight line, and hence if the sum of the moments of the forces about this point is also zero, the resultant itself must be zero and the body is in equilibrium.

Hence, in examining a system of coplanar forces acting on one rigid body in equilibrium we can obtain three and only three independent relations between the forces. We may obtain two relations by equating to zero the resolved parts of the forces in two directions and a third by equating to zero the sum of the moments about some point, or, alternatively, we may obtain three equations by equating to zero the sum of the moments about three points not in the same straight line.

Example 2. *Forces X, $2X$, $3X$, $2X$, $5X$ act along the lines AB, CA, FC, FD, ED respectively of a regular hexagon ABCDEF and forces P, Q and R act along the lines BC, FA, FE. If the system is in equilibrium find the values of P, Q and R.*

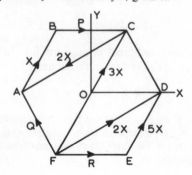

FIG. 41.

Taking OD (Fig. 41) as the x-axis, we have for the components of the eight forces in the order in which they are given

$$X_1 = \frac{1}{2}X, \qquad Y_1 = \frac{\sqrt{3}}{2}X,$$

$$X_2 = -\sqrt{3}X, \qquad Y_2 = -X,$$

$$X_3 = \frac{3}{2}X, \qquad Y_3 = \frac{3\sqrt{3}}{2}X,$$

$$X_4 = \sqrt{3}\,X, \qquad Y_4 = 0,$$

$$X_5 = \frac{5}{2}X, \qquad Y_5 = 5\frac{\sqrt{3}}{2}X,$$

$$X_6 = P, \qquad Y_6 = 0,$$

$$X_7 = -\frac{Q}{2}, \qquad Y_7 = \frac{\sqrt{3}}{2}Q,$$

$$X_8 = R, \qquad Y_8 = 0.$$

Since the sums of the components must each be zero we have

$$P + R - \frac{1}{2}Q + \frac{9}{2}X = 0 \tag{1}$$

$$\frac{\sqrt{3}}{2}Q + 9\frac{\sqrt{3}}{2}X = 0 \tag{2}$$

Also, the sum of the moments of the forces about O must be zero, that is, if $AB = a$,

$$\frac{\sqrt{3}}{2}a(-X + 5X - P - Q + R) + \frac{a}{2}(2X + 2X) = 0,$$

i.e.
$$P + Q - R = 4\left(1 + \frac{1}{\sqrt{3}}\right)X \tag{3}$$

From these three equations we have

$$P = 2 + \frac{2}{\sqrt{3}}\ X$$

$$Q = -9X$$

$$R = -\left(11 + \frac{2}{\sqrt{3}}\right)X.$$

EXERCISES 4 (a)

1. Forces of magnitudes P, $2P$, $3P$, $4P$ act respectively along the sides AB, BC, CD, DA of a square $ABCD$, and further forces each of magnitude $8\sqrt{2}P$ act along the diagonals BD and AC. Determine the magnitude of the resultant of these six forces, the inclination of its line of action to AC, and the perpendicular distance of this line of action from A. (L.U.)

2. ABC is an equilateral triangle; forces $4g$ N, $2g$ N and $2g$ N act along the sides AB, AC and BC respectively, in the directions indicated by the letters. Prove that, if E is the point where the perpendicular to BC at B meets CA produced and if F bisects AB, the resultant is $2\sqrt{7}g$ N acting along EF. (O.C.)

3. Forces 13P, 2P, 3P, 8P act along the sides AB, BC, CD, AD respectively of a square ABCD in the sense indicated by the order of the letters. Find the magnitude and direction of their resultant and prove that its line of action passes through the mid-point of AB. (L.U.)

4. ABCD is a plane non-re-entrant quadrilateral, in which the sides AD and BC are parallel. Show that forces whose magnitudes are proportional to the lengths of AB, AD, CD, BC acting in suitable senses along AB, BC, CD, DA respectively will be in equilibrium and determine the senses in which they act. (O.C.)

5. Forces of magnitudes 1, 2, 3, 6, 5, 4 units act respectively along the sides AB, CB, CD, ED, EF, AF of a regular hexagon, the sense of each force being indicated by the order of letters. Prove that the six forces are equivalent to a couple, and find its moment if the side of the hexagon is a. (L.U.)

6. ABC is an equilateral triangle of side a and AD is a median. Forces of 4, 3, 3 and 2 N act along BC, CA, AB and AD respectively, the direction being indicated by the order of the letters. Find the resultant of the forces in magnitude and direction, and the distance from D of the point where its line of action intersects BC produced. (L.U.)

7. ABCD is a plane quadrilateral in which the angles A and B are right angles, the angle ADC is 60°, and the sides AD and DC are equal. A force P acts along BC in the direction from B to C. Find three forces along CD, DA and AB respectively which will be in equilibrium with P. (O.C.)

8. A rectangular lamina ABCD lying on a smooth horizontal table is acted upon by forces P along AB, 4 along CB, 3 along CD and 4 along AD. Equilibrium is maintained by a fifth force applied at the middle point of BC. If AB = 2a and BC = 3a, find the magnitude of P. (L.U.)

9. The angles A, B, C of a triangle ABC are 45°, 75°, 60° respectively. D is a point on AC such that BDA = 75°, and E lies between DA and DB such that EDA = 45°. A force F acts in the line DE in the sense D to E. Find three forces P, Q, R in CA, AB, CB respectively which together are equivalent to F.

(L.U.)

10. Find the resultant of the following forces acting along the sides of a square ABCD; 17 N along DA, 7 N along CB, 19 N along CD, 5 N along BA; and prove that the line of action of the resultant bisects two of the sides of the square. (L.U.)

11. A, B, C are 3 points on a line ABCD, such that AB = BC = a. Forces of 3, 6 and 4 N respectively act at A, B, C in directions making angles 60°, 120° and 270° with AD. Show that they reduce to a single force, and find where its line of action cuts AD. (L.U.)

12. Forces of magnitude F, 2F, 3F, 4F act along the sides BA, BC, CD, DA of a quadrilateral ABCD in the directions indicated by the order of the letters, the quadrilateral being such that AB and BC are two sides of a square ABCE and D is the mid-point of CE. Find the magnitude and direction of the resultant and the distances from B at which its line of action meets AB and BC. (L.U.)

13. Forces of magnitude 4 N, 3 N, 1 N and 2 N act along the sides AB, CB, CD, AD respectively of a rectangle ABCD in the directions indicated by the order of the letters. The sides AB and BC have lengths 7a and 5a. If this system of forces is equivalent to a force P acting at A and a force Q acting along DB, find the magnitudes of P and Q and the direction of P. Find also where the line of action of the resultant of the system meets AB. (L.U.)

14. Show that forces 1, 5, 3, 4, 2, 6 acting in order round the sides of a regular hexagon, which touch a circle of radius a, are equivalent to a couple. Find its moment and show that, if the forces 2, 5 be replaced by forces $8\frac{1}{2}$, $5\frac{1}{2}$ acting along the same sides but in directions opposite to the forces 2, 5 respectively, the system will be in equilibrium.   (L.U.)

15. Two unit vectors i and j are such that j is at an angle $+90°$ to i. A force represented by $ai + bj$ acts through a point P whose position vector relative to an origin O is $xi + yj$. Show that the moment of the force about O is $(bx - ay)$ and that the moment does not depend on the particular point P chosen on the line of action of the force.   (O.C.)

16. Forces $4i + 2j$, $i - 2j$ and $i - 3j$ have their lines of action passing through points whose position vectors relative to O are $2i + 3j$, $i + j$ and $2i - j$ respectively. Find the resultant of the forces and, if its line of action passes through $xi + 0j$, find x and state the angle which the resultant makes with the vector i.

                              (O.C.)

4.5 Equilibrium Under the Action of Three Forces

If three forces act on a rigid body in equilibrium the forces must be coplanar, and either concurrent or parallel.

Let the forces be P, Q and R. Let A (Fig. 42) be a point on the line of

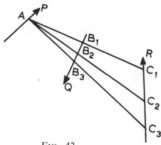

FIG. 42.

action of P, and let B_1, B_2, B_3... be points on the line of action of Q. Then, since the forces P and Q have no turning moments about the lines AB_1, AB_2, AB_3..., the force R can have no turning moment about any of these lines, and hence each of these lines must intersect the line of action of R or be parallel to it, and only one of the lines can be parallel to it. It follows that the forces Q and R must be coplanar and, since these are any two of the forces, the three forces must be coplanar.

Again, if the forces are not all parallel let the lines of action of Q and R meet in O. Then the line of action of P must pass through O, for otherwise P would have a turning moment about this point. Hence, the lines of action of the forces must be concurrent or parallel.

In the large class of problems in which a body is in equilibrium under the action of three forces we may use the fact that the forces are concurrent as an alternative to a moment equation. Thus the concurrence of the forces and two equations of resolution establish three conditions of equilibrium. Further, in dealing with the equilibrium of three concurrent forces we may use the triangle of forces or Lami's theorem to establish the condition of equilibrium.

In problems dealing with the equilibrium of a body it is important that a clear figure be drawn and all the forces acting on the body marked on the figure. Wherever any body presses against another body an unknown reaction must be assumed to act which, if the bodies be smooth, will be perpendicular to the common tangent plane. If a body is supported by a string a tension must be assumed in the string, and this tension is unchanged when the string passes over a smooth peg or pulley. If a body is hinged to another body and there is no friction at the hinge the forces acting there on either body may be taken as a single force acting through the centre of the hinge. If the direction of this force is not known it may be taken as having two unknown components in directions at right angles, and when these have been found the magnitude and direction of the force may be deduced.

When all the forces have been marked, the three equations of equilibrium for a body should be written down and numbered. If there is more that one body to be considered the three equations for each body should be set down. When this has been done, the statical problem has been solved, although some algebraic manipulation may be required to complete the solution. Geometrical relations between the angles and lengths in the figure may need to be considered so as to simplify the statical equations.

Example 3. *A uniform beam AB of length l and weight W is free to turn in a vertical plane about a hinge at A and is supported in a horizontal position by a string attached to the beam at a point D at l/3 from A and to a point F at a height b vertically above A. Find the tension in the string and the magnitude and direction of the reaction at the hinge.*

The weight W acts vertically downwards through C, the mid-point of the beam (Fig. 43). The tension in the string T acts along the string, and its line of action intersects that of the weight in E. The reaction at the hinge R must therefore also pass through E.

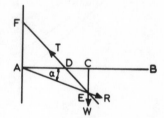

Fig. 43.

There are three unknown quantities to be found, namely, T, R and the direction of R. Let $AFD = \beta$ and $DAE = \alpha$.

Resolving horizontally we have

$$T \sin \beta - R \cos \alpha = 0 \tag{4}$$

Resolving vertically we have

$$T \cos \beta - R \sin \alpha - W = 0 \tag{5}$$

Taking moments about A we have

$$T . b \sin \beta - W . \frac{l}{2} = 0 \tag{6}$$

We have in addition the geometrical equation for β, namely,

$$\tan \beta = \frac{AD}{AF} = \frac{l}{3b},$$

whence

$$\sin \beta = \frac{l}{\sqrt{l^2 + 9b^2}}, \qquad \cos \beta = \frac{3b}{\sqrt{l^2 + 9b^2}}.$$

From equations (4), (5) and (6)

$$T = \frac{W}{2b}\sqrt{(l^2 + 9b^2)}.$$

$$R \sin \alpha = \frac{W}{2},$$

$$R \cos \alpha = \frac{Wl}{2b},$$

$$R = \frac{W}{2b}\sqrt{(l^2 + b^2)},$$

$$\tan \alpha = \frac{b}{l}.$$

Alternatively, since the triangles ADF and CDE are similar and $AD = 2DC$, we have $CE = \frac{b}{2}$ and hence $\tan \alpha = \frac{b}{l}$. Also, since FAE is a triangle of forces

$$\frac{T}{\sin(90 + \alpha)} = \frac{R}{\sin \beta} = \frac{W}{\sin(90 - \alpha - \beta)}.$$

Example 4. *A uniform ladder of length l and weight W rests with its top against a smooth vertical wall and its base held on the ground at distance b from the wall. Find the forces acting on the ladder.*

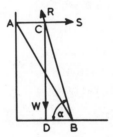

FIG. 44.

Let the force at the top be S perpendicular to the wall and the force at the base be R at an angle α to the horizontal (Fig. 44).

Then the ladder is in equilibrium under the action of the forces W, R and S.

Resolving horizontally
$$R \cos \alpha = S \tag{7}$$

Resolving vertically
$$R \sin \alpha = W \tag{8}$$

Taking moments about the base of the ladder
$$W\frac{b}{2} - S\sqrt{(l^2 - b^2)} = 0 \tag{9}$$

Hence,

$$S = \frac{W}{2}\frac{b}{\sqrt{l^2 - b^2}}$$

$$R = \frac{W}{2}\frac{\sqrt{4l^2 - 3b^2}}{\sqrt{l^2 - b^2}},$$

$$\tan \alpha = 2\frac{\sqrt{l^2 - b^2}}{b}.$$

Alternatively, the triangle BCD is a triangle of forces and we have

$$\frac{W}{\sin \alpha} = \frac{S}{\sin (90° - \alpha)} \quad \frac{R}{\sin 90°}.$$

Example 5. *A uniform heavy rod of length $2a$ rests with its lower end in contact with the inside of a smooth hermispherical cup, radius a, whose axis is vertical, the upper end of the rod projecting beyond the rim of the cup. Show that the inclination θ of the rod to the horizontal is given by $2 \cos 2\theta = \cos \theta$.*

Let AB (Fig. 45) be the portion of the rod inside the bowl, O the centre of the bowl and $OBA = \theta$. Then since $OA = OB = a$, $OAB = \theta$ and $AB = 2a \cos \theta$.

The reaction R at A will be normal to the surface of the bowl and will therefore pass through the centre of the bowl and be inclined at an angle 2θ to the horizontal.

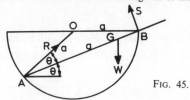

FIG. 45.

The reaction S at B will be perpendicular to the rod at B and therefore inclined at an angle θ to the vertical.

Resolving horizontally we have

$$S \sin \theta - R \cos 2\theta = 0 \tag{10}$$

Resolving vertically we have

$$S \cos \theta + R \sin 2\theta - W = 0 \tag{11}$$

Taking moments about A we have

$$S . 2a \cos \theta - W . a \cos \theta = 0 \tag{12}$$

Hence, $S = \dfrac{W}{2}$, and from (10) $R = \dfrac{W \sin \theta}{2 \cos 2\theta}.$

Substituting for R and S in (11) we have

$$\frac{W}{2} \cos \theta + \frac{W}{2} \frac{\sin \theta \sin 2\theta}{\cos 2\theta} - W = 0,$$

and hence,

$$\cos \theta = 2 \cos 2\theta.$$

Example 6. *Two smooth uniform spheres of equal masses but of radii 2 m and 3 m are placed in a fixed hemispherical bowl of radius 8 m. Show that in the position of equilibrium the inclination θ to the vertical of the line joining the centres of the spheres is given by $11 \tan \theta = 48$.*

Let O be the centre of the bowl and A and B the centres of the spheres (Fig. 46). $OA = 6$ m, $OB = 5$ m and $AB = 5$ m.

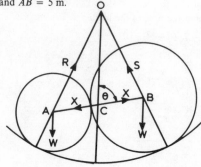

FIG. 46.

Reactions R and S between the spheres and the bowl will act along the lines AO and BO respectively. The reaction between the spheres X will act along the line AB on each sphere towards its centre.

For the sphere with centre at A the moment of its weight about O is equal to the moment of the force X about O.

For the sphere with centre at B the moment of its weight about O is equal to the moment of the force X about O in the opposite sense.

Hence the moments of the weights of the two spheres about O must be equal and opposite, that is, the vertical through O must bisect the line AB.

Let C be the mid-point of AB and θ the angle OCB, and let $OC = x$.

From the triangle OCB we have

$$5^2 = x^2 + (5/2)^2 - 5x \cos \theta \tag{13}$$

From the triangle OCA we have

$$6^2 = x^2 + (5/2)^2 + 5x \cos \theta \tag{14}$$

Subtracting these equations we have

$$10x \cos \theta = 11.$$

Substituting for x in (14) we have

$$36 = \frac{121}{100} \sec^2\theta + \frac{25}{4} + \frac{11}{2},$$

i.e.

$$\sec^2\theta = \frac{97 \times 25}{121} = 1 + \tan^2\theta.$$

$$\tan^2\theta = \frac{2304}{121},$$

$$\tan \theta = \frac{48}{11}.$$

EXERCISES 4 (b)

1. A uniform lamina of weight W in the form of an isosceles triangle ABC right-angled at B is freely hinged to a fixed point at A and rests with AC vertical and C above A, equilibrium being maintained by a horizontal string attached to C. Find the tension in the string and the magnitude and direction of the reaction at A. (O.C.)

2. A uniform beam AB is of mass 200 kg and is 5 m long. It is hinged to a vertical wall at A, and is kept horizontal and perpendicular to the wall by a tie attached to a point on the wall 4 m vertically above A, and to a point C of the beam, where $AC = 3$ m. A mass of 450 kg is suspended from B. Find the tension in the tie, and the magnitude and direction of the reaction at the hinge. (C.S.)

3. A uniform heavy rod AB, of length l, rests in equilibrium with the upper end B in contact with a smooth vertical wall and the other end A in contact with a smooth concave spherical surface of radius a (where $2l > a > l$) whose centre is at a point O on the wall vertically above B. If AB and OA are inclined to the horizontal at angles θ and ϕ respectively, prove that

(i) $\tan \phi = 2 \tan \theta$; (ii) $\sin \theta = \sqrt{\dfrac{a^2 - l^2}{3l^2}}$. (L.U.)

4. A uniform rod of weight W rests with one end against a smooth vertical wall and the other on a smooth plane which is inclined at an angle of 60° to the wall. Find the inclination of the rod to the vertical and the reactions at the ends of the rod. A graphical solution will be accepted. (C.S.)

5. AB is a uniform bar of weight W, movable about a smooth horizontal axis fixed at A; to B is attached a light cord which passes over a pulley C fixed vertically above A, and supports a mass of weight P at its free end. Show by applying the triangle of forces that in the position of equilibrium

$$CB = 2\frac{P}{W}.AC.$$ (L.U.)

6. A uniform rod AB, of mass 10 kg, is smoothly hinged at A and rests in a vertical plane with the end B against a smooth vertical wall. If the rod makes an angle of 40° with the wall, find the pressure on the wall and the magnitude and direction of the reaction at A. (O.C.)

7. A uniform sphere of radius a is to be kept at rest on a smooth plane inclined to the horizontal at an angle α by means of a string attached to a point on the surface of the sphere, and the tension in the string is not to exceed the weight of the sphere. Prove that the length of the string must not be less than $a(\sec \alpha - 1)$. (O.C.)

8. Two uniform rods AB, BC, alike in all respects and each of weight W, are rigidly jointed at B so that ABC is a right angle, and the end A is hinged freely to a fixed point from which the rods hang in equilibrium. Show that AB makes an angle $\tan^{-1} \frac{1}{3}$ with the vertical. If the rods are freely jointed at B but A and C are connected by a light inextensible string of such a length that ABC is a right angle, show that the tension in this string is $3W/2\sqrt{5}$. (O.C.)

9. A uniform square board the length of whose edge is $2a$ rests with one horizontal edge against a smooth vertical wall and is supported in an inclined position by means of a light string of length $a/2$ which is attached to a point P of the board and to a point of the wall. Show that for the board to be in equilibrium the point P must be at a distance $a/2$ from the edge of the board, whatever be the inclination of the board.

10. A uniform beam AB, 6 m long, has mass 40 kg. The end A, about which the beam can turn freely, is attached to a vertical wall, and the beam is kept in a horizontal position by a rope attached to a point of the beam 1·25 m from A and to a point of the wall vertically above A. If the tension in the rope is not to exceed $120g$ N, show that the height above A of the point of attachment of the string to the wall must not be less than $1\frac{2}{3}$ m. (L.U.)

11. A uniform circular disc of mass m and radius R is suspended by three strings of length $3R$, equally spaced round its periphery. The upper ends of the three strings are attached to a single fixed point. What is the magnitude of the least mass which attached to the disc will just reduce the tension in one string to zero? What will now be the tensions in the other two strings? (Q.E.)

12. A bar AB of length 70 cm has its centre of gravity 40 cm from A. A light string of length 210 cm is attached to the ends of the bar, which hangs in equilibrium with the string passing over a smooth peg. Show that the inclination θ of the bar to the vertical is given by $6 \sin^2 \theta = 5$. (L.U.)

13. A light inextensible string of length l has one end attached to the end A of a smooth uniform heavy rod AB whose length is $2a$. The other end of the string is attached to a small smooth ring C (whose weight may be neglected) which

slides on the rod. The rod is suspended with the string over a smooth peg P. Show that, in the position of equilibrium, (i) the portion PC of the string is at right angles to the rod; (ii) the length x of the portion PA is given by the equation

$$l(x^2 + a^2) = 2x^3.$$ (L.U.)

14. A heavy bar AB whose centre of gravity is at a point G such that $AG:GB = a:b$, is supported by a string attached to the end A. The other end B is pulled away from the vertical by a horizontal force, until the inclination of the string to the horizontal is ϕ. Prove that the inclination of the bar to the horizontal is given by

$$(a+b)\tan\theta = a\tan\phi.$$ (L.U.)

15. A uniform beam AB, of length $2l$ and weight W, rests tangentially against the rim of a smooth fixed circular disc of radius a whose plane is the vertical plane through the beam. The lower end A of the beam is in contact with a smooth horizontal plane passing through the lowest point O of the disc. If the end A of the beam is acted upon by a force T towards the point O, and the inclination of the beam to the horizontal is $60°$, prove that in the position of equilibrium $T = Wl/4a$. (L.U.)

16. A light elastic string, of natural length 60 cm, is stretched 12·5 cm when suspended from one end and carrying a mass of 3 kg at the other. If the mass be acted upon by a horizontal force of g newton, find the inclination of the string to the vertical in the equilibrium position and the corresponding length of the string.

(L.U.)

17. Five equal masses are attached to a light string which hangs from two points P and Q in the same horizontal. In equilibrium the horizontal projections of the six intervals of the string are all equal to a, and the depth below PQ of the lowest weight is $3a$. Show that the inclinations to the horizontal of the parts of the string are $\tan^{-1}(1/3)$, $\pi/4$, and $\tan^{-1}(5/3)$. (O.C.)

4.6 Equilibrium Under the Action of More than Three Forces

If there are four or more forces acting on a rigid body in equilibrium, the forces are not necessarily concurrent. If the forces are coplanar, the general conditions of equilibrium apply, giving three equations connecting the forces or their directions, and for a single body not more than three independent equations can be obtained. It should be noted that the fact that the force vectors placed end to end form a closed polygon is not a sufficient condition for equilibrium: this condition is equivalent to the condition that the sum of the resolved parts of the forces in two perpendicular directions be zero, and for equilibrium we require in addition that the sum of the moments of the forces about some point be zero: this condition is automatically satisfied if the forces are concurrent but not otherwise.

Example 7. *A uniform beam AB 6 m long is free to turn a vertical plane about a hinge at A. The beam has mass 200 kg and carries a mass of 300 kg at B. It is supported in a horizontal position by a rope attached to a point of the beam 4 m from A and to a point 3 m vertically above A. Find the tension in the rope and the magnitude and direction of the reaction at the hinge.*

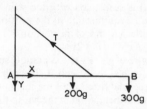

FIG. 47.

Let the tension in the rope be T newton (Fig. 47) and let the reaction at the hinge have horizontal and vertical components X and Y newton. The string makes an angle $\tan^{-1}\frac{3}{4}$ with the horizontal, and hence horizontal and vertical components of the tension T are $4T/5$ and $3T/5$.

Resolving horizontally $\quad X - \frac{4}{5}T = 0$ (15)

Resolving vertically $\quad \frac{3}{5}T - Y - 200g - 300g = 0$ (16)

Moments about A $\quad \frac{3}{5}T \times 4 - 200g \times 3 - 300g \times 6 = 0$ (17)

Hence
$$T = 1000g \text{ N}$$
$$X = 800g \text{ N}$$
$$Y = 100g \text{ N}.$$

The reaction at the hinge is therefore
$$\sqrt{X^2 + Y^2} = 100\sqrt{65}g \text{ N}$$
in a direction making an angle $\tan^{-1}\frac{1}{8}$ with the horizontal.

Example 8. *Two uniform smooth spheres, each of weight W and radius b, rest inside a hollow cylinder of radius $a(< 2b)$, fixed with its base horizontal. Show that the reaction between the curved surface of the cylinder and each sphere is $\dfrac{(a-b)W}{\sqrt{2ab-a^2}}$, and find the reaction between the two spheres.*

The condition $a < 2b$ ensures that one sphere shall rest on the other.

Let A and B be the centres of the spheres and ABC a triangle with AC horizontal and BC vertical (Fig. 48)

Then $AC = 2a - 2b$,
$\quad\quad AB = 2b$.

Writing the angle $BAC = \theta$ we have
$$\cos\theta = \frac{a-b}{b},$$
$$\sin\theta = \frac{\sqrt{2ab-a^2}}{b}.$$

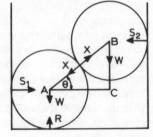

FIG. 48.

Let S_1 and S_2 be the reactions of the curved surface of the cylinder on the spheres, R the reaction of the base on the lower sphere and X the reaction between the spheres all in absolute units.

The forces acting on each sphere are concurrent, and hence we have two conditions of equilibrium for each sphere obtained by resolving the forces.

For the lower sphere

$$S_1 - X \cos \theta = 0 \tag{18}$$
$$R - W - X \sin \theta = 0 \tag{19}$$

For the upper sphere

$$S_2 - X \cos \theta = 0 \tag{20}$$
$$W - X \sin \theta = 0 \tag{21}$$

From (18) and (21) and from (20) and (21) we have

$$S_1 = S_2 = W \cot \theta = \frac{(a-b)}{\sqrt{2ab - a^2}} W.$$

Hence from (18)

$$X = \frac{W}{\sin \theta} \frac{bW}{\sqrt{2ab - a^2}}.$$

EXERCISES 4 (c)

1. A uniform beam AB is hinged at A to a wall and kept in a horizontal position by a light stay CD which joins a point C on the beam to a point D on the wall vertically below A. The beam has mass 10 kg and carries a mass of 20 kg at the end B. If $AC = 40$ cm, $AB = 120$ cm and the angle $ACD = 60°$, find the thrust in the stay and the magnitude and direction of the reaction at the hinge.

2. A pole of mass 50 kg is held in a vertical position with its base on horizontal ground by two ropes attached to the pole at heights 8 m and 10 m respectively from the ground, and to the ground at equal distances of 8 m from the base of the pole, the ropes being in the same vertical plane. If the vertical component of the reaction of the ground is $100g$ N, find the tensions in the ropes and the angle which the reaction of the ground makes with the vertical.

3. A uniform spar of mass 250 kg rests with one end on rough ground and is held inclined at 20° to the vertical by a guy-rope attached to its other end. The guy-rope makes an angle of 30° with the horizontal. A mass of 560 kg is suspended from the top end of the spar. Find the tension in the guy-rope and the reaction at the ground.   (C.S.)

4. A heavy bar AB, of mass 40 kg and length 240 cm, is hinged at A to a point in a vertical wall, and is maintained in a horizontal position by means of a chain attached to B and to a point in the wall 150 cm above A. If the bar carries a mass of 20 kg at a point 180 cm from A, calculate the tension in the chain and the magnitude and direction of the action at A.   (L.U.)

5. A ladder 3 m long and 35 kg in mass rests with the end A against a smooth vertical wall and the other end B on smooth ground at 180 cm from the wall; it is maintained in this position by a horizontal cord attached at B. Find the tension in the cord if the centre of gravity of the ladder is 120 cm from B. Find also the magnitude and direction of the force which, applied at A, will keep the ladder in position without the help of the cord.   (L.U.)

6. A hollow circular cylinder of internal radius 20 cm, open at both ends, rests with its axis vertical on a rough horizontal table. Two equal smooth spheres, each of weight W and radius 12·5 cm, are placed inside the cylinder; show that the two spheres exert a couple on the cylinder and find the moment of this couple.
                                                                                        (L.U.)

7. A lamina $ABCDEF$ is in the form of a regular hexagon and can turn freely about a fixed axis through A perpendicular to its plane. It is in equilibrium under the

reaction of the axis and forces $6g$ N along BC, $10g$ N along FC and Pg N along CD. Find the value of P and the magnitude and direction of the force exerted on the lamina by the axis. (L.U.)

8. A composite solid consists of a uniform right circular cone of vertical angle 60° and a uniform solid hemisphere of similar material whose radius is equal to that of the base of the cone. The cone and hemisphere are hinged together at a point common to the rim of the hemisphere and the circumference of the base of the cone so that the bases of the two solids coincide when the hinge is closed. The composite solid is then suspended from the apex of the cone with the hemisphere free to swing about the hinge. Show that, in the position of equilibrium, the axis of the cone makes an angle $\cot^{-1}\dfrac{8\sqrt{3}+9}{8}$ with the vertical. Hence show that the angle between the bases of the cone and the hemisphere is about 88° 44'.

It may be assumed that the centre of gravity of the cone divides the axis in the ratio $1:3$ and that the centre of gravity of a hemisphere of radius a is distant $\frac{3}{8}$ from the centre of its base. (L.U.)

9. The ends of a uniform heavy rod 240 cm long and of mass 10 kg slide in two smooth grooves AO and BO which are made in two planes inclined respectively at 30° and 45° to the horizontal. AO and BO are lines of greatest slope of the planes. Find the mass which should be attached to the rod at a point 60 cm from the end in contact with the plane inclined at 30° so that the rod may rest in equilibrium in a horizontal position.

10. A uniform smooth ladder rests with its extremities against a vertical wall and a horizontal plane, and is held by a rope one end of which is attached to a rung of the ladder one quarter of the way up, the other end being fixed to a point of the base of the wall vertically below the top of the ladder. Show that if the base and top of the ladder be distant a and b respectively from the base of the wall, the ratio of the reactions P and Q between the ladder and the ground and wall respectively is given by $Q/P = 3a/5b$. (L.U.)

11. A uniform bar AB, 3 m long and of mass 4 kg, has a cord 5 m long attached to its ends. The cord passes through a smooth ring O fixed in a smooth vertical wall, and the rod is placed in a vertical plane perpendicular to the wall with the end A against the wall and vertically below O. Prove that the rod will be in equilibrium if OA is 2 m and show that the tension of the string is $3g$ N. (O.C.)

12. A man wishes to pull a smooth lawn-roller of diameter 50 cm and mass 100 kg over a kerb stone 10 cm high. Find the direction in which he should pull, in any position of the roller, so as to raise the roller with the least effort; and show that the greatest force he need exert is $80g$ newton. (O.C.)

13. Two smooth planes, each inclined to the horizontal at an angle α, have a common horizontal line. A uniform cylinder, of weight W, rests in the space between them touching each plane along a generator. A second uniform cylinder, of weight W', is placed between the first cylinder and one of the planes, and its radius is such that, in this position, the plane through the axes of the two cylinders is horizontal. If the system remains in equilibrium, find the reactions between the planes and the two cylinders and the reaction between the two cylinders, and show that equilibrium cannot exist if W' is greater than W. (O.C.)

14. Three smooth circular cylinders with plane ends, equal in all respects, are in contact along generators with their axes horizontal and the plane containing the axes of the lower cylinders also horizontal. They are kept in equilibrium by strings, attached to the ends of the axes of the lower cylinders at right angles to these axes and each inclined at θ to the vertical. Prove that the pressure between the lower cylinders is $(3\sqrt{3} \tan \theta - 1)W/2\sqrt{3}$, where W is the weight of each cylinder.   (O.C.)

4.7 Jointed Rods

The conditions for the equilibrium of a body under the action of coplanar forces may be applied to each of a number of heavy rods freely jointed at their ends. Each rod must be in equilibrium under the action of its weight and the forces acting at its ends. The forces at each end of a *light* rod must be equal and opposite, and hence must be forces of tension or compression along the line of the rod, but the forces at the ends of a *heavy* rod must balance the weight of the rod, and hence cannot be equal and opposite.

In assuming unknown forces acting at the ends of a rod it is usually more convenient to specify horizontal and vertical components of the forces, and when these have been found the magnitude and direction of their resultant are easily deduced. To facilitate marking these forces on a diagram it is better to leave a space between the ends of the rods in the diagram.

Example 9. *Three equal uniform rods, each of weight W, are freely jointed at their ends so as to form an equilateral triangle. Find the forces at the joints when the triangle is suspended by a string from the mid-point of one of the sides*

By symmetry the force at each end of the horizontal rod *AB* (Fig. 49) will be the same; let its components be X and Y in absolute units. Then the force at the end A of the rod

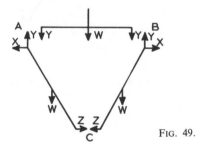

Fig. 49.

AC will also have components X and Y in the opposite directions. By symmetry also we may assume that the vertical component of the forces at C on AC and BC are zero; let the horizontal component be Z in absolute units.

Equating to zero the horizontal and vertical components of the forces acting on *AC* we have

$$X = Z,$$
$$Y = W.$$

Taking moments of the forces acting on AC about A we have

$$Z \times AC \sin 60° = W \times \frac{AC}{2} \cos 60.$$

Hence,

$$Z = \frac{W}{2\sqrt{3}}$$

$$X = \frac{W}{2\sqrt{3}}$$

$$Y = W,$$

$$\sqrt{X^2 + Y^2} = \frac{\sqrt{13}W}{2\sqrt{3}}$$

$$\tan^{-1} \frac{Y}{X} = 2\sqrt{3}.$$

Example 10. *A step ladder of weight 2W consists of two equal parts, jointed at the top, and held together by a rope half-way between the top and bottom so that when the rope is tight the angle between the two halves of the ladder is $2 \tan^{-1} \frac{6}{13}$. A man of weight 5W mounts the ladder and stops two-thirds of the way up. Neglecting friction between the ladder and the ground, find the tension in the rope and the reaction at the hinge.*

Let l be the length of the ladder and $\tan \alpha = \frac{6}{13}$ (Fig. 50). The forces in absolute units acting on the two halves of the ladder are shown in the figure.

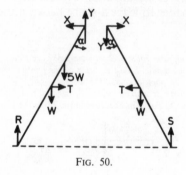

Fig. 50.

For the left-hand half we have, equating components to zero

$$X - T = 0 \tag{22}$$

$$R - 6W + Y = 0 \tag{23}$$

Taking moments about the top we have

$$W \times \frac{l}{2} \sin \alpha + 5W \times \frac{l}{3} \sin \alpha + T \times \frac{l}{2} \cos \alpha - R \times l \sin \alpha = 0,$$

that is,

$$26W - 12R + 13T = 0 \tag{24}$$

Similarly, for the right-hand half we have, equating components to zero,

$$X - T = 0 \tag{25}$$

$$S - W - Y = 0 \tag{26}$$

Taking moments about the top we have

$$S \times l \sin \alpha - W \times \frac{l}{2} \sin \alpha - T \times \frac{l}{2} \cos \alpha = 0,$$

that is, $12S - 6W - 13T = 0$ (27)

Hence,

$$T = 2W,$$
$$X = 2W,$$
$$Y = \tfrac{5}{3}W.$$

EXERCISES 4 (d)

1. Four equal uniform rods, each of weight W, are freely jointed at their ends so as to form a square. The rods are suspended from one of the corners and kept in the form of a square by a vertical string to the opposite corner. Find the tension in the string.

2. Four equal uniform rods, each of weight W, are freely jointed at their ends so as to form a square. The rods are suspended from one of the corners and kept in the form of a square by a light rod joining the mid-points of the two lower rods. Find the force in this rod, and the forces at the joints.

3. AB and BC are two rods of equal length freely jointed at B; the weight of AB is W and that of BC is $2W$. They are placed in a vertical plane inclined to one another at $90°$ with the ends A and C on a horizontal plane. What horizontal forces must be applied at A and C to maintain equilibrium?

(L.U.)

4. Two equal uniform rods AB, AC, smoothly jointed at A, each of length $2a$ and weight W, rest in equilibrium in a vertical plane astride a smooth fixed cylinder of radius r whose axis is horizontal. The ends B, C of the rods are jointed by an inextensible string of length $4l$ (where $l < a$) which passes underneath and remains clear of the cylinder. Show that the string is taut if $r > \dfrac{l^3}{a\sqrt{a^2 - l^2}}$, and find an expression for the reaction between a rod and the cylinder in terms of W, a and l.

(L.U.)

5. AB and BC are two uniform similar rods, each of weight W, freely hinged together at B and carrying small rings of negligible weight which enable the ends A and C to move without friction on a fixed horizontal wire. The rods are placed so as to include a right angle, with B below the wire, and are prevented from closing up by a light stay joining the middle points of the rods. Find the stress in this stay and the reactions at A, B and C.   (O.C.)

6. AB and BC are two uniform rods of weights W and W' respectively. They are freely hinged together at B, and the end A is freely pivoted to a fixed point, while the end C is constrained to move on a fixed horizontal wire, passing through A, by means of a small smooth ring of negligible mass. Show that the horizontal force which must be applied at C to keep the rods in the position in which the angles CAB and ACB are θ and ϕ and B is below AC, is

$$\tfrac{1}{2}(W + W') \cos \phi \cos \theta \operatorname{cosec} (\theta + \phi).$$ (O.C.)

7. Three equal rods AB, BC, CD and a rod AD of double their length are freely hinged at A, B, C, D, and the framework is suspended from the middle point of BC. If W is weight of each of the equal rods and $2W$ that of the longest rod, find the magnitudes of the forces at the hinges. Show that the lines of action of the forces at A and B meet at a depth $\dfrac{BC}{\sqrt{3}}$ below BC.   (L.U.)

8. AB, BC, CD, DE, EA are five equal uniform rods, each of weight W, freely jointed at their extremities and suspended from the joint A in the form of a regular pentagon, this configuration being maintained by light strings joining A to C and to D. Find the reactions at B and E, and show that the tension in either string is $2W \cos 18°$.   (L.U.)

9. Two rods AB and BC, a m and b m long, of the same material and cross-section, are freely jointed at B and hang with their ends A and C attached to two points at the same level, and at such a distance apart that ABC is a right angle. If the material of the rods weighs w kg/m, find the reactions at the joint B.

10. Two uniform rods AB, BC, of equal lengths but of different masses, are freely jointed at B, and jointed at A and C to two fixed points in the same horizontal line, at such distance apart that ABC is a right angle. Show that the tangent of the angle which the direction of the reaction at B makes with the rod BA is the ratio of the weight of AB to that of BC.   (L.U.)

11. Each half of a step ladder is 165 cm long and the two parts are connected by a cord 70 cm long attached to points distant 40 cm from their extremities. The half with the steps has mass 8 kg and the other half has mass 2 kg. Find the tension in the cord when a man of 77 kg is standing on the ladder 45 cm from the top, it being assumed that the reactions at the ground are vertical.   (L.U.)

12. Two uniform rods, AB, AC, of weight W_1, W_2, and of equal length, are smoothly hinged at A, and rest with B, C on a smooth horizontal plane, being kept in equilibrium by an inextensible string joining BC. A weight W is suspended from a point in AC at a distance of $\frac{3}{4} AC$ from A. Prove that the tension in the string is

$$\tfrac{1}{4} \ (W_1 + W_2 + \tfrac{1}{2}W) \tan \tfrac{1}{2}A. \qquad \text{(L.U.)}$$

13. Three uniform rods, AB, BC, CD, of weights W, $2W$ W respectively, are freely jointed at B and C and are freely hinged to fixed points at A and D. They rest in equilibrium with AD uppermost and horizontal. If $AB = CD = 2a$, $BC = 4a$, $AD = 6a$, calculate the magnitudes and directions of the reactions at A and B.   (L.U.)

14. Two equal uniform rods, AB, BC, each of length $2a$ and weight W, are freely jointed at B and rest, in a vertical plane, across two smooth horizontal pegs at the same horizontal level and distant a apart. Show that in the position of equilibrium the inclination θ of each rod to the vertical is given by $2 \sin^3 \theta = 1$. Determine the magnitude and direction of the reaction at the joint B.   (L.U.)

15. AOB and COD are two uniform rods, each of weight W, freely hinged at O. $AO = CO = a$ and $BO = DO = 3a$. The rods are in equilibrium in a vertical plane, the ends B and D resting on a smooth horizontal plane and being connected by a light string of length $3a$. Show that the tension in the string is $\dfrac{2\sqrt{3}}{9} W$, and find the reaction at the hinge.   (L.U.)

16. *AB* and *BC* are two uniform bars of the same material weighing w gm per cm length, and are smoothly jointed together at *B*. *AB* is 25 cm long and is smoothly hinged to a fixed pivot at *A*. *BC* is 52 cm long and the end *C* is constrained to slide in a smooth horizontal groove which is in line with *A*, the bars and the groove being in the same vertical plane with *B* 20 cm above *AC*. What horizontal force, acting along the groove, is necessary to preserve equilibrium, and what is then the direction of the reaction at the hinge *A*? (L.U.)

17. *AB* and *BC* are two equal uniform rods, each of weight *W* freely hinged at *B*, and the end *C* is freely hinged to a fixed point. The rods are in a vertical plane with *B* higher than *C*, and equilibrium is maintained by a horizontal force *W* and an upward vertical force $W/2$, both acting at *A*. Find the horizontal and vertical components of the reaction at the hinge *B*. Prove that the rod *AB* is horizontal and find the inclination of the rod *BC* to the horizontal. (L.U.)

18. Two uniform planks, *AB* and *AC*, each of length 3 m, are freely hinged at *A*, and stand in a vertical plane in equilibrium with *B* and *C* on a smooth horizontal plane. The mid-points of the planks are joined by a light inextensible rope of length 1·5 m, and the masses of *AB* and *AC* are 50 kg and 30 kg respectively. Find the tension in the rope and the horizontal and vertical components of the reaction at the hinge. (L.U.)

19. Two uniform rods, *AB* and *AC*, of equal mass and each of length a are freely jointed at *A*. They rest in equilibrium with *A* above *B* and *C*, and with *AB* and *AC* in contact with two smooth pegs in the same horizontal line at a distance $b(< a)$ apart. If each rod makes an angle α with the horizontal, show that $a\cos^3\alpha = b$. (L.U.)

CHAPTER 5

FRICTION

5.1 Laws of Friction

Smooth surfaces have been defined by the property that when they are in contact the action between such surfaces is always perpendicular to their common tangent plane. It can, however, be verified experimentally that no surfaces are perfectly smooth and that whenever there is a tendency for two bodies which are in contact to move relative to each other, a force known as the force of friction tends to prevent the relative motion. The mathematical discussion of the force of friction depends on certain assumptions which are embodied in the following so-called *laws of friction* and are found to be in close agreement with experiment.

Law 1. When two bodies are in contact the direction of the force of friction on one of them at its point of contact is opposite to the direction in which the point of contact tends to move relative to the other.

Law 2. If the bodies are in equilibrium the force of friction is just sufficient to prevent motion, and may therefore be determined by applying the conditions of equilibrium of all the forces acting on the body.

The amount of friction that can be exerted between two surfaces is limited and if the forces acting on the body are made sufficiently great motion will ensue. Hence, we define *limiting friction* as the friction which is exerted when equilibrium is on the point of being broken by one body sliding on another. The magnitude of limiting friction is assumed to be given by the following three laws:

Law 3. The ratio of the limiting friction to the normal reaction between two surfaces depends on the substances of which the surfaces are composed, and not on the magnitude of the normal reaction.

This ratio is usually denoted by the Greek letter μ. Thus if the normal reaction is R newton, the limiting friction is μR newton and for given materials polished to the same extent μ is found to be constant and independent of R. μ is called the *coefficient of friction*.

Law 4. The amount of limiting friction is independent of the area of contact between two surfaces and of the shape of the surfaces, provided that the normal reaction is unaltered.

Law 5. When motion takes place the direction of friction is opposite to the direction of relative motion and independent of velocity. The magnitude of the force of friction is in a constant ratio to the normal reaction, but this ratio may be slightly less than when the body is just on the point of moving.

It should be emphasised that the above laws are experimental and are accepted as the basis for the mathematical treatment of friction. Modern theory suggests that the force of friction is in fact due to the non-rigidity of bodies. When one body rests on another there is always an *area* of contact, much smaller than the apparent area of contact, which depends on the normal pressure between the bodies, and friction is considered to be due to the fusion of the materials of which the bodies are composed over the area of contact. Thus friction would be proportional to the area of contact, and therefore proportional to the normal pressure as assumed in the above laws.

5.2 Angle of Friction: Cone of Friction

Let R be the normal reaction at a point of contact O (Fig. 51) and F the force of friction acting in a direction perpendicular to R. Then

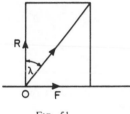

FIG. 51.

the total action at O is a force of magnitude $\sqrt{R^2 + F^2}$ acting in a direction making an angle $\tan^{-1}\dfrac{F}{R}$ with the normal reaction.

If the friction is limiting $F = \mu R$ and the action at O makes an angle $\tan^{-1}\mu$ with the normal reaction. This angle is called the *angle of friction* and is denoted by the Greek letter λ.

Thus $$\mu = \tan \lambda,$$

and the magnitude of the limiting friction may be found if either μ or λ is given.

If the direction in which the body tends to move is varied, the force of limiting friction will always lie in the plane through O perpendicular to the normal reaction, and the direction of total action at O will always lie on a cone with vertex at O, axis along the line of the normal reaction and semi-vertical angle λ (Fig. 52). This cone is called the *cone of friction*. If the friction is not limiting, the angle made by the total action at O with the normal reaction will be less than λ. Hence, whether the friction be limiting or not the direction of the total action at O must lie inside or on the cone of friction. It follows that if P be the resultant of the other

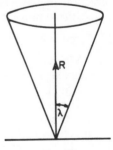

FIG. 52.

forces acting on the body in equilibrium, the direction of P must lie inside or on the cone of friction, since P must balance the total action at O.

5.3 Body on a Rough Inclined Plane

Suppose that a particle of weight W rests on a rough plane inclined at an angle α to the horizontal (Fig. 53). If there were no friction the particle would slide down the line of greatest slope of the plane, hence, the force of friction F will act upwards along this line. Let R be the normal reaction. Since the particle is in equilibrium we have by resolving the forces along and perpendicular to the plane

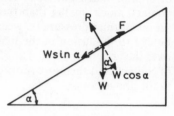

Fig. 53.

$$F = W \sin \alpha,$$
$$R = W \cos \alpha.$$

If the particle is on the point of moving, the friction will be limiting, that is, $F = \mu R$, and we have

$$\mu = \tan \alpha.$$

Hence, since $\mu = \tan \lambda$, where λ is the angle of friction, we have

$$\lambda = \alpha.$$

Therefore, the plane of greatest slope on which the particle can rest is one inclined at an angle equal to the angle of friction.

The same argument applies to a *body* on a rough inclined plane, provided that there is no question of equilibrium being broken by rolling or toppling.

5.4 The Least Force Problem

If a particle is on an inclined plane we may find the magnitude and direction of the least force required (i) to prevent it sliding down the plane, (ii) to move it up the plane.

(i) *Force required to prevent sliding down the plane.*

We assume that the plane is inclined at an angle greater than the angle of friction, since otherwise no force would be required. Let the force be P and let its direction make an angle θ with the line of greatest slope (Fig. 54). Let W be the weight of the particle, α the inclination of the plane, R the normal reaction and F the force of friction.

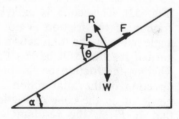

Fig. 54.

The particle is in equilibrium under the action of the forces W, R, F and P. Resolving along and perpendicular to the plane we have

$$P \cos \theta + F = W \sin \alpha, \tag{1}$$

$$-P \sin \theta + R = W \cos \alpha. \tag{2}$$

If the force P is only just sufficient to prevent sliding, the friction is limiting and $F = \mu R = R \tan \lambda$; therefore, eliminating R between equations (1) and (2) we have

$$(W \sin \alpha - P \cos \theta) = \tan \lambda (W \cos \alpha + P \sin \theta),$$

$$P(\cos \theta \cos \lambda + \sin \theta \sin \lambda) = W(\sin \alpha \cos \lambda - \cos \alpha \sin \lambda),$$

$$P = \frac{W \sin (\alpha - \lambda)}{\cos (\theta - \lambda)}.$$

Hence, P will have its least value when $\cos (\theta - y) = 1$, that is, when $\theta = \lambda$, and then $P = W \sin (\alpha - \lambda)$.

(ii) *Force required to make the particle move up the plane.*

In this case the direction of the frictional force will be down the plane and we have (Fig. 55)

$$F = P \cos \theta - W \sin \alpha,$$

$$R = P \sin \theta + W \cos \alpha.$$

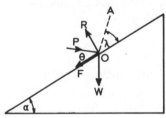

FIG. 55

Hence, the friction being limiting we have

$$P \cos \theta - W \sin \alpha = \tan \lambda (P \sin \theta + W \cos \alpha),$$
$$P(\cos \theta \cos \lambda - \sin \theta \sin \lambda) = W(\sin \alpha \cos \lambda + \cos \alpha \sin \lambda),$$

$$P = \frac{W \sin (\alpha + \lambda)}{\cos (\theta + \lambda)}.$$

P will have its least value when $\cos (\theta + \lambda) = 1$, that is when $\theta + \lambda = 0$, that is, the force must act in the direction OA making an angle λ with the upward direction of the line of greatest slope, and in this case $P = W \sin (\alpha + \lambda)$ is the least force required.

EXERCISES 5 (a)

1. Show that the least force that will move a weight W along a rough horizontal plane is $W \sin \lambda$ in a direction making an angle λ with the horizontal.

2. A block of wood, mass 4 kg, rests on a horizontal plank 6 m long. It is found that when one end of the plank is raised 2 m the block will just slide: find the coefficient of friction. If the vertical height of the end is increased to 3 m, find the least force perpendicular to the plank which will maintain equilibrium.   (O.C.)

3. A plane is inclined to the horizontal at an angle of 30° and on it is a mass of 40 kg. If the plane is rough, the coefficient of friction being $\frac{1}{4}$, find the least force parallel to the plane which will just drag the load up the plane.   (O.C.)

4. Find the least force which will move a mass of 80 kg up a rough plane inclined to the horizontal at 30° when the coefficient of friction is 0·75.   (L.U.)

5. The least force which will move a mass up an inclined plane is P. Show that the least force acting parallel to the plane which will move the mass upwards is $P\sqrt{1+\mu^2}$, where μ is the coefficient of friction.   (L.U.)

6. A body of weight W can just be supported on a rough inclined plane by a horizontal force P; it can also just be supported by a force Q acting up the plane. Find the cosine of the angle of friction in terms of P, Q and W only.   (L.U.)

7. A particle of weight W is placed on a rough inclined plane the inclination of which exceeds the angle of friction. The least horizontal force required to prevent motion down the plane is W; the least horizontal force required to produce motion up the plane is $W\sqrt{3}$. Find the inclination of the plane and the angle of friction. Find also the magnitude and direction of the least force that can maintain the particle in equilibrium.   (L.U.)

8. A body of mass 40 kg rests on an inclined plane of slope 10°, the coefficient of friction being 0·35. Find the magnitude and direction of the least force which will just pull the body up the plane.   (L.U.)

5.5 Problems Involving Sliding Only

Problems of this type are dealt with by applying the conditions of equilibrium as in the preceding chapter. Wherever two rough bodies are in contact, a frictional force F, whose direction is usually obvious, must be assumed to act in the common tangent plane. When limiting conditions of equilibrium are required the friction will be limiting and we may take $F = \mu R$, where R is the normal reaction.

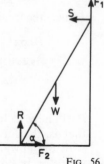

Example 1. *One end of a uniform ladder, of length l and weight W, rests against a rough vertical wall and the other end rests on rough horizontal ground, the coefficient of friction at each contact being μ. Find the inclination of the ladder to the horizontal when it is on the point of slipping.*

Let the inclination of the ladder to the horizontal be α. The ladder is in equilibrium under the action of the five forces R, S, F_1, F_2 and W as shown (Fig. 56).

FIG. 56.

Hence, resolving in two directions and taking moments about the base of the ladder we have

$$R + F_1 = W \tag{3}$$

$$S = F_2 \tag{4}$$

$$S \times l \sin \alpha + F_1 \times l \cos \alpha = W \times \frac{l}{2} \cos \alpha,$$

that is,

$$S = \left(\frac{W}{2} - F_1\right) \cot \alpha \tag{5}$$

In the limiting position when slipping is about to occur we have

$$F_1 = \mu S \tag{6}$$

$$F_2 = \mu R \tag{7}$$

Hence, $$R + \mu S = W,$$

$$S - \mu R = 0,$$

$$R = \frac{W}{1 + \mu^2},$$

$$S = \frac{\mu W}{1 + \mu^2},$$

and from (5) $$\cot \alpha = \frac{2\mu}{1 - \mu^2} = \tan 2\lambda.$$

Example 2. *A uniform solid hemisphere of radius r rests with its curved surface in contact with a rough plane inclined at an angle α to the horizontal. Show that if the hemisphere is about to slip the angle of friction is α, and find the inclination of the plane base of the hemisphere to the horizontal.*

The centre of gravity of a hemisphere of radius r is at a distance $3r/8$ from the centre. The hemisphere (Fig. 57) is in equilibrium under the action of the three forces R, F

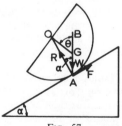

FIG. 57.

and W, therefore these three forces must be concurrent, that is, the centre of gravity G must be vertically above the point of contact A of the hemisphere and plane. The reaction R, being perpendicular to the plane, which is tangential to the hemisphere, must pass through its centre O. Therefore the angle $OAG = \alpha$.

Resolving along and perpendicular to the plane we have

$$F = W \sin \alpha \tag{8}$$

$$R = W \cos \alpha \tag{9}$$

Also, since the friction is limiting

$$F = \mu R \qquad (10)$$

Therefore, $\mu = \tan \alpha,$

and the angle of friction is α.

The angle made by the plane face with the horizontal is the angle made by OG with the vertical, namely the angle OGB. Denoting this angle by θ, we have in the triangle OAG

$$OA = r,$$
$$OG = \tfrac{3}{8}r,$$
$$OAG = \alpha,$$

therefore, $$\frac{\sin \theta}{r} = \frac{\sin \alpha}{\tfrac{3}{8}r},$$

and $$\theta = \sin^{-1}(\tfrac{8}{3}\sin \alpha),$$
$$= \sin^{-1}\left(\frac{8\mu}{3\sqrt{1+\mu^2}}\right).$$

EXERCISES 5 (b)

1. A uniform ladder rests with one end on the ground and the other end against a vertical wall in a plane perpendicular to the line of intersection of wall and ground. The coefficients of friction between the ladder and the ground and between the ladder and the wall are each $\tan 15°$. Show that the inclination of the ladder to the ground cannot be less than $60°$. Show that the ladder can just rest at an inclination of $30°$ if a mass $(\sqrt{3}+1)/2$ of its own is attached to the lower end. (O.C.)

2. A car with four equal wheels has a wheel base a and its centre of mass is equidistant from all four wheels and at a height h above the ground. Find the pressures on the wheels when the car rests with the back wheels locked on a slope of inclination α facing (i) uphill, (ii) downhill. (O.C.)

3. A circular cylinder of weight W, with its axis horizontal, is supported in contact with a rough vertical wall by a string wrapped partly round it and attached to a point on the wall and making an angle α with the wall. Show that the coefficient of friction must not be less than cosec α, and that the normal pressure on the wall is $W \tan \alpha/2$. (O.C.)

4. A uniform circular disc, of radius a and weight w, stands in a vertical plane on a rough horizontal floor with a point of its circumference in contact with an equally rough vertical wall and its plane at right angles to the wall. A particle of equal weight w is attached to a point P of the disc at the same height as the centre O, and between O and the wall. Show that the disc is on the point of slipping when

$$OP = \frac{2a\mu(1+\mu)}{1+\mu^2}, \text{ where } \mu \text{ is the coefficient of friction.} \qquad \text{(L.U.)}$$

5. A plank, whose mass can be neglected, rests with one end on rough ground and part of its length overreaching a rough vertical wall of height h, on which the plank rests in a vertical plane at right angles to the wall. The plank is inclined at θ to the horizontal and its coefficient of friction with the ground and with the wall is μ in each case.

Show that, if $\mu < \tan \theta < 1/\mu$, the distance x measured from the ground through which a man may walk along the plank before it slips, is given by

$$x = \frac{\mu h}{(1+\mu^2)\sin^2 \theta \cos \theta}.$$

(L.U.)

6. A thin hemispherical shell rests with its curved surface in contact with a rough horizontal plane whose coefficient of friction is μ, and with a rough vertical plane whose coefficient of friction is μ'. If the shell is on the point of slipping when the plane of its rim makes 30° with the horizontal, find the relation connecting μ and μ', and prove that if $\mu' < 1/3$, μ must lie between $\frac{1}{3}$ and $\frac{1}{4}$. (The centre of gravity of a thin hemispherical shell bisects the radius.) (O.C.)

7. A uniform cube, of weight W, has one edge AB in contact with a rough horizontal plane and is supported in an inclined position by a string attached to the middle point of the edge opposite to AB. If the cube is on the point of slipping on the plane when one of the faces through AB is inclined at 15° to the horizontal and the string (in the plane perpendicular to AB) is inclined upwards at 30° to the horizontal, show that the coefficient of friction is $\sqrt{3}/7$ and find the tension in the string. (L.U.)

8. A thin uniform rod rests in equilibrium with one end on the smooth face of a wedge of inclination 60° to the horizontal, and with the other end on rough horizontal ground the vertical plane through the rod intersecting the face of the wedge in a line of greatest slope. If the rod is about to slip when inclined at 30° to the horizontal, show that the coefficient of friction between the rod and the ground is $1/\sqrt{3}$. (L.U.)

5.6 Problems Involving Toppling

If a cube is placed on a rough inclined plane it may slide down the plane, or it may tilt about its lowest edge. Equilibrium may therefore be broken either by sliding or toppling, depending on the magnitude of the coefficient of friction.

In general, the axis about which a body may topple is the horizontal which is perpendicular to the line of greatest slope of the plane through the lowest point of the body. If it is about to topple, the reaction of the plane on the body and the frictional force will act through this point, and the body will topple if the moment of the other forces acting on the body about this point is such as to increase the tendency to tilt. This is so if the resultant of the other forces meets the inclined plane below the lowest point of the body.

Example 3. *A uniform circular cylinder of height h and radius a is placed on a rough inclined plane with its plane base in contact with the plane, the coefficient of friction being μ. If the inclination of the plane is gradually increased find the manner in which equilibrium will be broken.*

Let W be the weight of the cylinder and α the inclination of the plane in the limiting position (Fig. 58). Let R be the reaction of the plane and F the friction. If equilibrium is broken by sliding we have

$$R = W \cos \alpha,$$
$$F = \mu R = \mu W \cos \alpha,$$

Therefore, $\qquad W \sin \alpha = \mu W \cos \alpha.$

and $\qquad \tan \alpha = \mu.$

If equilibrium is broken by toppling, taking moments about the lowest point of the cylinder we have

$$W \sin \alpha \times \frac{h}{2} = W \cos \alpha \times a,$$

$$\tan \alpha = \frac{2a}{h}.$$

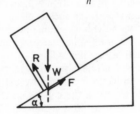

Fig. 58.

Therefore, the cylinder will topple before it slides if

$$\frac{2a}{h} < \mu.$$

EXERCISES 5 (c)

1. A uniform cubical block of side $2a$ and weight W rests on a rough horizontal plane. A man pushes it at right angles to one of its faces. Prove that the least push that will move it is the smaller of the two Wa/h, μW, where h is the height of the man's hands above the ground and μ the coefficient of friction between the block and the ground.

    If the coefficient of friction between the man and the ground is μ', what must be the least weight of the man to move the block?   (O.C.)

2. A cube rests on a rough plane, inclined to the horizontal at an angle $\alpha(< \pi/4)$, with two of its upper and two of its lower edges horizontal. Show that it will not be possible to drag the cube up the plane without upsetting it, by means of a rope attached to the middle point of the uppermost edge of the cube and pulled parallel to the inclined plane if the coefficient of friction between the plane and the cube exceeds $\frac{1}{2}(1 - \tan \alpha)$.   (O.C.)

3. A uniform cube, whose edges are each $4a$, stands on a rough horizontal plane. A gradually increasing horizontal force is applied to one of its vertical faces at a height a vertically above the centre of that face. Determine how equilibrium will be broken

    (i) when the coefficient of friction between the plane and the cube is $0{\cdot}5$;

    (ii) when this coefficient is $0{\cdot}7$.   (O.C.)

4. A uniform rod AB lies on rough horizontal ground. A cord attached to the end B passes over a small pulley fixed at a point D, vertically over a point C lying in the line AB produced beyond B. Prove that, if the cord is pulled with a gradually increasing force, the rod will begin to slide along the ground, if μ, the coefficient of friction between the rod and the ground, is less than $\cot DBC$; but that, otherwise, it will turn about the extremity A, and the extremity A will not slip till $\mu(\tan \beta - 2 \tan \alpha) = 1$, where α and β are the angles which AB and BD respectively then make with the horizontal.   (O.C.)

5. A heavy uniform cubical block of weight W is placed on a rough table with a face parallel to, and at a distance of half the side of the block from, an edge. To the centre of this face a light inextensible string is attached which passes over the smooth edge of the table and carries a mass at its free end. If the mass is gradually increased, show that equilibrium will be broken by the cube tilting about an edge if the coefficient of friction between the block and the table is greater than $\frac{1}{2}$, and find the load which just destroys equilibrium in this case.   (L.U.)

6. A uniform rod AB has a light ring attached at A, the ring being free to move on a rough horizontal straight rigid wire, the coefficient of friction between the ring and the wire being μ. The rod hangs vertically in equilibrium and a gradually increasing horizontal force is applied to the end B in a direction parallel to the wire. Prove that the rod will turn through an angle θ, where $\tan \theta = 2\mu$, from the vertical before the ring begins to slip.   (L.U.)

5.7 Problems Involving Two or More Bodies

Problems of friction with more than one body involved may be solved by applying the conditions for equilibrium to each of the bodies and eliminating unknown forces between the bodies.

Example 4. *Two rings of equal weight, connected by a light inextensible string, can slide one on each of two fixed equally rough rods in the same vertical plane inclined at equal angles of 45° in opposite directions to the horizontal. Prove that the extreme angle which the string can make with the horizontal is twice the angle of friction.*

Let AB (Fig. 59) be the string inclined at an angle θ to the rod at A, A being the lower of the two rings. We suppose that friction is limiting and that the ring at A is tending

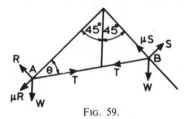

Fig. 59.

to slide upwards and the ring at B downwards.

Resolving along and perpendicular to the rod the forces acting on the ring at A we have

$$\mu R = T\cos\theta - \frac{W}{\sqrt{2}} \tag{11}$$

$$R = T\sin\theta + \frac{W}{\sqrt{2}} \tag{12}$$

and hence,

$$\mu = \frac{T\cos\theta - \dfrac{W}{\sqrt{2}}}{T\sin\theta + \dfrac{W}{\sqrt{2}}}.$$

Resolving along and perpendicular to the other rod the forces acting on the ring at B we have

$$\mu S = \frac{W}{\sqrt{2}} - T\sin\theta \tag{13}$$

$$S = \frac{W}{\sqrt{2}} + T\cos\theta \tag{14}$$

and hence

$$\mu = \frac{\dfrac{W}{\sqrt{2}} - T\sin\theta}{\dfrac{W}{\sqrt{2}} + T\cos\theta}.$$

Eliminating T between the two expressions obtained for μ we have

$$\tan\theta = \frac{1 - 2\mu - \mu^2}{1 + 2\mu - \mu^2},$$

$$\tan(45° - \theta) = \frac{2\mu}{1 - \mu^2},$$

$$= \frac{2\tan\lambda}{1 - \tan^2\lambda},$$

$$= \frac{2\tan\lambda}{1 - \tan^2\lambda},$$

$$= \tan 2\lambda.$$

Therefore, $(45° - \theta) = 2\lambda.$

Example 5. *Two equal uniform rods AB, BC, smoothly jointed at B, are in equilibrium with the end C resting on a rough horizontal plane and the end A freely pivoted at a point above the plane. Prove that if α and β are the inclinations of CB and BA to the horizontal, the coefficient of friction must exceed*

$$\frac{2}{\tan\beta + 3\tan\alpha}.$$

Let the reaction perpendicular to the ground at C (Fig. 60) be R, let X and Y be the components of the force at B, W the weight of each road and $2a$ its length. When the

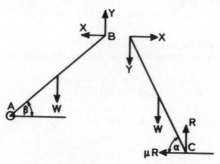

Fig. 60.

friction is limiting, the frictional force at C will be μR.

Equating to zero the horizontal and vertical components of the forces acting on the rod BC and taking moments about C we have the three equations

$$W + Y = R \tag{15}$$

$$X = \mu R \tag{16}$$

$$X \times 2a \sin \alpha = W \times a \cos \alpha + Y \times 2a \cos \alpha \tag{17}$$

Hence

$$W = 2R(1 - \mu \tan \alpha).$$

Equating to zero the sum of the moments about A of the forces acting on AB we have

$$X \times 2a \sin \beta + Y \times 2a \cos \beta = W \times a \cos \beta \tag{18}$$

and hence

$$3W = 2R(1 + \mu \tan \beta).$$

Eliminating R we have

$$3(1 - \mu \tan \alpha) = 1 + \mu \tan \beta,$$

$$\mu = \frac{2}{3 \tan \alpha + \tan \beta}.$$

EXERCISES 5 (d)

1. A uniform solid cube stands on a rough horizontal plane and an exactly similar cube is placed on it so that the faces coincide. The coefficient of friction between the two cubes is μ' (< 1) and between the lower cube and the plane is μ. A gradually increasing horizontal force is applied to the upper cube at right angles to one of its faces at the centre of that face. Prove that when equilibrium is broken, the upper cube will slide on the lower, while the lower remains at rest, or both cubes will move together as a single rigid body according as 2μ is greater or less than μ'.
(O.C.)

2. Two equal uniform rods AB, BC are freely jointed at B and rest in equilibrium in a vertical plane with the ends A and C on a rough horizontal plane. If μ is the coefficient of friction between each rod and the plane, show that the greatest angle that the rods can make with the vertical is $\tan^{-1}(2\mu)$.

3. Two uniform rods AB and BC of the same thickness and material, and of length 3 m and 2 m respectively, are freely hinged together and rest in a vertical plane with the ends A and C on a rough horizontal plane. If the greatest possible value of the angle ABC consistent with equilibrium is $90°$, find the coefficient of friction between the rods and the ground, and determine how equilibrium will be broken if the inclination of the rods is slightly increased beyond $90°$. (O.C.)

4. Two uniform ladders AB, BC of equal lengths and weights W, W' ($W > W'$) are hinged together at the top B and will stand on rough ground when containing an angle 2θ. Show that the total reaction at A makes a smaller angle with the vertical than at C. Assuming the coefficients of friction at A and C are each equal to μ, show that, as θ is increased, slipping will occur at C, and that

$$\mu = \tan \alpha \, (W + W')/(W + 3W')$$

where α is the value of θ for which slipping first occurs. (O.C.)

5. An equilateral triangle formed of wire is placed in a vertical plane with one side horizontal. On each side is strung a bead of weight W, and the beads are connected by an endless string, in tension, and passing through small smooth rings

at the corners of the triangle. Prove that, if a gradually increasing horizontal force be applied to the bead on the horizontal side, the system will begin to move when the force is equal to $2\mu W$, where μ is the coefficient of friction between the beads and the wire.   (L.U.)

6. A wedge of weight W, lying on rough ground, has its thin end pushed against a smooth vertical wall, the sloping face of the wedge making an angle 2θ with the wall. A smooth right circular cylinder of weight W_1 lies between the wedge and the wall. Find the relation between W and W_1 when the wedge is just on the point of sliding, the coefficient of friction between the ground and the wedge being μ.   (O.C.)

7. Two equal particles, each of weight W, are placed on a rough horizontal table and connected by a taut inextensible string. Prove that the least horizontal force that can be applied to one of them in a direction making an angle θ with the string so as to cause them both to be on the point of motion is $2\mu W \cos \theta$, where μ is the coefficient of friction between either particle and the table.   (O.C.)

8. Two cylinders each of radius a and weight W rest on a rough table with their axes horizontal and parallel and at a distance $3a$ apart; a third cylinder of the same radius and weight rests between them, friction being just sufficient to preserve equilibrium. Find the least coefficient of friction required between the upper and lower cylinders and between the lower cylinders and the table.

EXERCISES 5 (e)

1. A uniform sphere of weight W is placed on a rough plane which is inclined to the horizontal at an angle $\alpha \, (< 45°)$ which is less than the angle of friction. Show that a particle of weight $W \sin \alpha/(\cos \alpha - \sin \alpha)$, fastened to the sphere at the upper extremity of the diameter parallel to a line of greatest slope, will just prevent the sphere rolling down the plane.   (L.U.)

2. A force P acting parallel to a line of greatest slope of a rough plane of inclination α is just sufficient to maintain a heavy particle in equilibrium on the plane. Prove that the least force acting on the particle, parallel to the plane, such that the particle is on the point of moving up a line of greatest slope, is $P \sin (\alpha + \lambda)/ \sin (\alpha - \lambda)$, where λ is the angle of friction.   (L.U.)

3. A rough circular cylinder of radius a is fixed with its axis horizontal, and on it rests symmetrically a rod of length $2l$ and weight W, at right angles to the axis. A particle of weight w is attached to one end of the rod, which is allowed slowly to rotate without slipping until it is in equilibrium. If it now makes an angle θ with the horizontal and is on the point of slipping, show that the angle of friction between rod and cylinder is θ and that $w = Wa\theta/(l - a\theta)$.   (L.U.)

4. One end of a string, of length twice the radius of a metal sphere, is attached to a point A on a vertical wall, the other end being attached to a point on the surface of the sphere. The sphere, whose mass is 8 kg, then hangs in equilibrium against the wall. If the wall is smooth, find the tension in the string and the thrust of the sphere on the wall.

If, instead, the wall is rough, the coefficient of limiting friction between the wall and the sphere being $1/\sqrt{2}$, and the sphere is in the same position against the wall and attached to the same point A on the wall but with a different length of string, so that it is in equilibrium but just about to slip down the wall, prove

that the angle between the string and the wall is now $\tan^{-1} (\sqrt{2}/3)$.   (C.S.)

5. A solid hemisphere of weight W and radius a has its centre of gravity on the axis. at a distance x from the centre. It rests in equilibrium with its curved surface in contact with a rough plane inclined at an angle α to the horizontal. Prove that its plane base is inclined to the horizontal at an angle θ given by $x \sin \theta = a \sin \alpha$. If ϕ is the inclination of the base to the horizontal when a particle of weight W is attached to the centre of the base, the hemisphere again resting in equilibrium on the inclined plane, prove that $\sin \phi = 2 \sin \theta$.

6. A particle of weight W rests on a rough inclined plane of angle α, the coefficient of friction being $\sqrt{2} \tan \alpha$. Prove that the maximum horizontal force acting on the particle along the plane which will not disturb equilibrium is $W \sin \alpha$. If the force just exceeds this value, prove that the initial direction of motion of the particle makes an angle of $45°$ with the line of greatest slope of the plane.

(L.U.)

7. A uniform ladder of weight W leans against a smooth vertical wall, and its foot is on rough ground which slopes down from the wall at an inclination α to the horizontal. Prove that if the ladder is in limiting equilibrium its inclination to the wall is $\tan^{-1} 2 \tan(\epsilon - \alpha)$, where ϵ is the angle of friction. Prove also that the resultant reaction with the ground is then $W \sec(\epsilon - \alpha)$. (L.U.)

8. Two equal uniform rods AB, BC, of length $2l$, are rigidly connected at B so that ABC is a right angle. Prove that if the rods rest in limiting equilibrium in contact with a fixed circular hoop of radius a, so that AB is horizontal and BC a vertical tangent to the circle, then $2a(1-\mu) = l(1+\mu^2)$, where μ is the coefficient of friction between the rods and the hoop. (L.U.)

9. A uniform stick of length l is placed in the rough ring of an umbrella-stand at a height h above the ground. It rests also on a smooth floor. Show the equilibrium is impossible unless the stick is vertical, if the coefficient of friction is less than $h/\sqrt{(l^2 - h^2)}$. (L.U.)

10. A uniform rod of length l rests in a vertical plane against (and over) a smooth horizontal bar at a height h, the lower end of the rod being on level ground. Show that if the rod is on the point of slipping when its inclination to the horizontal is θ, then the coefficient of friction between the rod and the ground is

$$\frac{l \sin 2\theta \sin \theta}{4h - l \sin 2\theta \cos \theta}.$$

(L.U.)

11. The triangle ABC, in which BC is horizontal and AB and AC are equal and greater than BC, represents the cross-section of a triangular prism standing on a rough horizontal plane on one of its rectangular faces, and the face represented by AB is subject to wind pressure. Show that when this pressure, assumed normal to AB, becomes sufficiently great the prism will topple over or slide according as the angle of friction is greater or less than $\pi - 2\alpha$, where α is the inclination of either sloping face to the base. (L.U.)

12. A cylinder rests on a rough horizontal floor touching a rough vertical wall so that its axis is parallel to the floor and the wall. The mass of the cylinder is M and the coefficient of friction at both contacts is μ. A vertical force P is applied to the cylinder so as to cause it to rotate while pressing against the wall. Determine the minimum value of P. (Q.E.)

13. A light rod of length $2a$ rests horizontally between two planes each inclined at $45°$ to the horizontal, the rod being in a vertical plane perpendicular to their line of intersection, and the coefficient of friction between the rod and each plane is

0·5. A particle of weight w is placed at the centre of the rod. If the particle is gradually moved along the rod, show that the rod will not slip until the particle has been moved a distance $4a/5$.   (L.U.)

14. A uniform bar AB of weight W and length $2a$ rests with its upper end A against a rough vertical wall and its lower end B on equally rough horizontal ground. A concentrated load of weight $\frac{1}{2}W$ is rigidly attached to the bar at a point C, where $AC = 2a/5$. If the bar is just about to slip when its inclination to the horizontal is 45°, prove that the coefficient of friction is $1/2$.   (N.U.)

15. A solid homogeneous right circular cone of mass 10 kg has base radius 10 cm and height 24 cm, and stands on a horizontal rough plane, the coefficient of friction being 0·5. A string is attached to the apex of the cone.

(i) If the string is pulled horizontally with a gradually increasing force, prove that the cone will tip, not slide.

(ii) Find what is the least concentrated mass which, when added to the cone at a point on the rim of the base, will make the cone slide rather than tip when pulled as in (i).   (Q.E.)

16. A uniform rod AB, of length $2a$ and weight W, rests in a vertical plane with the end A on a rough horizontal floor OX and the end B on a smooth vertical wall OY; a string of length a, attached to O and the mid-point of AB, is in tension T. Prove that, if AB makes an angle θ with the vertical when A is on the point of slipping away from O, then

$$T = W(\sin\theta - 2\mu\cos\theta)/(2\mu\cos^2\theta)$$

and $$S = W\sin\theta(\sin\theta - \mu\cos\theta)/(2\mu\cos^2\theta),$$

where S is the reaction of the wall at B and μ is the coefficient of friction between the rod and the floor.   (O.C.)

17. Two equal uniform cylinders are placed in contact with their axes parallel and horizontal on a horizontal plane. A third equal cylinder is rested symmetrically on the first two with its axis parallel to theirs. Determine, graphically or otherwise, the limiting values of the coefficients of friction between cylinders and between cylinder and the plane for equilibrium to be possible.   (Q.E.)

18. A uniform beam rests over two pegs, which are not at the same level, so that it is inclined at an angle θ to the horizontal. The angle of friction between the beam and the upper peg is λ_1, and that between the beam and the lower peg is λ_2, where $\lambda_2 > \theta > \lambda_1$. Show that the beam will just slip over the pegs when the ratio of the distances from its centre of mass to the lower and upper pegs respectively is

$$\frac{\sin(\lambda_2 - \theta)\cos\lambda_1}{\sin(\theta - \lambda_1)\cos\lambda_2}.$$ (L.U.)

19. A light ladder 3 m long stands on a horizontal floor and rests against a smooth vertical wall. The bottom of the ladder is 1·25 m from the wall, and the coefficient of friction between it and the floor is 0·25. What is the minimum mass of a man standing on the bottom rung if the ladder is not to slip when a man of 105 kg stands on the top rung? The end rungs are each 25 cm from an end of the ladder.   (Q.E.)

20. Two planes, each initially at 45° to the horizontal, form a 90° V-channel with the line AA', in which the planes meet, horizontal. A thin uniform rod is placed

horizontally with one end in contact with each plane, and lying perpendicular to AA'. The angle of friction between the rod and each plane is λ. Through what angle can the whole system be rotated about the line AA' before the rod slips relative to the channel.   (Q.E.)

21. The shaft of a flywheel rests horizontally in two **V**-grooves, the angle of each being 60°. A rope round the wheel supports a weight P. The coefficient of friction is μ and the wheel and shaft weigh W. Show that the least value of P which will cause the shaft to rotate in the grooves is given by

$$P = \frac{2\mu d}{(1+\mu^2)\,D - 2\mu d}\,W,$$

where d is the diameter of the shaft and D the diameter of the wheel   (Q.E.)

CHAPTER 6

GRAPHICAL STATICS

6.1 Resultant of Coplanar Forces

We have seen that the magnitude and direction of the resultant of a system of coplanar forces can be found by drawing the polygon of forces; the force vectors are placed end to end in any order, and the line which with the vectors forms a closed polygon represents the resultant of the forces in magnitude and direction. The *line of action* of this resultant is found by drawing, in addition, what is called a *funicular polygon*.

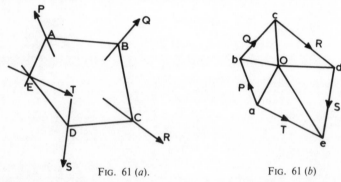

FIG. 61 (*a*).   FIG. 61 (*b*)

Let *P*, *Q*, *R*, *S* be the given forces and let their lines of action be as shown in Fig. 61 (*a*). Let the sides *ab*, *bc*, *cd*, *de* of the polygon *abcde*, Fig. 61 (*b*), represent the forces *P*, *Q*, *R*, *S*, respectively in magnitude and direction. Then *ae* represents the resultant of the forces in magnitude and direction.

Let *o* be any point in the plane of the polygon *abcde*; join *oa*, *ob*, *oc*, *od*, *oe*.

Let *A* be any point on the line of action of *P*; draw *AE* parallel to *ao*, and *AB* parallel to *ob* to meet the line of action of *Q* in *B*. Draw *BC* parallel to *oc* to meet the line of action of *R* in *C*, *CD* parallel to *od* to meet the line of action of *S* in *D*, *DE* parallel to *oe* to meet *AE* in *E*. Then the figure *ABCDE* is called the funicular polygon of the forces, and their resultant passes through the point *E*.

From the triangle *aob*, the force *P* is equivalent to forces represented in magnitude and direction by *ao* and *ob*, therefore, it is represented in magnitude, direction and line of action by magnitudes *ao* and *ob* along the lines *AE* and *AB* respectively. Similarly, the force *Q* is completely represented by magnitudes *bo* and *oc* along *BA* and *BC* respectively, and in taking the resultant of P and Q the forces along the line AB balance. The force R is completely represented by magnitudes co and od along CB and CD respectively; the force S is completely represented by magnitudes do and oe along DC and DE respectively.

In the summation, the components of P, Q, R and S along the lines AB, BC and CD balance; we are left with two forces of magnitudes ao and oe whose lines of action are AE and DE. Hence, the resultant of the forces P, Q, R, S passes through the point E.

If the given forces are in equilibrium their resultant will be zero and the polygon of forces will close, that is, the points a and e will coincide.

The converse is not true, since the given system of forces may reduce to a couple; if the points a and e coincide the lines AE and DE will be parallel, but the resultant couple will not be zero unless AE and DE are the same line.

Hence, for equilibrium, the polygon of forces and the funicular polygon must both close.

Example 1. *Forces of* 1, 2, 3, 4 N *act along the sides of a square. Find graphically the magnitude, direction and line of action of the resultant.*

Drawing the force polygon *abcde* (Fig. 63) we have the resultant represented by $ae = 2\cdot83$ N acting in a direction making an angle of 45° with a side of the square.

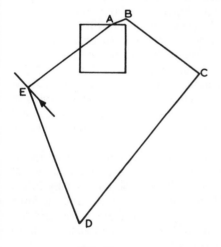

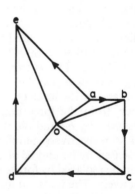

FIG. 62.   FIG. 63.

Taking any pole o we draw the funicular polygon *ABCDE* (Fig. 62) whose vertices A, B, C, D lie on the sides of the square and whose sides are parallel respectively to ob, oc, od, oe and oa. The point E is a point on the line of action of the resultant, and it may be seen that the resultant cuts a side of the square at 1·5 times the length of a side from a corner.

6.2 Resultant of Parallel Forces

The graphical method of finding the resultant of parallel forces is that of the preceding section, but in this case the polygon of forces, having all its sides parallel, will reduce to a straight line. We shall consider the important problem of finding the reactions at the supports of a beam loaded with various weights.

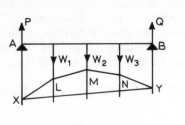

Fig. 64 (a)

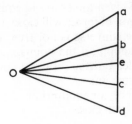

FIG. 64 (b)

Let the beam AB rest on supports at the same level at A and B and carry loads W_1, W_2, W_3. Let the reactions at A and B be P and Q respectively. In the force polygon, Fig. 64 (b), let ab, bc, cd represent the forces W_1, W_2, W_3, in the same vertical line. Then the line da will represent the sum of the forces P and Q. Take any point o and join oa, ob, oc, od.

Take any point L on the line of action of W_1 (Fig. 64 (a)) and through L draw LX parallel to oa to meet the line of action of P in X and LM parallel to ob to meet the line of action of W_2 in M. Through M draw MN parallel to oc to meet the line of action of W_3 in N, and through N draw NY parallel to od to meet the line of action of Q in Y. Join XY and through o draw oe parallel to XY to meet ad in e. Then ea represents the force P and de the force Q.

Since, from the force diagram, the force W_1 is equivalent to forces represented by ao and ob, it can be replaced by these forces along LX and LM respectively. Similarly the force W_2 can be replaced by forces represented by bo and oc along ML and MN respectively, and the force W_3 can be replaced by forces represented by co and od along NM and NY respectively. The forces along LM and MN balance, and hence we have the forces W_1, W_2, W_3 together equivalent to forces ao along LX and od along NY.

For the equilibrium of the system the resultant of the force P at X and the force ao along LX must be equal and opposite to the resultant of the force Q at Y and the force od along NY. Hence each of these resultants must act along XY. Therefore, oe is the direction of the resultant of P and ao, and it follows that ea represents P and de represents Q.

Example 2. *A light horizontal beam* 100 *cm long carries masses of* 2, 4 *and* 3 *kg at* 10, 30 *and*
70 *cm respectively from one end, and is supported at its ends. Find graphically the reactions*
at the supports.

Let the reactions be *P* and *Q* (Fig. 65 (*a*)).
The force polygon is the line *ad* (Fig. 65 (*b*)). Taking a point *o* join *oa, ob, oc, od.*

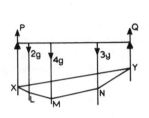

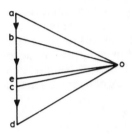

FIG. 65 (*a*)   FIG. 65 (*b*).

From any point *L* on the line of action of 2*g* parallels to *oa* and *ob* meet the lines of
action of *P* and 4*g* in *X* and *M* respectively; *MN* parallel to *oc* meets the line of action
of the 3*g* in *N* and *NY* parallel to *od* meets the line of action of *Q* in *Y. oe* is drawn
parallel to *XY* to meet *ad* in *e*. Then *ea* represents the force *P* and *de* the force *Q*. We
have $P = 5\cdot5g$, $Q = 3\cdot5g$.

EXERCISES 6 (*a*)

1. Forces of 2, 3, 4 N act along the sides *AB, BC, CA* respectively of an equilateral
   triangle *ABC* of side 30 cm. Find graphically the magnitude and direction of the
   resultant and the distance from *C* at which it cuts *BC*.

2. Forces of 1, 3, 2, 2, 1 N act along the sides *AB, BC, CD, DE, EF*, respectively, of
   a regular hexagon *ABCDEF* of side 20 cm. Find graphically the magnitude and
   direction of the resultant and the distance from *B* of the point in which it cuts *AB*.

3. Forces 13, 2, 3, 8 N act along the sides *AB, BC, CD, AD*, respectively, of a square
   ABCD in the sense indicated by the order of the letters. Find graphically the
   magnitude and direction of their resultant and show that its line of action passes
   through the mid-point of *AB*.

4. Masses of 5, 7, 3 kg are placed on a beam of length 100 cm at distances 10, 30,
   60 cm from one end. Find graphically the line of action of the resultant.

5. A horizontal beam 20 m long is supported at its ends and carries masses of 2, 3,
   4, 5 kg at distances 3, 5, 9, 15 m respectively from one end. Find graphically the
   thrusts at the supports.

6. A horizontal beam *AB* is 20 m long and is supported at 5 m from *A* and 3 m from
   B. Masses of 5, 7, 9, 6, 4 kg are carried at 1, 4, 7, 12, 16 m from *A*. Find graphically
   the forces at the supports.

6.3 Light Frameworks. Bow's Notation

If a rod of negligible weight is in equilibrium under the action of the forces at its ends, and the forces at each end do not reduce to couples, the resultants of the forces acting on each end must balance each other, and hence the line of action of each of these resultants must be along the rod. It follows that the forces acting on the rod can only be direct tensions or compressions, and such a rod is called a tie if in tension and a strut if in compression. Couples acting on the ends of rods are excluded by assuming that the rods are pin-jointed without frictional forces to other members. If a rod is in tension it exerts a force on the joint at each end away from the joint; if in compression the force is towards the joint at each end.

The forces of compression or tension in the various members of a framework of light rods may conveniently be found by graphical methods by drawing a triangle or polygon of forces for each point at which two or more rods join. The procedure is simplified by the use of Bow's Notation, by which each member of a framework is specified in the force diagram by the same letters in small type. This is done by lettering the spaces between the lines of action of the forces in the space diagram.

Example 3. *The framework shown in the diagram consists of seven light rods freely jointed and forming three equilateral triangles. Masses of 4 tonnes and 8 tonnes are carried at the upper joints and the framework is supported at its lower extremities. Find the stresses in the members of the framework.* (1 tonne = 1000 kg.)

The spaces between the forces are lettered (Fig. 66) so that, for example, AE denotes the member joining the support to the point where the 4 tonne load acts.

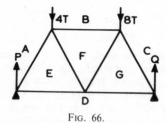

Fig. 66.

The reactions P and Q at the supports may be found graphically. Alternatively, if the length of a side of each triangle by 2 units, taking moments about each of the supports, we have

$$4P = (4 \times 3 + 8 \times 1)10^3 g = 20 \times 10^3 g,$$
$$4Q = (8 \times 3 + 4 \times 1)10^3 g = 28 \times 10^3 g,$$
$$P = 5 \times 10^3 g, \quad Q = 7 \times 10^3 g.$$

We now consider the equilibrium of the point where the forces AE, ED and DA (or P) meet. We may conveniently call this the point AED, and since the directions of all the forces and the magnitude of DA are known, we may draw the triangle of forces dae (Fig. 67) and measure the forces ae and ed.

The direction in which the forces act is evident from the triangle, and we have that the force in *AE* is a compression of $5 \cdot 77 \times 10^3 g$ and the force in *ED* a tension of $2 \cdot 89 \times 10^3 g$.

We now consider the four forces at the point *EABF*, where the directions of all the forces and the magnitudes of two of them are known. The compressive force *ea* will act towards the point in the direction *ea*, and we may add to the previous diagram to

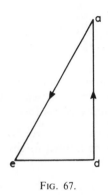

Fig. 67.

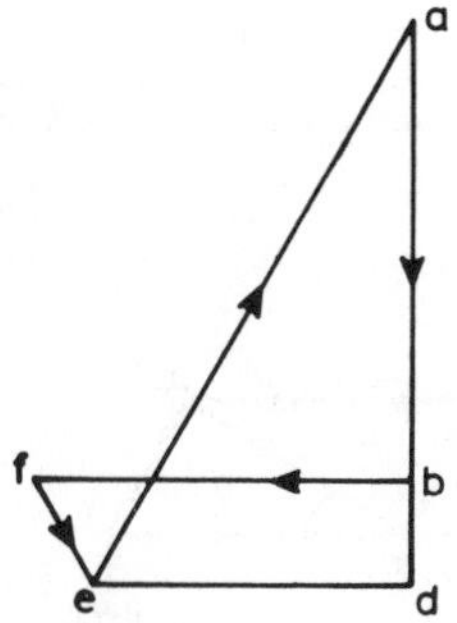

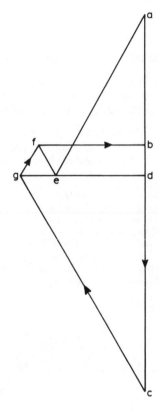

Fig. 69.

Fig. 68.

complete the polygon of forces *eabf* (Fig. 68).

By measurement $bf = 3 \cdot 46$, $fe = 1 \cdot 15 \times 10^3 g$ N. From the directions in which these forces act relative to the point considered we have that the member *BF* is in compression and the member *FE* in tension.

We may now consider the equilibrium of the point *FBCG*, where two of the four forces are known, and add to the previous diagram the quadrilateral of forces *fbcg*, starting from the force *fb* already drawn (Fig. 69).

By measurement $cg = 8 \cdot 08$, $gf = 1 \cdot 15 \times 10^3 g$ N and the members *CG* and *GF* are in compression.

The triangle of forces for the point *CDG* is already on the diagram; by measurement the force $dg = 4 \cdot 04 \times 10^3 g$ and the member *DG* is in tension. The quadrilateral of forces for the point *GDEF* need not be considered, although it is automatically included in the force diagram.

Hence we have the results:

Compressive forces		
	AE	5·77g kN
	BF	3·46g kN
	CG	8·08g kN
	GF	1·15g kN
Tensions	ED	2·89g kN
	EF	1·15g kN
	GD	4·04g kN

The following points may be noted:

(1) In lettering the space diagram the minimum number of letters must be used to ensure that each member or force is represented by two letters and that each pair of adjacent letters represents a force.

(2) The forces acting at each point should be drawn in the order of the letters describing the point beginning with the known forces and going around each point in the same sense.

Example 4. *The diagram (Fig. 70) represents a framework of seven light rods freely jointed at their ends. OC, CD are horizontal and the various angles are as shown. A mass of 1 tonne is suspended vertically from D, and the frame is kept in equilibrium by a force P applied at A in the direction CA and another force at O. Determine the magnitude of this force at O and find the stress in each rod, distinguishing tension from compression.*

To use Bow's notation the figure is redrawn (Fig. 71) and the spaces lettered. The unknown force *Q* must pass through the intersection of *P* and the force of *g* kN and its direction is roughly as shown.

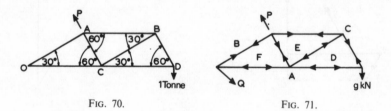

FIG. 70.   FIG. 71.

The force diagram is drawn for the points *ADC, CDE, EDAF, EFBC, BFA* in this order (Fig. 72).

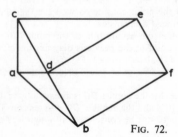

FIG. 72.

Then *ab* represents the force $Q = 1.53g$ kN

$$dc = 1.15g \text{ kN}$$
$$ad = 0.58g \text{ kN}$$
$$de = 2.0g \text{ kN}$$
$$ec = 2.31g \text{ kN}$$
$$ef = 1.15g \text{ kN}$$
$$fa = 2.89g \text{ kN}$$
$$fb = 2.0g \text{ kN}$$

The members *CE*, *EF* and *FB* are in tension.

EXERCISES 6 (*b*)

1. The diagonals *AC*, *BD* of a quadrilateral *ABCD* intersect at right angles at *O*, and *AO* = *CO* = *BO* = 5, *DO* = 10. A framework in the form of the above quadrilateral consists of five light rods *AB*, *BC*, *CD*, *DA*, *DB*, freely jointed, and the frame is in equilibrium under compressive forces of 5000 N acting at *A* and *C* in the line *AC*. Find the stress in each rod. (L.U.)

2. The framework shown (Fig. 73) consists of nine light rods freely jointed at *A*, *B*, *C*, *D*, *E*, *F*. *AEC* is an isosceles triangle right-angled at *E*, and *B*, *D*, *F* are

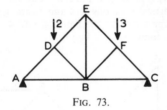

Fig. 73.

respectively the mid-points of *AC*, *AE*, *CE*. Vertical forces of 2000 N and 3000 N act downwards at *D* and *F*, and the framework is supported at *A* and *C*. Draw a stress diagram for the framework; state the stress in each rod and distinguish between struts and ties. (L.U.)

3. The framework shown (Fig. 74) consists of seven light rods, freely jointed at *A*, *B*, *C*, *D*, *E*. *BCE* is an equilateral triangle, *AB* = *BC* = *CD*, the plane of the

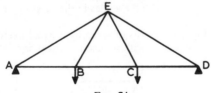

Fig. 74.

framework is vertical and *ABCD* is horizontal. Vertical forces of 5000 N and 3000 N act at *B* and *C*, and the framework is supported at *A* and *D*. Draw a stress diagram for the framework; state the stress in each rod, and distinguish between struts and ties. (L.U.)

4. The diagram (Fig. 75) shows a framework of five freely jointed light rods AB, BC, CD, DA, AC, in the form of a parallelogram $ABCD$ in a vertical plane with AB horizontal, and acted on by vertical forces, as shown, at the four corners. Prove that the frame is in equilibrium, and find graphically the stresses in all the rods, distinguishing tension from compression.   (L.U.)

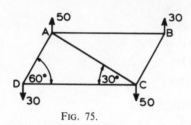

FIG. 75.

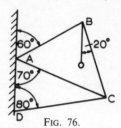

FIG. 76.

5. The diagram (Fig. 76) shows a smoothly jointed framework of light rods AB, BC, AC, CD, smoothly pivoted at A and D to a vertical wall. A mass of 100 kg is suspended from B and the system is at rest in a vertical plane. Find the stresses in all the rods, distinguishing tension from compression, and find also the forces exerted on the wall at A and D.   (L.U.)

6. The diagram (Fig. 77) represents a framework of nine smoothly jointed light rods, supported by vertical reactions at A and D, and loaded with 6 tonnes at F and 9 tonnes at E. The angles in the figure are all 45° or 90°. Determine the stresses in the rods. (1 tonne = 1000 kg.)   (O.C.)

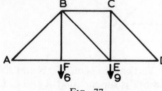

FIG. 77.

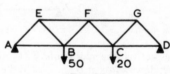

FIG. 78.

7. The diagram (Fig. 78) represents a framework of pin-jointed light rods resting on two supports at A and D, and carrying loads of 50 tonnes at B and 20 tonnes at C. Calculate the pressures on the supports and draw a stress diagram to show the stresses in all the rods. (All the angles in the diagram are either 45° or 90°.)   (O.C.)

8. The framework (Fig. 79) consists of seven light equal freely jointed rods. It is freely supported at A and C, with its plane vertical and ABC horizontal, and

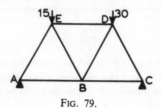

FIG. 79.

carries masses of 30 kg and 15 kg at D and E respectively. Find graphically the stress in each rod, distinguishing struts from ties.   (L.U.)

9. The diagram (Fig. 80) shows a cantilever consisting of six straight, rigid light rods freely jointed to one another and to a vertical wall at A and E. In the diagram, $ABDE$ is a square, ABC a straight horizontal line and $AB = BC$. A load of 200 kg is suspended from C. Find the stresses in the rods AB, BC, BD, and state which of these are in tension.   (L.U.)

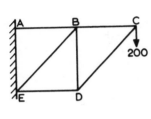

FIG. 80.

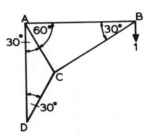

FIG. 81.

10. The diagram (Fig. 81) represents a framework consisting of five light rods freely jointed at their ends with AD vertical. A mass of 1000 kg is suspended from B, and equilibrium is maintained by a horizontal force at A and a force at D. Determine the magnitude of these forces and find the stress in each rod, distinguishing tension from compression.   (L.U.)

6.4 Method of Sections

The forces in the members of a framework may be calculated by considering a portion of the framework as being in equilibrium under the action of the external forces which act on it and the forces in the members joining this portion to the remainder of the framework. A line of section is drawn cutting not more than three members in which the forces are unknown, and if the lines of action of the forces in these members are not concurrent we have three conditions of equilibrium involving the external forces and the forces in the members. Hence, these forces can be found, and by repeated sections the forces in all the members of the framework can be calculated.

Example 5. *Calculate the forces in the members of the Warren girder shown in Fig. 82, in which the triangles are equilateral of side a and the loads are in tonnes.* (1 tonne = 1000 kg.)

By taking moments we find the reactions at the supports

$$P = 15, Q = 19 \times 10^3 g \text{ N}.$$

We may denote the forces in the members as $T_1, T_2, \ldots T_{11}$ newton, taking them all as tensions in the first instance, so that a negative value of T will indicate a compression.

Consider the section LM cutting AB and AC. Then the point A is in equilibrium (Fig. 83) under the action of the forces P, T_1, T_2 and hence

$$P + T_1 \sin 60 = 0,$$
$$T_2 + T_1 \cos 60 = 0,$$
$$T_2 = 5\sqrt{3}, \; T_1 = -10\sqrt{3} \times 10^3 g \text{ N}.$$

Consider the section NO cutting BD, DC and CE.

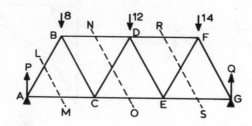

FIG. 82.

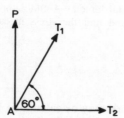

FIG. 83.

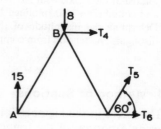

FIG. 84.

The triangular portion ABC (Fig. 84) is in equilibrium under the action of the forces P, $8 \times 10^3 g$ N, T_4, T_5, T_6.

Hence we have the three equations

$$T_5 \sin 60 + 15 \times 10^3 g = 8 \times 10^3 g,$$
$$T_4 + T_6 + T_5 \cos 60 = 0,$$
$$10^3 g \left(-15a + 8\frac{a}{2} \right) - T_4 a \frac{\sqrt{3}}{2} = 0,$$
$$T_4 = -\frac{22}{\sqrt{3}} \times 10^3 g, \; T_5 = -\frac{14}{\sqrt{3}} \times 10^3 g, \; T_6 = \frac{29}{\sqrt{3}} \times 10^3 g.$$

Consider the section RS cutting DF, EF, EG.
The portion $ABDEC$ (Fig. 85) is in equilibrium under the action of the forces P, $8 \times 10^3 g$, $12 \times 10^3 g$, T_8, T_9, T_{10}.

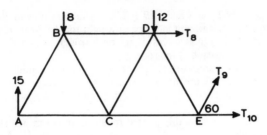

FIG. 85.

We have the three equations:

$$T_9 \sin 60 + 15 \times 10^3 g = 20 \times 10^3 g,$$

$$T_8 + T_{10} + T_9 \cos 60 = 0,$$

$$10^3 g\left(-15 \times 2a + 8 \times \frac{3a}{2} + 12 \times \frac{a}{2}\right) - T_8 a\frac{\sqrt{3}}{2} = 0,$$

and $$T_8 = -\frac{24}{\sqrt{3}}, \; T_9 = \frac{10}{\sqrt{3}}, \; T_{10} = \frac{19}{\sqrt{3}} \times 10^3 g.$$

By considering other sections the remaining forces are easily seen to be

$$T_3 = \frac{14}{\sqrt{3}}, \; T_7 = -\frac{10}{\sqrt{3}}, \; T_{11} = -\frac{38}{\sqrt{3}} \times 10^3 g.$$

EXERCISES 6 (c)

1. In the symmetrical framework of pin-jointed rods shown (Fig. 86), the triangles *ABC, ADC* are equilateral and the angle *AEC* is 30°. The framework carries masses of 20 kg at each of the points *A, B, C, E*, and is supported at *D*. Find the stresses in the rods *AE, AD, AB, AC*.   (O.C.)

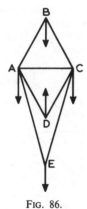

FIG. 86.

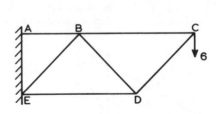

FIG. 87.

2. A rectangle *ABCD*, in which $AB = 2BC$, is formed of four light rods freely hinged together, and is kept in shape by a light rod *BD* freely hinged at its ends to the framework. Equal forces *X* act outwards at *A* and *C* in the line *AC*. Find the stresses in each of the rods.   (L.U.)

3. The freely jointed framework of light rods (Fig. 87) is in equilibrium in a vertical plane; *ABC* and *DE* are horizontal and *AE* is vertical with $AB = AE$ and $BC = 2AB = DE$. Find the stress in each bar and the reaction on the wall at *E*.
(L.U.)

4. A framework of five smoothly jointed rods is in the form of a rhombus *ABCD* and its diagonal *BD*, where $AC = 80$ cm, $BD = 60$ cm. The frame is in equilibrium under the action of opposite forces $10g$ N at *A* and *C*, each acting in the line *AC* towards the centre of the rhombus. Find the stress in each rod.
(L.U.)

5. The framework shown (Fig. 88) consists of six light rods freely jointed at *B, C, E*, and freely hinged to a vertical wall at *A* and *D*. The plane of the framework is vertical, *ABC* and *DE* are horizontal, and $AB = BC = AD = 2DE$. Find, graphically or otherwise, the stress in each rod, distinguishing struts from ties.
(L.U.)

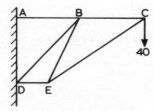

FIG. 88.

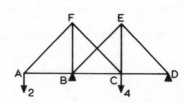

FIG. 89.

6. The figure (Fig. 89) represents a smoothly jointed light frame with all the angles 45° or 90°. *BE* and *FC* cross each other without interference. The frame has vertical loads at *A* and *C* as shown, and vertical supports at *B* and *D* which keep *ABCD* horizontal. Draw a stress diagram and find the stresses in *CF* and *BC*, distinguishing struts from ties.   (L.U.)

7. The framework in the figure (Fig. 90) consists of five light rods, smoothly jointed at *A, B, C, D*, hinged to a fixed support at *A* and further supported by a vertical reaction at *B*. Find the magnitude and direction of the reaction at *A* and the stresses in the rods, when a mass of 80 kg is suspended from *D*.   (O.C.)

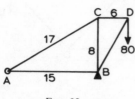

FIG. 90.

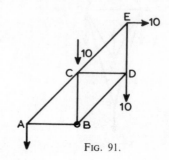

FIG. 91.

8. The framework (Fig. 91) consists of seven light, smoothly jointed rods, the horizontal and vertical rods being equal. It is loaded at C and D with equal masses 10 kg, and a horizontal force $10g$ N acts at E. The framework is hinged at B to a fixed support and anchored at A; find the stresses in the rods. (O.C.)

9. Seven light rods, AB, BC, CA, BD, CD, DE, CE, are jointed together to form a framework in which ABC, BCD, CDE are equilateral triangles. The framework rests on smooth vertical supports at A and E with AE and BD horizontal and BD above AE. It carries masses of 5 kg at each of the joints B, C, D. Determine the stresses in the various rods. (O.C.)

10. Determine the stresses in the rods composing the framework of light rods represented by the figure (Fig. 92), which rests on vertical supports at A and F with $ABEF$ horizontal, and carries masses of 10 kg at each of the joints C and E. Each of the triangles ABC, BCD, DBE, DEF, is a right-angled isosceles triangle. (O.C.)

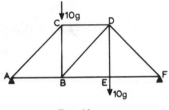

FIG. 92.

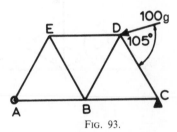

FIG. 93.

11. The framework shown (Fig. 93) consists of seven equal light rods in a vertical plane, smoothly hinged together at their ends. It is supported by a smooth hinge at A and a smooth horizontal platform at C, and is acted on by a force of $100g$ N at D, as shown in the figure. By drawing or calculation find (i) the supporting forces at A and C, (ii) the forces in the rods, distinguishing compression and tension. (L.U.)

12. Five light rods form the sides of a square hinged frame $ABCD$ and the diagonal BD. The frame is supported by vertical forces at A and C with the rod BD vertical and D above B. Find the stresses in the rods when a mass W is suspended from B.

13. In the frame $ABCDE$ (Fig. 94) of freely jointed bars, $AD = DC = CE = EB = DE$, and $AC = CB = 1.8AD$. It is freely supported at A, and B is hinged to a fixed support at the same level. A force of $1000g$ N acts at C as shown; find the reactions at A and B, and show how to draw a stress diagram for the bars. (L.U.)

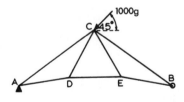

FIG. 94.

14. A framework consists of seven equal light rods OA, OB, OC, OD, AB, BC, CD, freely jointed at the ends to form three equilateral triangles. The framework is freely supported at D, and carries masses of 3 kg at A and 1 kg at B. A horizontal force P is applied at C and in the equilibrium position AB is horizontal. Determine, graphically or otherwise, the force P, the reaction at D and the stress in each rod, indicating the rods which are in tension.   (L.U.)

15. The frame of smoothly jointed rods represented in the figure (Fig. 95) is supported at A and B, AB being horizontal, and masses of 8 and 4 kg are suspended from C and D. The acute angles in the figure are 30° and 60°. Find by a stress diagram the stresses in each member of the figure.   (L.U.)

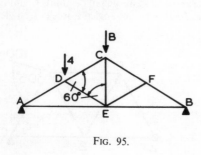

FIG. 95.

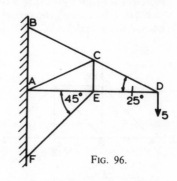

FIG. 96.

16. Find the stresses in the bars of the wall crane shown (Fig. 96), due to a mass of 5 tonnes hanging from a chain at D. The chain passes over pulleys at D and E; it is fixed to the wall at F, and $AE = ED$.   (L.U.)
   (In the figure EF is a chain, not a bar.)

CHAPTER 7

CENTRE OF GRAVITY

7.1 Centre of Gravity of Simple Forms

We have seen, §3.2, that the weights of the constituent particles of a body are a system of parallel forces whose resultant passes through a fixed point for any orientation of the body, and this point is the centre of gravity of the body.

If a body has a centre of symmetry G, such that for every particle A of the body there is a corresponding particle A' of equal mass, and G is the mid-point of AA', then the resultant weight of A and A' may be taken to act at G, and similarly for every other pair of particles, and hence G is the centre of gravity of the body.

Thus, the centre of gravity of a thin uniform rod is at its mid-point; the centre of gravity of a rectangle or a parallelogram is at the intersection of the diagonals; the centre of gravity of a circle, an ellipse, a sphere or an ellipsoid is at the centre of symmetry.

Triangular Lamina

The centre of gravity of a triangular lamina may be found by considering the triangle to be made up of a large number of thin strips parallel to one of its sides. Thus if ABC be the triangle

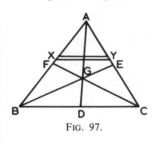

FIG. 97.

(Fig. 97) and XY a thin strip parallel to BC, the centre of gravity of XY is at its mid-point, and hence the centre of gravity of the whole triangle lies on the line joining the mid-points of all such strips, that is, on the median AD. Similarly, by taking strips parallel to AC and AB we see that the centre of gravity lies on the medians BE and CF. Hence the centre of gravity of the triangle is at the intersection of the medians G, that is, at a point G on AD such that $DG = \frac{1}{3}AD$.

If we consider three equal particles each of weight w to be placed at the vertices A, B, C, respectively of the triangle ABC, the resultant of the weights at B and C is a weight of $2w$ at D the mid-point of BC. The resultant of w at A and $2w$ at D is $3w$ at G where $AG = 2GD$.

Hence, the centre of gravity of a uniform triangular lamina is the same as that of three equal particles placed at the vertices of the triangle.

Triangle Formed by Three Uniform Rods

Let BC, CA, AB, be three uniform rods of lengths a, b, c and weights

107

wa, *wb*, *wc* respectively, and let *D*, *E*, *F* be
the mid-points of the rods (Fig. 98).

The centre of gravity of the rods *AB* and
AC together is at a point *L* in *FE* such that

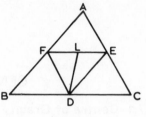

$$wc . FL = wb . EL$$

From similar triangles, $FD = \frac{1}{2}b$ and $DE = \frac{1}{2}c$

$$\frac{FL}{FD} = \frac{EL}{ED}.$$

Fig. 98.

Therefore, *DL* divides the side *EF* of the triangle *DEF* in the ratio of the
remaining sides and consequently bisects the angle *FDE*.

Hence, the centre of gravity of the three rods must lie on the bisector of
the angle *FDE*. Similarly, it must lie on the bisector of the angles *DEF*
and *EFD* and, therefore, the centre of gravity of the three rods is at the
centre of the inscribed circle of the triangle *DEF*.

Tetrahedron

Let *ABCD* be a uniform tetrahedron (Fig. 99) and let *E* be the mid-
point of the side *BD* and *F* the centre of gravity of the base *BCD*. We

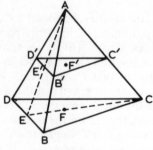

Fig. 99.

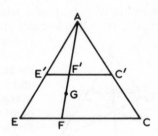

Fig. 100.

consider the tetrahedron as made up of thin, triangular sections such as
B'C'D' parallel to *BCD*. Since *D'B'* is parallel to *DB*, *AE* bisects *B'D'* at *E'*,
and in the section *AEC* (Fig. 100) the centre of gravity of the triangle
B'C'D' is at *F'* on *E'C'*. Since *E'C'* is parallel to *EC* and $E'F' = \frac{1}{3}E'C'$,
$EF = \frac{1}{3}EC$, *F'* lies on *AF*. Hence, the centres of gravity of all sections
parallel to *BCD* lie on *AF*, and therefore the centre of gravity of the
tetrahedron lies on *AF*.

The centre of gravity of the tetrahedron is, therefore, at the intersection of the lines joining the vertices to the centres of gravity of the
opposite faces.

It follows that the centre of gravity of a tetrahedron will be the same as that of four equal particles placed at its vertices.

The centre of gravity of four particles of weight w placed at A, B, C and D respectively, will be the same as that of w at A and $3w$ at F; therefore the centre of gravity will be a point G on AF such that

$$AG = 3GF.$$

Therefore, the centre of gravity G of the tetrahedron lies on AF at a distance $\frac{1}{4}AF$ from F. Also, if h be the length of the perpendicular from A on BCD, the centre of gravity will be at a height $\frac{1}{4}h$ above BCD.

Pyramid

Consider a solid pyramid $OABCDE$...(Fig. 101) whose vertex is O and whose base is a polygon $ABCDE$...Let F be the centre of gravity of

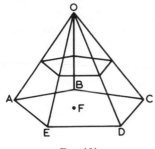

$ABCDE$...Sections parallel to the base will cut the pyramid in figures similar to $ABCDE$ ...and the centres of gravity of these sections will be similarly placed and will all lie on OF.

If h be the height of the pyramid, it may be considered as a number of tetrahedrons $OABC$, $OACD$, $OADE$...each of height h. The centre of gravity of each tetrahedron will be at a height $\frac{1}{4}h$ above the base, and hence the centre of gravity of the pyramid will be at a height $\frac{1}{4}h$ above the base on the line joining the vertex to the centre of gravity

FIG. 101.

of the base.

Solid Cone

A solid cone may be considered as a limiting case of a pyramid whose base is a polygon as the number of sides of the polygon is increased indefinitely. Hence, the centre of gravity of a cone of height h is on the line joining the vertex to the centre of gravity of the base at a height $\frac{1}{4}h$ above the base.

Curved Surface of a Cone

The surface of a cone may be considered as a limiting case of the surface of a pyramid. The centre of gravity of each triangle joining the vertex of a pyramid to its base is one-third of the way up the median of the triangle through its vertex, and is therefore at a height $\frac{h}{3}$ above the base, where h is the height of the pyramid. Hence, the centre of gravity of the curved surface of a cone is at a height $\frac{h}{3}$ above the base, where h is the height of the cone.

If the cone is a right circular one, by symmetry the centre of gravity of the curved surface lies on the axis, and is therefore a point on the axis at a height $\frac{1}{3}h$ above the base.

EXERCISES 7 (a)

1. *ABC* is a triangular lamina and *D, E, F* are the mid-points of the sides. Show that if the triangle *DEF* is removed the position of the centre of gravity of the lamina is unaltered.
2. *ABCD* is a uniform quadrilateral lamina in which the area of the triangle *ABD* is four times that of the triangle *BCD*. Show that the centre of gravity of the quadrilateral and the point *C* are equidistant from *BD*.
3. *ABCD* is a uniform quadrilateral lamina in which *BC* is parallel to *AD*. The length of *BC* is *a* and the length of *AD* is *b*. Prove that the centre of gravity of the lamina coincides with that of masses placed at *D, A, B, C*, proportional to *b*, $a+b$, *a*, $a+b$ respectively.   (O.C.)
4. Show that the centre of gravity of a quadrilateral *ABCD* is the same as that of three particles of masses proportional respectively to *AO, OC*, 2*AC* placed at *A, C*, and the mid-point of *BD*, where *O* is the intersection of *AC* and *BD*. (L.U.)

7.2 General Formula for Centre of Gravity

Consider a number of particles in a plane whose weights are $w_1, w_2, \ldots w_n$ and whose coordinates with respect to rectangular axes OXY (Fig. 102) in the plane are $(x_1, y_1), (x_2, y_2), \ldots (x_n y_n)$. If the plane OXY is horizontal, the weights of the particles will act in a direction perpendicular to the plane. The resultant of the parallel forces will be $w_1 + w_2 + \ldots + w_n$. Let this resultant act at the point $(\bar{x}, \bar{y})$. Then the moment of the resultant about OY is equal to the sum of the moments of the weights about OY; that is

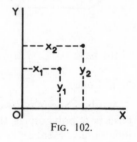

Fig. 102.

$$(w_1 + w_2 + \ldots + w_n)\bar{x} = w_1 x_1 + w_2 x_2 + \ldots + w_n x_n.$$

Writing

$$\Sigma w = w_1 + w_2 + \ldots + w_n,$$
$$\Sigma wx = w_1 x_1 + w_2 x_2 + \ldots + w_n x_n,$$

we have

$$\bar{x} = \frac{\Sigma wx}{\Sigma w},$$

and, similarly

$$\bar{y} = \frac{\Sigma wy}{\Sigma w}.$$

Since the centre of gravity of the weights must lie in the plane OXY, its coordinates are therefore $(\bar{x}, \bar{y})$.

Strictly speaking, the above formulae give the position of what is called the *centre of mass*. It is also the centre of gravity on the assumption that the weights of the particles act in parallel directions, and since bodies considered are usually small compared with the earth no distinction is necessary between the centre of mass and centre of gravity.

7.3 Compound Bodies

The formulae of the previous section may be used to find the centre of gravity of compound bodies. Thus if we have two bodies of weights W_1 and W_2 whose centres of gravity are at the points (x_1, y_1) and (x_2, y_2) respectively, the coordinates of the centre of gravity of the compound body will be

$$\bar{x} = \frac{W_1 x_1 + W_2 x_2}{W_1 + W_2}, \quad \bar{y} = \frac{W_1 y_1 + W_2 y_2}{W_1 + W_2}.$$

Example 1. *ABCD is a uniform square board whose edge is of length 2a. A triangular piece is removed by making a straight cut from A to the middle point of BC. Find the distances of the centre of gravity of the remainder from AD and CD (Fig. 103).*

The remainder may be considered as a rectangle *FECD* of area $2a^2$ and a triangle *AEF* of area a^2, and the weights of the portions may be taken as $2\rho a^2$ and ρa^2 respec-

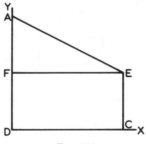

Fig. 103

tively. Taking *DC* and *DA* as the x and y-axes respectively, we have for the coordinates (x_1, y_1) of the centre of gravity of the rectangle, $x_1 = a$, $y_1 = \dfrac{a}{2}$.

We have for the coordinates (x_2, y_2) of the centre of gravity of the triangle $x_2 = \frac{2}{3}a$, $y_2 = \frac{4}{3}a$.

Hence,

$$\bar{x} = \frac{2\rho a^2 \times a + \rho a^2 \times \frac{2}{3}a}{2\rho a^2 + \rho a^2} = \frac{8}{9}a,$$

$$\bar{y} = \frac{2\rho a^2 \times \frac{a}{2} + \rho a^2 \times \frac{4}{3}a}{2\rho a^2 + \rho a^2} = \frac{7}{9}a.$$

Alternatively, the centre of gravity of the triangle is the same as that of weights $\rho\frac{a^2}{3}$ at each of the points A, E, F, and the centre of gravity of the rectangle is the same as that of weights $\rho\frac{a^2}{2}$ at each of the points F, E, C, D, and the centre of gravity of the whole is the same as that of the weights at A, E, F, D, C.

7.4 Centre of Gravity of a Remainder

If a portion of a body is removed, the centre of gravity of the remainder may be found by considering the difference of the moments of the weight of the whole acting at the centre of gravity of the whole, and of the weight of the portion removed acting at the centre of gravity of the portion removed.

Example 2. *ABCD is a uniform square board of side 8 cm. From the board a circular portion, of radius 2 cm whose centre is distant 3 cm from AB and BC, is removed. Find the distances of the centre of gravity of the remainder from DC and AD.*

We may take the weights of the whole and of the portion removed as 64ρ and $4\pi\rho$ respectively. Taking DC and DA as the axes of x and y respectively (Fig. 104), we have

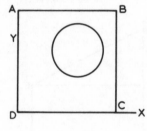

Fig. 104.

for the coordinates of the centre of gravity of the whole $(4, 4)$, and of the portion removed $(5, 5)$.

Hence, for the centre of gravity of the remainder we have

$$\bar{x} = \frac{64\rho \times 4 - 4\pi\rho \times 5}{64\rho - 4\pi\rho},$$

$$= \frac{64 - 5\pi}{16 - \pi} = 3.76.$$

Similarly $\bar{y} = 3.76.$

The centre of gravity of the remainder is, therefore, distant 3·76 cm from AD and from DC.

Example 3. *The radii of a frustum of a right circular cone are a and b (a > b) and its height is h. Find the distance of its centre of gravity from the larger face.*

If h_1 be the height of the whole cone, we have from similar triangles (Fig. 105)

$$\frac{h_1 - h}{b} = \frac{h_1}{a},$$

$$h_1 = \frac{ah}{a-b}.$$

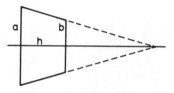

FIG. 105.

Thus the volume

of the whole cone $\qquad = \frac{1}{3}\pi a^2 h_1 = \frac{1}{3}\pi a^3 \frac{h}{a-b},$

of the portion removed $\qquad = \frac{1}{3}\pi b^2 (h_1 - h) = \frac{1}{3}\pi b^3 \frac{h}{a-b}.$

The distance from the larger face of the centre of gravity

of the whole cone $\qquad = \frac{h_1}{4} = \frac{1}{4}\frac{ah}{a-b},$

of the portion removed $\qquad = h + \frac{h_1 - h}{...4} = \frac{(4a - 3b)h}{4(a-b)}.$

Therefore, the distance from the larger face of the centre of gravity of the frustum is

$$\frac{\dfrac{1}{3}\pi a^3 \dfrac{h}{a-b} \times \dfrac{1}{4}\dfrac{ah}{a-b} - \dfrac{1}{3}\pi b^3 \dfrac{h}{a-b} \times \dfrac{1}{4}\dfrac{(4a-3b)}{a-b}h}{\dfrac{1}{3}\pi a^3 \dfrac{h}{a-b} - \dfrac{1}{3}\pi b^3 \dfrac{h}{a-b}}$$

$$= \frac{a^4 - 4ab^3 + 3b^4}{(a^3 - b^3)(a-b)} \cdot \frac{h}{4}$$

$$= \frac{a^2 + 2ab + 3b^2}{a^2 + ab + b^2} \cdot \frac{h}{4}.$$

EXERCISES 7 (b)

1. A uniform wire *ABCD* is bent at right angles at *B* and *C* in such a way that *BA* and *CD* are in the same sense, and the lengths of the parts *AB*, *BC*, *CD* are 15, 10, 5 cm respectively. Find the distances of the centre of gravity of the wire from *AB* and *BC*. Show that the wire can be suspended with each part equally inclined to the vertical by a string attached at a point *P*, and give the length of *BP*.

(O.C.)

2. A circular plate, centre O and radius a, is pierced with four circular holes, each of radius c. The centres of these holes are at A, B, C and D, where ABC is an equilateral triangle in a circle, centre O and radius $b(> 2c)$, and D is the other end of the diameter of this circle through A. Find the centre of gravity of the plate.

(O.C.)

3. A rigid framework $ABCDE$ of four equal rods, forming part of a regular hexagon, is suspended from A. Show that the angle made by AB with the vertical is

$$\tan^{-1}\left(\frac{4\sqrt{3}}{7}\right).$$

(O.C.)

4. A piece of solid metal shafting is 3 m long and tapers uniformly from a diameter of 30 cm at one end to a diameter of 10 cm at the other end. Find the distance of the centre of gravity from the thicker end. (L.U.)

5. A uniform solid body consists of a right-circular cone of slant height 3 m and base radius 180 cm, mounted on the plane base of a hemisphere also of radius 180 cm. Determine the distance, in centimetres, of the centre of gravity of the whole body from the centre of the hemisphere. (L.U.)

6. A uniform solid body consists of a square pyramid mounted on a cube such that each of the sixteen edges of the solid is of length a. Show that the centre of gravity of the whole lies in the cube at a distance from the common interface of $\dfrac{11a}{24+4\sqrt{2}}$

(L.U.)

7. From a cone of height $2h$, a cone of height h, having the same circular base, is removed; find the distance of the centre of gravity of the remainder from the vertex of the original cone. (L.U.)

7.5 Toppling

If a body be placed with its base in contact with a horizontal plane it may rest or topple over, according to the position of its centre of gravity. If it topples, moving initially parallel to a vertical plane, it turns about an axis perpendicular to the vertical plane through one or other extremity of the projection of the base on this vertical plane. When the body is about to topple, therefore, the reaction of the horizontal plane on its base will act through this axis (Fig. 106), and if the vertical through the centre of gravity of the body passes outside this axis it cannot balance the reaction and toppling will ensue.

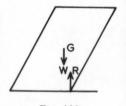

FIG. 106.

Hence, toppling in any vertical plane depends on whether or not the vertical through the centre of gravity passes outside the projection of the base on that vertical plane.

Example 4. *A pile in the shape of a flight of stairs is formed of n uniform cubical blocks, of edge a, each block being displaced a small distance c horizontally with reference to the the block below. Determine the position of the centre of gravity of the pile and deduce that the pile must topple over if $(n-1)c > a$.*

The horizontal distances of the centres of gravity of the n blocks from the clear edge of the first are (Fig. 107)

$$\frac{a}{2}, \frac{a}{2}+c, \frac{a}{2}+2c,\ldots\frac{a}{2}+(n-1)c.$$

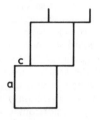

FIG. 107.

The distance x of the centre of gravity of the pile from the same edge is given by

$$\bar{x} = \frac{\frac{a}{2}+\left(\frac{a}{2}+c\right)+\ldots+\left(\frac{a}{2}+(n-1)c\right)}{n},$$

$$= \frac{a}{2}+\frac{n-1}{2}c.$$

Hence, the vertical through the centre of gravity will pass outside the edge of the lowest block if $\frac{a}{2}\ldots+\frac{n-1}{2}c > a$, that is if $(n-1)c > a$.

EXERCISES 7 (c)

1. $ABCD$ is the vertical face of a rectangular block, the horizontal face which has BC for an edge being in contact with the ground. BC is 40 cm, CD is 25 cm; E is a point in BC 15 cm from B. Find the position of a point F in CD, such that the block will be on the point of toppling over when a prism is cut from it by cutting it along EF at right angles to the face $ABCD$. (O.C.)

2. A square $ABCD$ is of side a, E is the mid-point of BC and F a point on CD distant x from C. The triangle EFC is cut away, and the remaining pentagon represents the middle cross-section of a uniform bar which rests on a horizontal table, the face represented by DF being in contact with the table. Find the distances of the centre of gravity of the bar from the faces represented by BE and DF. What is the greatest value of x consistent with equilibrium? (L.U.)

3. $ABCD$ is a square lamina of side a, from which a triangle ADE is removed, E being a point in CD distant c from C. Show that the centre of gravity of the remaining lamina is distant $\dfrac{a^2+ac+c^2}{3(a+c)}$ from BC.

Deduce that, if this lamina be placed in a vertical plane with CE resting on a horizontal table, equilibrium will not be possible if c is less than the positive root of $2x^2+2ax-a^2 = 0$. (L.U.)

4. A cubical block of edge a rests on a horizontal plane and is gradually under-mined by cutting away slices by planes parallel to a horizontal edge, inclined at 45° to the horizontal. Find the centre of mass of the remainder when a length x has been removed from each of four edges, and show that the block will fall when $9x = 5a$, approximately. (L.U.)

5. An isosceles triangle is cut off a corner of a uniform square lamina. Show that the remainder can stand on a shortened edge if the part cut off is 0·5 of an edge, but not if the part cut off is 0·6 of an edge. (O.C.)

6. A table consists of a 1-cm board, 48 cm square, and having at its corners legs of the same material 54 cm long, and of 2 cm square cross-section. Find the height of the centre of mass and the greatest angle through which the table can be tilted on two legs without being overturned.

7. A uniform right prism, whose cross-section is an isosceles triangle BAC, lies on a table with the face containing BC horizontal. The prism is gradually sliced away by cutting slices parallel to the face in which AB lies, beginning from the edge through C. What fraction of the whole prism can be cut away without the re-mainder toppling over, AB, AC being the equal sides? (L.U.)

7.6 Centre of Gravity by Integration

The general formula for the area enclosed by a curve and the x-axis between values of x, $x = a$ and $x = b$ is $A = \int_a^b y\,dx$. The element of area $y\,dx$ is at a distance x from the y-axis, and hence the moment of area about the y-axis is $xy\,dx$. Taking the mass as proportional to the area we have therefore for the x-coordinate of the centre of gravity, from the general formula of §7.2,

$$\bar{x} = \int_a^b xy\,dx \div \int_a^b y\,dx.$$

Since the centre of gravity of the strip $y\,dx$ is at a distance $y/2$ from the x-axis we have for the y-coordinate of the centre of gravity

$$\bar{y} = \int_a^b \frac{1}{2}y^2\,dx \div \int_a^b y\,dx.$$

The point $(\bar{x}, \bar{y})$, found by assuming uniform density of material over the area, is usually called the *centroid* of the area. When the density is uniform the centroid and the centre of gravity of the area are identical.

Centre of Gravity of Circular Arc

Consider an arc of a circle of radius r with centre at the origin and subtending an angle 2α at the centre, and let the x-axis bisect the arc (Fig. 108). By symmetry, the centre of gravity lies on OX and we require its x-coordinate.

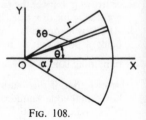

Fig. 108.

An element of the arc whose x-coordinate is $r \cos \theta$, subtending an angle $\delta\theta$ at the centre, is of length $r\delta\theta$, and we have for the centroid

$$\bar{x} = \int_{-\alpha}^{\alpha} r^2 \cos \theta d\theta \div \int_{-\alpha}^{\alpha} r d\theta,$$

$$= 2r^2 \sin \alpha \div 2r\alpha,$$

$$= \frac{r \sin \alpha}{\alpha}.$$

Centre of Gravity of a Sector of a Circle

Let the sector with centre at the origin (Fig. 109) have radius r and subtend an angle 2α at the centre, the x-axis bisecting the sector. By symmetry, the centre of gravity lies on OX and we require its x-coordinate. An element which is a sector inclined at an angle θ to the x-axis and containing an angle $\delta\theta$ has area $\frac{1}{2}r^2\delta\theta$ and, since it is triangular in shape, its centre of gravity is $\frac{2}{3}r$ from the origin and therefore $\frac{2}{3}r \cos \theta$ from the y-axis.

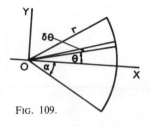

Fig. 109.

Therefore, the x-coordinate of its centroid is

$$\bar{x} = \int_{-\alpha}^{\alpha} \frac{1}{3}r^3 \cos \theta d\theta \div \int_{-\alpha}^{\alpha} \frac{1}{2}r^2 d\theta,$$

$$= \frac{2}{3}r^3 \sin \alpha \div r^2\alpha,$$

$$= \frac{2}{3} \frac{r \sin \alpha}{\alpha}.$$

Centre of Gravity of a Semicircle

When $\alpha = \frac{\pi}{2}$, the sector becomes a semi-circle, and hence the centroid of a semi-circle is on a central radius at a distance $\frac{4r}{3\pi}$ from the centre.

Centre of Gravity of a Uniform Solid Hemisphere

Consider a hemisphere of radius r with its centre at the origin and with the x-axis as its axis of symmetry (Fig. 110). An element which is

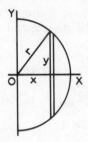

Fig. 110.

a disc of radius y has a volume $\pi y^2 dx$, and its centre of gravity is at a distance x from the origin, where $x^2 + y^2 = r^2$.

The centre of gravity lies on OX and its x-coordinate is

$$\bar{x} = \int_0^r \pi y^2 x dx \div \int_0^r \pi y^2 dx,$$

$$= \int_0^r (r^2 - x^2) x dx \div \int_0^r (r^2 - x^2) dx,$$

$$= \tfrac{1}{4} r^4 \div \tfrac{2}{3} r^3 = \tfrac{3}{8} r.$$

Centre of Gravity of a Uniform Hemispherical Shell

Let the hemisphere be of radius r with its centre at the origin and with the x-axis as an axis of symmetry (Fig. 111). Let a zonal strip subtend an angle θ at the origin and let the width of the strip by $r\delta\theta$. Its radius is $r \sin \theta$. Then the area of the strip is $2\pi r \sin \theta . r\delta\theta$ and its centre of

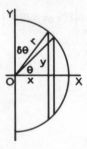

Fig. 111.

gravity is distant $r \cos \theta$ from the origin on the x-axis. Therefore, the centre of gravity of the shell has as its x-coordinate

$$\bar{x} = \int_0^{\pi/2} 2\pi r^3 \sin \theta \cos \theta d\theta \div \int_0^{\pi/2} 2\pi r^2 \sin \theta d\theta,$$

$$= r \int_0^{\pi/2} \sin 2\theta d\theta \div 2 \int_0^{\pi/2} \sin \theta d\theta,$$

$$= r/2.$$

Example 5. *A thin strip of metal of uniform width and thickness has part of it bent into the form of a semi-cylinder of radius r, leaving a plane piece of length l tangential to the semi-cylinder of radius r along one of its edges. Show that the body can rest with the plane piece in contact with a horizontal plane provided that l is greater than 2r.*   (L.U.)

The lengths of the curved and plane portions (Fig. 112) are πr and l. The strips may be taken as thin wires of uniform density ρ and masses $\pi \rho r$ and $l \rho$. The centre of gravity

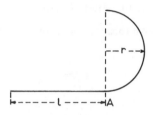

FIG. 112.

of the semicircular portion is distant $\dfrac{r \sin \pi/2}{\pi/2} = \dfrac{2r}{\pi}$ horizontally from the point of junction A, and the centre of gravity of the plane portion is distant $l/2$ from A. Therefore, the centre of gravity of the whole will lie to the left of A if

$$l\rho \times l/2 > \pi \rho r \times 2r/\pi,$$

that is, if $l > 2r$, and this is the condition that the body will not topple.

7.7 Theorem of Pappus

If a plane area is revolved about an axis in its own plane, the volume generated is the product of the area and the length of the path described by the centre of gravity of the area.

Let A be the area and OX be the axis of rotation (Fig. 113). Consider a small element of the area δA distant y from OX. Then, if the area be rotated through an angle α, the volume generated by the element δA is $\alpha y \delta A$.

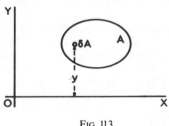

FIG. 113.

Hence, the volume described by the whole area is

$$\Sigma \alpha y dA = \alpha \Sigma y \delta A = \alpha A \bar{y},$$

and this is the total area multiplied by the length of the path of its centroid.

If the axis divides the area into two parts of areas A_1 and A_2 whose centres of gravity are distant $\bar{y}_1$ and $\bar{y}_2$ respectively from the axis, the volumes generated by the parts are $\alpha \bar{y}_1 A_1$ and $\alpha \bar{y}_2 A_2$. The *difference* of these volumes

$$= \alpha(\bar{y}_1 A_1 - \bar{y}_2 A_2),$$

$$= \alpha A \bar{y}.$$

For example, if a semicircle of radius a be rotated through an angle 2π about its diameter, the solid generated is a sphere of volume $\frac{4}{3}\pi a^3$.

Hence, if $\bar{y}$ be the distance of the centroid of the semicircle from its diameter, we have

$$\frac{\pi}{2}a^2 \times 2\pi \bar{y} = \frac{4}{3}\pi a^3,$$

$$\bar{y} = \frac{4a}{3\pi}.$$

Again, if a circle of radius a be rotated through an angle 2π about an axis in its plane at a distance $b(> a)$ from its centre, the length of the path described is $2\pi b$ and the volume generated is

$$2\pi b \times \pi a^2 = 2\pi^2 a^2 b.$$

The solid thus generated is called an anchor-ring or tore.

Thus the theorem of Pappus may be used to find the position of the centre of gravity when the volume generated is known, or to find the volume generated when the position of the centre of gravity is known.

EXERCISES 7 (d)

1. From a circular lamina of radius a, a quadrant is removed. Find the distance of the centre of gravity of the remainder from the centre of the circle.

2. A lamina is bounded by a semicircle on a diameter AB, a semicircle on the diameter AO, where O is the mid-point of AB, on the same side of AB, and a semicircle on the diameter OB on the opposite side of OB. Find the position of the centre of gravity of the lamina. (L.U.)

3. A thin uniform flywheel of mass 50 kg and radius 30 cm has its axis 0·05 cm out of centre. Static balance about the axis is restored by fixing a length of thin uniform wire, of mass 5/18 kg per m length, suitably along the rim of the disc. Prove that the length of wire required is about 31·4 cm. (L.U.)

4. A sheet of paper in the form of a sector of a circle AOB, centre O, of angle α and radius r, is formed into a right circular conical shell by bringing the edge OA into coincidence with the edge OB. Prove that the distance from O of the centre of mass of the shell is $(2r \cos \theta)/3$, where $\sin \theta = \alpha/(2\pi)$.

   If the above shell be closed by affixing a circular base of paper whose mass is equal to that of the shell, prove that the distance of the centre of mass of the combination from O is $5r \cos \theta/6$. (L.U.)

5. A uniform thin hemispherical cup of radius r stands on a circular base of the same material, thickness and radius as the cup, while the intervening stem is of length r and weight one quarter of that of the hemisphere. Find the height of the centre of gravity above the base. (L.U.)

EXERCISES 7 (*e*)

1. A body is built up of a solid right circular cone and a solid hemisphere (both of the same uniform density) on the same circular base as the cone. Find the vertical angle of the cone if the centre of gravity of the body lies in the common circular base. (L.U.)

2. A thin hemispherical shell of weight W rests with its curved surface on a horizontal plane. To a point on the rim a particle of weight $\dfrac{W}{2}$ is attached. Show that in the position of equilibrium, the plane of the rim makes an angle of 45° with the horizontal. (L.U.)

3. A uniform cube is attached by one of its faces to the base of a uniform hemisphere, a diagonal of this face of the cube being a diameter of the base of the hemisphere. If ρ_1 be the density of the material of the hemisphere and ρ_2 of the material of the cube, show that the combined solid will be in equilibrium with any point of the curved surface of the hemisphere in contact with a horizontal plane if $\pi \rho_1 = 8 \rho_2$. (L.U.)

4. A right circular cylindrical can, of height 45 cm and diameter 30 cm, made of uniform thin material, stands with its axis vertical and its plane base in contact with a horizontal table. The can is fitted with a lid of diameter 30 cm which is hinged about a tangent to its circumference, and the lid is opened so that it stands in a vertical plane at right angles to its closed position. Find the distances of the centre of gravity of the can with its lid from the base and the axis. (L.U.)

5. A uniform lamina is in the form of a square $ABCD$, of side $2a$, from which the isosceles triangle ABE is cut away; in this triangle $AE = BE$ and the distance of E from AB is h. Prove that the centre of gravity of the lamina is at a distance $\dfrac{12a^2 - h^2}{3(4a - h)}$ from AB.

   If $h = \dfrac{a}{2}$ and the lamina is suspended by a vertical string from A, find the angle which AD makes with the vertical. (O.C.)

6. A uniform wire of length 44 cm is bent into the form of a closed plane pentagon $ABCDE$ having $AB = BC = AE = ED = 10$ cm, $BE = 16$ cm, and the angles at C and D equal. Find the position of the centre of gravity of the wire. If the wire is supported by a vertical string from a point P of AB, find the distance AP if AB is horizontal in the equilibrium position. (L.U.)

7. $ABCD$ is a uniform solid tetrahedron, from which the tetrahedral portion $AEFG$ is removed, E, F, G being the mid-points respectively of AB, AC, AD. Find the distance of the centre of mass of the remaining portion from the plane BCD, given that the distance of A from this plane is h. (L.U.)

8. The height of the frustum of a uniform solid circular cone is h, and the radii of its circular ends are r_1 and r_2, the centres of these ends being A and B respectively. If G is the centre of mass, prove that
$$\frac{AG}{GB} = \frac{r_1^2 + 2r_1 r_2 + 3r_2^2}{3r_1^2 + 2r_1 r_2 + r_2^2}.$$
(L.U.)

9. The corners A and C of a thin uniform sheet of material in the form of a regular hexagon $ABCDEF$ are folded over to the centre of the hexagon. Determine how far the centre of gravity of the resulting body is from the centre of the original hexagon. (Q.E.)

10. $ABCD$ is a rectangular plate. $AB = 20$ cm, $BC = 30$ cm, and E is the mid-point of BC. If the triangular portion ABE is removed from the plate and the remainder is then suspended from A, find the inclination of the side AD to the vertical. (L.U.)

11. A uniform lamina $AOBCD$ consists of a square $ABCD$ and an isosceles triangle with equal sides OA, OB which make angles of 70° with AB. The lamina is suspended freely from its corner A. Find to the nearest tenth of a degree the angle which AD makes with the downward drawn vertical when the lamina is in its equilibrium position. (C.S.)

12. A solid body consists of a hemisphere surmounting a cylinder of the same radius whose height is three times the radius of its base. It is placed with its plane face in contact with a rough plane whose inclination to the horizontal is gradually increased. Prove that it will slide down the plane without toppling over, provided the coefficient of friction is less than 44/81. (L.U.)

13. An aircraft has a mass of 30 000 kg, and its centre of gravity is at a point A. Two vehicles are put on board the aircraft; the first weighs 11·2 tonnes, and its centre of gravity is placed 75 cm horizontally behind A and 30 cm vertically above A; the second weighs 2 tonnes, and its centre of gravity is placed 180 cm horizontally forward from A and 45 cm vertically above A. Find the horizontal and vertical distances from A of the centre of gravity of the loaded aircraft. (1 tonne = 1000 kg.) (C.S.)

14. A gun-barrel 3 m long tapers uniformly from a diameter of 20 cm at the breech to 12·5 cm at the muzzle, and the diameter of the bore is uniform at 7·5 cm. Find the distance of the centre of mass from the breech.

15. Assuming that the centre of gravity of a uniform circular arc subtending an angle 2θ at the centre of a circle of radius a is $a \sin \theta/\theta$ from the centre, find the centre of gravity of the uniform sector bounded by that arc and the radii to its extremities. Find the centre of gravity of the segment cut off by a chord equal to the radius. (L.U.)

16. A solid hemisphere and a solid cylinder have the same radii and are made of the same homogeneous material, and one end of the cylinder is cemented to the base of the hemisphere. The height of the cylinder is $\frac{2}{3}$ of its radius. Show that the centre of gravity of the whole solid is 1/48 of the radius from the common plane. (L.U.)

17. A uniform solid prism has a cross-section which is a trapezium $ABCD$. $AB = 1·8$ m, $CD = 3$ m, and the angles ADC and BCD are each 60°. Determine whether the prism can rest with the face containing BC in contact with a horizontal plane. (L.U.)

18. Use the theorem of Pappus to find the position of the centre of gravity of a uniform semicircular lamina.

   A uniform plane lamina consists of an isosceles triangle ABC, in which $AB = AC$ and $BAC = 90°$, and a semicircle BDC on BC as diameter. The lamina is suspended freely from A and a horizontal force P is applied at B in the same vertical plane as the lamina, and maintains equilibrium with the axis of symmetry of the lamina inclined at an angle θ to the vertical. If the sense of P is such as to tend to increase θ, prove that

$$\frac{P}{W} = \frac{8 + 3\pi}{3\pi(\cot\theta - 1)}$$

where W denotes the weight of the semicircle.   (L.U.)

19. A solid of uniform material consists of a frustum of a right circular cone surmounted by a hemisphere whose base is congruent with the smaller end of the frustum to which it is glued. The height of the frustum is 10 cm, the radii of its plane ends are 12·5 cm and 7·5 cm. Find the distance of the centre of gravity from the base of the solid.   (L.U.)

CHAPTER 8

WORK. MACHINES

8.1 Work

The work done by a force on a moving body is defined as the product of the force and the distance moved by its point of application along the line of action of the force. Thus if a force P acts on a particle which

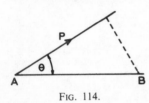

Fig. 114.

moves from A to B (Fig. 114), in a constant direction making an angle θ with AB, the distance moved by the particle along the line of action of the force is the projection of AB on the line of action of P, that is, $AB \cos \theta$. Hence, by definition, the work done by the force is $P \times AB \cos \theta$.

We note (see §1.8) that the work done is the scalar product of the force vector $\mathbf{P}$ and the displacement vector $\mathbf{AB}$ so that

$$W = \mathbf{P} \cdot \mathbf{AB}$$

If P is a varying force, AB must be an infinitesimal displacement δx and the work done in the displacement is then

$$\delta W = \mathbf{P} \cdot \delta \mathbf{x}$$

If the angle θ is a right angle, $\cos \theta = 0$, and the work done by P during the motion is zero, that is, a force does no work in a displacement perpendicular to its line of action. If $\theta = 180°$, $\cos \theta = -1$ and the work done will be $-P \times AB$; in this case the work done by the force is negative, that is, work is done against the force.

8.2 Units of Work

In SI units the unit of force is the newton and the unit of length the metre and hence the unit of work is 1 newton-metre and this unit is called a *joule* (symbol J).

When the force is in dynes and the length in centimetres the work is in dyne-centimetres and the dyne-centimetre is called an *erg*. Since 1 dyne $= 10^{-5}$ N and 1 cm $= 10^{-2}$ m, 1 erg $= 10^{-7}$ joule. The erg is now an outmoded unit.

124

When the force is in pounds weight and the distance in feet the work is in pounds force-feet, commonly called *foot-pounds* (ft lbf) and (see §16.11) 1 ft lbf = 1·356 joule. The foot-pound also is now outmoded.

If a particle of weight w N is lifted from a position of equilibrium at a height a m above the ground to a position of equilibrium at a height b m above the ground, the work done by the lifting force is $w(b-a)$ joule, and this quantity depends only on the initial and final heights of the particle. If the particle is lifted to a height x m $(x > b)$ and then lowered to a height b m, the work done by the lifting force is $w(x-a)-w(x-b)$ $= w(b-a)$, and if there is also a horizontal displacement the lifting force will do no work in such a displacement.

Theorem

The work done in raising a system of particles from one position to another position is Wh, where W is the total weight of the particles, and h is the distance through which the centre of gravity of the particles is raised.

Let the weights of the particles be $w_1, w_2, \ldots w_n$, and let $x_1, x_2, \ldots x_n$, respectively, be their heights above some standard position. Then if $\bar{x}$ be the height of their centre of gravity, we have

$$W\bar{x} = w_1 x_1 + w_2 x_2 + \ldots + w_n x_n.$$

When the masses have been raised let $x_1'.x_2', \ldots x_n'$ be the heights of the particles above the standard position; then if $\bar{x}'$ be the height of their centre of gravity we have

$$W\bar{x}' = w_1 x_1' + w_2 x_2' + \ldots + w_n x_n'.$$

Hence

$$W(\bar{x}' - \bar{x}) = w_1(x_1' - x_1) + w_2(x_2' - x_2) + \ldots + w_n(x_n' - x_n).$$

The right-hand side in this equation is the sum of the work done in raising the individual particles, and the left-hand side is Wh, hence the theorem is proved.

It should be noted that the work done depends on the initial and final positions of the centre of gravity, and is independent of the path followed by the particles.

Example 1. *A right circular cone of weight W, base radius a and height h, rests with a generator in contact with a horizontal plane. Find the work done in raising it so that its base is in contact with the plane.*

In the initial position (Fig. 115) the centre of gravity of the cone is at a height $\frac{3}{4}h \sin \alpha$

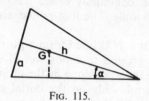

FIG. 115.

above the plane, where α is the semi-vertical angle and $\tan \alpha = a/h$. In the final position the centre of gravity is at a height $\frac{1}{4}h$ above the plane. Hence, the work done is

$$W\left(\frac{h}{4} - \frac{3}{4}h \sin \alpha\right)$$

$$= W\frac{h}{4}\left(1 - \frac{3a}{\sqrt{a^2 + h^2}}\right).$$

8.3 Work Done in Stretching an Elastic String

The work done in stretching an elastic string is the product of the extension and the mean of the initial and final tensions.

It has been seen (§2.1) that if λ be the modulus of an elastic string, l its unstretched length and x its extension, the tension in the string is

$$T = \lambda\frac{x}{l}.$$

If the string is stretched a further small distance δx the work done in this further extension is to the first order of small quantities

$$\lambda\frac{x}{l}\delta x.$$

Hence, the work done in stretching the string from an extension x_1 to an extension x_2 is

$$\int_{x_1}^{x_2} \lambda\frac{x}{l}dx = \frac{\lambda}{2l}(x_2{}^2 - x_1{}^2),$$

$$= \frac{\lambda}{l}\left(\frac{x_2 + x_1}{2}\right)(x_2 - x_1).$$

Now, $\frac{\lambda}{l}x_1$ is the initial tension, $\frac{\lambda}{l}x_2$ the final tension, therefore $\frac{\lambda}{l}\left(\frac{x_2 + x_1}{2}\right)$ is the mean of the initial and final tensions, and $x_2 - x_1$ is the extension.

8.4 Work Done by the Resultant of Two Forces

The work done by the resultant of a system of forces in any displacement is equal to the total work done by the forces of the system in that displacement.

The work done by a force in any linear displacement is the product of the displacement and the component of the force in the direction of the displacement. The component of the resultant of a number of forces in any direction is equal to the sum of the components of the forces in that direction, and hence the work done by the resultant is equal to the sum of the quantities of work done by the forces.

8.5 Work Done by a Couple

The work done by a couple whose moment remains constant in turning through any angle is the product of the moment of the couple and the angle.

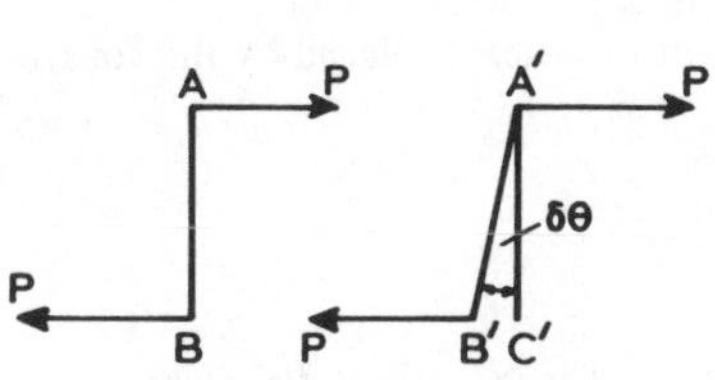

FIG. 116.

Let the forces of the couple be each P and the arm AB, and let AB move to the position $A'B'$, so that the angle between AB and $A'B'$ is the small angle $\delta\theta$ (Fig. 116). The movement of AB may be considered as one of translation from AB to $A'C'$, followed by a rotation from $A'C'$ to $A'B'$. During the translation the work done by the forces P will be equal and opposite in sign, and hence the total work done will be zero. In the rotation about A' the force P at A' does no work, the other force P moves its point of application through the distance $AB \sin \delta\theta \doteqdot AB\delta\theta$. Hence, the work done by the force is $P.AB.\delta\theta$, that is, the moment of the couple multiplied by the small angle through which it turns.

Hence, in turning through an angle α, the work done by the couple is

$$\int_0^\alpha P.AB.d\theta$$
$$= P.AB.\alpha,$$

if the moment of the couple remains constant. The angle α is measured in radians, and if the moment of the couple is in newton-metres the work will be in joules.

EXERCISES 8 (a)

1. A mass of 75 kg is drawn up a slope of 1 in 20 a distance of 40 m. Find the work done.

2. A uniform solid hemisphere of mass 10 kg and radius 15 cm rests with its plane face on a horizontal table. Find the work required.

    (a) to turn it over so that it rests with its curved surface in contact with the table,

    (b) to turn it about a tangent to its plane face until it is about to fall on to its curved surface.

3. A uniform log is in the form of a right prism whose cross-section is a triangle of sides 45, 60, 75 cm and has mass 500 kg. It rests with its smallest rectangular face on a horizontal plane. Find the least work needed to raise it on one edge so that it may fall over on to its largest rectangular face.   (L.U.)

4. An elastic string of natural length 2 m is stretched 50 cm by a force of $8g$ N. Find the amount of work required to stretch it an additional 100 cm.

5. A sphere of weight W N, and radius a m lies at the bottom of a cylinder of radius b m. Water is poured into the cylinder until the sphere is just covered. Show that the work done in lifting the sphere just clear of the water is
$(2W - W')(a - 2a^3/3b^2)$ where W' is the weight of water displaced by the sphere.

8.6 Machines

A machine is any apparatus by which a force, called the Power or Effort, is applied to overcome a resistance or move a weight. A simple example is a lever, by means of which a heavy load can be lifted by exerting a relatively small effort.

Mechanical Advantage

If an effort P has to be applied to a machine to overcome a resistance W, the ratio W/P is called the mechanical advantage of the machine.
Thus

$$\text{mechanical advantage} = \frac{\text{resistance}}{\text{effort}} = \frac{W}{P}.$$

Velocity Ratio

The ratio of the distance moved by the point of application of the effort to the distance moved by the point of application of the resistance or weight is called the velocity ratio of a machine.
Thus

$$\text{velocity ratio} = \frac{\text{distance moved by } P}{\text{distance moved by } W}.$$

8.7 Efficiency

If a machine were perfectly frictionless and its moving parts weightless, it would be found that its mechanical advantage would be equal to its velocity ratio. That is

$$\frac{W}{P} = \frac{\text{distance moved by } P}{\text{distance moved by } W},$$

or $\quad P \times \text{distance moved by } P$

$$= W \times \text{distance moved by } W.$$

In other words, the work done by the effort would be equal to the work done against the resistance. This is called the *Principle of Work*. In all machines, however, some part of the work done by the effort is consumed in overcoming friction on moving parts of the machine, and hence the mechanical advantage is less than the velocity ratio.

The ratio of the mechanical advantage to the velocity ratio is called the efficiency of the machine, and this is the same as the ratio of the work done by the machine against the resistance to the work done by the effort.

Thus

$$\text{efficiency} = \frac{\text{mechanical advantage}}{\text{velocity ratio}},$$

$$= \frac{\text{work done by a machine}}{\text{work supplied to the machine}}.$$

The efficiency is often expressed as a percentage.

8.8 Law of a Machine

The velocity ratio depends only on the arrangement of the parts of a machine and is a quantity independent of the effort applied. The mechanical advantage, and therefore the efficiency, of a machine varies with the effort applied and may be found by experiment. It is usually found that P and W are connected by a linear relation of the form $P = a + bW$, where a and b are constants. Such a relation is called the 'Law of the Machine'. Thus the mechanical advantage and the efficiency of a machine vary with the load, and efficiency as calculated is always related to a particular load.

8.9 Pulleys

Weights may be lifted by means of pulleys arranged in different ways, and it is usual to distinguish between three systems of pulleys commonly used. The weight of the pulleys themselves and of the rope used is generally

First System of Pulleys

In this system a separate rope passes around each pulley and is attached to a supporting beam and to the next pulley, the effort being applied at the free end of the last rope, whose direction may be changed by means of fixed pulley.

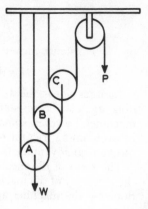

Let A, B, C (Fig. 117) be three pulleys in such a system. Then if the effort P moves through a distance x, the rope supporting the pulley C is shortened by x, and therefore the pulley C rises through a distance $x/2$. Similarly, the pulley B rises through a distance $x/4$ and the pulley A and W rise through a distance $x/8$. The velocity ratio is therefore 8, and if there were n movable pulleys it would be 2^n.

The mechanical advantage may be found on the assumption that the pulleys and rope are perfectly smooth and weightless.

Fig. 117.

Thus the tension in the rope supporting pulley A would be $\dfrac{W}{2}$, and since this load is carried by the two parts of the rope supporting pulley B the tension in this rope would be $\dfrac{W}{4}$ and $\dfrac{W}{8}$ in the third rope. The mechanical advantage would then be equal to the velocity ratio.

If the pulleys A, B, C are assumed to be frictionless but of weights w_1, w_2, w_3 respectively, taking T_1, T_2, T_3 as the tensions in the three strings we have

$$2T_1 = W + w_1,$$
$$2T_2 - T_1 = w_2,$$
$$2T_3 - T_2 = w_3,$$
$$T_3 = P.$$

Hence, $$P = \frac{W}{8} + \frac{1}{8}w_1 + \frac{1}{4}w_2 + \frac{1}{2}w_3.$$

Second System of Pulleys

In this system there are two blocks of pulleys, the upper block being fixed and the lower movable with the same rope passing around all the

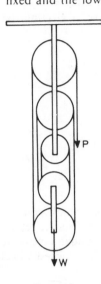

pulleys. Although the pulleys in each block are usually concentric and of the same diameter, it is convenient to show them as in Fig. 118, since the lengths of rope between the blocks are approximately vertical. The fixed end of the rope may be attached to the upper block, in which case the number of pulleys in each block will be the same, or to the lower block, in which case the upper block will have one more pulley than the lower. Suppose there are n vertical lengths of rope between the upper and lower blocks. Then if the effort moves through a distance x the shortening of the rope x will be equally shared between the n lengths of rope between the upper and the lower block, and hence the weight will rise through a distance x/n.

The velocity ratio is therefore n, and this is also the mechanical advantage if the system is weightless and frictionless.

Fig. 118.

If the weight w of the lower block is taken into account, since this is supported by n lengths of rope in each of which the tension is P, we have

$$nP = W + w,$$

and hence the mechanical advantage is $n - \dfrac{w}{P}$.

Third System of Pulleys

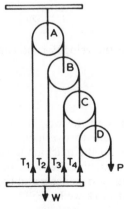

In the third system there are as many ropes as there are pulleys, each rope being attached to the weight and to another pulley. The system is shown diagramatically in the figure.

Let A, B, C, D be four pulleys in such a system (Fig. 119). Then if the weight rises a distance x, the pulley B descends a distance x and is therefore $2x$ nearer to the weight. The pulley C descends a distance $2x$ from pulley B, that is a distance $3x$ from A and is therefore $4x$ nearer to the weight. The pulley D descends $4x$ from the pulley C, that is $7x$ from A, the rope from pulley D to the weight is shortened by $8x$, and the effort moves through a distance $15x$. Hence, the velocity ratio is 15.

Fig. 119.

If there are n pulleys, it is easily seen that the velocity ratio is $2^n - 1$.

If T_1, T_2, T_3, T_4 be the tensions in the ropes we have, neglecting the weights of the ropes and pulleys,

$$T_1 + T_2 + T_3 + T_4 = W,$$
$$T_1 = 2T_2,$$
$$T_2 = 2T_3,$$
$$T_3 = 2T_4 = 2P,$$

and hence $15P = W$, that is, the mechanical advantage is 15.

8.10 The Differential Pulley

In the differential pulley (Fig. 120), the fixed upper block consists of two concentric cogged wheels of different diameters, fixed together. A continuous chain passes over the larger cogged wheel, under a movable pulley supporting the weight and then round the smaller cogged wheel in the opposite sense. The effort is applied to the slack portion of the chain. If the diameters of the larger and smaller cogged wheels be a and b respectively, it follows that if the effort moves through a distance x, a length x of the chain in the loop carrying the weight is wound on to the larger wheel, while a length $\frac{b}{a}x$ is at the same time unwound from the smaller wheel.

Therefore, the weight rises a distance $\frac{1}{2}\left(x - \frac{b}{a}x\right)$ and the velocity ratio is

$$\frac{2a}{a-b}.$$

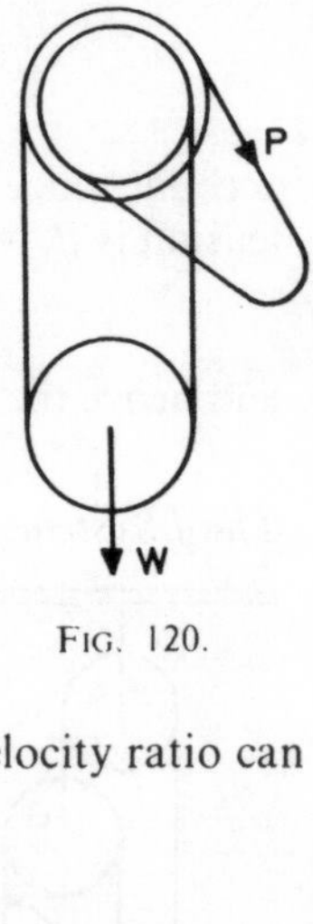

Fig. 120.

By taking the diameters of the wheels nearly equal the velocity ratio can be made as great as desired.

Overhauling

With a frictionless machine if the effort is removed the weight runs back to its original position and the machine is said to overhaul. To prevent overhauling, the friction between the parts of the machine must be so great that the load by itself cannot move the machine. Let F be the work done by friction when the effort moves through a distance a and the load through a distance b. Then by the principle of work we have

$$Pa = Wb + F.$$

Assuming that when the effort is removed the amount of friction is the same but its direction is reversed and just balances the weight, we have $Wb = F$ by the principle of work.

Therefore, $Pa = 2Wb$,

and since a/b is the velocity ratio and W/P the mechanical advantage the efficiency must be 50 per cent. Hence, the efficiency of a machine must be less than 50 per cent. to prevent overhauling.

8.11 The Wheel and Axle

The machine consists of a wheel fixed on an axle of smaller radius. The effort is applied to a rope wound around the wheel and fixed to

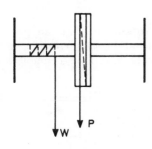

it. The weight is lifted by a rope wound around the axle in the opposite sense and fastened to the axle (Fig. 121).

It is easily seen that if the radii of the wheel and axle be a and b respectively, when the effort moves through a distance $2\pi a$ the weight rises $2\pi b$, and hence the velocity ratio is a/b. If the axle can turn without friction the moments of P and W about the axis of rotation must balance, that is,

Fig. 121. $Pa = Wb$,

and hence the mechanical advantage is a/b.

A capstan is a particular case of a wheel and axle.

Differential Wheel and Axle

In this case the axle consists of two portions of different radii. The weight is lifted by a pulley which is carried in the loop of a rope which is wound round the two portions of the axle in opposite directions (Fig. 122). If a, b, c be the radii of the wheel and the larger and smaller portions of the axle respectively, when the effort moves through a distance $2\pi a$, a length $2\pi b$ of rope is wound on to the axle, while a length $2\pi c$ of rope is unwound. The weight therefore rises through a distance $\frac{1}{2}(2\pi b - 2\pi c)$ and the velocity ratio is $\dfrac{2a}{b-c}$.

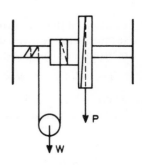

Fig. 122.

If b is nearly equal to c the velocity ratio will be very large.

8.12 The Screw

A screw is a cylindrical body with a projecting thread running round it in a spiral curve whose inclination to the axis of the cylinder is constant.

The pitch of a screw is the distance measured parallel to the axis in which the thread makes a complete circuit of the cylinder and is denoted by p. The screw works in a fixed support containing a groove of the same shape as the thread along which the screw slides. The effort may be applied by an arm perpendicular to the axis to overcome a resistance in the direction of the axis of the screw (Fig. 123).

If the radius of the arm be a, and p the pitch of the screw, in one complete rotation of the arm the screw advances a distance equal to the pitch parallel to its axis, and hence the velocity ratio is $\dfrac{2\pi a}{p}$.

The Differential Screw

This consists of a hollow screw of pitch p_1 working in a fixed support and a second screw of smaller pitch p_2 which cannot rotate but slides in grooves inside the hollow screw as this rotates (Fig. 124). Thus a complete

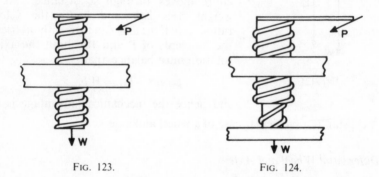

Fig. 123.   Fig. 124.

rotation of the arm drive the hollow screw forward a distance p_1, but the second screw moves a distance p_2 into the hollow screw so that the resistance moves a distance $p_1 - p_2$.

The velocity ratio is therefore $\dfrac{2\pi a}{p_1 - p_2}$,

where a is the radius of the arm. By taking p_1 nearly equal to p_2, a very high velocity ratio can be obtained.

EXERCISES 8 (b)

1. A block and tackle has four pulleys in each block, and a mass of 112 kg is supported by the movable lower block, of mass 8 kg. What is the velocity ratio of the machine? If 25 per cent. of the work done is lost in overcoming friction find the effort required to raise the load.   (L.U.)

2. There are three pulleys in each block of a block and tackle. The rope is attached to the fixed block, passes round each pulley, and the free end comes off a pulley of the fixed block. Find the effort needed to raise a mass of 60 kg if the weight of the movable block is negligible and the efficiency is 63 per cent.   (L.U.)

3. Find the force necessary to sustain three movable pulleys, each of weight W, in that system of pulleys in which each movable pulley hangs in the loop of a separate string, the hanging parts of the strings being vertical and one end of each string attached to a fixed point. A, B are two such movable pulleys, each of weight W; a third pulley, also of weight W, hangs in the loop of a string whose ends are attached one to the axle of A and the other to the axle of B. If B is the upper of the pair A, B, what force must be applied to the free end of the string which passes under B so as to maintain equilibrium?   (L.U.)

4. Find the condition of equilibrium for a system of pulleys in which each pulley hangs in the loop of a separate string, the strings being all parallel and attached to the beam. The weights of the pulleys are to be taken into account. If there are five pulleys, each of mass 1 kg, what mass will a force of $5g$ N support on such a system, and what will be the total pull on the beam?   (L.U.)

5. If the fixed pulleys of a differential block have ten and eleven teeth, and the effect of friction in the machine is to increase the effort by an amount which is a fixed proportion of the load, find that proportion when the efficiency is 1/3.
     (L.U.)

6. A differential wheel and axle consists essentially of three cylinders A, B, C fixed rigidly together so as to have a common horizontal axis, their radii being a, b, c respectively. The power P is applied to the rim of the cylinder A with the largest radius. The load W is attached to a pulley supported by a rope which is wrapped one way round the cylinder B and the opposite way round the cylinder C of least radius. If the system is in equilibrium find the relation between P and W.
     (L.U.)

7. In a differential wheel and axle the radius of the wheel is 30 cm, while the radii of the axles are 4 cm and 5 cm respectively. Find the effort needed to raise a mass of 1200 kg, the efficiency then being 72 per cent.   (L.U.)

8. If a capstan is turned by a double arm of length 4 m, and for each revolution a mass of 100 tonnes is raised 1 cm, find the force applied at both ends of the arm if all friction is neglected.   (L.U.)

9. A man of mass 65 kg sits in a seat of mass 7 kg, which is suspended from a smooth pulley supported by the two parallel portions of a rope which is coiled in opposite directions round the two drums of a differential wheel and axle of radii 30 cm and 24 cm respectively. He raises himself by pulling one side of the rope. State which side, and show that to raise himself he must exert a pull exceeding $8g$ N.   (L.U.)

10. In a differential wheel and axle the radius of the wheel is 24 cm, and the radii of the axle are 4 cm and 6 cm. It requires an effort of $144g$ N to lift 2 240 kg; calculate the efficiency of the machine for this load.   (L.U.)

11. A screw, whose axis is vertical, advances a distance p for each complete turn. If the screw is used to lift a weight, show that the mechanical advantage is $2\pi a/p$, where a is the distance from the axis of the line of action of the horizontal force which operates the screw. When the effort is $100g$ N, a mass of 500 kg can be lifted. Find the efficiency of the screw given that $p = a$.   (L.U.)

12. A copying press has a lever 50 cm long fastened at its centre to a screw the thread of which makes six complete turns per 5 cm of length. Forces equal to $12g$ N (in opposite directions) are applied at the two ends of the lever. Find the pressure exerted by the press.   (L.U.)

13. If the two screws in a differential screw have two and three threads to the cm respectively, and a couple of moment 20·8 N m applied to the larger screw produces a thrust equal to a weight of half a tonne, calculate the efficiency of the machine.   (L.U.)

14. A bucket is lowered into a well by means of a windlass and pulley. The end of the rope of the windlass is attached to the frame of the windlass, and the pulley, with bucket attached, slides in the loop of the rope, the hanging parts of the rope being vertical. Neglecting friction and the weight of the rope, determine by the principle of work, or otherwise, the force that must be applied at the arm of the windlass to maintain the bucket in equilibrium, having given the weight W of the bucket and its load, b the diameter of the barrel of the windlass and a the length of the arm. What is the efficiency if the force that will just raise the bucket is nW?   (L.U.)

15. The velocity-ratio of a machine for lifting loads is 44, and its efficiency for a load of 800 kg is 32 per cent. Show that the effort required to lift this load is 56·8g N, and find the work done against friction when the load is raised 1 m.

If the efficiency of the same machine for a load of 1000 kg is 36 per cent, find a law for the machine of the form $P = a + bW$ giving the effort P newton required to lift any weight W newton.

16. A continuous rope system of pulleys consists of two blocks each of three pulleys, the rope being fastened to the fixed block. Draw a diagram showing the arrangement of the pulleys and rope.

A man of mass 75 kg is raising a mass of 120 kg by means of the system. Find the thrust exerted by the man on the ground when he pulls vertically downwards assuming the system to be (i) 100 per cent efficient; (ii) 70 per cent efficient.   (C.S.)

17. A screw-jack is to be used to lift two wheels of a motor-car off the ground. The load on each of these wheels is 250 kg and the springs deflect 10 cm under this load, the jack is applied to the frame of the car at a point midway between the wheels. The velocity ratio between the handle and the lifting point of the jack is 200:1, and the friction in the jack is such that the applied force is 200 per cent greater than it would be without friction. Find the greatest force which has to be applied to the handle, and the total work done, in lifting the car until there is 1 cm clearance between the wheels and the road. The weight of the wheels and axle parts may be neglected.

CHAPTER 9

BENDING MOMENTS AND SHEARING FORCES

9.1 Internal Stresses in a Beam

In the previous chapters the external forces acting on bodies have been considered. In this chapter it will be seen how internal forces between the constituent particles of a body may in certain cases be measured.

Consider a beam of negligible mass with one end built into a wall so that the beam projects horizontally from the wall; let a weight W act at its free end (Fig. 125).

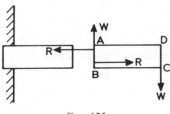

FIG. 125.

If the beam were cut across any section AB, the outer portion $ABCD$ would fall. When it has not been cut the portion $ABCD$ is held in position by the forces exerted by the fibres of the beam. These forces may be reduced to a force and a couple. Since for equilibrium the force must balance the weight W, it must be equal to W and acting vertically upwards at the section. Also, the couple must balance the couple of the two forces W and its moment must be equal to $W \times AD$. Hence, at the section AB the fibres of the beam exert a force W vertically upwards and a couple whose moment is $W \times AD$.

9.2 Shearing Force

The vertical force at any section of a loaded beam is equal and opposite to the algebraic sum of the external forces on one side of the section, and this algebraic sum of forces is called the *Shearing Force* at the section.

9.3 Bending Moment

The couple at any section is equal and opposite to the sum of the moments of the external forces on one side of the section about the section. The algebraic sum of the moments of the external forces on one side of a section about the section is called the *Bending Moment* at the section.

9.4 Convention of Signs

Since the whole beam is in equilibrium, the Shearing Force calculated by summing the external forces on one side of a section must be equal and opposite to that found by summing the external forces on the other side of the section; similarly the moment of the external forces on one side of a section about the section must be equal and opposite to the moment of the external forces on the other side of the section about the section. Hence, the magnitude of the Bending Moment or Shearing Force at a section may be found by considering the external forces on either side of the section. To ensure consistency in the signs of bending moments and shearing forces certain conventions are used.

In calculating the shearing force for any section the positive direction for forces on the left of the section is taken as vertically downwards and for forces on the right of the section vertically upwards (Fig. 126). Thus if a light beam of length l is supported at its ends (Fig. 127) and carries a

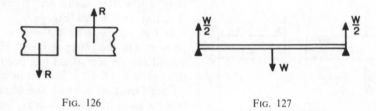

Fig. 126   Fig. 127

load W at its centre, the reactions at the supports will be each $\dfrac{W}{2}$. The shearing force at any section in the left-hand half of the beam will be $-\dfrac{W}{2}$; at any section in the right-hand half of the beam it will be

$$-\frac{W}{2} + W = +\frac{W}{2}.$$

Corresponding to this convention of signs for shearing forces, in calculating a bending moment, the moment of any external force about the section is taken as positive if it tends to stretch the uppermost fibres of the beam. Thus in the case of the end-supported beam, at a distance x from the left-hand support the bending moment will be

$$-\frac{W}{2}x \text{ if } x < \frac{l}{2},$$

If $x > \dfrac{l}{2}$ the bending moment will be

$$-\frac{W}{2}x + W\left(x - \frac{l}{2}\right),$$

where l is the length of the beam.

9.5 Graphical Representation

The bending moment and shearing force at sections along the length of a beam may be shown graphically by plotting the values of the bending moment and the shearing force at points along the beam. The graphs of bending moment and shearing force thus drawn may be straight lines or curves; they show the variation of stress along the beam and indicate the points where breaking is most likely to occur, that is, at points where the bending moment is a maximum or the shearing force a maximum.

Example 1. *A light beam AB, 4 m long, is supported at its ends in a horizontal position and carries loads of 9 kg and 12 kg at 4/3 m and 7/3 m respectively from A. Draw bending-moment and shearing-force diagrams for the beam.*

Let the weights act at points C and D respectively and let P and Q be the reactions at the supports (Fig. 128). By taking moments we have $P = 11g$ N, $Q = 10g$ N.

At any point in AC at x m from A the shearing force is $-11g$, and the bending moment $-11gx$ N m.

At any point in CD at x m from A, the shearing force is

$$-11g + 9g = -2g,$$

and the bending moment is $-11gx + 9g(x - 4/3)$.

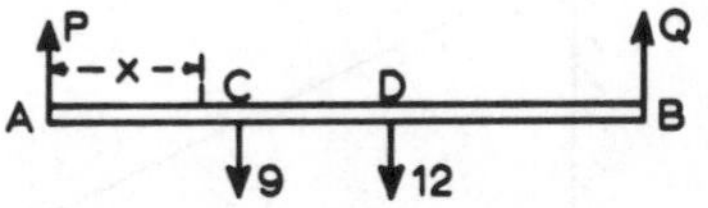

FIG. 128

At any point in DB at x m from A, the shearing force is $-11g + 9g + 12g = 10g$, and the bending moment is $-11gx + 9g(x - 4/3) + 12g(x - 7/3)$. Hence, as x varies along the beam, the shearing-force graph consists of three horizontal lines, and the bending moment for each of the three portions of the beam is a linear expression in x, and its graph is therefore a straight line.

By giving particular values to x the graphs may be drawn as in Fig. 129.

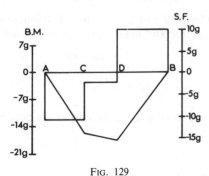

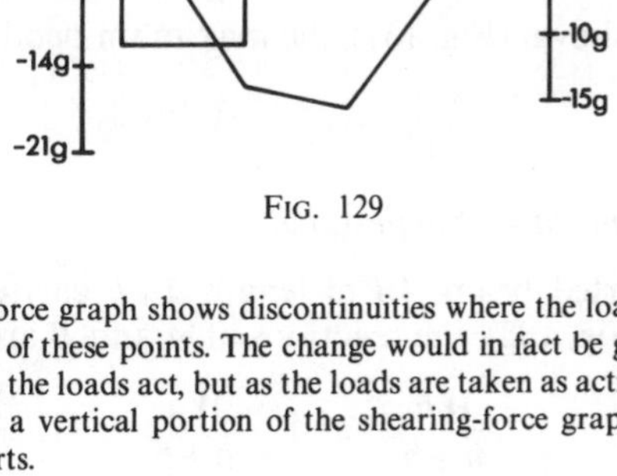

FIG. 129

The shearing-force graph shows discontinuities where the loads act and has different values either side of these points. The change would in fact be gradual over the lengths of beam on which the loads act, but as the loads are taken as acting at points, the change is represented by a vertical portion of the shearing-force graph where each load acts and at the supports.

9.6 Standard Cases

Light Cantilever with Load at Free End

For a cantilever of length l and load W at its free end, the shearing force and bending moment at x from the wall are

$$S = -W$$
$$M = W(l-x).$$

The bending-moment and shearing-force graphs are as shown (Fig. 130), the maximum bending moment being Wl at $x = 0$.

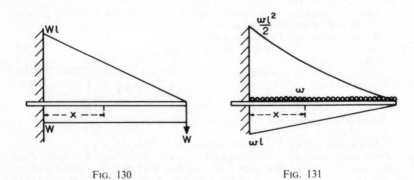

FIG. 130   FIG. 131

Cantilever with Uniformly Distributed Load

For a cantilever of length l with a uniformly distributed load of w per unit length, the shearing force and bending moment at x from the wall are

$$S = -w(l-x),$$
$$M = w\frac{(l-x)^2}{2}.$$

The graphs are as shown (Fig. 131), the maximum bending moment being $\frac{1}{2}wl^2$ at $x = 0$.

End-supported Beam with a Single Load

If an end-supported beam AB of length $a+b$ carries a load W at C, distant a from A (Fig. 132), the reactions at A and B are

$$\frac{Wb}{a+b} \quad \text{and} \quad \frac{Wa}{a+b}.$$

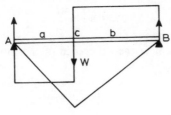

FIG. 132

Hence in AC at x from A

the shearing force $\quad S = -\dfrac{Wb}{a+b},$

the bending moment $M = -\dfrac{Wb}{a+b}x.$

In CB at x from B,

the shearing force $\quad S = +\dfrac{Wa}{a+b},$

the bending moment $M = -\dfrac{Wa}{a+b}x.$

The bending-moment and shearing-force graphs are as shown, the maximum bending moment being at C and equal to $\dfrac{Wab}{a+b}.$

End-supported Beam with Uniformly Distributed Load

Let an end-supported beam AB of length l carry a uniformly distributed load of w per unit length (Fig. 133). The reaction at each support is

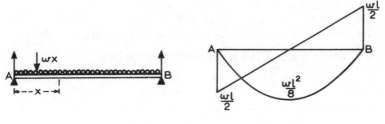

FIG. 133   FIG. 134

$\dfrac{wl}{2}$ and at x from A the shearing force is the difference of wx and $\dfrac{wl}{2}$.

That is,
$$S = wx - \frac{wl}{2}.$$

The bending moment is the difference of the moments of wx and $\frac{wl}{2}$ about the section, that is

$$M = \frac{wx^2}{2} - \frac{wl}{2}x.$$

The bending-moment and shearing-force graphs are as shown (Fig. 134), the maximum bending moment being $\frac{wl^2}{8}$ at the mid-point of the beam and the shearing force at this point is zero.

9.7 Relation of Bending Moment, Shearing Force and Load

Let w be the load per unit length along a horizontal beam. The quantity w, usually called the intensity of load, may include the weight of the beam itself and may vary with x, the distance along the beam. Let S be the shearing force and M the bending moment at distance x along the beam.

Consider a small length AB of the beam of length δx (Fig. 135). Let S and $S + \delta S$ be the shearing forces and M and $M + \delta M$ the bending moments at A and B respectively. In the figure S and M are taken as positive, that is, the sum of the forces on the beam to the left of A is a force S downwards, and to the right B a force $S + \delta S$ upwards; the forces to the left of A have a moment about A tending to stretch the upper fibres of the beam, as have the forces to the right of B about B. The portion of the load on AB will be to the first order of small quantities $w\delta x$ acting at the mid-point of AB.

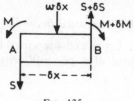

FIG. 135

Then, since the length AB is in equilibrium, we have
$$\delta S = w\delta x,$$
and, taking moments about B,
$$M + S\delta x + w\delta x \cdot \frac{\delta x}{2} = M + \delta M,$$
that is,
$$\frac{\delta M}{\delta x} = S + \frac{1}{2}w\delta x.$$

In the limit as δx tends to zero, we have

$$\frac{dS}{dx} = w,$$

$$\frac{dM}{dx} = S,$$

and hence, $$\frac{d^2 M}{dx^2} = w.$$

We also have $$S = \int_0^x w \, dx + \text{constant},$$

$$M = \int_0^x S \, dx + \text{constant}.$$

It should be noted that the expression for the bending moment has a maximum or minimum at points at which the shearing force is zero.

Example 2. *A beam AB, 12 m long, is supported at points C, 1 m from A, and D, 3 m from B. It carries a uniformly distributed load of 2 tonne/m. Draw the bending-moment and shearing-force diagrams for the beam and find the maximum bending-moment.*

By taking moments, we find the reactions P and Q at C and D (Fig. 136) are

$$P = 9000g, \quad Q = 15\,000g.$$

The intensity of load $w = 2000$ kg/m.

F_IG. 136

In AC at x from A we have for the shearing force and bending moment in kilonewtons and metres.

$$S = \int_0^x wg \, dx = 2xg,$$

$$M = \int_0^x 2xg \, dx = x^2 g.$$

The additive constants are zero, since S and M are both zero at A.
In CD at x from A

$$S = \int_0^x wg \, dx - P = (2x-9)g,$$

$$M = \int_0^x (2x-9)g \, dx + Cg,$$

$$= (x^2 - 9x + C)g.$$

But $M = 1$ when $x = 1$, therefore $C = 9$, and $M = (x^2 - 9x + 9)g$.
In DB at x from A

$$S = \int_0^x wg\,dx - P - Q = (2x - 24)g,$$
$$M = \int_0^x (2x - 24)g\,dx + D,$$
$$= (x^2 - 24x + D)g.$$

But $M = 0$ when $x = 12$, therefore $D = 144$
and $M = (x^2 - 24x + 144)g$.

From these expressions the graphs for bending moment and shearing force are drawn (Fig. 137). The maximum bending moment is in CD where the shearing-force

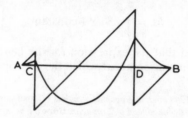

FIG. 137

is zero, that is, where $2x - 9 = 0$, $x = 4\frac{1}{2}$, and its value is $-11\,250g$ N m.

Example 3. *A light beam AB, 10 m long, is end supported and carries a mass which varies in intensity from 10 kg/m at A to 30 kg/m at B. Find expressions for the bending moment and shearing-force at x from A; sketch the bending-moment and shearing-force graphs, and find the maximum bending moment.*

At x m from A (Fig. 138) the intensity of mass is $10 + 2x$.

Hence, on an element δx at x from A we have a force $(10 + 2x)g\,\delta x$ whose moment about A is $x(10 + 2x)g\,\delta x$.

Hence, if Q be the reaction at B

$$10Q = \int_0^{10} x(10 + 2x)g\,dx = \frac{3500}{3}g,$$
$$Q = \frac{350}{3}g \text{ N}.$$

Similarly, the reaction at A is

$$P = \frac{250}{3}g \text{ N}.$$

Hence, for the shearing-force at x from A we have

$$S = \int_0^x (10 + 2x)g\,dx - P,$$
$$= \left(x^2 + 10x - \frac{250}{3}\right)g.$$

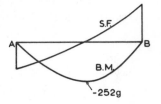

FIG. 138 FIG. 139

For the bending moment at x from A we have

$$M = \int_0^x \left(x^2 + 10x - \frac{250}{3}\right) g \, dx + \text{constant}.$$

The constant is zero since the bending moment is zero when x is zero, and hence

$$M = \left(\frac{x^3}{3} + 5x^2 - \frac{250}{3}x\right) g$$

The expression for M has a maximum where $\frac{dM}{dx} = 0$, that is, where $S = 0$, that is,

$$x^2 + 10x - \frac{250}{3} = 0,$$

$$x = 5 \cdot 41.$$

The maximum bending moment is therefore

$$\frac{(5 \cdot 41)^3}{3} + 5(5 \cdot 41)^2 - \frac{250}{3}(5 \cdot 41) = -252g \text{ N m.}$$

The bending-moment and shearing-force graphs are as shown in Fig. 139.

9.8 Graphical Construction for Bending Moments

When a beam carries a number of loads at points along its length, a funicular polygon may be drawn (§6.2) to determine the reactions at the supports, and this polygon may be used as a bending-moment diagram showing the magnitude of the bending moment at points along the beam.

Let AB be an end-supported beam carrying loads W_1, W_2, W_3 at points C, D, E (Fig. 140). A funicular polygon is drawn in the usual way to determine the reactions at A and B, which are represented in the force diagram by ea and de respectively, oe being parallel to XY.

Let Z be any point on the beam and let the vertical through Z meet the funicular polygon at R and S. Then the bending moment at Z is proportional to the length RS. Taking the point Z in CD, the bending moment at Z is the moment about Z of the forces P and W_1. But the forces P and W_1 are together equivalent to a force oe along XY, which may be taken to act at R, and a force ob along LM, which may be taken to act at S. From the force diagram, the horizontal component of each of these forces is equal to the perpendicular h from o on the line $abcd$.

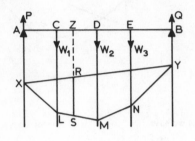

Fig. 140

Hence the difference of their moments about Z is $h \times RS$. Similarly, the bending moment at any point of the beam is the product of the force h and the intercept made on the vertical through the point by the funicular polygon.

EXERCISES 9

1. An end-supported beam AB is 10 m long and carries loads of 20 kg at C, 2 m from A, and 30 kg at D, 4 m from B. Draw bending-moment and shearing-force diagrams and find the bending moment at C, at D, and at the centre of the beam.
2. A beam AB, 16 m long, is supported at points C and D, 3 m from each end. Masses of 20 kg and 50 kg are suspended from A and B respectively, and 40 kg and 50 kg from E, 7 m from A, and F, 10 m from A, respectively. Draw bending-moment and shearing-force diagrams and find the maximum shearing force and the maximum bending moment.
3. A beam ABC, 16 m long, is supported at A and at B 6 m from the end C. It carries a uniform load of 300 kg/m. Find the maximum bending moment.
4. An end-supported beam AB is 15 m long and a point C of the beam is 2 m from A. The beam carries a uniformly distributed load of 20 kg/m over 10 m of its length, beginning at C. Find the maximum bending moment. If, in addition, it carries a uniformly distributed load of 10 kg/m over its whole length, find the maximum bending moment.
5. A beam 20 m long carries a uniformly distributed load of 100 kg/m from the support at one end to the mid-point of the beam. The second support is 4 m from the other end. Draw bending-moment and shearing-force diagrams and find the maximum bending moment.
6. An end-supported beam is 15 m long and carries a load of 20 kg/m over 6 m of its length from one support. Draw bending-moment and shearing-force diagrams and find the maximum bending moment.
7. An end-supported beam is 20 m long. It carries a uniformly distributed load of 200 kg/m and also a concentrated load of 1200 kg at 5 m from one end. Draw bending-moment and shearing-force diagrams and find the maximum bending moment.

8. A light beam 10 m long carries loads of 83 kg and 107 kg at its ends and is balanced on a support in a horizontal position. Find the maximum bending moment.

9. A beam AB, 50 m long, is end supported and carries loads of 3 tonnes at C, 7 tonnes at D and 4 tonnes at E, where $AC = 5$ m, $AD = 20$ m, $AE = 35$ m. In addition, it carries a uniformly distributed load of $\frac{1}{2}$ tonne/m. Draw bending-moment and shearing-force diagrams and find the maximum bending moment.

10. A beam AB, 12 m long, is end supported. It carries a uniformly distributed load of 5 kg/m from A to its mid-point and a uniformly distributed load of 3 kg/m over the remainder of the beam. Draw bending-moment and shearing-force diagrams and find the maximum bending moment.

11. A rod of length l, whose weight is negligible, rests horizontally with its ends supported and carries a movable weight w; the rod will break if the bending moment at any points is L. Prove that the least value of w which can break the rod is $4L/l$. (L.U.)

12. A train of weight W and length l is in the centre of a bridge of twice its own length. Assuming that the weight of the train is uniformly distributed throughout its length, calculate the bending moment at the centre of the bridge, and compare it with the value when one end of the train just reaches one of the piers of the bridge. (L.U.)

13. A beam AB, 10 m long, is end supported and carries a uniform load of 100 kg/m together with a concentrated load of 1 000 kg at 3 m from A. Find the maximum bending moment.

14. Infantry in threes, equivalent to a uniformly distributed load of 700 kg/m, march across a bridge of 5 m span. Find the maximum bending moment due to this load (i) when the bridge is covered, (ii) when the first half of the bridge is covered.

15. A uniform rigid rod, LM, 20 cm long and of weight 10 kg, rests in a horizontal position supported at the ends L and M. A mass of 12 kg is suspended from the point C of the rod at a distance of 8 cm from L. Calculate the shearing force and bending moment at a point 7 cm from M. (L.U.)

16. A bridge AB of 15 m span is end supported. The portion CD, where $AC = 3$ m, $CD = 10$ m, is covered with a uniformly distributed load of 200 kg/m. Find the magnitude and position of the maximum bending moment.

17. A load W, uniformly distributed over a length $2a$, traverses a span of length l greater than $2a$. Prove that the maximum bending moment will have its greatest value when the load is symmetrically placed on the span, and find this value.

18. A uniform beam 10 m long, and weighing 2 kg per m run, is supported in a horizontal position at its two ends and carries a load of 30 kg at a point distant 4 m from one end. Draw curves of shearing force and bending moment for any point of the beam and determine where the bending moment is greatest. (L.U.)

19. A uniform beam AC, 32 m long, whose middle point is B, rests on supports at the same level at its ends and carries a load of 4 tonnes uniformly distributed along the half AB. Assuming that the weight of the beam itself is negligible, draw a bending-moment diagram indicating the magnitude of the maximum bending moment and the point at which it acts. (L.U.)

20. A uniform steel bar, of mass 32 kg and length 40 cm, rests horizontally on two supports at its ends. A mass of 8 kg is suspended from the bar at a point 10 cm from one end. Find by calculation at what point of the bar the shearing force is zero and evaluate the bending moment at this point. Draw a diagram showing the distribution of shearing force along the bar. (L.U.)

21. A light beam of length 12 m carries a uniform load of 100 kg/m and is supported at one end and at 4 m from the other end. Draw bending-moment and shearing-force diagrams and find the magnitude and position of the maximum bending moment.

22. A beam of length l carries a uniformly distributed load and is propped horizontally on two supports, one of which is at one end of the beam. Find the position of the second support which makes the maximum bending moment for the beam least.

23. A light 12 m beam AB is supported at its ends, and carries masses of 2 tonnes at C and 4 tonnes at D, where $AC = 4$ m, $DB = 2$ m. Draw the shearing-stress and bending-moment diagrams. Draw the corresponding diagrams when the load is not concentrated at C and D, but is uniformly distributed over the beam.

(L.U.)

24. A uniform beam of weight W and length l rests on two supports, each distant a from the middle section of the beam. Find the bending moment at the middle and at one support, and find a in terms of l if these two bending moments are equal in magnitude, but opposite in sign.   (L.U.)

CHAPTER 10

MOMENTS OF INERTIA

10.1 Second Moments and Moments of Inertia

If δA be an element of an area distant x from a given axis, $\Sigma x \delta A$, where the sum is taken over the area, is called the first moment of area about the axis. As has been seen, the first moment about an axis in the plane of the area, $\Sigma x \delta A = A\bar{x}$, where A is the total area and $\bar{x}$ the distance of its centroid from the given axis.

The sum $\Sigma x^2 \delta A$, in which each element of area is multiplied by the square of its distance from the axis, is called the *second moment of area* about the given axis. If the surface density of the area be σ, so that the mass of an element δA is $\sigma \delta A$, then $\Sigma \sigma x^2 \delta A$ is called the moment of inertia of the area about the given axis.

The units of a moment of inertia are mass $\times$ (distance)^2, and hence writing

$$Mk^2 = \Sigma \sigma x^2 \delta A,$$

where M is the total mass, k is a length which is called the *radius of gyration* of the area about the axis. If the surface density is constant, so that $M = A\sigma$, where A is the total area, then the second moment of area is

$$\Sigma x^2 \delta A = Ak^2.$$

Similarly, if δV be an element of volume of a solid distant x from a given axis, $\Sigma x^2 \delta V$ is called the *second moment of volume* about the axis. If ρ be the volume density, so that the mass is $M = \Sigma \rho \delta V$, then

$$\Sigma \rho x^2 \delta V = Mk^2$$

is the moment of inertia and k is the radius of gyration of the solid about the axis. If the density is constant so that $M = \rho V$, where V is the volume of the solid, we have

$$\Sigma x^2 \delta V = Vk^2.$$

The problem of finding the second moment of area or volume of a uniform body about an axis is the same as that of finding its moment of inertia, but it is more usual to calculate second moments of area of plane areas and moments of inertia of solids.

Second moments of areas and volumes will be used considerably in later work. In this chapter we shall see how these quantities can be calculated in simple cases.

10.2 Second Moment of a Thin Rod

Consider the second moment of a thin uniform rod of length $2a$ about an axis through its centre perpendicular to its length (Fig. 141).

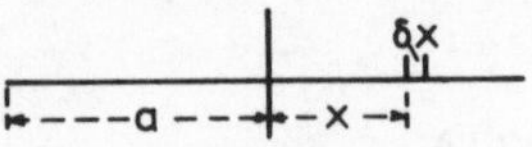

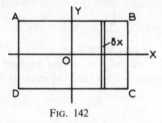

FIG. 141

Let A be the cross-sectional area of the rod. Since this is small, we may consider an element of length δx and volume $A\delta x$ as being distant x from the axis. Values of x are from $-a$ to $+a$, and the second moment about the axis

$$= \Sigma x^2 A\delta x,$$

$$= A\int_{-a}^{a} x^2 dx,$$

$$= \tfrac{2}{3}Aa^3,$$

$$= \tfrac{1}{3}Va^2.$$

Hence, the radius of gyration is given by

$$k^2 = \tfrac{1}{3}a^2,$$

and the moment of inertia is $\tfrac{1}{3}Ma^2$.

10.3 Second Moment of Rectangular Lamina

Consider the second moment of a rectangular lamina about an axis through its centre parallel to one of its sides. Let $ABCD$ be the rectangle

FIG. 142

(Fig. 142) with centre O, $AB = 2a$, $BC = 2b$, and OY parallel to CB. Taking a strip parallel to OY of width δx and area $2b\delta x$ the second moment of area about OY

$$= \Sigma 2bx^2\delta x,$$

$$= 2b\int_{-a}^{a} x^2 dx,$$

$$= \frac{4}{3}ba^3,$$

$$= (4ab)\frac{a^2}{3}.$$

Hence, since the area is $4ab$, the radius of gyration is given by $k^2 = \frac{1}{3}a^2$.
Similarly, about the perpendicular axis OX the second moment is
$(4ab)\dfrac{b^2}{3}$.

10.4 Parallel Axes Theorem

If the moment of inertia of a body of mass M about an axis through its centre of mass is Mk^2, the moment of inertia about a parallel axis at a distance a from this axis is $M(k^2 + a^2)$.

Let any section of the body perpendicular to the given axes meet the axis through the centre of mass in G and the other axis in O, so that $OG = a$ (Fig. 143).

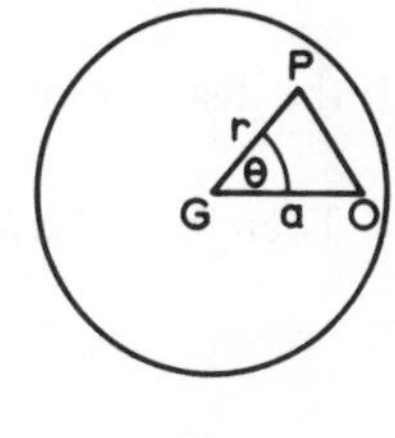

Let P be any particle of mass m in the section distant r from G, and let the angle OGP be θ.

Then $OP^2 = r^2 + a^2 - 2ar \cos \theta$.

The moment of inertia about the axis through G is given by $Mk^2 = \Sigma mr^2$, where the summation is taken over the whole body.

The moment of inertia about the axis through O is

FIG. 143

$$\Sigma mOP^2 = \Sigma m(r^2 + a^2 - 2ar \cos \theta),$$
$$= \Sigma mr^2 + a^2 \Sigma m - 2a \Sigma mr \cos \theta,$$
$$= Mk^2 + Ma^2 - 2a \Sigma mr \cos \theta.$$

The distance of the centre of mass of the body from a plane through G perpendicular to OG is $\Sigma mr \cos \theta / M$, and since the centre of mass lies in this plane, we have $\Sigma mr \cos \theta = 0$. Hence, we have

$$\Sigma mOP^2 = M(k^2 + a^2),$$

and the theorem is proved.

The theorem proved for moments of inertia holds for second moments of area if the mass is replaced by the area. Thus, if the second moment of an area A about an axis through its *centroid* be Ak^2, its second moment about a parallel axis distant a from this axis is $A(k^2 + a^2)$.

For example, the moment of inertia of a uniform thin rod of mass M and length $2a$ about an axis through its centre perpendicular to its length is $M\dfrac{a^2}{3}$. The moment of inertia of the rod about a parallel axis through one of its ends is therefore $M\left(\dfrac{a^2}{3} + a^2\right) = \dfrac{4}{3}Ma^2$.

Similarly, the second moment of area of a rectangular lamina of sides $2a$ and $2b$ about an axis through its centre parallel to the side of length $2b$ is $(4ab)a^2/3$. The second moment about the side of length $2b$ is, therefore,
$(4ab)\left(\dfrac{a^2}{3} + a^2\right) = (4ab)\dfrac{4}{3}a^2$.

10.5 Moments of Inertia of a Lamina

If the moments of inertia of a lamina about two perpendicular axes in its plane meeting in a point O are A and B respectively, its moment of inertia about an axis through O perpendicular to its plane will be $A + B$.

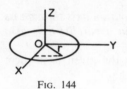

Let OX and OY be the axes in the plane of the lamina and OZ a perpendicular axis (Fig. 144). Let an element of mass m have coordinates (x, y) with respect to the axes OX and OY.

Then we have for moments of inertia about OX and OY

FIG. 144

$$A = \Sigma m y^2$$
$$B = \Sigma m x^2.$$

If the distance of the element from OZ be r we have

$$r^2 = x^2 + y^2.$$

Therefore, the moment of inertia about OZ

$$= \Sigma m r^2,$$
$$= \Sigma m (x^2 + y^2),$$
$$= A + B.$$

The theorem holds for second moments of area in which an element of area replaces an element of mass.

For example, the second moments of area of a rectangle of sides $2b$ and $2a$ about axes through its centre parallel to its sides are $(4ab)\dfrac{a^2}{3}$ and $(4ab)\dfrac{b^2}{3}$. The second moment about a perpendicular axis through its centre is therefore

$$(4ab)\left(\frac{a^2 + b^2}{3}\right).$$

10.6 Moment of Inertia of a Uniform Rectangular Prism

Let the prism have sides $2a$, $2b$, $2c$ and consider its moment of inertia about an axis through its centre parallel to the edge of length $2a$ (Fig. 145). Let ρ be the density, so that the mass is $M = 8abc\rho$.

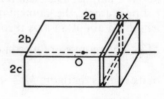

FIG. 145

Consider an element perpendicular to the axis which is a thin prism of sides $2b$, $2c$ and thickness δx, distant x from the centre. The mass of the element is $\rho \cdot 4bc\delta x$, and its moment of inertia about the axis is

$$(\rho 4bc\delta x)\frac{b^2 + c^2}{3}.$$

Hence, the total moment of inertia is

$$\int_{-a}^{a} 4bc\rho \cdot \frac{b^2+c^2}{3}dx = (8abc\rho)\frac{b^2+c^2}{3},$$

$$= M\frac{b^2+c^2}{3}.$$

Similarly, about axes through O parallel to the other edges the moments of inertia are

$$M\frac{c^2+a^2}{3} \quad \text{and} \quad M\frac{a^2+b^2}{3}.$$

10.7 Moment of Inertia of a Circular Ring

A uniform circular ring of radius a has each particle at the same distance a from an axis perpendicular to the plane of the ring through its centre, hence its moment of inertia about this axis is $\Sigma ma^2 = Ma^2$.

10.8 Moment of Inertia of a Uniform Circular Disc

First, consider the moment of inertia about an axis through its centre perpendicular to the plane of the disc.

Let O be the centre and a the radius of the disc (Fig. 146). Consider an element which is a ring of radius r, thickness δr and mass $2\pi r \delta r \cdot \sigma$, where σ is the surface density. The moment of inertia of the ring about the axis is

$$2\pi r \delta r \cdot \sigma \cdot r^2 = 2\pi \sigma r^3 \delta r.$$

Fig. 146

The moment of inertia of the disc is, therefore,

$$2\pi\sigma \int_0^a r^3 dr = \pi\sigma\frac{a^4}{2}.$$

The total mass is $M = \pi a^2 \sigma$, and hence the moment of inertia is $M\frac{a^2}{2}$.

Let the moment of inertia of the disc about a diameter be A, then, by symmetry, the moment of inertia about a perpendicular diameter will also be A. Therefore, the moment of inertia about an axis through the centre perpendicular to the plane of the disc will be $A+A = 2A$.

Hence

$$2A = M\frac{a^2}{2},$$

$$A = M\frac{a^2}{4}.$$

Example 1. *The moment of inertia of a uniform circular disc of mass M and radius a about a tangent in its plane will be by the parallel axis theorem,*

$$M\left(\frac{a^2}{4}+a^2\right) = \frac{5}{4}Ma^2.$$

Example 2. *The second moment of area of a disc of radius a with a concentric hole of radius b about a perpendicular through its centre is the difference of the second moments of discs of radius a and radius b and is, therefore,*

$$\pi a^2 \cdot \frac{a^2}{2} - \pi b^2 \cdot \frac{b^2}{2} = \pi\left(\frac{a^4-b^4}{2}\right).$$

Similarly, about a diameter the second moment is $\quad \pi\left(\frac{a^4-b^4}{4}\right).$

10.9 Moment of Inertia of a Uniform Solid Sphere

Let the sphere be of mass M and radius a and consider its moment of inertia about a diameter $X'OX$ (Fig. 147).

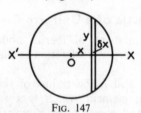

Fig. 147

Let an element which is a disc of radius y and thickness δx be perpendicular to OX and distant x from the centre.

Then $x^2 + y^2 = a^2$, and the volume of the element is

$$\pi(a^2 - x^2)\delta x.$$

Its mass is $\qquad \dfrac{M}{\frac{4}{3}\pi a^3}\pi(a^2 - x^2)\delta x.$

Its moment of inertia about OX is

$$\frac{M}{\frac{4}{3}\pi a^3}\pi(a^2 - x^2)\delta x \cdot \frac{(a^2 - x^2)}{2}.$$

Hence, the total moment of inertia of the sphere is

$$\frac{3M}{8a^3} \int_{-a}^{a} (a^2 - x^2)^2 dx,$$

$$= \frac{3M}{4a^3}\left(a^5 - \frac{2}{3}a^5 + \frac{1}{5}a^5\right),$$

$$= \frac{2}{5}Ma^2.$$

Cor. The moment of inertia of a hemisphere about any diameter $= \frac{1}{2} \cdot \frac{2}{5} Ma^2$, where M is the mass of the whole sphere, $= \frac{2}{5} M'a^2$, where M' is the mass of the hemisphere.

10.10 Moment of Inertia of a Uniform Thin Hollow Sphere

The moment of inertia of a thin hollow sphere about a diameter may be considered as the difference of the moments of inertia of two spheres. Let the outer and inner spheres have radii a and $a-\delta$ respectively, where δ is small. Then, if ρ be the volume density, the difference of the moments of inertia is

$$\tfrac{2}{5}(\tfrac{4}{3}\pi\rho a^3)a^2 - \tfrac{2}{5}\{\tfrac{4}{3}\pi\rho(a-\delta)^3\}(a-\delta)^2$$
$$= \tfrac{8}{15}\pi\rho\{a^5-(a-\delta)^5\}.$$

To the first order of small quantities

$$(a-\delta)^5 = a^5 - 5a^4\delta.$$

Hence, the difference is

$$\tfrac{8}{15}\pi\rho \times 5a^4\delta,$$
$$= \tfrac{2}{3}a^2(4\pi\rho a^2\delta).$$

But $4\pi\rho a^2\delta$ is the mass M of the shell, therefore the moment of inertia is $\frac{2}{3}Ma^2$.

10.11 Moment of Inertia of a Uniform Solid Circular Cylinder

Let the cylinder be of mass M, radius a and length l (Fig. 148). Since any thin section of the cylinder perpendicular to its axis has moment of

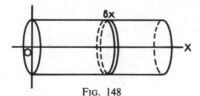

Fig. 148

inertia about the axis $ma^2/2$, where m is the mass of the section, the total moment of inertia about its axis is

$$\Sigma m\frac{a^2}{2} = M\frac{a^2}{2}.$$

Consider the moment of inertia about a diameter of one of its ends. Let an element which is a disc of thickness δx be distant x from the end and let the density of the material be ρ.

The mass of the element $= \pi \rho a^2 \delta x$.

The moment of inertia of the element about its own diameter

$$= \pi \rho a^2 \delta x \cdot \frac{a^2}{4}.$$

Its moment of inertia about the end diameter, by the parallel axis theorem,

$$= \pi \rho a^2 \delta x \left(\frac{a^2}{4} + x^2 \right).$$

Hence, the total moment of inertia about an end diameter is

$$\int_0^l \pi \rho a^2 \left(\frac{a^2}{4} + x^2 \right) dx,$$
$$= \pi \rho a^2 \left(\frac{a^2 l}{4} - \frac{l^3}{3} \right),$$
$$= M \left(\frac{a^2}{4} + \frac{l^2}{3} \right).$$

Cor. The moment of inertia of the cylinder about a diameter through its centre of gravity is, by the parallel axis theorem,

$$M \left(\frac{a^2}{4} + \frac{l^2}{3} \right) - M \frac{l^2}{4} = M \left(\frac{a^2}{4} + \frac{l^2}{12} \right).$$

10.12 Moment of Inertia of a Uniform Solid Circular Cone

Let the cone be of mass M, height h, base radius a, and density ρ.

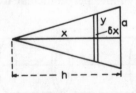

Fig. 149

Consider an element which is a disc of radius y and thickness δx, distant x from the vertex of the cone (Fig. 149).

We have

$$y = \frac{a}{h} x.$$

The moment of inertia of the disc about the axis of the cone is

$$(\pi y^2 \rho \delta x)\frac{y^2}{2} = \frac{\pi \rho}{2}\frac{a^4}{h^4}x^4 \delta x.$$

Hence, the total moment of inertia about the axis is

$$\frac{\pi \rho a^4}{2h^4}\int_0^h x^4 dx = \frac{1}{10}\pi \rho a^4 h,$$

$$= \frac{3}{10}Ma^2.$$

The moment of inertia of the element about its diameter is

$$(\pi \rho y^2 \delta x)\frac{y^2}{4}.$$

About a diameter of the base it is

$$(\pi \rho y^2 \delta x)\left(\frac{y^2}{4}+(h-x)^2\right).$$

Hence, the total moment of inertia about a diameter of the base is

$$\pi \rho \frac{a^2}{h^2}\int_0^h x^2\left(\frac{a^2 x^2}{4h^2}+(h-x)^2\right)dx,$$

$$= \pi \rho a^2 h\left(\frac{a^2}{20}+\frac{h^2}{30}\right),$$

$$= M\left(\frac{3}{20}a^2+\frac{h^2}{10}\right),$$

$$= \frac{3}{10}M\left(\frac{a^2}{2}+\frac{h^2}{3}\right).$$

10.13 Moments of Inertia of Composite Bodies

It is sometimes required to find the moments of inertia of a composite body about axes through its centre of gravity when moments of the separate bodies are known. The parallel axes theorem is used to find the moment of inertia of each part about an axis through the centre of gravity of the whole, and the total moment is the sum of the moments of inertia of the parts.

Example 3. *A uniform hemisphere of radius a has its plane face joined to the base of a uniform circular cylinder of radius a and height 2a, ρ being the density of each body (Fig. 150). Find the moments of inertia of the composite body about its axis of symmetry and a perpendicular axis through its centre of gravity.*

Volume of cylinder $= 2\pi a^3$.

Volume of hemisphere $= \frac{2}{3}\pi a^3$.

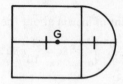

FIG. 150

Distance of centre of gravity G of the body from the centre of gravity of the hemisphere

$$= \frac{2\pi a^3 \left(a + \frac{3}{8}a\right)}{2\pi a^3 + \frac{2}{3}\pi a^3} = \frac{33}{32}a.$$

Moment of inertia about the axis of symmetry

of cylinder $= (2\pi a^3 \rho)\dfrac{a^2}{2}$,

of hemisphere $= \left(\dfrac{2}{3}\pi a^3 \rho\right)\dfrac{2}{5}a^2$.

Total $= \dfrac{19}{15}\pi\rho a^5 = \dfrac{19}{40}Ma^2$.

Moment of inertia of hemisphere about a diameter $= \left(\dfrac{2}{3}\pi a^3 \rho\right)\left(\dfrac{2}{5}a^2\right)$,

about a parallel through its C.G. $= \left(\dfrac{2}{3}\pi a^3 \rho\right)\left(\dfrac{2}{5}a^2 - \dfrac{9}{64}a^2\right)$,

about a parallel through $G = \left(\dfrac{2}{3}\pi a^3 \rho\right)\left(\dfrac{2}{5}a^2 - \dfrac{9}{64}a^2 + \left(\dfrac{33}{32}\right)^2 a^2\right)$,

$$= \frac{6773}{7680}\pi\rho a^5.$$

Moment of inertia of cylinder about a perpendicular to its axis

through its C.G. $= (2\pi\rho a^3)\left(\dfrac{7}{12}a^2\right)$,

through G $= (2\pi\rho a^3)\left(\dfrac{7}{12}a^2 + \left(\dfrac{11}{32}\right)^2 a^2\right)$,

$$= \frac{2155}{1536}\pi\rho a^5.$$

Total moment of inertia about axis through $G = \dfrac{17548}{7680}\pi\rho a^5$,

$$= \frac{4387}{5120}Ma^2.$$

EXERCISES 10

1. Show that the moment of inertia of a thin uniform rod about an axis through its centre inclined at an angle θ to the rod is $M\frac{a^2}{3}\sin^2\theta$, where M is the mass of the rod.

2. Find the moment of inertia of a uniform thin circular ring of mass M and radius a, about a diameter.

3. Find the moment of inertia of a uniform rectangular lamina of sides $2a$ and $2b$ about an axis through one corner perpendicular to its plane.

4. Find the moment of inertia of a uniform thin hollow cylinder of mass M, radius a and length l, about (i) its axis, (ii) a perpendicular axis through its centre of gravity.

5. Find the radius of gyration of a uniform right circular cone mass M, radius a and height h, about an axis through its vertex perpendicular to the axis of the cone.

6. Find the moment of inertia of a cube of mass M each of whose edges is of length a, about one of its edges.

7. Show that the radius of gyration of a triangular lamina, of base a and height h, about its base is $h/\sqrt{6}$, and about a parallel to its base through its vertex $h/\sqrt{2}$.

8. A hole of 1 m diameter is punched in a uniform circular plate of 5 m diameter, the centre of the hole being 1·5 m from the centre of the plate. Find the moment of inertia of the plate.

    (i) about the diameter through the centre of the hole,
    (ii) about the diameter which is perpendicular to this.

                                                              (L.U.)

9. AB and BC are two uniform rods of the same material of lengths $2a$ and $2b$ respectively joined at B so that the angle ABC is a right angle. Find the radii of gyration of the rods about axes through the centre of gravity of the rods parallel to AB and BC respectively.

10. AB and CD are two uniform rods of the same material of lengths $2a$ and $2b$ respectively. The end C of the rod CD is joined to the mid-point of AB so that the rods are at right angles. Find the radius of gyration of the rods (i) about an axis perpendicular to their plane through C, (ii) about a parallel axis through their centre of gravity.

11. Three rectangular areas, 60 cm by 5 cm, 90 cm by 5 cm, and 30 cm by 3·75 cm, are fitted together to form an I figure, the longest and shortest areas forming the cross-pieces. Find the moment of inertia of the area about the outer edge of the shortest area.   (L.U.)

12. A uniform solid right-circular cylinder has mass M, radius a, length h. Find the moment of inertia (i) about a diameter of a circular face, (ii) about a tangent to the mid-circular section.   (L.U.)

13. $ABCD$ is a uniform square lamina of side $2a$ and E is the mid-point of BC. The triangular portion ABE is removed; find the second moment of the remaining area about AD.

14. ABC is a triangular lamina; A is a right angle, $AB = AC$, $BC = a$. Find the second moment of area about an axis in the plane of the lamina parallel to and distant a from BC, on the opposite side of BC to A.

15. The radii of the ends of a frustum of a uniform cone are a and $2a$, its mass is M and its height h. Find its moment of inertia (i) about its axis, (ii) about a diameter of its larger face.

16. A uniform thin rod of mass m and length $2a$ has a particle of mass m attached to one end. Find the radius of gyration of the body (i) about an axis perpendicular to the rod through its centre of gravity, (ii) about a parallel axis through the other end of the rod.

17. A uniform body of mass M consists of a hemisphere of radius a and a right circular cylinder of radius a and height a with one of its circular faces attached to the plane face of the hemisphere. Find the moments of inertia of the body about its axis of symmetry and about a diameter of the free circular face of the cylinder.

18. A uniform body consists of a solid hemisphere of radius a with a right circular cone, whose base radius and height are also a, attached so that two circular faces coincide. Show that the moment of inertia about an axis through the circumference of the common bases perpendicular to those bases is $41Ma^2/38$, where M is the total mass.   (L.U.)

19. A uniform thin hollow cylinder of radius a and length $2a$ has one of its ends joined to the rim of a uniform thin hemispherical shell of radius a. Find the moments of inertia of the body about its axis of symmetry and about a perpendicular axis through its centre of gravity.

20. A wind measuring instrument consists of two hemispherical thin shells, each of radius a and mass m, attached to the ends of a uniform thin rod of mass m and length $4a$, the rims of the hemispheres being in the same plane and their centres $6a$ apart. Find the moment of inertia of the body about an axis through its centre of gravity perpendicular to the rod and in the same plane as the rims.

21. A uniform circular disc of radius $2a$ has a concentric hole of radius a. The mass of the annulus is M. Find the moment of inertia of the annulus about an axis through a point on the circumference of the circle of radius a (i) if the axis is perpendicular to the plane of the annulus, (ii) if the axis lies in the plane of the annulus and touches the circle.   (L.U.)

PART III—HYDROSTATICS

CHAPTER 11

FLUID PRESSURE

11.1 Introductory

Whereas Statics deals with the equilibrium of a rigid body, Hydrostatics deals with the equilibrium of fluids. A *fluid* is defined as a body whose constituent particles act on each other with a pressure which is normal to their common surface when the fluid is at rest. When a fluid is in motion this pressure may have a component in the plane of the common surface, and this component of the pressure is called *viscosity*. A *perfect fluid* is defined as one in which there is no viscosity, and which therefore offers no resistance to the separation of its particles. Since in hydrostatics we are dealing with fluids which are at rest, we need make no distinction between viscous and non-viscous fluids, and we have that *the pressure of a fluid in equilibrium is always normal to any surface with which it is in contact.*

Fluids are divided into *liquids* and *gases*. A liquid is a fluid which may be taken as incompressible, such liquids as water or mercury can only be appreciably compressed by very great pressures. A gas, on the other hand, is easily compressible and is capable of indefinite expansion to fill the space which contains it.

11.2 Pressure at a Point

The pressure of a fluid on a given area of surface may be uniform or varying. The mean pressure on a given area is measured by dividing the total thrust on the area by the area. Thus a thrust of P newton on an area of A square metres gives a mean pressure of P/A newton per square metre. The SI standard unit of pressure is the newton per square metre (abbreviation N/m^2).

The pressure at a point is the mean pressure over an indefinitely small area surrounding the point, and is measured in newtons per square metre.

The pressure at a point in a fluid in equilibrium is the same in all directions.

This means that if a surface could be made to pass through any point of the fluid without disturbing equilibrium, the pressure on the surface at the point would be independent of the orientation of the surface.

The theorem is proved by considering the thrusts of the remainder of the fluid on the faces of a small triangular prism of the fluid. Let the right-angled triangles ABC and DEF (Fig. 151) be end faces of the prism perpendicular to its length with BC and EF horizontal, AB and DE

161

vertical. Let p_1, p_2, p_3 be the mean pressures on the faces $ADEB$, $BEFC$,

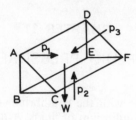

FIG. 151

$ADFC$ respectively. Let w be the weight per unit volume of the fluid and l the length AD of the prism. The weight of the prism W, is given by

$$W = \tfrac{1}{2}AB \cdot BC \cdot l \cdot w.$$

The thrusts on the three faces are

$$p_1 AB \cdot l, \quad p_2 BC \cdot l, \quad p_3 CA \cdot l, \text{ respectively,}$$

normal to the faces, and the thrusts on the end faces ABC and DEF will be equal and opposite. Hence for equilibrium, resolving horizontally and vertically we have

$$p_1 AB \cdot l = p_3 CA \cdot l \cos BAC,$$
$$p_2 BC \cdot l = p_3 CA \cdot l \cos ACB + \tfrac{1}{2}AB \cdot BC \cdot l \cdot w.$$

Hence,

$$p_1 AB \cdot l = p_3 AB \cdot l,$$
$$p_2 BC \cdot l = p_3 BC \cdot l + \tfrac{1}{2}AB \cdot BC \cdot l \cdot w.$$

Therefore,

$$p_1 = p_3,$$
$$p_2 = p_3 + \tfrac{1}{2}AB \cdot w.$$

In the limit, as AB tends to zero and the size of the prism decreases indefinitely, we have

$$p_1 = p_2 = p_3,$$

that is, the pressure at the point in the three directions considered are equal.

This result is confirmed experimentally by introducing pressure-gauges in a fluid which record the same pressures at a point for different orientations.

The pressure at a point in a fluid in equilibrium is the same for points at the same horizontal level.

This theorem is proved by considering the thrust of the remainder of the fluid on a small right circular cylinder of the fluid whose axis is horizontal (Fig. 152).

Let a be the area of each end of the cylinder, and let the mean pressures on the ends be p_1 and p_2 respectively.

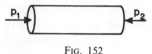

FIG. 152

The pressure at any point on the curved surface of the cylinder will be perpendicular to the surface, and therefore perpendicular to the axis of the cylinder. Hence the only forces parallel to the axis of the cylinder will be the thrusts on the ends, and since the cylinder is in equilibrium, we have

$$p_1 a = p_2 a,$$

that is,

$$p_1 = p_2.$$

p_1 and p_2 are the mean pressures over the ends of the cylinder, and when the radius of the cylinder is diminished indefinitely they become the pressures at points at the same horizontal level, and the theorem is proved.

The pressure at a point in a fluid in equilibrium increases in proportion to the depth of the point.

This theorem is proved by considering the thrust of the remainder of the fluid on a small right circular cylinder of the fluid whose axis is vertical (Fig. 153). Let a be the area of each end section; let the mean pressures on the upper and lower ends be p_0 and p_1 respectively, let h be the height of the cylinder and w the density of the fluid. Then, since the pressure at any point of the curved surface is perpendicular to the axis of the cylinder, the only vertical forces are the thrusts on the ends and the weight of the cylinder and we have for equilibrium

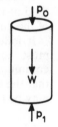

$$p_1 a = p_0 a + ahw,$$

that is,

$$p_1 = p_0 + hw.$$

FIG. 153

In the limit as the radius of the cylinder diminishes indefinitely p_0 and p_1 are the pressures at points whose difference in level is h, and the theorem is proved.

Since p_0 and p_1 are pressures per unit area, it follows that the difference between p_1 and p_0 is the weight of a column of the fluid of unit cross-sectional area and height h.

Example 1. *Find the increase in pressure on descending a depth of* 20 *m in water, the density of the water being* 1000 *kg/m^3.*

Let p_0 and p_1 be the upper and lower pressures in N/m^2.

The mass of a column of water of cross-sectional area 1 m^2 and height 20 m is 20 000 kg.

Hence,

$$p_1 - p_0 = 20\,000\,g$$

$$= 196\,200\ N/m^2$$

$$= 196 \cdot 2\ kN/m^2.$$

11.3 Atmospheric Pressure

The pressure on the surface of a liquid will be that due to the atmosphere. This pressure varies with the prevailing atmospheric conditions, but is generally about 10^5 N/m^2. The atmospheric pressure is usually given as the height of the mercury barometer, and the pressure is the weight of a column of mercury of unit cross-sectional area whose height is that of the barometer.

The average height of a mercury barometer is about 75 cm. The corresponding height of a water barometer would be about 10·2 m. Hence the pressure at a depth x m in water when the water barometer records 10 m will be that due to a column of water of height $x + 10$ m.

The additional atmospheric pressure is frequently omitted when calculating pressure in a liquid.

11.4 Transmissibility of Fluid Pressure

We have seen that pressure in a fluid at rest is the same at points at the same level, and that the difference in pressure at different levels is the product of the density and difference in height.

It follows that if an additional pressure is applied to any point of a fluid at rest in a closed vessel, this pressure is transmitted to every point of the fluid.

It follows also that the free surface of a liquid at rest under gravity must be horizontal, and that the free surfaces of liquids in intercommunicating vessels must be at the same level. This assumes, of course, that the extent of the liquid is limited and that the weights of its particles may be taken as acting in parallel directions.

The Hydraulic Press

The hydraulic press is a machine which makes use of the transmissibility of fluid pressure to obtain mechanical advantage. Essentially it consists of two inter-communicating cylinders containing liquid (Fig. 154). A force P applied by a piston in the smaller cylinder is used to overcome a resistance W to a piston in the larger cylinder. Let the cross-sectional areas of the larger and smaller cylinders be a and b respectively. The force P on the smaller piston causes an increase in pressure P/b throughout the liquid, and therefore at every point on the larger piston. Hence, the additional thrust on this piston is

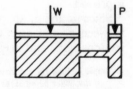

Fig. 154

$a \times \dfrac{P}{b} = \dfrac{a}{b}P$, and if this thrust equals W the mechanical advantage is a/b.

If the smaller piston descends a distance x, a volume xb of liquid moves into the larger cylinder and lifts the larger piston a distance xb/a. Hence the velocity ratio of the machine is a/b and the principle of work is verified.

The hydraulic press is sometimes called Bramah's press, after the inventor of a U-shaped leather collar for the large piston, which is pressed against the sides of the cylinder by the liquid pressure to prevent leakage.

11.5 Density and Specific Gravity

The *density* of any substance is the mass of a unit volume of the substance. The density of water is usually taken as 1 gm/cc $= 1000$ kg/m^3 or 62·5 lb/ft^3. The density of a substance, therefore, relates to certain units of mass and of volume. In general, the density of a substance varies with its temperature, but in the case of liquids this variation is slight and is usually neglected.

The *specific gravity* of a substance is the ratio of its density to that of water and is a number independent of the units in which the densities are given. Thus, if the specific gravity of a substance is 4, its density is 4000 kg/m^3.

Example 2. *Five litres of a liquid of specific gravity* 1·3 *are mixed with* 7 *litres of a liquid of specific gravity* 0·78. *If the bulk of the liquid shrinks* 1 *per cent on mixing, find the specific gravity of the mixture.*   (L.U.)

Let w grammes be the mass of a litre of water. Then the total mass of the mixture is

$$5 \times 1\cdot3w + 7 \times 0\cdot78w \text{ grammes.}$$

The volume of the mixture is

$$12 \times 0\cdot99 \text{ litres.}$$

The mass of one litre of the mixture is therefore

$$\frac{5 \times 1\cdot3 + 7 \times 0\cdot78}{12 \times 0\cdot99}w \text{ grammes.}$$

$$= 1\cdot007w \text{ grammes.}$$

Hence, the specific gravity of the mixture is 1·007.

EXERCISES 11 (a)

1. The pressure in a water pipe at the bottom of a building is 4×10^5 N/m^2; at the top it is 4×10^4 N/m^2. Find the height of the building.
2. Find the pressure at a depth of 1000 fathoms in sea water. (1 fathom $= 1\cdot85$ m, specific gravity of sea water 1·024.)
3. A bottle is filled with liquid of specific gravity σ and is weighed. A solid body, whose weight in air is W gm and whose specific gravity is σ', is put into the bottle and the overflow removed. Prove that the increase in weight is $W(\sigma' - \sigma)/\sigma'$.

If $W = 2.45$, and if water is the liquid used, the increase in weight is 1.95 gm. Calculate the specific gravity of the solid. (L.U.)

4. A hollow spherical shell of external and internal radii a and b respectively has a specific gravity S. If the shell can float in water, prove that $b/a > (1-1/S)^{1/3}$.

Deduce that for iron (sp. gr. 7.8), the thickness cannot exceed 0.045 of the external radius. (L.U.)

5. If 16 cc of sulphuric acid of specific gravity 1.85 are mixed with 7 cc of water, and if the specific gravity of the dilute acid is 1.64, find the contraction in volume which has taken place. (L.U.)

6. Find the atmospheric pressure which is equivalent to that at a depth of 75 cm in mercury (sp. gr. 13.6).

7. Two vertical cylinders of cross-sectional area 120 and 200 cm^2 respectively contain water and are connected at their bases by a pipe. On top of the water in the smaller cylinder is a light piston which fits the cylinder. A mass of 1 kg is placed on the piston. Find the amount by which the piston is lowered and the free surface in the other cylinder raised.

11.6 Common Surface of Liquids

It can be shown that the common surface of two liquids of different densities which do not mix is a horizontal plane.

Let the densities of the liquids be ρ_1 and ρ_2, where $\rho_1 < \rho_2$. Let C and C' (Fig. 155) be two points in the same horizontal plane in the lower liquid, and let verticals through C and C' meet the common surface in B and B' and the free surface of the upper liquid in A and A' respectively. If p_0 be the pressure at the free surface and p the pressure of C and C', we have by considering the equilibrium of small columns of the liquids of heights AC and $A'C'$

Fig. 155

$$p - p_0 = \rho_1 ABg + \rho_2 BCg,$$
$$p - p_0 = \rho_1 A'B'g + \rho_2 B'C'g.$$

Hence

$$\rho_1 AB + \rho_2(AC - AB) = \rho_1 A'B' + \rho_2(A'C' - A'B'),$$

and since $AC = A'C'$ we have

$$AB = A'B'.$$

Therefore, since the free surface is horizontal, the common surface of the liquids must be horizontal.

11.7 Measurement of Relative Density

The relative density of liquids which do not mix may be measured

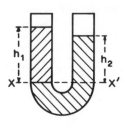

FIG. 156

in a U-tube. With the heavier liquid filling the bottom of the tube, let XX' be the level of the common surface of the liquids (Fig. 156). Let ρ_1 and ρ_2 be the densities of the liquids ($\rho_1 < \rho_2$) and let their free surfaces be at heights h_1 and h_2 above XX'.

Then, since the pressure at the level XX' must be the same in the two arms of the tube, we have

$$\rho_1 h_1 g = \rho_2 h_2 g,$$

and hence by measuring h_1 and h_2 the relative density may be found.

Similar calculations may be made when more than two columns of liquids balance in a U-tube.

Example 3. *Some mercury (sp. gr. 13·6) is poured into a uniform U-tube and into one arm alcohol (sp. gr. 0·8) is poured which occupies a length 6·8 cm of the tube. What is the difference in level of the free surfaces of the liquids? If now chloroform (sp. gr. 1·5) is poured into the other arm until the free surfaces of the chloroform and alcohol are at the same level, what length of the tube is occupied by the chloroform?*

In the first case let h cm be the height of the column of mercury above the level of the common surface of mercury and alcohol.

Then we have

$$6{\cdot}8 \times 0{\cdot}8w = h \times 13{\cdot}6w,$$

where w is the mass of water that would fill 1 cm of the tube.

Hence,

$$h = 0{\cdot}4 \text{ cm},$$

and the difference in level is $6{\cdot}8 - 0{\cdot}4 = 6{\cdot}4$ cm.

When chloroform is added let h_1 cm be the length of tube it fills.

Then, since the free surfaces are at the same level, the pressures at depth h_1 in either arm will be the same. That is

$$h_1 \times 1{\cdot}5w = 6{\cdot}8 \times 0{\cdot}8w + (h_1 - 6{\cdot}8) \times 13{\cdot}6 ,$$

$$h_1 = 7{\cdot}2 \text{ cm}.$$

11.8 Thrust on a Plane Area

If the area is horizontal, the pressure at any point will be ρhg, where will be perpendicular to the area and the total thrust is the sum of these parallel pressures over the area.

If the area is horizontal, the pressure at any point will be ρh, where h is the height of the free surface above the area and ρ the density of the liquid. Hence, if A be the total area, the thrust on it will be

$$\rho A h g.$$

If the area is not horizontal, let $\bar{y}$ be the depth of its centroid G below the free surface (Fig. 157). Let a small element of area δA be at a depth

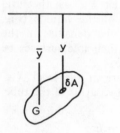

FIG. 157

y below the free surface. Then the thrust on the element δA will be

$$\rho y \delta A g.$$

Summing such quantities over the whole area we have the total thrust $= \Sigma \rho y \delta A g$.

But the depth of the centroid of the area is given by

$$A\bar{y} = \Sigma y \delta A.$$

Therefore, if the density of the liquid is uniform the total thrust is

$$\rho A \bar{y} g.$$

Hence, the total thrust on a plane area immersed in a given liquid depends only on the area and the depth of its centroid. It follows that if the area, while remaining immersed, be rotated about an axis through its centroid, the total thrust on the area is unchanged.

We have found that the *magnitude* of the total thrust on a plane area depends on the depth of the centroid; the point where this force may be taken to act is called the *centre of pressure*, which is not at the centroid unless the area is horizontal.

11.9 Thrusts in Liquids of Differing Densities

Suppose we have a plane area immersed in two layers of liquids of densities ρ_1 and ρ_2 $(\rho_1 < \rho_2)$, so that the common surface of the liquids divides the area into two parts.

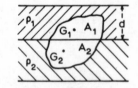

Let the areas of the two parts be A_1 and A_2, and the depths of their centroids below the free surface $\bar{x}_1$ and $\bar{x}_2$. Let d be the depth of the upper layer (Fig. 158).

Then the thrust on the area A_1

FIG. 158

$$= A_1 \bar{x}_1 \rho_1 g,$$

which is the product of the area A_1 and the pressure at its centroid. At each point of the area A_2 there is a pressure $\rho_1 d$ due to the upper layer of liquid, equivalent to a thrust $A_2 \rho_1 dg$ at its centroid. In addition, due to the liquid of density ρ_2, there is a thrust $A_2 \rho_2 (\bar{x}_2 - d)g$ on the area A_2.

Hence, the total thrust on the area A_2

$$= A_2 \{\rho_1 d + \rho_2 (\bar{x}_2 - d)\}g,$$

and this is the product of the area A_2 and the pressure at its centroid.

It should be noted that the thrust on a plane area immersed in a liquid may be greater than the entire weight of the liquid. For example, if a vessel in the form of a hollow pyramid of base area A and height h be filled with liquid of density ρ through a hole at the vertex, the base, being horizontal, is at a depth h below the free surface of the liquid, the pressure at any point of the base is ρh and the total thrust on the base is $\rho A h g$.

The weight of the liquid is $\frac{1}{3}\rho A h g$.

The difference between the thrust on the base and the weight of the liquid arises from the downward thrust of the sides of the pyramid on the liquid. Hence, the *upward* thrust of the liquid on the sides of the pyramid will be $\frac{2}{3}\rho A h g$.

Example 4. *A tank whose base is 3 m by 4 m and height 2 m is half filled with water. It is turned about one of the shorter edges of its base until the water just begins to overflow. Find the thrust on one of its vertical sides and on its base in this position.*

When the tank has been tilted, a diagonal of its vertical faces will be horizontal (Fig. 159).

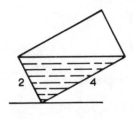

Fig. 159

Area immersed of a vertical face
$$= 4 \text{ sq m,}$$

length of the diagonal $\quad = 2\sqrt{5} \text{ m,}$

maximum depth of water $\quad = \dfrac{4}{\sqrt{5}} = 0.8\sqrt{5} \text{ m,}$

depth of centroid of immersed area $= \dfrac{1}{3} \times 0.8\sqrt{5} \text{ m,}$

thrust on vertical side $\quad = 1000g \times 4 \times \dfrac{1}{3} \times 0.8\sqrt{5},$

$$= 2.34 \times 10^4 \text{ N.}$$

Depth of centroid of base $\quad = 0.4\sqrt{5} \text{ m.}$

Area of base $\quad = 12 \text{ sq m.}$

Thrust on base $\quad = 1000g \times 12 \times 0.4\sqrt{5},$

$$= 1.05 \times 10^5 \text{ N.}$$

Example 5. *A vertical rectangular area ABCD, with AB horizontal and DC below AB, is subject to the pressure of a homogeneous liquid at rest under gravity. E is the middle point of AB. Show that the ratio of the thrusts on the triangles CED and DEA lies between 2:1 and 4:1, depending on the depth of AB below the free surface of the liquid. Find the depth of AB when this ratio is 5:2 and AD is 4 m.*

Let h be the depth of AB below the free surface, a the length of AD and ρ the density of the liquid (Fig. 160).

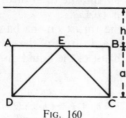

FIG. 160

Area CED	$= \frac{1}{2}a \cdot AB,$
area DEA	$= \frac{1}{4}a \cdot AB,$

depth of centroid of $CED = h + \frac{2}{3}a,$

depth of centroid of $DEA = h + \frac{1}{3}a,$

thrust on CED $\quad = \frac{1}{2}\rho a AB\left(h+\frac{2}{3}a\right)g,$

thrust on DEA $\quad = \frac{1}{4}\rho a AB\left(h+\frac{1}{3}a\right)g,$

ratio of thrusts $\quad = \dfrac{2(3h+2a)}{3h+a}.$

If $h = 0$ this ratio is $4:1$, if h is very large compared with a it is approximately $2:1$. If the ratio is $5:2$ and $a = 4$ m we have

$$\frac{5}{2} = \frac{2(3h+8)}{3h+4},$$

and $\qquad\qquad\qquad\qquad\qquad h = 4$ m.

Example 6. *The figure (Fig. 161) represents a mould for casting a metal hemisphere of diameter 1 m, molten metal being poured into the mould through a small aperture at O. The metal has a mass of 8500 kg/m³.*

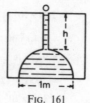

FIG. 161

(i) *Find the upward thrust of the molten metal on the mould when h = 50 cm.*

(ii) *If the mould is of mass 8 tonnes, find the value of h when the mould is on the point of being lifted.*   (L.U.)

When	$h = 0.5$
area of circular base	$= \pi/4$ m^2
depth below free surface	$= 1.5$ m.
Thrust on base	$= (\pi/4) \times 1.5 \times 8500g,$
	$= 3187\pi g$ N
Weight of metal	$= \frac{2}{3}\pi \times (\frac{1}{2})^3 \times 8500g$
	$= 708\pi g$ N.
Difference	$= 2479\pi g$ N,
	$= 7.79g$ kN.

This difference is the upward thrust of the metal on the mould.

If the upward thrust is $8g$ kN we have

$$\tfrac{1}{2}\pi(h+1) \times 8500 - 708\pi = 8000$$
$$h = 0.53 \text{ m.}$$

EXERCISES 11 (b)

1. Two liquids of specific gravities 1·2 and 0·84 are poured into the limbs of a U-tube until the differences in level of their upper surfaces is 9 cm. Find the heights of these surfaces above the common surface and the pressure at the common surface.

2. A U-tube with open ends of 1 cm^2 cross-section whose vertical branches rise to a height of 33 cm, contains mercury in both branches to a height of 6·8 cm. Find the greatest amount of water than can be poured into one of the branches, assuming the specific gravity of mercury to be 13·6.   (L.U.)

3. A square lamina ABCD, of side 3 m, is placed vertically in a homogeneous liquid with the edge AB in the surface. A straight line LM parallel to AB divides the square into two parts, so that the thrusts on the two parts are equal. Find the depth of LM. If E is a point in BC such that the thrust on the triangle ECD is one half of the thrust on the square, find the length EC.   (L.U.)

4. A circular hole of 18 cm diameter is cut in the vertical side of a tank filled with liquid of specific gravity 1·1. The highest point of the hole is 27 cm below the free surface of the liquid. What force is needed to hold a plate on the side to cover the hole?

5. A closed barrel with circular ends 75 cm in diameter and 1 m deep is filled with sea-water (sp. gr. 1·025) and then slowly tilted through an angle of 30°. Find the thrust of the water on the bottom of the barrel.

6. A closed cubical box of side 2 m is half full of oil (sp. gr. 1·3) and half full of water. It is tilted about one edge which is horizontal until the faces about this edge are inclined at 45° to the horizontal. Find the liquid thrust on one of the vertical faces of the box (i) if the oil and water are not mixed, (ii) if they are thoroughly mixed.   (L.U.)

7. A rectangular area of height h is immersed vertically in water with one edge in the free surface. A horizontal line divides the area at a depth $2h/3$. Find the ratio of the thrusts on the two parts. (L.U.)

8. A cubical tank of 1 metre edge with its base horizontal has its lower half filled with water and its upper half filled with oil of specific gravity 0·8. Determine the total fluid thrusts on the upper half and on the lower half of one of its vertical sides. (L.U.)

9. A circular lamina of radius 6 cm is held in a vertical position with its centre in the plane of separation of two liquids, the upper layer being water of depth 12 cm, and the lower layer oil (sp. gr. 1·2). Find the total liquid thrust on the lamina.

10. A rectangular lock gate 4 m wide can just bear a resultant force of 100g kN. If the depth of water on the lower side is 3 m, to what depth can the water on the other side be allowed to rise? (L.U.)

11. A vertical triangular area ABC with $AB = AC = 5$ m, $BC = 6$ m, has its vertex A in the free surface of a liquid of specific gravity 1·3 and its base BC horizontal. Find the thrust of the liquid. If it is lowered until A is at a depth of 4 m in the liquid, find the additional thrust.

12. A closed rectangular tank is 10 m high and stands on a base 4 m square. It is filled with water and tilted through an angle of 40° about one of the edges of the base. Find the thrust on the top and on the base in this position.

13. A pair of equal lock-gates are kept shut by the thrust of water 3·5 m deep. Taking the gates as rectangular and plane, each measuring 4·5 m vertical by 3 m horizontal, and supported by vertical hinges at their outer edges 5 m apart, show that the reaction between the gates across the line where they abut is equal to the resultant reaction on the hinges, and find its value. (L.U.)

14. A rectangular dam of a reservoir is 10 m wide and 2·5 m deep; calculate the thrust on the dam, the surface of the water being 25 cm below the top of the dam. (L.U.)

15. A reservoir is closed by a sluice-gate 2 m broad and 3 m high. Calculate the pressure of the water upon it, assuming that the top of the sluice is in the surface of the water. (L.U.)

16. A square plate is immersed with an edge of length a in the surface of water, find the position of the two horizontal lines which divide the square into three rectangles, on each of which the total water pressure is the same. (L.U.)

17. A rectangular vessel contains three liquids which do not mix, of specific gravities 1·0, 1·2, 1·6, the thicknesses of which are 4, 3 and 2 cm respectively. Compare the total normal thrusts of the liquids on a side of the vessel. (L.U.)

11.10 Centre of Pressure

The centre of pressure of a plane area immersed in a liquid is the point at which the total thrust of the liquid on the area may be assumed to act. We are usually concerned with the distance of the centre of pressure from the line in which the plane of the area meets the free surface of the liquid, and we shall prove that for a uniform liquid this distance is the second moment of the area about the line divided by the first moment of the area about the same line.

Centre of Pressure of a Vertical Area

Consider a vertical plane area A completely immersed in a uniform liquid of density ρ, and let the plane in which the area lies meet the free surface of the liquid in the line XX' (Fig. 162). Let a small element of area δA be at a depth y below the free surface.

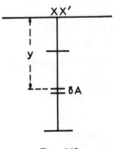

Then the thrust on the element δA is $\rho y \delta A g$ and the total thrust on the area is $\Sigma \rho y \delta A g$, where the summation is over the whole area. The moment of the thrust on the element δA about the line XX' is $\rho y^2 \delta A g$, and the sum of the moments of the thrusts on all elements of the body is $\Sigma \rho y^2 \delta A g$.

Fig. 162

Hence, since the moment of the total thrust about XX' must be equal to this quantity, we have that the distance p of the centre of pressure from the line XX' is given by

$$p = \frac{\Sigma \rho y^2 \delta A g}{\Sigma \rho y \delta A g} = \frac{\Sigma y^2 \delta A}{\Sigma y \delta A},$$

$$= \frac{\text{the second moment of area about } XX'}{\text{the first moment of area about } XX'}.$$

If h be the distance of the centroid of the area from XX' and k its radius of gyration about XX' we have

$$p = \frac{Ak^2}{Ah},$$

$$= \frac{k^2}{h}.$$

Centre of Pressure of Inclined Area

Suppose the area considered is inclined at an angle θ to the horizontal (Fig. 163). As before, let the plane of the area meet the free surface of the liquid in the line XX' and let a small element of area δA be at a distance y from the line XX'. Then the thrust on an element δA is $\rho g y \sin \theta \, \delta A$ and the total thrust on the area

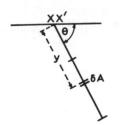

$$= \Sigma \rho g y \sin \theta \delta A = \rho g \sin \theta \, \Sigma y \delta A.$$

The moment of the thrust on the element δA about XX' is $\rho g y^2 \sin \theta \, \delta A$ and the total moment

$$= \Sigma \rho g y^2 \sin \theta \, \delta A$$

Fig. 163

$$= \rho g \sin \theta \, \Sigma y^2 \delta A.$$

Hence, as before, the distance p of the centre of pressure of the area

from XX' is given by

$$p = \frac{\rho g \sin \theta \, \Sigma y^2 \delta A}{\rho g \sin \theta \, \Sigma y \delta A} = \frac{k^2}{h}.$$

Hence, the position of the centre of pressure in the area is unaltered by turning the area about the line in which its plane meets the free surface of the liquid.

Distance from Centroid to Centre of Pressure

Let $Ak_1{}^2$ be the second moment of area about an axis parallel to XX' through the centroid. Then by the parallel axis theorem

$$Ak^2 = A(k_1{}^2 + h^2).$$

Therefore

$$p = \frac{k^2}{h} = \frac{k_1{}^2 + h^2}{h},$$

$$= \frac{k_1{}^2}{h} + h.$$

Hence, the distance of the centre of pressure from XX' is always greater than the distance of the centroid from XX', that is, the centre of pressure always lies below the centroid at a distance measured at right angles to XX' of $k_1{}^2/h$.

When the distance of the centre of pressure from XX' is known its position is in many cases evident. When the area has an axis of symmetry perpendicular to XX' the centre of pressure obviously lies on this axis.

If a triangular lamina has its base parallel to the line in which its plane cuts the free surface, the pressure on any thin strip of its area parallel to its base may be taken as acting at the mid-point of the strip, and hence the centre of pressure of the triangle must lie on the median from the mid-point of its base.

11.11 Standard Cases

Centre of Pressure of a Rectangle

Consider a rectangle $ABCD$ immersed in a uniform liquid with the side AB in the free surface (Fig. 164). Let $AB = a$, $BC = h$. The second

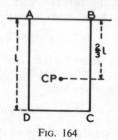

Fig. 164

moment of the rectangle about $AB = \dfrac{ah^3}{3}$ and its first moment about AB is $ah \times \dfrac{h}{2}$.

Hence
$$p = \frac{2}{3}h.$$

Centre of Pressure of a Triangle

Consider a triangle ABC of height h with its base BC in the surface of the liquid (Fig. 165).

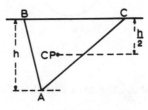

FIG. 165

The second moment of the triangle about BC is $\dfrac{1}{2}h \cdot BC \times \dfrac{h^2}{6}$ and the first moment about BC is $\dfrac{1}{2}h \cdot BC \times \dfrac{h}{3}$.

Hence
$$p = \frac{h}{2}.$$

If the vertex A be in the surface of the liquid and the base BC horizontal (Fig. 166), we have the second moment about a parallel to BC through A is

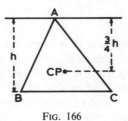

FIG. 166

$\dfrac{1}{2}h \cdot BC \times \dfrac{h^2}{2}$ and the first moment is $\dfrac{1}{2}h \cdot BC \times \dfrac{2h}{3}$.

Hence
$$p = \frac{3h}{4}.$$

Centre of Pressure of Circular Area

Consider a circular area of radius a whose centre is distant h from the line XX' in which its plane meets the free surface (Fig. 167).

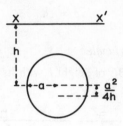

Fig. 167

The second moment of the area about a diameter is $\pi a^2 \times \dfrac{a^2}{4}$, and hence about XX' $\pi a^2\left(\dfrac{a^2}{4}+h^2\right)$.

The first moment of the area about XX' is $\pi a^2 \times h$.

Hence
$$p = \frac{h^2 + a^2/4}{h} = h + \frac{a^2}{4h}.$$

The centre of pressure is therefore at a distance $\dfrac{a^2}{4h}$ from the centre of the circle.

11.12 Increase of Depth

When the centre of pressure of a plane area has been found and the depth of the area is then increased, the increase in depth causes an equal additional pressure proportional to this increase at every point of the area. Hence the additional thrust due to the increase in depth may be taken as acting at the centroid of the area. By finding the position of the resultant of this additional thrust at the centroid and the original thrust at the centre of pressure, the new centre of pressure may be found.

Example 7. *A rectangle of sides a and b has its sides of length a vertical and its upper edge at a depth h below the surface of a liquid of density ρ. Find the distance of the centre of pressure from its centroid.*

Let A be the higher edge of the rectangle and B its centroid (Fig. 168).

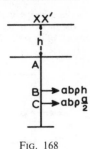

Fig. 168

If the liquid just covered the rectangle the thrust would be $\dfrac{a^2 b \rho g}{2}$ at the centre of

pressure C at $\dfrac{2}{3}a$ below A.

The additional head of liquid h causes a thrust $abh\rho g$ at the centroid B.

The total thrust is $ab\left(h+\dfrac{a}{2}\right)\rho g$ at a point x below B where

$$abh\rho g x = \frac{a^2 b \rho g}{2}\left(\frac{a}{6}-x\right).$$

Therefore

$$x = \frac{a^2}{6(2h+a)}.$$

Example 8. *A lamina in the form of a regular hexagon is half immersed in a liquid, a diagonal being in the free surface. Prove that the centre of pressure of the immersed half is at a depth of 5r/8, where r is the radius of the inscribed circle of the hexagon.* (L.U.)

The problem is not altered by taking the immersed portion of the hexagon as vertical.

We have three equilateral triangles A, B, C, of area $\dfrac{r^2}{\sqrt{3}}$ and height r (Fig. 169).

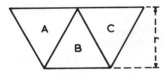

Fig. 169

The triangles A and C have each a thrust $\dfrac{r^2}{\sqrt{3}}\times\dfrac{r}{3}\rho g$ acting at a depth $\dfrac{r}{2}$ below the

surface. The triangle B has a thrust $\dfrac{r^2}{\sqrt{3}}\times\dfrac{2r}{3}\rho g$ acting at a depth $\dfrac{3r}{4}$ below the surface.

Now, the thrust on B is equal to the sum of the thrusts on A and C, and hence the total thrust is at a depth midway between the depths of the centres of pressure of A and B, that is, at a depth $\dfrac{1}{2}\left(\dfrac{r}{2}+\dfrac{3r}{4}\right) = \dfrac{5r}{8}$.

Example 9. *A circular manhole 2 m in diameter in the vertical side of a water tank has its centre at a depth 3·5 m below the surface of the water. It is covered by a circular plate held in position by bolts at the ends of its vertical diameter. Find the tensions in the bolts.*

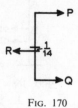

FIG. 170

The thrust on the plate is (Fig. 170).

$$R = \pi \times 3{\cdot}5 \times 1000g \text{ N},$$

acting at a depth

$$\frac{1}{4 \times 3{\cdot}5} = \frac{1}{14} \text{ m}$$

below the centre of the circle.

Forces P and Q at the end of the diameter must balance R and we have

$$P + Q = \pi \times 3{\cdot}5 \times 1000g,$$

$$P\left(1 + \frac{1}{14}\right) = Q\left(1 - \frac{1}{14}\right),$$

$$P = 3347 \text{ N},$$

$$Q = 3862 \text{ N}.$$

Example 10. *The depths of water on the two sides of a rectangular lock gate 4 m wide are 3 m and 1·5 m. Find the resultant thrust on the gate and its turning moment about the bottom of the gate.*

On the deeper side the resultant thrust is

$$4 \times 3 \times 1{\cdot}5 \times 10^3 g = 18\,000g = 177\,000 \text{ N}$$

acting at a height 1 m above the bottom.

On the other side the thrust is

$$4 \times 1{\cdot}5 \times 0{\cdot}75 \times 10^3 g = 4500g = 44\,100 \text{ N}$$

acting at a height 0·5 m above the bottom.

Hence, the resultant thrust is 132 900 N and the turning moment about the bottom is

$$(18\,000 \times 1 - 4500 \times 0{\cdot}5)g = 154\,000 \text{ N m}$$

$$= 154 \text{ kN m}.$$

EXERCISES 11 (c)

1. The triangular lamina ABC is vertically immersed with the edge AB in the free surface and C at depth h. If D is the mid-point of BC, show that the depth of the centre of liquid pressure on the triangular portion ADC is $7h/12$, and find the ratio of the thrusts on ADC and ADB. (L.U.)

2. A triangle ABC, right-angled at C, is immersed vertically in water with AB in the free surface. It is then rotated about A until AC is vertical. Show that the depths of the centre of pressure on the triangle ABC in the two positions are in the ratio $2 \sin \alpha : 3$, where α is the angle BAC.   (L.U.)

3. A square plate, of side a, is immersed vertically in water with one side in the surface. Calculate the ratio of the depths of the centres of liquid pressure on each of the two triangles into which the plate is divided by a diagonal.   (L.U.)

4. $ABCD$ is a square lamina of side $2a$ from which the portion AEB is removed, where E is the mid-point of AD. The lamina $BCDE$ is immersed in liquid with B in the surface and BC vertical. Show that the depth of the centre of gravity of $BCDE$ is $11a/9$, and that the depth of the centre of liquid pressure on one side of $BCDE$ is $31a/22$.   (L.U.)

5. ABC is a triangular lamina in which the angle A is a right-angle, $AB = AC$ and $BC = a$. It is immersed vertically in liquid with BC horizontal, and at a depth a below the surface, and with A below BC. Find the distance from A of the centre of liquid pressure on one side of the lamina.   (L.U.)

6. The vertical end of a tank is a trapezium whose upper and lower horizontal sides are 4 m and 2m respectively, and whose depth is 2 m. Calculate the thrust on the vertical end of the tank and the depth of the centre of pressure, when the tank is filled with water.   (L.U.)

7. A triangular lamina ABC, right-angled at A, is immersed in water with its plane vertical and B in the free surface. If $BC = a$ and the angle ACB is θ, find the depth of the centre of pressure of the triangle when BC is vertical.   (L.U.)

8. $ABCD$ is a square lamina of side $2a$ and P is the mid-point of CD. The triangle CBP is removed, and the remaining lamina is immersed vertically in liquid with AB in the surface. Find the depth of the centre of liquid pressure.   (L.U.)

9. A hollow cube of edge a with one face horizontal has its lower half filled with water, whilst the upper half is filled with liquid of specific gravity 0.9. If the liquids do not mix, show that the depth of the centre of liquid pressure on a vertical face of the cube is $149a/222$.   (L.U.)

10. A square $ABCD$, of side a, is immersed vertically in liquid, with the side AB in the free surface. Show that, if P is a point in BC such that $BP = \frac{2}{3}a$, the liquid thrust on the triangle PCD is twice that on the triangle ABP. What is then the depth of the centre of pressure of the trapezium $APCD$?   (L.U.)

11. A lamina $ABED$ has the shape of a square $ABCD$ of side a from which a triangular portion BCE has been removed, E being a point on CD. The lamina is immersed vertically in a uniform liquid with AB in the surface. If the depth of the centre of liquid pressure is $3a/5$, find the length of DE.   (L.U.)

12. A layer of liquid of density ρ and depth a rests on top of a liquid of density 3ρ and depth greater than a. A square lamina of side $2a$ is immersed vertically with one edge in the free surface. Prove that the depth of the centre of liquid pressure is $13a/9$.   (L.U.)

13. A, B, C, D are consecutive vertices of a regular hexagon of side a, and AD is a diagonal. A plane area $ABCD$ of this form is immersed vertically in liquid with BC in the surface. Show that the depth of the centre of liquid pressure is $7\sqrt{3}a/20$.   (L.U.)

14. A rectangular area of height h is immersed vertically in water with one edge in the free surface. A horizontal line is drawn across the area at a depth $2h/3$. Find the thrusts on the two parts into which the area is divided, and show that the

distances of the centres of pressure on the two parts from the line of division
are in the ratio 4 : 5.   (L.U.)

15. A rectangular lock-gate 3 m wide can just bear a resultant force of $100g$ kN.
If the depth of water on the lower side is 2·5 m, to what depth can the water on
the other side be allowed to rise? When this depth is as great as possible, at
what height above the bottom of the gate does the resultant thrust act?   (L.U.)

16. A cubical tank of 1 metre edge with its base horizontal has its lower half filled
with water and its upper half filled with oil of specific gravity 0·8. Determine
the total fluid thrusts on the upper and lower halves of one of the vertical sides
and find the depth of the centre of pressure of the upper half.   (L.U.)

17. The depths of water on the two sides of a rectangular lock-gate are h_1 and h_2.
Prove that the resultant pressure on the gate acts at a point whose depth below
the mean level of the surface is $(h_1{}^2 + h_2{}^2 + 4h_1h_2)/6(h_1 + h_2)$.   (L.U.)

18. A trapezium is formed by cutting a square $ABCD$ of side a along the line joining
A to the mid-point of BC, and is immersed in water with AD in the surface.
Find the distances of the centre of pressure from AD and DC.   (L.U.)

19. A cube of edge 1 m is full of water, and is placed with two faces vertical and
four faces making 45° with the vertical. Find the thrust on one of the upper inclined faces, and the moment of this thrust about the highest edge of the cube.
          (L.U.)

20. A rectangular door in the vertical side of a reservoir can turn freely about its
lower edge, and is fastened at its two upper corners. The door is 1 m wide and
2 m high, and its upper edge is 2 m below the water level. Determine the reactions
at the upper corners, assuming them equal.   (L.U.)

21. A dam 10 m high has a triangular cross-section. If the water side of the dam is
vertical and the base is 7 m thick, determine the density of the material con-
stituting the dam, given that the water surface is level with the top and that the
resultant of the water pressure and weight of the dam passes through a point
on the base 5 m from the water side.   (Q.E.)

CHAPTER 12

BUOYANCY

12.1 Principle of Archimedes

If a body be at rest wholly or partly immersed in a liquid, the resultant of the liquid pressures on the body is a vertical force equal to the weight of the liquid displaced by the body and acting upwards through the centre of gravity of the displaced liquid.

This resultant force is called the *force of buoyancy*, and the centre of gravity of the displaced liquid is called the *centre of buoyancy*.

The principle of Archimedes, which holds for gases as well as liquids, enables us to study floating bodies, to measure specific gravities and to find liquid thrusts on curved surfaces. The principle is established by considering the horizontal and vertical components of the thrust on a submerged surface.

Horizontal Component of Thrust on a Surface

The horizontal component of the thrust in any given direction on a submerged surface is equal to the thrust on the projection of the surface on a vertical plane perpendicular to the given direction, and acts through the centre of pressure of the projection.

Let ρ be the density of the liquid and δA a small element of the area of the surface at a depth y (Fig. 171). Let the element δA be considered

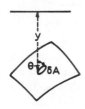

FIG. 171

as a plane area inclined at an angle θ to the plane of projection. The thrust on δA is $\rho g y \delta A$ perpendicular to δA. The horizontal component in the given direction of this force is $\rho g y \delta A \cos \theta$. But $\delta A \cos \theta$ is the area of the projection of δA on the perpendicular plane of projection. Hence the horizontal component of the thrust on δA is the same as the thrust on its projection; therefore the horizontal thrust on the whole surface is the same as that on its projection and acts through the centre of pressure of the projection. It follows that if a *body* is immersed in a liquid, it may be considered as two surfaces having the same horizontal projections on any vertical plane, and hence, the horizontal components of the thrusts on the two surfaces being equal and opposite, the total horizontal thrust on the body is zero.

Vertical Component of Thrust on a Surface

The vertical component of the thrust on a submerged surface is equal to the weight of the liquid contained above the surface by the verticals through the boundary of the surface.

Let ρ be the density of the liquid and δA a small element of the surface at depth y inclined at an angle θ to the horizontal (Fig. 172).

δA being considered as a plane area, the thrust on the element will be $\rho g y \delta A$ normal to δA, and the vertical component of this thrust will be $\rho g y \delta A \cos \theta$. The projection of the area δA on a horizontal plane is $\delta A \cos \theta$, and hence $\rho g y \delta A \cos \theta$ is the weight of the column of liquid which is vertically above δA. Hence, the vertical component of thrust on the whole surface is the sum of such columns, and is therefore the total weight of liquid above the surface.

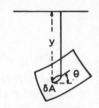

Fig. 172

This is the downward thrust on the upper face of the surface. If the surface is of negligible thickness, the pressure at any point on its lower face will be equal and opposite to that at the same point on its upper face, and hence the vertical component of thrust on the lower face will be equal and opposite to that on the upper face.

Vertical Component of Thrust on a Body

A body may be considered as two surfaces, the dividing line being points at which vertical tangents can be drawn to the body (Fig. 173).

The downward thrust on the upper surface is equal to the weight of liquid above this surface; the upward thrust on the lower surface is equal to the weight of liquid above this surface. Hence the resultant thrust on the body is the difference between the weights of these quantities of liquid, that is, the weight of liquid that would fill the space between the the two surfaces.

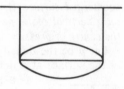

Fig. 173

This is the force of buoyancy. This force, being the sum of the weights of small columns of liquid contained between the upper and lower surfaces, may be taken to act at the centre of gravity of this liquid, that is, at the centre of buoyancy.

If the body is not completely immersed, the upper surface must be taken as the section of the body by the free surface of the liquid, and the volume of liquid displaced is the volume of the body below this section.

12.2 Floating Bodies

If a body floats in a liquid, its weight acts downwards through its centre of gravity G, and the force of buoyancy acts upwards through the centre of buoyancy B (Fig. 174). Hence the force of buoyancy must be equal to the weight of the body, that is, the weight of the liquid displaced by the body must be equal to the weight of the whole body.

Also, the two forces must be in the same vertical line, that is, the centres

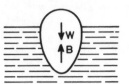

Fig. 174

of gravity of the body and of the liquid displaced must be in the same vertical line.

It follows that if a body of uniform material floats in water its specific gravity s must be less than unity. If V be the volume of the body and v the volume of water displaced, then $Vs = v$, and s is the fraction of the volume immersed.

Flotation in Liquids of Different Densities

In establishing the principle of Archimedes it was not assumed that the liquid was of uniform density. Hence, we may use the principle to find the force of buoyancy when a body is immersed in liquid with layers of different densities, the liquid displaced in each layer being considered as having the density of the layer.

Example 1. *A pontoon has vertical sides, a rectangular base 20 m long and 4 m wide and ends sloping at 45° to the horizontal. It floats in water with its base 16 cm below the surface. Find the mass of the pontoon. Find also how much it is immersed when a mass of 60 tonnes is placed centrally on it.*

The mass of the pontoon (Fig. 175) is the mass of the volume of water it displaces.

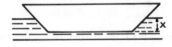

Fig. 175

A section of the displaced liquid parallel to a side is a trapezium of sides 20 and 20·32 m and width 16 cm.

Therefore

volume displaced $= 4 \times 20 \cdot 16 \times 0 \cdot 16 = 12 \cdot 90$ m^3,

mass of water displaced $= 12 \cdot 90$ tonnes,

and this is the mass of the pontoon.

Let x m be the height of the free surface above the base when a load of 60 tonnes is added.

Total mass $= 72 \cdot 90$ tonnes,

volume displaced $= 4 \times (20 + x) \times x$ m^3,

mass of water displaced $= 4x(x + 20)$ tonnes.

Therefore $4x(x + 20) = 72 \cdot 90$,

$$x = 0 \cdot 87 \text{ m approximately.}$$

Example 2. *A beam 1·5 m long, of cross-section 20 cm by 8 cm and of mass 15 kg, floats vertically in water with a piece of iron (sp. gr. 7·5) attached to its lower end. If the mass of the iron is 5 kg what length of the beam is immersed?*

Let x m of the beam be immersed.

Mass of water displaced by the beam $= x \times 0.20 \times 0.08 \times 10^3 = 16x$ kg.

Mass of water displaced by the iron $= \dfrac{5}{7.5} = \dfrac{2}{3}$ kg.

Total mass of water displaced $= 20$ kg.

Therefore

$$16x + \frac{2}{3} = 20,$$

$$x = 1.21 \text{ m}.$$

Example 3. *A 5 g mass is placed on the base of a conical piece of wood (sp. gr. 64/125) which floats with its base horizontal and vertex downwards partly immersed in water in a large vessel. The 5 g mass causes the circular base of the cone to sink to the level of the surface of the water. This mass is now removed and a brass mass (sp. gr. 8) attached to the apex under water. Find this mass if the cone sinks half as far as before.* (L.U.)

Let h cm be the vertical height of the cone and α its semi-vertical angle.
Volume of cone $= \frac{1}{3}\pi h^3 \tan^2\alpha$.
Let h_1 cm be the length of the axis under water when the cone floats alone.
Volume immersed $= \frac{1}{3}\pi h_1^3 \tan^2\alpha$.
This volume is $\frac{64}{125}$ of the whole,

therefore $\qquad\qquad\qquad\qquad h_1 = \frac{4}{5}h$.

The additional volume of water displaced by the 5 g mass itself has a mass of 5 g, that is,

$$\frac{61}{125} \times \frac{1}{3}\pi h^3 \tan^2\alpha = 5. \tag{1}$$

Let w g be the mass of brass, the mass of water it displaces is $\dfrac{w}{8}$ g and the additional mass of water now displaced by the cone is

$$\frac{1}{3}\pi(\tfrac{9}{10}h)^3 \tan^2\alpha - \frac{1}{3}\pi(\tfrac{4}{5}h)^3 \tan^2\alpha.$$

Therefore $\qquad\qquad \frac{7}{8}w = \frac{1}{3}\pi h^3 \tan^2\alpha(\tfrac{729}{1000} - \tfrac{64}{125})$,
hence, using (1),

$$w = 2.54 \text{ gm}.$$

Example 4. *A cylinder of wood 12 cm long floats in water with its axis vertical and 10 cm of its length immersed. Oil of specific gravity 0·75 is poured on to the water until the top of the cylinder is in the oil surface. What is the depth of the layer of oil?*

Let x cm be the depth of the layer of oil, and A sq cm the cross-sectional area of the cylinder.

The specific gravity of the wood is $\dfrac{10}{12}$, therefore its mass is

$$\frac{10}{12}A \times 12 = 10A \text{ g}.$$

Mass of oil displaced $\qquad\qquad = 0.75 \times A \times x$ g.
Mass of water displaced $\qquad\qquad = A(12 - x)$ g.
Therefore $\qquad\qquad 12 - x + 0.75x = 10$,

$$x = 8 \text{ cm}.$$

EXERCISES 12 (a)

1. A cubical lump of ice (sp. gr. 0·92) has embedded in it a piece of iron (sp. gr. 7·76) of mass 1 gm. The lump of ice floats in water and gradually melts, but retains its cubical form. Find the length of the edge of the cube when it sinks.   (L.U.)

2. Find the weight of iron (sp. gr. 7·76) that would just be sufficient to submerge a block of wood (sp. gr. 0·72) of volume 1000 cm^3 floating in water.

    (a) if the iron is on top of the wood and out of the water,
    (b) if the iron is attached to the underside of the block.

3. A hollow spherical ball is made of copper (sp. gr. 8·8), and its external diameter is 8 cm. If it just floats in water completely immersed, find the thickness of the metal.

4. A closed cubical box whose edges are 1 m long weighs 100 kg. A piece of iron (sp. gr. 7·76) is to be attached to the mid-point of one edge so that the cube may float in sea-water (sp. gr. 1·025) with that edge 40 cm below the surface and horizontal. Find the mass of iron required.

5. A cubical block of wood of mass 50 kg floats in water with three-quarters of its bulk immersed, and floats in oil just totally immersed when a mass of 10 kg is placed on top of it clear of the oil. Find the specific gravity of the oil.

6. A piece of metal which has a mass 10 kg floats in mercury with 5/9ths of its volume immersed. Find the volume and density of the metal, assuming the specific gravity of the mercury to be 13·5.   (L.U.)

7. A uniform solid cork cube floats in water with two faces vertical and with two-thirds of its surface area exposed. Find the specific gravity of the cork.

8. A cube of ice (sp. gr. 0·918) floats in sea-water (sp. gr. 1·026) with two faces horizontal and projects 1 cm above the surface of the water. Find to what height it will project if transferred to float in fresh water.   (L.U.)

9. A spherical piece of ice (sp. gr. 0·918) of radius 10 cm has a lump of iron (sp. gr. 7·8) inside it and floats in water with 19/20ths of its volume immersed. Find the volume of the iron.   (L.U.)

10. A square slab of wood, 25 cm thick, floats in water with three-quarters of its volume immersed. If the wood is of mass 120 kg, what is the length of the side of the square? If the block is floating with its square faces horizontal and oil (sp. gr. 0·72) is poured on top of the water until the upper surface of the wood is just immersed, find the depth of the layer of oil.

12.3 Determination of Specific Gravity

The specific gravity of a solid is simply determined by weighing it in air and in water.

If W be the weight of the body and s its specific gravity, the weight of water displaced by the body is W/s. This is therefore the force of buoyancy acting on the body when it is immersed in water, and its apparent weight is then $W - W/s$.

Hence, the apparent loss of weight when the body is weighed in water is W/s. The weighing is, of course, done by suspending the body from the arm of a balance which is outside the water. If the body is weighed in a liquid of specific gravity s_1, the force of buoyancy is $\dfrac{W}{s} \times s_1$, and this is then the apparent loss of weight.

The specific gravity of a liquid is measured by means of a *hydrometer*. This is, essentially, a cylindrical body which floats in the liquid with its axis vertical. The length of the axis which is immersed depends on the specific gravity of the liquid, and the cylinder may be graduated so that the specific gravity of the liquid may be read off at the level of its free surface.

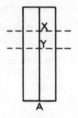

FIG. 176

Let W be the weight of the cylinder, a its cross-sectional area and X and Y (Fig. 176) the levels of the free surface when it floats in water and in a liquid of specific gravity s respectively. Then if A be the lower end of the axis of the cylinder and ρ the density of water in newtons,

$$a \,.\, AX \,.\, \rho = W,$$

$$a \,.\, AY \,.\, \rho s = W,$$

$$s = \frac{AX}{AY}.$$

In the usual type of hydrometer there is a portion of the body of different shape below the lower end of the cylinder. If V be the volume of this portion the above equations become

$$(V + aAX)\rho = W,$$
$$(V + aAY)\rho s = W,$$

$$s = \frac{V + a \,.\, AX}{V + a \,.\, AY},$$

and the cylinder is graduated accordingly.

Another hydrometer commonly used is known as Nicholson's hydrometer. This is made to float in water and in the liquid whose specific gravity is being measured with the same proportion of its volume immersed, by adding weights to a scale-pan which is above the surface.

If W be the weight of the hydrometer, V the volume immersed and w the weight to be added to keep the same volume immersed in liquid of specific gravity s, we have

$$V\rho = W,$$

$$V\rho s = W + w,$$

$$s = \frac{W + w}{W}.$$

Example 5. *A piece of wood weighs 144 N in air, and a piece of metal weighs 36 N in water. When fastened together the two weigh 24 N in water and 8 N in a solution of specific gravity* $1 \cdot 1$. *Find the specific gravities of the wood and the metal.* (L.U.)

Let s_1 and s_2 be the specific gravities of the wood and metal respectively, and let W N be the weight of the metal in air.

The weight of the two in water is 24 N, therefore

$$144\left(1-\frac{1}{s_1}\right)+36 = 24,$$

$$s_1 = \frac{12}{13}.$$

The weight of the metal in water is 36 N, therefore

$$W\left(1-\frac{1}{s_2}\right) = 36.$$

The weight of the two in liquid of specific gravity 1·1 is 8 N, therefore

$$144\left(1-\frac{1·1\times13}{12}\right)+W\left(1-\frac{1·1}{s_2}\right) = 8.$$

Hence, eliminating W we have

$$s_2 = 10.$$

EXERCISES 12 (b)

1. A piece of an alloy of mass 96 g is composed of two metals whose specific gravities are 11·4 and 7·4. If the weight of the alloy is $86g$ mN in water, find the mass of each metal in the alloy.   (L.U.)

2. A piece of metal weighs 11·4 N in air and 9·6 N in a liquid of specific gravity 1·2. Calculate the specific gravity of the metal. A piece of wood weighs 1·8 N in air. When the metal is attached to the wood the two together weigh 9 N in the liquid. Calculate the specific gravity of the wood.   (L.U.)

3. A body weighing 12·4 N appears to weigh 2·4 N in water. It is then weighed in a mixture of a liquid A of specific gravity 0·8 and water, and appears to weigh 3·6 N. Find how many cc of the liquid A are added to 10 cc of water to form the mixture.   (L.U.)

4. A piece of a material A weighs 30·4 N in air and 26·4 N in water; a piece of a material B weighs 67·2 N in air and 61·2 N in water. A piece of an alloy formed from A and B weighs 54·6 N in air and 48·6 N in water. Find the volume of each material in the piece of alloy, assuming there to have been no diminution of volume when the alloy was made.   (L.U.)

5. A cubical block of wood (sp. gr. 0·83) contains inside it a piece of lead (sp. gr. 11·35). It floats in water with one-tenth of its volume above the surface, and can just be immersed by putting a mass of 100 g on its upper surface. Calculate the length of an edge of the cube and the volume of the piece of lead.   (L.U.)

6. A uniform rod has a mass attached to one end to make it float upright in liquid. If 3 cm of the rod is immersed when it floats in water and 3·5 cm when it floats in liquid of specific gravity 0·9, what length of it will be immersed when it floats in liquid of specific gravity 1·2?   (L.U.)

7. A bottle with a long straight neck floats vertically upright in water, part of the neck alone emerging. It is then placed in a solution of specific gravity 1·2, and 8 cm more of the neck are above the surface. If the neck be circular, 1 cm in radius, find the mass of the bottle.   (L.U.)

8. A piece of glass weighs 5 N in air, 3·2 N in water, and 1·7 N in sulphuric acid. Find the specific gravity of the glass and of the sulphuric acid.   (L.U.)

9. A mixture of two uniform substances weighs 25 N in water and 28 N in liquid of specific gravity 0·8. A mass of one of the substances of equal weight with the mixture weighs 30 N in the second liquid, and a mass of the other substance of equal weight with the mixture weighs 15 N in water. Find the specific gravity of each substance and their volumes in the mixture.   (L.U.)

10. A nugget of quartz and gold weighs 260 g in air and 180 g in water; taking the specific gravities of quartz and gold to be 2·6 and 19·5 respectively, find the mass of gold in the nugget.   (L.U.)

12.4 Equilibrium of a Body in a Liquid

If a body is held in any way in a liquid, the general conditions of equilibrium may be applied by resolving and taking moments of all the forces including the force of buoyancy acting at the centre of buoyancy.

Example 6. *A beam whose cross-section is a rectangle is held horizontally with a diagonal of its cross-section in the surface of water by a vertical rope attached to the mid-point of its lowest edge. Find the specific gravity of the beam.*

Consider the central cross-section of the beam. Let C be the mid-point of the horizontal diagonal, A the point of the lowest edge and B the centroid of the immersed triangle (Fig. 177).

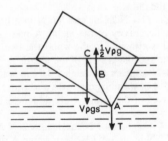

Fig. 177

Let V be the volume of the block, s its specific gravity and ρ the density of water.
Then the weight of the block is $V\rho g s$ and the force of buoyancy is $\frac{1}{2}V\rho g$ acting at B.
Since $AB = \frac{2}{3}AC$, we have, by equating the moments of the weight and the buoyancy about A,

$$V\rho g s = \tfrac{2}{3} \times \tfrac{1}{2}V\rho g.$$

Therefore,

$$s = \tfrac{1}{3}.$$

Example 7. *A uniform rod of specific gravity s is free to turn about its lower end, which is fixed at a depth h in water. Prove that the rod can float in an inclined position provided $sl^2 > h^2$, where l is the length of the rod. Determine s if the rod floats with half of its length immersed.*
          (L.U.)

Let x be the length of the rod immersed, a its cross-sectional area and ρ the density of water (Fig. 178).

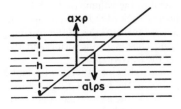

Fig. 178

The weight of the rod $= al\rho gs$,

the force of buoyancy $= ax\rho g$.

These forces act at distances $l/2$ and $x/2$ respectively from the hinge, therefore, taking moments about the hinge we have

$$\frac{x}{2} \times ax\rho g = \frac{l}{2} \times al\rho gs,$$

$$x^2 = l^2 s,$$

x must be greater than h, and hence $l^2 s > h^2$.

Also, if $x = l/2$ we have $\qquad s = \frac{1}{4}$.

EXERCISES 12 (c)

1. ABC is a triangular lamina, the angle A being a right angle and the angle B 30°. It can turn freely in its own plane, which is vertical, about A, which is fixed in the surface of water. If it is in equilibrium with C immersed and AC making an angle of 60° with the horizontal, show that the specific gravity of the material of the lamina is $\frac{3}{8}$.   (L.U.)

2. A solid lighter than water is held completely immersed in a vessel containing 100 cc of water by means of a string fastened to a point in the base of the vessel, and the tension in the string is $1 \cdot 6g$ mN. When 60 cc of a second liquid of specific gravity $1 \cdot 2$ are added and thoroughly mixed with the water, the tension in the string is $2 \cdot 2g$ mN. Find the specific gravity and the mass of the solid.
(L.U.)

3. A bucket containing water is suspended by a cord which passes over a smooth pulley, the pulley being sufficiently small for the other end of the cord, to which is attached a ball, to hang inside the bucket. If W be the weight of the water and $s(>2)$ the specific gravity of the ball, prove that equilibrium is possible if the weight of the ball lies between W and $Ws/(s-2)$.   (L.U.)

4. A uniform thin rod AB of length 150 cm is freely hinged to a point A 50 cm above the surface of a tank of deep water. The rod is in equilibrium when partially immersed and making an angle of 60° with the vertical. Find its specific gravity.
(L.U.)

5. A uniform rod is free to rotate about a fixed horizontal axis through its upper end. The lower end dips into water and rests in an inclined position with one-third of its length immersed. Show that the specific gravity of the rod is $\frac{5}{9}$.

A piece of metal (sp. gr. 4·6) is now attached to the lower end of the rod, and the system rests with one-half of the length of the rod immersed. Find the ratio of the volume of the metal to the volume of the rod.   (L.U.)

6. Two solid uniform spheres, each of radius 4 cm, are connected by a light string and totally immersed in a tank of water. If the specific gravities of the spheres are 0·4 and 1·8, find the tension in the string and the pressure between the bottom of the tank and the heavier sphere.   (L.U.)

7. A buoy is in the form of a right circular cone of height 3 m and base diameter 2 m. The vertex is fastened to the bottom of the sea by a chain, and it floats at low tide with the chain slack, the axis of the cone vertical and two-thirds of it immersed. Find the mass of the buoy, assuming that the mass of the chain is negligible and that the density of the water is 1024 kg/m³. Calculate also the pull on the chain at high tide when the buoy is completely immersed.   (L.U.)

8. A thin uniform rod of length $2a$ and specific gravity $\frac{3}{4}$ is hinged at one end to a point at a height $a/2$ above the surface of water, with the other end immersed. Find the inclined position of equilibrium.   (L.U.)

9. The cross-section of a uniform prism is a rectangle with unequal sides, and it floats in water with two opposite edges in the surface, supported by a string attached to the edge which is out of the water. Show that the specific gravity of the prism is $\frac{2}{3}$, that the string is vertical, and the tension in it is one-fourth of the weight of the prism.   (L.U.)

10. A uniform thin rod floats in water in an inclined position with one-half of its length immersed, the upper end of the rod being supported by a string. Prove that the string is vertical and that the density of the rod must be three-quarters of that of the water.   (L.U.)

12.5 Thrust on a Curved Surface

Body Immersed in Liquid

When a body is immersed in a liquid, the force of buoyancy is the *resultant* of the liquid thrusts on the surfaces of the body. Hence, if the body has a plane surface and a curved surface, and the force of buoyancy and the thrust on the plane surface are known, the thrust on the curved surface is easily found. This is not a question of the equilibrium of the body as a whole, but of using the fact that the force of buoyancy is caused by the liquid thrusts on the surfaces of the body.

Example 8. *A quadrant of a solid sphere of radius a is held with one of its plane semicircular faces in the surface of water. Find the thrust on the curved surface of the quadrant.*

Assuming that there is no thrust on the horizontal face, let P be the thrust on the vertical face and B the force of buoyancy (Fig. 179).

Then if ρ be the density of water

$$P = \frac{1}{2}\pi a^2 \times \frac{4a}{3\pi} \times \rho g = \frac{2}{3}a^3 \rho g.$$

$$B = \frac{1}{4} \times \frac{4}{3}\pi a^3 \times \rho g = \frac{\pi}{3}a^3 \rho g.$$

Let X and Y be the horizontal and vertical components of the thrust on the curved surface. Then the force B is the *resultant* of the forces P, X, Y.

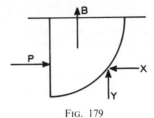

Fig. 179

Therefore

$$X = P = \frac{2}{3}a^3\rho g,$$

$$Y = B = \frac{\pi}{3}a^3\rho g,$$

$$\sqrt{X^2+Y^2} = \frac{1}{3}\sqrt{\pi^2+4}\,.\,a^3\rho g.$$

Since the pressure at any point of the curved surface is normal to the surface, the resultant thrust must pass through the centre of the sphere and its inclination to the horizontal is $\tan^{-1}\dfrac{Y}{X} = \tan^{-1}\pi/2$.

Body Containing Liquid

When a hollow body contains liquid, the liquid exerts thrusts on the plane and curved surface of the body. The liquid is in equilibrium under the action of its weight and the thrusts on the liquid exerted by the surfaces of the body, which are equal and opposite to the thrusts of the liquid on the body. This is equivalent to saying that the weight of the liquid is equal to the *resultant* of the thrust of the liquid on the plane and curved surfaces of the body. If therefore the weight of the liquid and the thrust on the plane surface of the body are known the thrust on the curved surface may be found.

Example 9. *A hollow right circular cone of height h and semi-vertical angle α is filled with liquid of density ρ and rests with a generator in contact with a horizontal plane. Find the thrust of the liquid on the curved surface of the cone.*

Let P be the liquid thrust on the base of the cone, X and Y the horizontal and vertical components of the liquid thrust on the curved surface and W the weight of the liquid

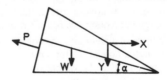

Fig. 180

(Fig. 180). Then W is equal to the resultant of the forces P, X and Y.

$$W = \frac{1}{3}\pi h^3 \tan^2\alpha \cdot \rho g.$$

The depth of the centroid of the base below the free surface of the liquid, which is assumed to be at the highest point of the cone, is $h \sin \alpha$.
Hence

$$P = \pi h^2 \tan^2\alpha \times h \sin \alpha \times \rho g,$$

and this force is inclined at an angle α to the horizontal.
Therefore

$$X = P\cos\alpha = \pi\rho gh^3 \tan^2\alpha \sin\alpha \cos\alpha,$$

$$Y = W + P\sin\alpha = \pi\rho gh^3 \tan^2\alpha\left(\frac{1}{3} + \sin^2\alpha\right),$$

$$\sqrt{(X^2 + Y^2)} = \frac{1}{3}\pi\rho gh^3 \tan^2\alpha\sqrt{(1 + 15\sin^2\alpha)},$$

$$= W\sqrt{(1 + 15\sin^2\alpha)}.$$

EXERCISES 12 (d)

1. A closed vessel of thin sheet metal consists of a right circular cylinder of radius a and height a closed at one end, and having the rim of the other end soldered to the rim of the base of a circular cone of radius a and height a. It is held with its axis vertical and conical part uppermost, and filled with water through a small orifice at the vertex of the cone. If the orifice is then closed and the vessel inverted, find the ratio of the thrusts on the curved conical surface in the two positions.
(L.U.)

2. A thin hollow cone of base radius r and height h, just filled with liquid of density w, is fixed with its axis horizontal. Find the magnitude of the thrust on the curved surface due to the liquid.
(L.U.)

3. A closed circular cylinder is completely immersed in water with its centre at a depth h and its axis inclined at an angle θ to the vertical. Calculate the resultant liquid thrust on the curved surface of the cylinder in terms of the weight W of water displaced by the cylinder.
(L.U.)

4. A closed hollow hemisphere is completely filled with liquid. Compare the magnitude of the liquid thrusts on its curved surface in the three positions (i) with its plane face horizontal and uppermost, (ii) with its plane face horizontal and lowermost, (iii) with its plane face vertical.
(L.U.)

5. A conical vessel contains enough fluid to fill it to a depth equal to half the depth of the vessel when the vertex is downwards. If the vessel is inverted, show that the resultant thrust of the curved surface is altered in the ratio $(23 - 12 \times 7\frac{1}{3}):1$.

6. A closed vessel in the form of a right circular cone is placed on its flat base, and liquid is poured in through a hole at the top until the depth of liquid is one-third of the height of the cone. If W is the weight of liquid that would fill the cone, show that the pressures on the base and curved surface are respectively W and $8W/27$.
(L.U.)

EXERCISES 12 (e)

1. A uniform cube, of edge a and weight W, floats partly immersed in a liquid of density ρ with a pair of opposite faces horizontal. A load w evenly distributed along one edge of the upper face tilts the cube until that edge is in the free surface of the liquid. Show that the inclination θ of the upper face of the cube to the horizontal is given by $\tan\theta = 2\left(1 - \dfrac{W+w}{\rho a^3}\right)$. (L.U.)

2. A uniform solid cone of volume V and density ρ_1 is held completely immersed with its axis vertical in a liquid of density $\rho_2(>\rho_1)$ by means of a string attached to its vertex and to the base of the vessel containing the liquid. Find the tension in the string.

   The liquid slowly drains out of the vessel, and when the string becomes slack two-thirds of the axis of the cone is still immersed. Find the ratio ρ_1/ρ_2.
   (L.U.)

3. A uniform cube of side a and specific gravity σ floats in water with two faces horizontal. When a second liquid of specific gravity $\sigma_1(<1)$ is poured on to the water to a depth b the upper face of the block is in the free surface. Find the value of σ in terms of σ_1, a and b. Show also that when the depth of the liquid is $b/2$ the height of the upper face above the free surface is $b(1-\sigma_1)/2$. (L.U.)

4. A solid hemisphere of radius 10 cm is held with its circular base vertical and its centre in the plane of separation of two layers of liquid, the upper layer of depth 10 cm being water and the lower layer liquid of specific gravity 1·2. Find the total thrust on the vertical plane and the magnitude and direction of the resultant thrust on the curved surface of the hemisphere. (L.U.)

5. Two equal light hemispherical shells can be fitted together to form a sphere which is water-tight on closing two small catches at A and B, the opposite ends of a diameter of the common rim. If the sphere is placed with the point A resting on a horizontal table and is filled with a weight W of water, find the least pair of equal and opposite forces that must be applied at B to prevent the hemispheres from separating when the catch B is released. (L.U.)

6. A sea-wall slopes from the bottom at $30°$ to the horizontal for 10 m, and is then continued vertically upwards. Find the resultant horizontal and vertical pressures on it in newtons per metre of its length when there is a depth of 10 m of water (density of sea water 1024 kg/m^3). (L.U.)

7. A closed hemispherical bowl of radius 6 cm is filled with water. It is held with its plane face making an angle of $50°$ with the horizontal and the curved surface above this face. Find the magnitude and direction of the thrust on the curved surface.

8. A trough whose cross-section is a triangle with vertex downwards is partly filled with water of weight W. A block of wood of weight W' is then introduced and floats on the water. Show that the pressure on either of the vertical plane ends of the trough is increased in the ratio $(1 + W'/W)^{3/2}$. (L.U.)

9. A cylinder of specific gravity 0·45 floats in water with its axis vertical. If its height be 30 cm and radius 5 cm, find what volume of lead (sp. gr. 11·4) must be suspended from the centre of its lower face to make it sink so that only 2·5 cm emerges from the water. (L.U.)

10. The cross-section of a block of wood is a trapezium $ABCD$. AB and CD are the parallel sides 10 cm apart, $AB = 16$ cm. $CD = 6$ cm, $AD = BC$. The specific gravity of the wood is $\frac{3}{5}$, and the block floats with the face containing AB immersed and horizontal. Show that the depth of AB is about 4·86 cm.

(L.U.)

11. A ship with sides practically vertical near the water-line is observed to sink 34 cm deeper when loaded with 400 tonnes of cargo in sea-water. Find the water-line area, taking the density of sea-water as 1024 kg/m^3. The displacement of the ship is 4500 tonnes; find how far it sinks when passing from salt water to fresh water. (L.U.)

12. A buoy in the form of a hollow spherical shell, of external diameter 1 m and uniform thickness, floats in water with half of its volume immersed. Find the thickness of the shell if the material is of specific gravity 8. (L.U.)

13. An iron cylinder of diameter 25 cm and height 10 cm stands in a cylindrical jar of diameter 30 cm. Mercury is now poured into the jar until the iron begins to float. Calculate the depth of the mercury. Oil is now poured on top of the mercury until the upper face of the cylinder is just level with the surface of the Find the volume of oil required and the height of the base of the cylinder above the bottom of the jar. Take the specific gravities of iron, mercury and oil to be 7·9, 13·6 and 0·9 respectively. (L.U.)

14. A rectangular barge is 20 m long and 5 m broad, and when unloaded has a mass of 30 tonnes. It is floating in water. Find what added load will increase the draught of the barge so that it is uniformly 1 m. What is then the resultant force arising from water-pressure on one of the long sides of the barge, and where does it act?

15. A cylinder vessel, 15 cm in diameter and 30 cm deep, is filled with water to a depth of 13·5 cm. A steel cylinder, of diameter 7·5 cm and height 10 cm, is then suspended in the water with its axis vertical and its lower end 2·5 cm from the bottom of the vessel; the wire is attached to the top face of the cylinder. What is (a) the tension in the wire, (b) the increase in the force exerted by the water on the bottom of the vessel, and (c) the tension in the cylinder across a horizontal section through its centre of gravity? (Specific gravity of steel 7·8.)

PART IV—DYNAMICS

CHAPTER 13

VELOCITY, ACCELERATION, LINEAR MOTION

13.1 Velocity

Velocity is defined as the rate of change of position. Consider a particle moving in a straight line so that its distance from a fixed point O in the line at time t is x. At time $t + \delta t$ let the particle be distant $x + \delta x$ from O. Then the particle has moved a distance δx in time δt and $\dfrac{\delta x}{\delta t}$ is the average rate of displacement or *average velocity* during the interval δt.

The velocity v at time t is defined as the limiting value of this quantity as δt tends to zero, that is

$$v = \lim_{\delta t \to 0} \frac{\delta x}{\delta t} = \frac{dx}{dt}.$$

Thus if the distance x is given in terms of the time t by an equation of the form

$$x = ct^2, \text{ where } c \text{ is a constant,}$$

$$v = \frac{dx}{dt} = 2ct,$$

and the velocity is a constant multiple of the time.

If

$$x = ct,$$

$$v = c,$$

and the velocity has a constant value. Hence, if the velocity is constant the distance x through which the particle moves in time t is

$$x = vt.$$

Units of velocity are units of distance divided by units of time and velocity is usually calculated in metres per second.

Centimetres per second, feet per second and miles per hour are also used and

$$1 \text{ cm/sec} = 10^{-2} \text{ m/sec}$$
$$1 \text{ ft/sec} = 0.3048 \text{ m/sec}$$
$$1 \text{ mile/h} = 22/15 \text{ ft/sec} = 0.477 \text{ m/sec}$$
$$1 \text{ km/h} = 5/18 \text{ m/sec}.$$

If a particle is moving along a curved path, let s be its distance measured along its path from a point of the path at time t and $s + \delta s$ the corresponding

195

distance at time $t + \delta t$. Then $\dfrac{\delta s}{\delta t}$ is the average rate of change of position in time δt and the velocity v at time t is

$$v = \lim_{\delta t \to 0} \frac{\delta s}{\delta t} = \frac{ds}{dt}.$$

Since the particle is moving along the curve, its direction of motion at any instant is along the tangent to the curve. Hence, the velocity of the particle has magnitude and direction. The magnitude of the velocity of a particle is called its *speed*. Thus a particle may move along a curved path with constant speed; but, as its direction of motion is continually changing, its velocity is not constant.

The velocity at any point on the path of a particle may be represented by a straight line whose length is proportional to the speed and whose direction is that of the tangent to the path, the sense in which the particle is moving along the tangent being indicated by an arrow. Thus velocity is a vector quantity (see §1.9).

A particle may have at the same time more than one velocity from different sources. A man in a ship has the velocity of the ship and has also the velocity with which he moves about the ship, that is, his velocity relative to the ship. His resultant velocity is a combination of these two velocities, and this resultant is found by the law for the addition of vectors.

13.2 Parallelogram of Velocities

If a particle has at the same time velocities represented in magnitude, direction and sense by straight lines OA and OB, they are equivalent to a velocity which is represented in magnitude, direction and sense by the diagonal OC of the parallelogram of which OA and OB are two sides.

This Theorem is merely a restatement of the fact that velocity is a vector quantity.

Let OA (Fig. 181) represent a velocity of magnitude u and OB a velocity of magnitude v. Then we may think of the particle as moving along

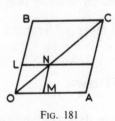

FIG. 181

OA with velocity u, while at the same time the line OA moves parallel to itself so that the point L moves along OB with velocity v.

OA also represents the *distance* moved in unit time with the velocity u, and OB the distance moved in unit time with the velocity v. At time t the particle will have moved a distance OM along OA, where $OM = ut$, and distance OL along OB, where $OL = vt$, so that at time t

the particle will be at N, the intersection of the sides of the parallelogram formed by OM and OL. The ratio of the sides of this parallelogram is

$$\frac{OM}{OL} = \frac{ut}{vt} = \frac{u}{v}.$$

But the ratio of the sides of the parallelogram $OBCA$ is

$$\frac{OA}{OB} = \frac{u}{v}.$$

Hence the parallelograms $OLNM$ and $OBCA$ are similar and N lies on the diagonal OC of $OBCA$. Therefore OC is the path of the particle. In unit time the particle will have moved to C, and therefore OC on the scale of velocities represents the velocity of the particle in magnitude and direction.

It follows that if the directions OA and OB include an angle α, the resultant velocity V is given by

$$V^2 = u^2 + v^2 + 2uv \cos \alpha.$$

In particular if the directions OA and OB are at right angles

$$V^2 = u^2 + v^2.$$

Also, a velocity may be resolved into component velocities in the same way as force. Thus, the velocity V of a particle at O in a direction making an angle α with a given direction OX is equivalent to a velocity $V \cos \alpha$ along OX and $V \sin \alpha$ along the perpendicular to OX.

13.3 Angular Velocity

Let A be a particle moving in a plane, O a given point in the plane and OX a fixed line (Fig. 182). Then the angular velocity of the particle about the point O is the rate at which the angle XOA is increasing.

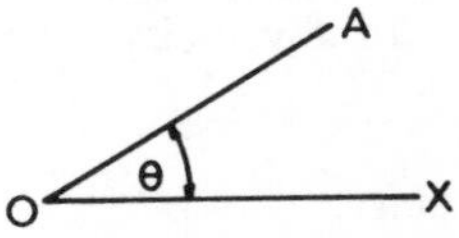

Let the angle XOA, measured in a counterclockwise sense, be θ.

Fig. 182

Then the angular velocity about O is $\dfrac{d\theta}{dt}$ in the direction of θ increasing.

The angle θ is usually measured in radians and the angular velocity, sometimes denoted by ω, in radians per second.

Thus $$\omega = \frac{d\theta}{dt} \text{ rad/sec.}$$

If a particle describes a circle of radius r with constant angular velocity ω, its speed at any instant is $r\omega$.

This follows at once, since if δs be any small element of the arc of the circle, the angle $\delta\theta$ which it subtends at the centre of the circle is given by

$$\delta s = r\delta\theta.$$

Therefore
$$\frac{\delta s}{\delta t} = r\frac{\delta\theta}{\delta t},$$

and in the limit as δt tends to zero

$$\frac{ds}{dt} = r\frac{d\theta}{dt} = r\omega.$$

13.4 Acceleration

Acceleration is defined as rate of change of velocity. Consider a particle moving in a straight line so that its velocity at time t is v and at time $t+\delta t$ is $v+\delta v$. Then δv is the change of velocity which occurs in time δt and the *average acceleration* during the period is $\frac{\delta v}{\delta t}$.

The acceleration a at time t is defined as the limiting value of this quantity as δt tends to zero.

That is
$$a = \lim_{\delta t \to 0} \frac{\delta v}{\delta t}$$
$$= \frac{dv}{dt}.$$

Thus if the velocity at any instant can be expressed in terms of the time, the acceleration may be found by differentiating the expression for the velocity with respect to the time.

If the velocity is proportional to the time, that is

$$v = ct,$$

then
$$a = c, \text{ a constant.}$$

If
$$v = ct^2,$$
$$a = 2ct,$$

and the acceleration is proportional to the time.

If x be the displacement of the particle along the straight line at time t, we have

$$v = \frac{dx}{dt},$$

therefore
$$a = \frac{d^2x}{dt}.$$

If the velocity at any instant can be expressed in terms of the displacement x

$$a = \frac{dv}{dt},$$

$$= \frac{dv}{dx} \cdot \frac{dx}{dt},$$

$$= v\frac{dv}{dx}.$$

We thus have three equivalent expressions for the acceleration at time t, namely,

$$a = \frac{dv}{dt} = \frac{d^2x}{dt^2} = v\frac{dv}{dx}.$$

The direction of the acceleration given by any of these quantities is that of x increasing, and for a particle being accelerated in the opposite direction these expressions would be negative. A negative acceleration is called a retardation.

A unit of acceleration is a change of a unit of velocity in unit time. Thus if the velocity is in metres per second, the unit of acceleration is one metre per second in one second. This is written as m per sec per sec or m/sec². If distances are measured in feet, the unit of acceleration is one foot per second in one second, or ft/sec².

13.5 Acceleration Due to Gravity

If a body is falling freely near the surface of the earth it has an acceleration due to gravity which is denoted by g towards the centre of the earth. The value of g is approximately 9·81 m/sec² or 32 ft/sec².

The value of g varies from about 9·78 m/sec² at the equator to about 9·83 m/sec² at the poles; in the latitude of England its value is approximately 9·81 m/sec² or 32·2 ft/sec².

In most problems sufficient accuracy is obtained by taking

$$g = 9·81 \text{ or even } 9·80 \text{ m/sec}^2 \text{ or } 32 \text{ ft/sec}^2.$$

The values of g are those for the acceleration of a particle falling in a vacuum. If a body falls through the air, the effect of the resistance of the air to its motion is to reduce its acceleration.

13.6 Acceleration as a Vector

A particle may have at the same time accelerations in different directions. Thus a particle falling under gravity may have at the same time an acceleration in some horizontal direction.

The acceleration of a particle has magnitude and acts in a definite sense along a straight line, and hence, like a velocity, it can be represented in magnitude, direction and sense by a straight line. Hence, (see §1.9) acceleration is a vector, and the resultant of accelerations in different directions may be found by the parallelogram law. This is easily seen from the fact that accelerations in two directions are changes of velocity in unit time in these two directions. These changes of velocity may be compounded by the parallelogram law giving a resultant change of velocity in unit time which is the resultant acceleration.

Thus if a particle has accelerations a_1 and a_2 in directions which include an angle α, the resultant acceleration of the particle a is given by

$$a^2 = a_1{}^2 + a_2{}^2 + 2a_1 a_2 \cos \alpha.$$

In particular, if the directions are at right angles

$$a^2 = a_1{}^2 + a_2{}^2.$$

It follows also that an acceleration in a given direction may be resolved into component accelerations. Thus if a particle at O has acceleration a in a direction OP making an angle α with a given direction OX and an angle $\frac{\pi}{2} - \alpha$ with OY, the acceleration is equivalent to the component accelerations

$$a \cos \alpha, \text{ along } OX,$$

$$a \sin \alpha, \text{ along } OY.$$

13.7 Angular Acceleration

The angular acceleration of a particle moving in a plane about a fixed point is the rate of change of its angular velocity about the point. Thus if θ be the angle made by the line joining the particle to the given point with a fixed direction, the angular velocity in the sense of θ increasing is

$$\omega = \frac{d\theta}{dt}.$$

The angular acceleration in the sense of θ increasing is

$$\frac{d\omega}{dt} = \frac{d^2\theta}{dt^2}.$$

13.8 Linear Motion of a Rigid Body

We have so far discussed the velocity and acceleration of a particle. If all the particles of a rigid body have the same velocity and acceleration in a straight line we may speak of the displacement, velocity or acceleration of the body, meaning the displacement, velocity or acceleration of each of its particles.

EXERCISES 13 (a)

1. In an amusement park cars are driven along a path whose shape is a regular octagon, at a speed which is kept constant at 30 m/sec. Find the magnitude and direction of the velocity given to each car at each angular point.

2. The minute hand of a clock is 1 metre long. Find its angular velocity and the velocity of its end.

3. A wheel of radius a rolls without slipping on horizontal ground, and its angular velocity is ω. Show that the velocity of its centre is $a\omega$ and that the greatest velocity of a point of the wheel is $2a\omega$. Show that the velocity of a point on the rim at a height h above the ground is $\omega\sqrt{2ah}$.

4. A wheel 1 m in diameter is rolling on horizontal ground, and the velocity of its centre is 5 m/sec. Find its angular velocity and the magnitude and direction of the velocity of a point on its rim $\frac{2}{3}$ m above the ground.

5. A ship is steaming on a course $30°$ east of north at a speed of $12\frac{1}{2}$ knots, and a man walks backwards and forwards across the deck perpendicular to the ship's course at a speed of $1\cdot524$ m/sec. Find the actual directions in which the man moves. (A knot is a speed of $0\cdot5148$ m/sec.)   (O.C.)

6. A shell moving with velocity 500 m/sec suddenly bursts, so that every piece of the shell is given an additional velocity of 80 m/sec in some direction by the explosion. Prove that after the explosion all the pieces will be moving in directions within about $9°$ of the original direction.

7. A particle moves in a circle of diameter d with uniform speed v. If A be the position of the particle at any instant, B a fixed point on the circumference and θ the angle subtended at the centre of the circle by the chord BA, prove that the component of the velocity of the particle at any instant perpendicular to BA is $v \sin (\theta/2)$. Hence show that the angular velocity of the particle about B is constant.

13.9 Motion in a Straight Line—Constant Acceleration

Let s be the distance moved in time t, then if the acceleration has a constant value a we have

$$\frac{dv}{dt} = \frac{d^2s}{dt^2} = v\frac{dv}{ds} = a.$$

Integrating with respect to the time we have

$$v = \frac{ds}{dt} = at + \text{constant.}$$

If u be the value of the velocity at time $t = 0$, we have

$$v = u + at \qquad (1)$$

Writing $\dfrac{ds}{dt}$ for v and integrating again with respect to the time we have

$$s = ut + \tfrac{1}{2}at^2 + \text{constant.}$$

If the distance is measured from the point where $t = 0$, the constant is zero and we have

$$s = ut + \tfrac{1}{2}at^2 \qquad (2)$$

Writing $v\dfrac{dv}{ds} = a$, we have on integrating with respect to s

$$\tfrac{1}{2}v^2 = as + \text{constant}.$$

If u is the initial velocity when $s = 0$, the value of the constant is $\tfrac{1}{2}u^2$ and we have

$$v^2 = u^2 + 2as \qquad (3)$$

From (1) $$a = \frac{v - u}{t}.$$

Substituting for a in (2) we have

$$s = ut + \tfrac{1}{2}(v - u)t,$$

that is $$s = \frac{u + v}{2}t. \qquad (4)$$

These four equations determine the motion of a particle or of a body moving in a straight line with *constant* acceleration, and do not apply to motion with variable acceleration.

If we think of these equations as applying to a definite period of motion, so that u is the initial velocity, v the final velocity, t the time and s the distance moved, it will be seen that each of the above equations involves four of the five quantities u, v, s, t, a. Hence, if any three of these quantities are known, the other two may be determined from the appropriate equations. Each of the above equations omits one of the four quantities v, s, t, a; an equation omitting u, which is less commonly used, may be found by eliminating u between any two of the equations, giving

$$s = vt - \tfrac{1}{2}at^2 \qquad (5)$$

Hence, the solution of problems involving constant acceleration in a straight line depends on choosing the appropriate equations to determine the unknown quantities for each stage of the motion. It is useful to draw up a table showing which of the quantities are known. Thus in a particular case the information might be summarised as follows:

$$u = 10 \text{ m/sec}$$

$$v = ?$$

$$a = 2 \text{ m/sec}^2$$

$$s = ?$$

$$t = 3 \text{ sec}.$$

In this case the quantities v and s are unknown, and appropriate equations
are $$v = u + at,$$

$$s = ut + \tfrac{1}{2}at^2,$$

giving $$v = 16 \text{ m/sec}, \ s = 39 \text{ m}.$$

Example 1. *A ball is thrown vertically upwards with a velocity of* 20 *m/sec. Find its height when it is moving at the rate of* 12 *m/sec and find the time between the instants at which it is at this height.* (O.C.)

If the distance be measured upwards from the ground, the acceleration due to gravity, which we shall take as 9·80 m/sec², is downwards and therefore negative.

We have for the motion:

$$u = 20 \text{ m/sec}$$
$$v = 12 \text{ m/sec}$$
$$a = -9·80 \text{ m/sec}^2$$
$$s = ?$$
$$t = ?$$

To find s we use the equation $v^2 = u^2 + 2fs$, and we have

$$s = \frac{20^2 - 12^2}{2 \times 9·80} = 13·1 \text{ m.}$$

The time is found by using the equation $s = ut + \frac{1}{2}at^2$, and we have

$$13·1 = 20t - 4·90t^2$$

giving

$$t = 0·82 \text{ or } 3·26 \text{ sec.}$$

Thus there are two values of t at which the height is 13·1 m, and the time between the two instants is 2·44 seconds.

Example 2. *A car moving with constant acceleration passes three posts A, B, C on a straight road. The distance from A to B is* 15 *m and from B to C* 20 *m. The car takes* 6 *sec to go from A to B and* 5 *sec to go from B to C. Find the acceleration of the car and its distance from A when its speed is* 5·5 *m/sec.*

Let V m/sec be the initial velocity of the car and α m/sec² its acceleration. We have for the two stages A to B and A to C:

A to B	A to C
$u = V$ m/sec	$u = V$ m/sec
$v = ?$	$v = ?$
$a = \alpha$ m/sec²	$a = \alpha$ m/sec²
$s = 15$ m	$s = 35$ m
$t = 6$ sec	$t = 11$ sec

Applying the formula $s = ut + \frac{1}{2}at^2$ to each of the stages A to B and A to C we have

$$15 = 6V + 18\alpha,$$
$$35 = 11V + 60·5\alpha.$$

Hence,

$$\alpha = \tfrac{3}{11} \text{ m/sec}^2,$$
$$V = 1\tfrac{15}{22} \text{ m/sec.}$$

If the speed be 5·5 m/sec at a point X, we have for the stage A to X,

$$u = 37/22 \text{ m/sec}$$
$$v = 5·5 \text{ m/sec}$$
$$a = 3/11 \text{ m/sec}^2$$
$$s = ?$$
$$t = ?$$

Using the formula $v^2 = u^2 + 2as$ we have

$$2 \times \tfrac{3}{11} \times s = (5 \cdot 5)^2 - (1 \cdot 682)^2$$
$$s = 50 \cdot 27 \text{ m}.$$

Hence, the speed is $5 \cdot 5$ m/sec at $50 \cdot 27$ m from A.

Example 3. *An electric train starts from rest at a station and comes to rest at the next station, one kilometre away, in 3 min. It has first a uniform acceleration for 40 sec, then a constant speed, and it is brought to rest by a constant retardation for 20 sec. Find the maximum speed of the train and its retardation when coming to rest.*

If the train has acceleration α m/sec² from A to B, zero acceleration from B to C, and retardation β m/sec² from C to D, we have for the three stages:

A to B	B to C	C to D
$u = 0$	$u = ?$	$u = ?$
$v = ?$	$v = ?$	$v = 0$
$a = \alpha$ m/sec²	$a = 0$	$a = -\beta$ m/sec²
$t = 40$ sec	$t = 120$ sec	$t = 20$ sec
$s = ?$	$s = ?$	$s = ?$

Stage A to B gives

$$v = 40\alpha,$$
$$s = 800\alpha.$$

In stage B to C, putting $u = v = 40\alpha$ we have

$$s = 4800\alpha.$$

In stage C to D, putting $u = 40\alpha$ we have

$$\beta = 2\alpha,$$
$$s = 400\alpha.$$

Hence, the total distance A to D is 6000α, and this distance is 1000 m.

Hence

$$\alpha = 0 \cdot 167 \text{ m/sec}^2$$
$$\beta = 2\alpha = 0 \cdot 333 \text{ m/sec}^2$$
$$v = 40\alpha = 6 \cdot 67 \text{ m/sec}.$$

Hence, the retardation is $0 \cdot 333$ m/sec² and the maximum velocity $6 \cdot 67$ m/sec.

EXERCISES 13 (b)

1. The driver of a train travelling at 80 km/h sees on the same track 200 m in front of him a slow train travelling in the same direction at 25 km/h. What is the least retardation that must be applied to the faster train so as to avoid a collision? (O.C.)

2. A train takes 4 min 7·5 sec between two stations 3 kilometres apart starting from and finishing at rest. The acceleration is uniform for 45 sec, and the retardation is uniform for the last 30 sec, the speed being constant for the remaining time. Find this speed and also the values of the acceleration and retardation. (O.C.)

3. A car is timed to take 15 sec over 200 m and 10 sec over the next 200 m. Assuming constant acceleration, what is the speed of the car at the end of the observed motion? (O.C.)

4. Two stations A and B are 500 m apart. A train starting from A is uniformly accelerated for 15 sec to a speed of 45 km/h, which is maintained until the train is 100 m from B when it slows up uniformly and stops at B. Find the values of the accelerations and the time taken.   (O.C.)

5. A train starts from A with uniform acceleration $\frac{1}{6}$ m/sec². After 2 min the train attains full speed and moves uniformly for 11 min. It is then brought to rest at B by a constant retardation 5/3 m/sec². Find the distance AB.   (O.C.)

6. A particle is projected vertically upwards, and at the same instant another is let fall to meet it. Show that, if the particles have equal speeds when they impinge, one of them has travelled three times as far as the other.   (O.C.)

7. A body moving in a straight line traverses distances AB, BC, CD of 153 m, 215 m and 217 m respectively in successive intervals of 3, 5 and 7 sec. Show that these facts indicate a uniform retardation, and find the time and distance traversed when the body comes to rest.   (O.C.)

8. A particle traverses a distance of 300 metres in a straight line at an average speed of 4 m/sec starting from rest and finishing at rest. It moves with a uniform acceleration for 10 sec and is brought to rest by a uniform retardation in the last 20 sec of its motion and moves with a uniform speed during the rest of its motion. Find the acceleration and retardation.

9. A car starting from rest at A travels to B with uniform acceleration $\frac{22}{135}$ m/sec²; from B to C its speed is constant; at C the brakes are applied, the subsequent retardation being uniform and equal to $\frac{11}{135}$ m/sec². If the total distance travelled is 2860 m and the total time is $5\frac{1}{2}$ min, find the time from B to C.   (O.C.)

10. A balloon leaves the ground with a vertical acceleration of 0·5 m/sec². How far has it risen and what is its velocity 30 sec later? If at this instant some ballast is dropped, how long will it take to reach the ground?

11. A particle moving in a straight line with constant acceleration passes a point A with a speed of 10 m/sec and reaches a point B, 105 m from A, in 6 sec. Find its speed when it is half-way between A and B.

12. A lift descends with uniform acceleration 0·5 m/sec² for the first part of its journey and a uniform retardation of 0·75 m/sec² for the remainder. The total time taken is 8 sec. Find the distance from start to stop.

13. A car running at 50 m/sec has a constant retardation for 10 sec followed by a constant acceleration for t sec, the acceleration and retardation being each 2 m/sec². Find t if the distance gone in the $(10 + t)$ sec is the same as it would have been if the original speed had not changed.

14. A body falls freely from a point O, passing three points A, B and C, the distances AB and BC being equal. The time from A to B is 2 sec and from B to C 1 sec. Find the distance AB.

15. A projectile leaves the muzzle of a gun with a velocity of 533 m/sec relative to the gun having travelled 2·5 m down the barrel. Assuming the acceleration to be uniform during the travel, find the time of discharge and the acceleration.

13.10 Motion in a Straight Line—Graphical Methods for Constant Acceleration

When the acceleration has a constant value the velocity at any instant is given in terms of the time by the equation $v = u + at$. Therefore, if a graph is drawn of velocity against time, it will be a straight line, and from the graph the velocity at any instant may be read off (Fig. 183).

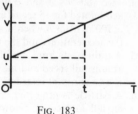

FIG. 183

The acceleration a is the slope of the straight line, and if the acceleration is negative the slope will be negative, that is, the angle made by the straight line with the positive direction of the t-axis OT will be obtuse.

The distance moved in time t is given by the formula $s = \dfrac{u+v}{2}t$. From the velocity–time graph, this is the area of the trapezium bounded by the ordinates which are the velocities u and v and included between the straight line and a length t of the axis OT. Thus for any value of t the distance is the area under the velocity time graph up to this value of t.

The graph of distance against time, called the space–time graph,

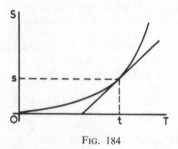

FIG. 184

may be drawn by using the formula $s = ut + \frac{1}{2}at^2$, and will be a parabola (Fig. 184). The distance gone at any instant may be read off from the curve, and its gradient at any instant, $\dfrac{ds}{dt}$, will be the velocity at that instant.

Many problems involving constant acceleration are simplified if a velocity-time graph for the motion is roughly sketched.

Example 4. *A tram takes 80 sec between two stops 367 m apart. On starting it is uniformly accelerated up to a speed of 22 km/h and maintains this speed until it is brought to a stop by a constant retardation. If the time occupied in accelerating is twice that occupied in retarding find the acceleration and the distance run at full speed.*

The velocity-time graph is as shown (Fig. 185).

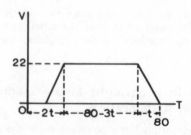

FIG. 185

If $2t$ be the time of acceleration and t sec the time of retardation, the area under the graph is

$$11 \times 2t + 22(80 - 3t) + 11 \times t,$$

$$= 1\,760 - 33t.$$

This divided by 3600 is the distance gone, which is 0·367 km, therefore

$$3\,600 \times 0\cdot367 = 1\,760 - 33t,$$

$$t = 13\cdot3 \text{ sec.}$$

Since, a velocity of 22 km/h is acquired in 26·6 sec, the acceleration is 0·23 m/sec². The distance travelled at full speed is $22(80 - 3t) \times 1\,000/3\,600 = 245$ m.

13.11 Graphical Methods for Variable Acceleration

When the acceleration is not constant, each of the quantities v, s, a will vary with the time t, and graphs may be drawn based on observations connecting any two of these four quantities. The distance, velocity or acceleration may be plotted against the time as the independent variable, and velocity or acceleration plotted against the distance as the independent variable. It is also possible, although less usual, to have the acceleration plotted against the velocity. The particular graph that will be drawn depends on the set of observational values obtained, but, as we shall see, if one of the above graphs can be drawn, all the values of the other quantities can be deduced from it.

(1) *Distance–Time Graph*

If an accurate graph of distance against time is drawn, the velocity for any value of t, $\dfrac{ds}{dt}$, is the gradient of the graph for that value of t (Fig. 186). This may be measured by drawing a tangent to the graph and

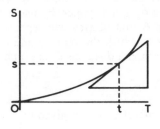

Fig. 186

measuring the gradient, that is, the tangent of the angle of slope, in units of distance divided by units of time. Thus the velocity for various values of t may be found and a velocity–time graph drawn.

(2) *Velocity–Time Graph*

If the velocity is plotted against the time, the acceleration for any value of t, $\dfrac{dv}{dt}$, is the gradient of the graph for that value of t, and may be measured by drawing a tangent to the graph (Fig. 187). Thus the

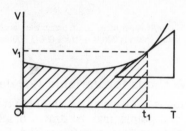

Fig. 187

acceleration for various values of t may be found and an acceleration–time graph drawn.

Since
$$\frac{ds}{dt} = v,$$

the distance gone between the times $t = 0$ and $t = t_1$ is

$$s = \int_0^{t_1} v \, dt.$$

This integral is the area under the velocity–time curve between these values of t. Hence the distance gone may be found for various values of t by finding the area under the velocity–time curve. The area may be found by counting the squares on graph paper, by using Simpson's rule or by the use of a planimeter. A unit of area will represent a certain distance, depending on the scales to which the velocity and time are plotted. Thus from the velocity–time graph a distance–time graph may be deduced.

(3) *Acceleration–Time Graph*

Since $\dfrac{dv}{dt} = a$ the velocity at time t_1 is given by

$$v = \int_0^{t_1} a \, dt.$$

Hence, the velocity may be found for various values of t by calculating the area under the acceleration–time curve up to each value of t (Fig. 188).

It should be noticed that between values of t for which the acceleration is negative the area under the graph represents a decrease in velocity,

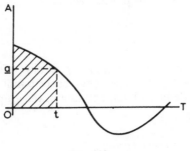

Fig. 188

and therefore must be taken as negative. Thus from the acceleration–time graph a velocity–time graph may be deduced.

The procedure of drawing tangents to a graph and measuring gradients is called *differentiating* the graph. That of calculating areas under a graph is called *integrating* the graph. The integration of a graph may be done with considerable accuracy, but differentiation involves drawing tangents to the curve by eye and is a less accurate procedure.

(4) *Velocity–Distance Graphs*

If a set of values of velocity and distance are given we may plot a graph of $\frac{1}{2}v^2$ against s (Fig. 189) or, alternatively, a graph of $\frac{1}{v}$ against s (Fig. 190).

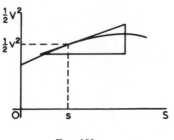

Fig. 189

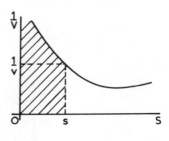

Fig. 190

In the first case, since

$$a = v\frac{dv}{ds} = \frac{d}{ds}\left(\frac{1}{2}v^2\right),$$

the gradient of the graph represents the acceleration, and values of the acceleration for various distances may be deduced.

In the second case, if $\frac{1}{v}$ is plotted against s

$$\int \frac{1}{v} ds = \int \frac{dt}{ds} \cdot ds = t,$$

and hence the area under the curve up to any value of s gives the time corresponding to this distance. Thus corresponding values of distance and time may be deduced by integration of the graph.

(5) *Acceleration–Distance Graph*

We have
$$\int a \, ds = \int v \frac{dv}{ds} \cdot ds,$$
$$\int v \, dv,$$
$$= \frac{1}{2} v^2.$$

Therefore, the area under the graph (Fig. 191) between any two values of s gives the change in the value of $\frac{1}{2} v^2$.

Thus
$$\int_0^{s_1} a \, ds = \frac{1}{2} v^2 - \frac{1}{2} u^2,$$

where u is the velocity at $s = 0$ and v the velocity at $s = s_1$. Thus cor-

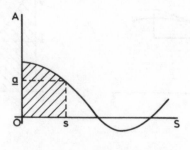

FIG. 191

responding values of velocity and distance may be found from the graph.

(6) *Acceleration–Velocity Graph*

In this case by plotting $\frac{1}{a}$ against v we have

$$\int \frac{1}{a}dv = \int \frac{dt}{dv}dv = t,$$

and hence the area under the graph (Fig. 192) gives the time, and corre-

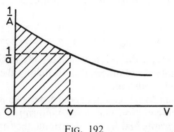

Fig. 192

sponding values of velocity and time may be found by integration of the graph.

Example 5. *Simultaneous values of speed and time for a train are given in the table below. Draw the speed-time curve, and find the acceleration at the end of the second minute and the distance in kilometres passed over in attaining a speed of 50 km/h.*

Time (seconds)	0	50	100	150	200	250	300
Speed (km/h)	0	24·6	36·3	43·7	48·3	51·3	53·5

The graph is as shown in Fig. 193.
The tangent is drawn for $t = 120$, and its gradient is an increase of 25 km/h in 175 sec. Therefore the acceleration is

$$\tfrac{25}{175} \times \tfrac{5}{18} \text{ m/sec}^2 = 0.59 \text{ m/sec}^2.$$

At $t = 225$ sec the speed is 50 km/h.

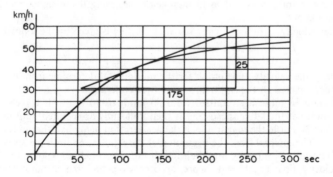

Fig. 193

Of each square under the graph one side represents 5 km/h or $5 \times \frac{5}{18}$ m/sec and one side represents 25 sec. Therefore the area of one small square represents

$$5 \times \frac{5}{18} \times 25 = \frac{625}{18} \text{ m} = 34 \cdot 7 \text{ m}.$$

There are approximately 67 small squares of area under the graph between $t = 0$ and $t = 225$, and hence the distance passed is

$$67 \times 0 \cdot 0347 = 2 \cdot 32 \text{ kilometres}.$$

EXERCISES 13 (c)

1. A body starting from rest moves in a straight line, and the following observations are taken:

Time	0	0·2	0·4	0·6	0·8	1·0	1·2	1·4	1·6 seconds
Distance	0	0·55	2·1	4·8	8·5	13·2	18·5	23·7	29·0 centimetres

Determine from a graph the velocity of the body in centimetres per second at the middle of each interval of time and show that for the first second the acceleration is approximately constant.   (O.C.)

2. A motor car is found to increase its speed from 8 to 80 kilometres per hour in 40 sec. Find the acceleration (supposed uniform) in centimetre–second units. Plot a space–time graph, and from it determine the time taken to travel the last 300 metres of the movement observed in the 40 sec.   (O.C.)

3. A train starting from rest is timed over successive distances of 220 m with the following result:

Distance in metres	220	440	660	880	1100	1320
Time in seconds	45	63·6	78	90	100·6	110·2

Plot a space–time graph and a velocity–time graph. What is the average value of the acceleration and at what point was the velocity 52·8 km/h?   (O.C.)

4. The velocity–time diagram of a particle consists of two straight lines AB, BC, where the coordinates of A, B, C are (0, 10), (10, 10), (20, 25), the first coordinate in each case being the time in seconds and the second coordinate the velocity in metres per second. Describe the motion of the particle and find the total distance covered.   (O.C.)

5. A train approaching a station does two successive quarters of a kilometre in 16 and 20 sec respectively. Assuming the retardation to be uniform, draw a graph to show the variation of the velocity with the time during the 36 sec. Prove that the train runs 334 m further before stopping if the same retardation is maintained.   (O.C.)

6. The velocity v km/h of a car t sec after starting is given by the following table:

t	0	5	10	15	20	25	30
v	0	5·8	8·7	10·7	12·2	13·3	14·0

Draw the velocity–time graph for the motion and determine from it (i) the distance covered by the car in 25 sec, (ii) the acceleration when $t = 10$.

7. A train is uniformly retarded from 30 km/h to 10 km/h. It travels a certain distance at the latter speed, and is then uniformly accelerated until its speed is again 30 km/h, the magnitude of the acceleration being half that of the retardation. The interval from the beginning of the retardation until the speed is again 30 km/h is $7\frac{1}{2}$ minutes, and the total distance covered is 2 kilometres. Sketch a velocity–time graph and, hence or otherwise, find the distance travelled at 10 km/h.   (L.U.)

8. The acceleration of a train starting from rest increases uniformly from 0.2 m/sec^2 to 0.7 m/sec^2 in the first 5 sec, it then increases uniformly to 0.9 m/sec^2 in the next 5 sec and remains constant at this value for 10 sec; the acceleration then decreases uniformly to zero in 5 sec. Draw an acceleration–time graph and find the velocity at the end of 25 sec. Draw a velocity–time graph and find the distance gone in the 25 sec.

9. The velocity of a particle at points measured along a straight line from a fixed point are given in the following table:

s m.	0	10	20	30	40	50
v m/sec.	30	20	15	12	10	8.57

Show that the graph $\dfrac{1}{v}$ against s is approximately a straight line and find the time to traverse the distance of 50 m.

10. The acceleration of a car starting from rest increases uniformly with the distance from an initial value of 0.25 m/sec^2 to a value 1.0 m/sec^2 at the end of 75 m. Draw a graph of the acceleration against the distance and find the velocity given to the car in this distance.

EXERCISES 13 (d)

1. A bicycle is travelling along a horizontal road at 10 km/h. If, at any instant, A is the highest point and P is any other point of the wheel, show that the velocity of P is along the line AP. Find also the speed and directions of motion of the points at the extremities of the horizontal diameter of the wheel. (L.U.)

2. Two trains, each of length 90 m, moving in opposite directions along parallel lines, meet when their speeds are 60 km/h and 40 km/h. If their accelerations are 30 cm/sec^2 and 15 cm/sec^2 respectively, find the time they take to pass each other. (L.U.)

3. A particle moving in a straight line with uniform acceleration describes 17 m in the third second of its motion and 29 m in the sixth second. Find its initial speed and the distance described in the tenth second. (L.U.)

4. A particle is projected vertically upwards with a velocity of 30 m/sec, and two seconds later another particle is projected vertically upwards from the same point with a velocity of 22 m/sec. Find the height above the point of projection at which they meet and the time which has then elapsed since the projection of the first particle. (L.U.)

5. Two particles A and B pass a point at the same instant in the same direction. A is moving with velocity u_1 and retardation f_1, and B with velocity $u_2(< u_1)$ and retardation $f_2(< f_1)$. Show that B will overtake A after a time $\dfrac{2(u_1 - u_2)}{f_1 - f_2}$ and find the greatest distance between the particles during this interval. (L.U.)

6. Prove that if a particle starts from rest and moves with constant acceleration, the difference between the distances traversed in successive seconds is constant. If the distance traversed in the seventh second from rest is 52 m, find the distance traversed in the tenth second. (L.U.)

7. A particle moving in a straight line with constant acceleration passes in succession through A, B, C. The time taken from A to B is t_1 and from B to C is t_2; $AB = a$, $BC = b$. Prove that the acceleration of the particle is $2(bt_1 - at_2)/t_1 t_2(t_1 + t_2)$, and find the velocity at B. (L.U.)

8. A cyclist A riding at 16 km/h is overtaken and passed by B riding at 19·2 km/h. If A immediately increases his speed with uniform acceleration, show that he will catch B when his speed is 22·4 km/h. If when he has increased his speed to 20·8 km/h he continues to ride at this speed and catches B after he has gone 200 m, find his acceleration. (L.U.)

9. A point moving in a straight line covers 12 m, 18 m and 42 m in successive intervals of 3, 2 and 3 sec. Prove that these distances are consistent with the supposition that the point is moving with uniform acceleration. (L.U.)

10. Prove that if a particle moves with uniform acceleration, the spaces described in successive equal intervals of time are in arithmetical progression. It is observed that a particle describes 396·9 metres in 3 sec, 392·0 metres in the next 4 sec, and 269·5 metres in the next 5 sec. Show that this is consistent with uniform retardation and find the time before it comes to rest. (L.U.)

11. The two ends of a train moving with constant acceleration pass a certain point with velocities u and v. Find in terms of u and v what proportion of the length of the train will have passed the point after a time equal to half that taken by the train to pass it. (L.U.)

12. A train starting from rest travels the first part of its journey with constant acceleration f, the second part with constant speed v and the third part to rest with constant retardation f'. If the average speed for the whole journey is $\frac{7}{8}v$, show that the train is travelling at constant speed for three-quarters of the time. Find also what fraction of the whole distance is described with constant speed. (L.U.)

13. A train has a maximum speed of 90 km/h. It can accelerate to this speed in 5 min and stop from this speed in 500 m. Assuming uniform acceleration and deceleration, determine the minimum time taken to travel from one stop to another 18 km distant if over the central mile the speed must not exceed 18 km/h, but is unlimited over the remaining portions. (Q.E.)

14. The cage of a pit performs the first part of its descent with uniform acceleration f and the remainder with uniform retardation $2f$. Prove that if h is the depth of the shaft and t the time of descent, $h = \frac{1}{3}ft^2$. (L.U.)

15. A cage goes down a mine-shaft 750 m deep in 45 sec. For the first quarter of the distance only, the speed is being uniformly accelerated, and during the last quarter uniformly retarded, the acceleration and retardation being equal. Find the uniform speed of the cage over the centre portion of the shaft. (L.U.)

16. A particle moving in a straight line with uniform acceleration f passes a certain point with velocity u. Three seconds afterwards another particle moving in the same straight line with constant acceleration $\frac{4}{3}f$ passes the same point with velocity $\frac{1}{3}u$. The first particle is overtaken by the second when their velocities are respectively 27 and 31 m/sec. Find the values of u and f and the distance travelled from the point. (L.U.)

17. If a sprinter can start with a velocity of 20 ft/sec and run with uniform acceleration, find graphically the greatest speed attained in running 100 yd in 10 sec, and the necessary acceleration. (L.U.)

18. The maximum possible acceleration of a body is 1 m/sec^2 and its maximum possible retardation is 3 m/sec^2. What is the least time in which it can travel 1 km from rest to rest? (L.U.)

19. A block falls from a mast-head, and is observed to take $\frac{2}{5}$ sec in falling from the deck to the bottom of the hold, a distance of 10 m. Calculate the height of the mast-head above the deck. (L.U.)

20. A particle is projected vertically upwards with a velocity of u m/sec and after t sec another particle is projected upwards from the same point with the same initial velocity. Prove that they will meet at a height of $\dfrac{4u^2 - g^2 t^2}{8g}$.   (L.U.)

21. A man sees a bus 100 m away starting from rest with constant acceleration. He then runs after it with constant speed and just catches it in one minute. Determine the speed of the man and the acceleration of the bus. If the man's speed is 2·5 m/sec find in yards the nearest he can get to the bus.   (L.U.)

22. A particle moves for 4 sec in a straight line under a constant acceleration f and describes 52 m. The acceleration then ceases and the particle describes a further 48 m in 3 sec. The particle is then brought to rest by a constant retardation $2f$. Find the initial velocity of the particle, its retardation and the total distance described.   (L.U.)

23. A train starts from rest with a constant acceleration of 6 cm/sec² which is maintained for 3 min. Steam is then gradually shut off, thereby reducing the acceleration at a uniform rate until the train is running at full speed 5 min after starting. The brakes are then applied and produce a retardation which increases uniformly until the train is brought to rest in 2·5 min more.

Draw the acceleration–time graph and record (i) the value of full speed, (ii) the value of the retardation at the instant of stopping. Using the same time-axis sketch the velocity–time graph for the journey.   (L.U.)

24. A train starts from a station with an acceleration 0·2 m/sec² which decreases uniformly with the time for 4 min, at the end of which time the train is running at full speed. The train is then subject to a constant retardation which brings it to rest at the next station in $1\frac{1}{2}$ min. Draw the acceleration–time graph, finding the values of full speed and the constant retardation. Use the graph, or any other method, to find the speed of the train at the end of each successive minute.   (L.U.)

25. The graph showing the velocity of a vehicle (v m/sec), as a function of the distance (s m) it has travelled from an initial point, is a straight line joining the points $s = 0$, $v = 10$ and $s = 100$, $v = 20$.

Find the time the vehicle takes to travel the 100 m, and its acceleration at $s = 0$ and at $s = 100$.   (Q.E.)

CHAPTER 14

RELATIVE MOTION; PARABOLIC MOTION

14.1 Resultant Velocity

When we speak of the velocity of a body we mean its rate of displacement with respect to some point which we regard as fixed. The fixed point may be a point on the surface of the earth, although this point is moving, due to the earth's rotation and to its motion about the sun. The point we regard as fixed may equally well be some point in the heavens or a point in a moving ship or vehicle. Thus any velocity which we can observe is a velocity relative to some point.

When a body is moving through the air or through water the velocity most easily observed is its velocity relative to the air or water. Thus the indicator on an aeroplane shows its air speed, that is, its velocity relative to the air. If the air has itself a certain speed the velocity of the aeroplane

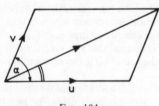

FIG. 194

relative to the ground is the resultant of its air speed and the velocity of the air, and this resultant may be found by the parallelogram of velocities. In the same way the velocity of a boat or of a swimmer is usually measured with respect to the water, and the velocity relative to the surface of the earth is the resultant of the velocity with respect to the water and the velocity of the water. If an aeroplane has an air speed u in a certain direction, and the air, that is to say, the wind, has a velocity v in a direction making an angle α with the direction of the air speed (Fig. 194), then the resultant velocity of the aeroplane with respect to the ground will be

$\sqrt{u^2+v^2+2uv\cos\alpha}$ in the direction of the diagonal of the parallelogram formed by the velocities u and v, that is, in a direction making an angle

$$\tan^{-1}\left(\frac{v\sin\alpha}{u+v\cos\alpha}\right)$$

with the direction of the air speed.

Hence, for an aeroplane to move along a certain course the aeroplane must be headed in such a direction that the resultant of its speed and the velocity of the wind will be directed along the given course. The line along which the aeroplane must be steered to follow a certain course may be found graphically. Thus, let a line AB represent the velocity of the wind v in magnitude and direction, and AX the course to be followed

(Fig. 195). Then, describing an arc of a circle with centre B and radius BC proportional to the air speed u to cut AX in C, we have AC as the resultant of u and v along the given course. The direction of the air speed and the

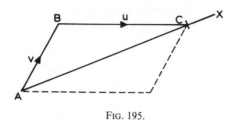

FIG. 195.

resultant velocity may also be found by calculation from the triangle ABC, of which two sides, AB and BC, and the angle BAC are known.

Example 1. *The wind is blowing from due west at 20 km/h. An aeroplane whose air speed is 100 km/h flies from its base X to a point Y, 40 km east and 80 km north of X, and then returns to its base, both journeys being in a straight line. Find the direction in which it is headed on the outward and inward journeys, and the times for the journeys.*

Let ABC be a triangle of velocities (Fig. 196) for the outward journey.
$AB = 20$ km/h, $BC = 100$ km/h, $AC = V$ km/h,

$$BAC = \tan^{-1}2 = 63° 26'.$$

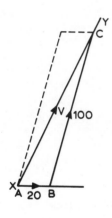

FIG. 196.

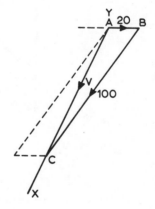

FIG. 197.

Then

$$\frac{100}{\sin 63° 26'} = \frac{20}{\sin ACB} = \frac{V}{\sin ABC}.$$

Hence, $ACB = 10° 18'$, $ABC = 106° 16'$, $V = 107·4$ km/h.

The direction is therefore N. 16° 16′ E., and the resultant velocity 107·4 km/h.

The distance is $\sqrt{80^2 + 40^2} = 89·44$ km.

$$\text{the time } \frac{89·44}{107·4} = 0·833 \text{ h.}$$

$$= 50 \text{ min approximately.}$$

On the return journey $BAC = 180° - 63° 26'$ (Fig. 197), and

$$\frac{100}{\sin 63° 26'} = \frac{20}{\sin ACB} = \frac{V}{\sin ABC}$$

$$ACB = 10° 18',$$

$$ABC = 53° 08',$$

$$V = 89·45 \text{ km/h,}$$

and the time is approximately 1 hour.

Example 2. *A stream with a current running at 4 km/h is 250 m wide between parallel banks. A boat whose speed in still water is 6 km/h wishes to cross. In what direction should it be headed so as to cross the stream (a) in the least possible time, (b) to a point directly opposite its starting point? Find the time in each case and the distance moved downstream in case (a).*

Let the boat be headed so as to make an angle α with the direction of the stream (Fig. 198). Then its velocity is the resultant of 6 km/h in this direction and 4 km/h downstream.

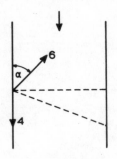

Fig. 198.

The component of its resultant velocity perpendicular to the stream is $6 \sin \alpha$ and along the stream $4 - 6 \cos \alpha$.

$$\text{Hence, the time is} \qquad \frac{\frac{1}{4}}{6 \sin \alpha} = \frac{1}{24 \sin \alpha} \text{ hours.}$$

For (a) the time must be a minimum, therefore $\sin \alpha = 1$ and the time is $\frac{1}{24}$ h $= 2·5$ min. In this time the distance moved downstream is

$$\frac{4 - 6 \cos \alpha}{24} = \frac{1}{6} \text{ km.}$$

For (b) the component of the resultant velocity downstream must be zero, therefore

$$4 - 6\cos\alpha = 0,$$

$$\cos\alpha = \tfrac{2}{3},$$

$$\alpha = 48°\ 11'.$$

The time is
$$\frac{1}{24\sin\alpha} = 0\cdot 0559 \text{ hours.}$$

$$= 3\cdot 35 \text{ min.}$$

14.2 Relative Velocity

If two bodies A and B are moving along a straight line in the same direction with velocities u and v respectively, where $u > v$, the distance between the bodies is increasing at the rate $u - v$, and this is therefore the velocity of A relative to B. If B is moving in the opposite direction to A with velocity v, the distance between them is increasing at the rate $u + v$, and this is the relative velocity of A with respect to B. In either case the relative velocity of A with respect to B is the sum of A's velocity and B's velocity reversed.

This is also true if A and B are moving in parallel straight lines. The distance between them measured perpendicularly to the direction of motion is unchanged; measured along the direction of motion it increases at the rate $u - v$ if they are moving in the same direction, $u + v$ if they are moving in opposite directions. Hence, the relative velocity of A with respect to B is independent of the relative positions of the bodies.

Suppose now that A and B are two ships moving on the surface of the sea with velocities u and v respectively in any two directions. The relative velocity of A with respect to B is the rate at which their relative position is changing. To find this relative velocity we may imagine a current to set in affecting both ships, of such magnitude and direction that it would bring B to rest. The current would therefore have a velocity v in a direction opposite to that of B's motion. The velocity of A would then be the resultant of its velocity u and the velocity of the current, that is, the resultant of A's velocity and B's velocity reversed. This current would not alter the relative positions of the ships, but it would bring B to rest, and A's velocity relative to B would be the same as its velocity relative to the surface of the earth.

Hence, for any two bodies A and B the relative velocity of A with respect to B may be found by adding to A's velocity B's velocity reversed. To find this relative velocity it is not necessary to know the positions of the bodies, but only the magnitudes and directions of their velocities.

It is evident that the relative velocity of B with respect to A is equal and opposite to the relative velocity of A with respect to B.

If the relative velocity of A with respect to B is known and the velocity of one body is known, the velocity of the other may be easily found.

14.3 Units

In problems involving the relative velocities of ships the unit of length is usually taken as a nautical or sea-mile, which is 1·853 km or 6080 ft. A speed of one sea-mile per hour is called a speed of one knot. The divisions of a sea-mile are in decimal units, thus

$$1 \text{ fathom } = 6·08 \text{ feet,}$$
$$1 \text{ shackle } = 10 \text{ fathoms,}$$
$$1 \text{ cable } = 10 \text{ shackles,}$$
$$1 \text{ sea-mile } = 10 \text{ cables.}$$

Also $1 \text{ knot } = 0·515 \text{ m/sec}$

$$= 1·15 \text{ mph approximately.}$$

Example 3. *To an observer in a train travelling due east at 40 km/h an aeroplane appears to be travelling due north at 75 km/h. Find the true course and speed of the aeroplane.* (O.C.)

If the true course and speed be in a direction N. $\alpha°$ E. at v km/h (Fig. 199), the relative

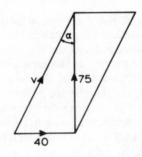

Fig. 199.

velocity of the aeroplane with respect to the train is the resultant of this velocity and the train's velocity reversed. This relative velocity is the velocity observed from the train, and is 75 km/h.

Hence $$v^2 = 40^2 + 75^2,$$
$$v = 85 \text{ km/h.}$$
$$\tan \alpha = \tfrac{40}{75} = 0·5333,$$
$$\alpha = 28° 04'.$$

14.4 Relative Path

If the positions of two bodies A and B at some instant are P and Q respectively, and the relative velocity of A with respect to B is known, the *relative path* of A with respect to B is a straight line through P in

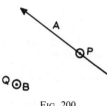

FIG. 200.

the direction of the relative velocity (Fig. 200). Hence, all questions of the nearest approach of two bodies may be dealt with by assuming B to be stationary at Q and A to move along the relative path with the relative velocity. This follows from the fact that if the same additional velocity were given to both bodies, and as a result B were brought to rest, the relative path would be A's real path.

The shortest distance apart of the bodies is therefore the perpendicular distance from Q on to the relative path.

Example 4. *A ship A is 5 sea-miles due north of a ship B. A is steaming due west at 15 knots and B is steaming due north-west at 10 knots. Find the distance and the time of their nearest approach to each other.*

The relative velocity of B with respect to A is the resultant of 10 knots north-west and 15 knots east (Fig. 201).

This is

$$V = \sqrt{15^2 + 10^2 + 2 \cdot 15 \cdot 10 \cdot \cos 135°},$$

$$= 10 \cdot 58 \text{ knots.}$$

The direction of this velocity is

$$\tan^{-1}\left(\frac{5\sqrt{2}}{15 - 5\sqrt{2}}\right) = 41° \, 44' \text{ north of east.}$$

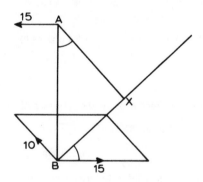

FIG. 201.

Hence, if X be the nearest point to A on the relative path BX

$$AX/AB = \cos 41° \, 44'.$$

$$AX = 3 \cdot 73 \text{ sea-miles.}$$

Also

$$BX = 5 \sin 41° \, 44',$$

$$= 3 \cdot 328 \text{ sea-miles.}$$

This distance is covered at 10·58 knots in time

$$\frac{3 \cdot 328}{10 \cdot 58} \text{ h} = 0 \cdot 3146 \text{ h} = 18 \cdot 88 \text{ min.}$$

Example 5. *Two cars are running towards a cross-roads along straight roads which include an angle of 105°. Their speeds are 60 km/h and 30 km/h respectively, and the second car passes the cross-roads 2 min after the first. What is the relative velocity of the second car with respect to the first? What is the shortest distance between the cars, and how far is each from the cross-roads when they are nearest to each other?*

When the first car is at the cross-roads, A, the second is 1 km away at B (Fig. 202). The relative velocity V is the resultant of 60 km/h and 30 km/h in directions including an angle of 75°.

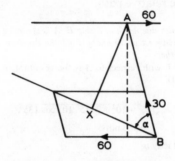

FIG. 202.

Therefore $V^2 = 60^2 + 30^2 + 2 \cdot 60 \cdot 30 \cos 75°,$

$$V = 73 \cdot 71 \text{ km/h.}$$

The angle α made by the relative path with BA is given by

$$\frac{60}{\sin \alpha} = \frac{30}{\sin (75° - \alpha)},$$

$$\alpha = 51° \, 51'.$$

The perpendicular AX from A on to the relative path is $1 \sin \alpha = 0 \cdot 7864$ km. $BX = \cos \alpha = 0 \cdot 6177$ km.

The time to cover the distance BX is

$$\frac{0 \cdot 6177 \times 60}{73 \cdot 71} = 0 \cdot 503 \text{ min.}$$

After this time the first car is 503 metres from the cross-roads, and the second car is $(1 - 0 \cdot 251)$ km = 749 metres from the cross-roads.

Example 6. *An aircraft is observed 140 km due east of A flying due west at 220 km/h to attack A. Ten minutes later a second aircraft leaves its base 40 km south-west of A to engage it and flies at 250 km/h. In what direction must it fly to intercept the first aircraft and at what distance from A may contact be expected?*

Let P and Q be the two aircraft when Q starts (Fig. 203); P is

$$140 - \frac{220}{6} = 103\tfrac{1}{3} \text{ km east of } A.$$

The relative velocity of Q with respect to P must be directly towards P.

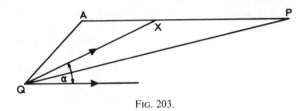

FIG. 203.

This is the resultant of P's velocity reversed, that is, 220 km/h due east, and Q's velocity of 250 km/h in a direction (say) α° north of east (Fig. 204).

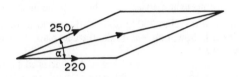

FIG. 204.

Hence the direction of the relative velocity is

$$\tan^{-1}\frac{250\sin\alpha}{220+250\cos\alpha}\text{ north of east.}$$

The direction of the relative path is

$$\tan^{-1}\frac{40\cos 45^\circ}{103\cdot3+40\sin 45}\text{ north of east.}$$

Therefore

$$\frac{220+250\cos\alpha}{250\sin\alpha}=\frac{103\cdot3+40\sin 45^\circ}{40\cos 45^\circ}=4\cdot653,$$

$$4\cdot653\sin\alpha-\cos\alpha=0\cdot88,$$

$$\alpha=23^\circ.$$

If the true path meets AP in X

$$\frac{AX}{\sin(45^\circ-\alpha)}=\frac{40}{\sin\alpha},$$

$$AX=\frac{40\sin 22^\circ}{\sin 23^\circ}=38\cdot35\text{ kilometres.}$$

Most problems in relative velocity can be solved graphically, involving as they do the finding of the resultant of two velocities, or the finding of the direction of one velocity of known magnitude when the other and the direction of the resultant velocity are known.

EXERCISES 14 (a)

1. Two football players A and B are running straight down the field in parallel lines 5 m apart. A, who has the ball, is 2 m ahead of B. If both are moving 20·3 m/sec, with what velocity (relative to himself) must A pass the ball to B in order that the pass may just not be "forward", i.e. in order that the ball may travel at right angles to the length of the field? Find also the velocity of the ball relative to the ground. (O.C.)

2. If an aeroplane travels at 100 km/h in still air, and the wind is blowing at 30 km/h from the south-west, find graphically the direction in which the pilot must steer in order to travel due north. Find also its velocity relative to the ground. (O.C.)

3. A cyclist observes that while cycling due north at 15 km/h the wind appears to come from due east, but when cycling due east at the same speed the wind appears to come from $22\frac{1}{2}°$ south of east. Determine the velocity and direction of the wind. (Q.E.)

4. A cruiser is proceeding due east at 20 knots, and a destroyer whose speed is 30 knots is 10 sea-miles due south of it. In what direction must the destroyer travel in order to meet the cruiser, and when will the meeting occur? (O.C.)

5. If an aeroplane can travel at 200 km/h in still air, and if the air is moving from the west at 80 km/h, how long will it take the aeroplane to reach a place 500 km off to the south-west? (O.C.)

6. A river 100 m wide is flowing at 4 km/h. A boat is to be rowed at 10 km/h (relative to the stream) from a point on one bank to a landing-stage on the opposite bank 50 m farther down. Give a graphical construction showing the direction in which the boat should be steered and find approximately the time taken in crossing. (O.C.)

7. An aeroplane travels in still air at 200 km/h. It starts from A to reach a point B due north 300 km away. There is a wind blowing due west at 40 km/h, but when half the distance has been covered the velocity of the wind increases to 60 km/h. Find the time taken over the flight to the nearest minute. (O.C.)

8. A steamer proceeding due west at 12 knots sights another straight ahead of it at a distance of 10 sea-miles proceeding due north at 15 knots. Find, graphically or otherwise, what will be their least distance apart in the subsequent motion. (O.C.)

9. A motor-boat with a speed of 15 knots is steered due south, but at the end of 10 min is 2 nautical miles S. 10° E. of its starting-point. Find the strength and direction of the tide. (O.C.)

10. A man swims at 3 km/h across a river 125 m wide, flowing at 5 km/h. How long will it take him if he swims so as to reach the opposite bank (a) as quickly as possible, (b) as little downstream as possible? (L.U.)

11. An aeroplane can travel at 120 km/h in still air, and the wind is blowing at 45 km/h. Compare the times taken from A to B and back again if the direction of the wind all the time is (i) A to B, (ii) at right angles to AB, (iii) at 45° to AB. (O.C.)

12. A destroyer, steaming N. 30° E. at 30 knots, observes at noon a steamer, which is steaming due north at 12 knots, and overtakes the steamer at 12.45 p.m. Find the distance and bearing of the steamer from the destroyer at noon. (O.C.)

13. Find the true course and true speed of a steamer travelling through the water at 12 knots and steering due north by the compass through a current of 3 knots

which sets south-east. Find also the direction in which the steamer should steer in order to make its true course due north, and the true speed on this course.

(O.C.)

14. A cruiser which can steam at 30 knots receives a report that an enemy vessel, steaming due north at 20 knots, is 29 nautical miles away in a direction 30° north of east. Show (i) graphically, (ii) by calculation, that the cruiser can overtake the vessel in almost exactly 2 hr. (O.C.)

15. A ship leaves a certain port and steams north-east at 15 knots; 5 hours later another ship leaves the same port and steams due west at 20 knots. Their wireless instruments can maintain communication up to 225 nautical miles; find to the nearest nautical mile the distances of the ships from the port when communication ceases. (O.C.)

16. A battleship is steaming 15 knots due north; a cruiser which steams 25 knots, is 5 nautical miles south-west, and is ordered to line up 1 nautical mile astern. Find, graphically or otherwise, the course the cruiser should steer to line up as quickly as possible. (L.U.)

17. Two ships are sailing at speeds of 10 and 12 km/h along parallel lines in the same direction. When they are opposite one another and 2 km apart, the faster ship turns its course through 30° in the direction of the other. Find how close they get to one another. (L.U.)

18. If a ship is moving north-east at 15 knots, and a second ship appears to an observer on the first to be moving due east at 7 knots, determine the actual direction and magnitude of the velocity of the second. (L.U.)

19. To an observer on a ship travelling due west at 16 km/h another ship 1 km due south appears to be travelling north-east at 12 km/h. Find the magnitude and direction of the velocity of the second ship, and the distance apart of the two ships when nearest to each other. (L.U.)

20. Two roads cross at right angles at P; a man A, walking along one of them at 6 km/h, sees another man B, walking on the other road at 8 km/h, at P when he is 100 m off. Find the velocity of A relative to B and show that they will be nearest together when A has walked 36 m. (L.U.)

21. From their point of intersection two straight roads lie respectively due east and 60° N. of E. At the same instant that a motor travelling at 35 km/h due east is at the crossing, a second motor is 5 km from it, and is travelling at 30 km/h towards it from 60° N. of E. Find by a graphical construction, or by calculation, the relative velocity of the first to the second motor. Find also when they will be at their shortest distance apart. (L.U.)

22. Two motor cars are proceeding, one on each road, towards the point of intersection of two roads which meet at an angle of 60°. If their speeds are 25 and 40 km/h, and they are respectively 350 and 200 m from the cross-roads, find their relative velocity and their distances from the cross-roads when they are nearest together. (L.U.)

23. An aeroplane A is flying horizontally due north at 250 km/h, and an aeroplane B is flying at the same height N. 35° W. at 220 km/h. B passes the point of intersection of their paths at 3 a.m., 2 min before A reaches the point. Find graphically or otherwise the shortest distance between A and B during their flight and the time at which they are nearest to one another. (L.U.)

24. A man travelling due west at 8 km/h observes that the wind appears to blow from the north. When he increases his speed to 16 km/h the wind appears to blow from the north-west. Find the speed and true direction of the wind. (L.U.)

25. PO and QO are two straight roads intersecting at right angles at O. Two cyclists A and B are riding in the directions PO and QO respectively, A at 9 km/h and B at 12 km/h. A is 2 km from O and moving towards O when B is at O. Calculate the least distance apart of the cyclists and the time after B passes O when they are nearest to each other.   (L.U.)

26. A swimmer crosses a river of width 40 m which has a uniform current. In crossing the river as quickly as possible he takes 90 sec and is carried downstream 30 m How long will it take him to swim in a straight line back to the original starting-point?   (Q.E.)

27. ABC is an equilateral triangle of side 200 km; an aeroplane flies from B towards C with a speed of 200 km/h relative to the air. When it is at a point X, 50 km from B, it changes its course so as to fly directly to A. If the wind blows at 40 km/h in the direction BC, find, graphically or otherwise, the angle through which the pilot changes his course, assuming that the aeroplane's speed relative to the air is unaltered.   (L.U.)

28. The actual directions of flight of two aeroplanes A and B moving horizontally are north-west and north-east respectively. There is a wind of 60 km/h from the east, and the velocity of each aeroplane relative to the ground is 200 km/h. Find, graphically or otherwise, the actual speed of each in still air, and the speed of A relative to B.   (L.U.)

29. A vessel A is steaming due north at a speed of 18 knots, and a vessel B is steaming south-east at a speed of 15 knots. Find, graphically or otherwise, the magnitude and direction of the velocity of A relative to B. If B is initially 30 sea-miles due north of A, find the shortest distance between the two vessels during the subsequent motion.   (L.U.)

30. An aircraft sets out to fly from one point to a second point 200 km due north. In what direction should the pilot set his course if he intends to fly at an air speed of 400 km/h and there is a wind of 100 km/h blowing from the north-east. If, when he has flown for 20 min on this course, the wind dies down to 60 km/h and he does not change course, how far from his calculated position will he be at the time when he expects to arrive over his destination?   (Q.E.)

31. A boy A is swimming due west at a speed of 0·8 m/sec; a second boy B is swimming at a constant speed in a converging direction. At one instant B is 10 m, 30° W. of N. of A and 10 sec later he is 6 m due north of A. Find by drawing or calculation the speed and direction of B.   (L.U.)

32. A man who can swim at 2 km/h wishes to cross a river 250 m wide, flowing at 3 km/h, as quickly as possible. Find, by calculation, in what direction with respect to the bank he should head and how many minutes he would take. Also calculate how far downstream from his starting-point he lands.   (L.U.)

33. An aerodrome A is 200 km due north of a point O; another aerodrome B is due east of O and the angle OBA is 30°. An aeroplane P starts from A at noon and flies with constant speed 400 km/h in a direction N. 75° E. Another aero-plane Q starts from B at noon with constant speed 300 km/h in a direction N. 15° W. Find, graphically or otherwise, the velocity of Q relative to P and the least distance between P and Q during their flight.   (L.U.)

34. A man falling vertically by parachute in a steady downpour of rain observes that when his speed is v_1 the rain appears to make an angle α with the vertical. When his speed is v_2 the rain appears to make an angle β with the vertical. Show that the rain actually falls at an angle θ with the vertical given by
$$(v_2 - v_1)\cot\theta = v_2\cot\alpha - v_1\cot\beta.$$ (L.U.)

35. A straight river between parallel banks is 250 m wide and its speed is 4 km/h. A man can row a boat at a speed of 2 km/h relative to the water. Find the direction in which the boat should be steered in order to cross the river (i) in the shortest possible time, (ii) by the shortest possible route. (L.U.)

36. Two particles P and Q move along two perpendicular lines with uniform speeds in the direction of O, the point of intersection of the lines. The speed of P is 6 cm/sec and of Q is 8 cm/sec, and the initial distances OP and OQ are 9 cm and 7 cm. Determine (i) the velocity of Q relative to P, (ii) their shortest distance apart, (iii) the times at which their distance apart is 5 cm. (L.U.)

37. To an observer in a ship steaming due west at 14 knots another ship appears to be steaming at 26 knots in the direction S. $\alpha°$ E., where $\cos \alpha = 5/13$. Find the true speed and direction of steaming of the ship observed. (L.U.)

38. When cycling at 12 km/h along a road which runs S.S.W., a cyclist finds that the wind appears to come from W.S.W. On turning into a road which runs S.E. and cycling at 10 km/h he finds that the wind appears to come from the east. Find the speed and direction of the wind. (L.U.)

39. Two bodies move in concentric circles, of centre O and radii a, b, with uniform speeds u, v in the same sense. If P, Q be the positions of the bodies at a moment when their relative velocity is along the line joining them, obtain expressions for the ratios $b:a$ and $v:u$ in terms of the angles of the triangle OPQ; and if angle $POQ = \theta$ show that

$$\cos \theta = \frac{au + bv}{bu + av}. \tag{L.U.}$$

40. A ship at A which cannot sail at more than 20 knots wishes to intercept a ship at B, 38 sea-miles due east of A, which is sailing at 24 knots in a direction 30° N. of W. Prove that in order to intercept, the first ship may steer any course that makes an angle of not more than $\tan^{-1} \frac{4}{3}$ with due north. Calculate the *least* time in minutes in which she can intercept. (L.U.)

14.5 Motion in Two Dimensions

We have defined the velocity of a particle moving on a plane curve as being a vector of magnitude $\frac{ds}{dt}$ whose direction is that of the tangent to the curve at the point considered. If the tangent makes an angle ψ with the positive direction of the x-axis and $\frac{\pi}{2} - \psi$ with the positive direction of the y-axis, the resolved parts of this velocity parallel to the axes are $\frac{ds}{dt} \cos \psi$ and $\frac{ds}{dt} \sin \psi$.

Now we have in general the differential relations between distance measured along a curve and its projection on the axes, namely

$$\frac{dx}{ds} = \cos \psi, \quad \frac{dy}{ds} = \sin \psi,$$

and hence the resolved parts of the velocity parallel to the axes are

$$\frac{dx}{ds} \cdot \frac{ds}{dt} = \frac{dx}{dt}, \text{ and } \frac{dy}{ds} \cdot \frac{ds}{dt} = \frac{dy}{dt}.$$

It is usual in dynamics to denote differentiation with respect to the time by a dot, thus

$$\dot{x} = \frac{dx}{dt}, \ \ddot{x} = \frac{d^2x}{dt^2}, \text{ etc.}$$

In this notation the components of velocity parallel to the axes of x and y are, respectively, $\dot{x}$ and $\dot{y}$ (see also § 1.15).

The acceleration of a particle is defined as a vector such that its projection in any direction is the rate of change of velocity in that direction. Thus if u, v be the components of the velocity at time t parallel to the axes of x and y respectively, and $u + \delta u, v + \delta v$ the components at time $t + \delta t$, then the components of acceleration parallel to the axes at time t are

$$\lim_{\delta t \to 0} \frac{\delta u}{\delta t} = \frac{du}{dt},$$

$$\lim_{\delta t \to 0} \frac{\delta v}{\delta t} = \frac{dv}{dt}.$$

Writing $u = \dot{x}$ and $v = \dot{y}$, we have for the components of acceleration at time t, $\ddot{x}$ and $\ddot{y}$ parallel to the axes (see also § 1.15).

The quantities $\dot{x}$, $\dot{y}$, $\ddot{x}$, $\ddot{y}$ are components of velocity and acceleration measured in the positive direction of the axes. Thus if a particle has an acceleration g parallel to the y axis and in the direction of y decreasing, that is towards the origin, we have $\ddot{y} = -g$.

14.6 Parabolic Motion

We now consider the two-dimensional motion of a particle which is projected with a given velocity in a given direction. We shall suppose the motion to take place near the earth's surface, so that the acceleration due to gravity may be taken as constant and in a constant direction throughout the motion. We shall also suppose that the resistance of the air is negligible. In practice, the resistance of the air is by no means

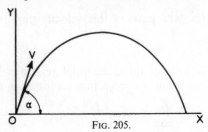

FIG. 205.

negligible when calculating the path of a body moving through it, and at high velocities may cause a retardation much greater than that due to gravity. We may, however, obtain a good approximation to the motion of a slowly moving body by neglecting the air resistance and considering the motion to be *in vacuo*. We shall see that in this case the path is a parabola.

Consider a particle projected with initial velocity V from a point O in a direction making an angle α with the horizontal. Let OX be a horizontal axis through O, and OY a vertical axis such that the motion takes place entirely in the vertical plane XOY, and the position of the particle at any instant may be described by coordinates (x, y) with reference to these axes (Fig. 205).

The only acceleration of the particle is that due to gravity, and is $-g$ parallel to the y-axis. Hence, we have for the components of acceleration parallel to the axes at any instant

$$\ddot{x} = 0, \qquad \ddot{y} = -g \tag{1}$$

Integrating these equations with respect to the time, we have

$$\dot{x} = \text{constant}, \qquad \dot{y} = -gt + \text{constant}.$$

The initial values of $\dot{x}$ and $\dot{y}$ when $t = 0$ are $V \cos \alpha$ and $V \sin \alpha$.

Hence, $\dot{x} = V \cos \alpha, \qquad \dot{y} = -gt + V \sin \alpha \tag{2}$

These equations show that the horizontal component of velocity remains constant throughout the motion, while the vertical component decreases to zero as t increases and eventually becomes negative.

Integrating again with respect to t, we have

$$x = V \cos \alpha \cdot t, \qquad y = -\tfrac{1}{2}gt^2 + V \sin \alpha \cdot t \tag{3}$$

No constants are added on integration, since x and y are both zero when $t = 0$.

These equations give the coordinates of the particle and its velocity at time t, and completely describe the motion. We may obtain the equation of the path of the particle by eliminating t between the two equations (3).

We have $t = \dfrac{x}{V \cos \alpha}$,

$$y = V \sin \alpha \frac{x}{V \cos \alpha} - \tfrac{1}{2}g\left(\frac{x}{V \cos \alpha}\right)^2,$$

that is

$$y = x \tan \alpha - \frac{g}{2V^2 \cos^2 \alpha}x^2 \tag{4}$$

This equation, being of the second degree in x only, is the equation of a parabola. Written in the form

$$-\frac{2V^2\cos^2\alpha}{g}\left(y-\frac{V^2\sin^2\alpha}{2g}\right) = \left(x - \frac{V^2\sin\alpha\cos\alpha}{g}\right)^2,$$

it may be seen that the vertex of the parabola is the point

$$\left(\frac{V^2\sin\alpha\cos\alpha}{g},\ \frac{V^2\sin^2\alpha}{2g}\right)$$

and its latus rectum $\dfrac{2V^2\cos^2\alpha}{g}$.

The Vertex

The vertex at a height $V^2\sin^2\alpha/2g$ is the highest point of the parabola. The vertical component of velocity at the vertex is therefore zero, and hence from (2) the time to the vertex is $\dfrac{V\sin\alpha}{g}$.

Range

The range is the distance measured horizontally to the point where the particle meets the horizontal through O.

At this point $y = 0$, and we have from (4)

$$0 = x\tan\alpha - \frac{gx^2}{2V^2\cos^2\alpha},$$

$$x = \frac{2V^2\cos^2\alpha\tan\alpha}{g},$$

$$= \frac{V^2\sin 2\alpha}{g}.$$

Time of Flight

The time of flight is the time taken for the range. Since the horizontal component of the velocity is constant and equal to $V\cos\alpha$, the time of flight is $\dfrac{V^2\sin 2\alpha}{g} \div V\cos\alpha = \dfrac{2V\sin\alpha}{g}$, that is, twice the time taken to reach the vertex.

Maximum Range

For a given velocity of projection V, the range varies with the angle of projection α. The range is $V^2\sin 2\alpha/g$, and this quantity has its greatest value when $\sin 2\alpha = 1$, that is, when $\alpha = 45°$. Hence the greatest range is $\dfrac{V^2}{g}$.

Angle of Projection for a Given Range

To obtain a range R with a given velocity of projection V, the angle of projection is given by

$$\frac{V^2 \sin 2\alpha}{g} = R,$$

$$\sin 2\alpha = \frac{gR}{V^2}.$$

This quantity must be less or equal to 1 if the range can be attained, and hence

$$2\alpha = \sin^{-1}\left(\frac{gR}{V^2}\right).$$

There are two values of α given by this equation, since

$$\sin 2\alpha = \sin(180° - 2\alpha),$$

and hence the angle of projection may be α or $90° - \alpha$.

The two directions α and $90° - \alpha$ are equally inclined to the horizontal and vertical respectively, and therefore to the direction required for maximum range.

Remaining Velocity

The velocity at time t has components from (2)

$$V \cos \alpha, \quad V \sin \alpha - gt.$$

Hence, the velocity is

$$\{V^2 \cos^2\alpha + (V \sin \alpha - gt)^2\}^{\frac{1}{2}},$$

$$= \{V^2 - 2V \sin \alpha . gt + g^2 t^2\}^{\frac{1}{2}},$$

in a direction inclined to the horizontal at an angle

$$\tan^{-1}\left(\frac{V \sin \alpha - gt}{V \cos \alpha}\right).$$

In particular, the remaining velocity at the vertex is $V \cos \alpha$, and the remaining velocity when $y = 0$, that is, when $t = \dfrac{2V \sin \alpha}{g}$, is V, in a direction making an angle $-\alpha$ with OX.

14.7 Range on an Inclined Plane

If a particle is projected from a point O with velocity V at an inclination α to the horizontal, we may find its range on a plane through O inclined at an angle β to the horizontal, the vertical plane of motion containing the line of greatest slope of the plane (Fig. 206). The path of the particle

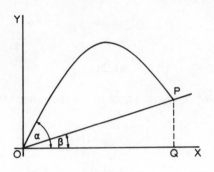

FIG. 206.

is unchanged, and its velocity and position at time t are given by the equations obtained in the previous section.

If it meets the plane at a point P at time t and (x, y) be the coordinates of P, we have

$$x = V \cos \alpha \cdot t,$$
$$y = V \sin \alpha \cdot t - \tfrac{1}{2}gt^2,$$

and also $y = x \tan \beta.$

Hence, $y = V \cos \alpha \tan \beta \cdot t = V \sin \alpha \cdot t - \tfrac{1}{2}gt^2,$

$$t = \frac{2V}{g}(\sin \alpha - \cos \alpha \tan \beta),$$

$$= \frac{2V}{g} \frac{\sin (\alpha - \beta)}{\cos \beta}.$$

$$x = V \cos \alpha \times \frac{2V \sin (\alpha - \beta)}{g \cos \beta},$$

$$= \frac{2V^2}{g} \cdot \frac{\cos \alpha \sin (\alpha - \beta)}{\cos \beta}.$$

If the range OP be R, we have

$$R = x \sec \beta,$$

$$= \frac{2V^2}{g} \frac{\cos \alpha \sin (\alpha - \beta)}{\cos^2 \beta},$$

$$= \frac{V^2}{g} \cdot \frac{\sin (2\alpha - \beta) - \sin \beta}{\cos^2 \beta}.$$

For a given velocity of projection the range is maximum when $\sin(2\alpha - \beta) = 1$,

that is,
$$2\alpha - \beta = 90°,$$

$$\alpha = 45° + \frac{\beta}{2}.$$

For this value of α

$$R = \frac{V^2}{g} \cdot \frac{1 - \sin\beta}{\cos^2\beta},$$

$$= \frac{V^2}{g} \cdot \frac{1 - \sin\beta}{1 - \sin^2\beta},$$

$$= \frac{V^2}{g} \cdot \frac{1}{1 + \sin\beta}.$$

To attain a range R on the inclined plane with the given velocity V we have

$$R = \frac{V^2}{g} \frac{\sin(2\alpha - \beta) - \sin\beta}{\cos^2\beta},$$

$$\sin(2\alpha - \beta) = \frac{gR}{V^2}\cos^2\beta + \sin\beta.$$

Hence, if
$$\sin\theta = \frac{gR}{V^2}\cos^2\beta + \sin\beta,$$

we have either
$$2\alpha - \beta = \theta,$$

or
$$2\alpha - \beta = 180° - \theta,$$

and
$$\alpha = \frac{\theta}{2} + \frac{\beta}{2}, \text{ or } \alpha = 90° + \frac{\beta}{2} - \frac{\theta}{2}.$$

It may easily be seen that these two directions are equally inclined to the direction for maximum range $45° + \frac{\beta}{2}$.

The range *down* the inclined plane is also given by the above formulae but the angle β is now negative.

14.8 Parabola of Safety

If a bomb explodes on the ground, pieces may be thrown off with a certain velocity in all directions. The parabola of safety is the boundary curve in a vertical plane through the point of projection, which includes all possible paths of particles with the given velocity.

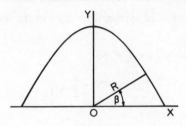

FIG. 207.

From the previous section, the maximum distance which can be reached from O on an imaginary plane of slope β (Fig. 207) is given by

$$R = \frac{V^2}{g} \cdot \frac{1}{1+\sin \beta}.$$

R and β are therefore polar coordinates of points on the bounding curve. Writing $R\cos \beta = x$, $R\sin \beta = y$, we have

$$R(1+\sin \beta) = \frac{V^2}{g},$$

$$R+y = \frac{V^2}{g},$$

$$R^2 = \left(\frac{V^2}{g}-y\right)^2 = x^2+y^2,$$

and hence

$$x^2 = -\frac{2V^2}{g}\left(y-\frac{V^2}{2g}\right).$$

This is the equation of a parabola whose vertex is at a height $\dfrac{V^2}{2g}$ above O and whose latus rectum is $\dfrac{2V^2}{g}$.

Example 7. *At a range of* 100 *m in vacuo a bullet fired horizontally strikes the target* 6 *cm below the point at which its initial direction produced would cut the target. Find the initial velocity of the bullet.*

Let V m/sec be the initial velocity of the bullet. As in the general case, the horizontal and vertical motions may be dealt with separately.

The time of the motion is the time taken by a particle to fall 6 cm vertically under gravity. If t be the time

$$6 = \tfrac{1}{2} \times 981t^2,$$

$$t = 0.1105 \text{ sec.}$$

During this time the bullet moves 100 m horizontally with constant velocity V, therefore

$$0\cdot1105\,V = 100,$$
$$V = 904\cdot2 \text{ m/sec.}$$

Example 8. *A projectile is fired from a point on a cliff to hit a mark 200 m horizontally from the point and 200 m vertically below it. The velocity of projection is that due to falling freely under gravity through 100 m from rest. Show that the two possible directions of projection are at right angles, and find the times of flight.* (O.C.)

The velocity due to a fall of 100 m is given by

$$V^2 = 2gs,$$
$$= 1962,$$
$$V = 44\cdot3 \text{ m/sec.}$$

If the projectile is fired at an angle α above the horizontal, the horizontal component of velocity is $V\cos\alpha$ and the horizontal distance of 200 m is described with this constant velocity.

Hence, the time of flight is

$$t = \frac{200}{44\cdot3\cos\alpha} = 4\cdot514\sec\alpha.$$

The initial vertical velocity is $V\sin\alpha$ and the distance *above* the point of projection after time t is -200 m. Therefore

$$-200 = 44\cdot3\sin\alpha\,(4\cdot514\sec\alpha) - \tfrac{1}{2}g\,(4\cdot514\sec\alpha)^2.$$

Hence
$$\sec^2\alpha - 2\tan\alpha - 2 = 0,$$
$$\tan^2\alpha - 2\tan\alpha + 1 = 2,$$
$$\tan\alpha = 1 \pm \sqrt{2}.$$

If
$$\tan\alpha_1 = 1 + \sqrt{2}.$$
$$\tan\left(\alpha_1 - \frac{\pi}{2}\right) = -\cot\alpha_1,$$
$$= \frac{-1}{\sqrt{2}+1},$$
$$= 1 - \sqrt{2}.$$

Therefore the two values of α differ by a right angle. The time of flight is

$$t = 4\cdot514\sec\alpha,$$
$$= 4\cdot514\sqrt{1+\tan^2\alpha},$$
$$= 4\cdot514\sqrt{1+2+1\pm2\sqrt{2}},$$
$$= 11\cdot8 \text{ or } 4\cdot9 \text{ sec, approximately.}$$

Example 9. *Show that, if R be the maximum horizontal range for a given velocity of projection, a particle can be projected to pass through a point whose horizontal and vertical distances from the point of projection are $\tfrac{1}{2}R$ and $\tfrac{1}{4}R$ respectively, provided that the tangent of the* *angle of projection is* 1 *or* 3, *and that in the second case the range on the horizontal plane is* $\frac{3}{5}R$.   (L.U.)

If V be the velocity of projection, the maximum range R is given by

$$R = \frac{V^2}{g},$$

and

$$V = \sqrt{gR}.$$

Using the equation of the trajectory

$$y = x \tan \alpha - \frac{1}{2} \frac{gx^2}{V^2 \cos^2 \alpha},$$

since $y = \frac{1}{4}R$ when $x = \frac{1}{2}R$ we have

$$\frac{1}{4}R = \frac{1}{2}R \tan \alpha - \frac{1}{2} \frac{g\frac{1}{4}R^2}{gR \cos^2 \alpha},$$

$$\sec^2 \alpha - 4 \tan \alpha + 2 = 0,$$

$$\tan^2 \alpha - 4 \tan \alpha + 3 = 0,$$

$$(\tan \alpha - 1)(\tan \alpha - 3) = 0.$$

Hence, $\tan \alpha = 1$ or 3, and we have when $\tan \alpha = 3$

$$\sin \alpha = \frac{3}{\sqrt{10}}, \quad \cos \alpha = \frac{1}{\sqrt{10}},$$

$$\sin 2\alpha = \frac{6}{10},$$

and the range is

$$\frac{V^2 \sin 2\alpha}{g} = \frac{3}{5}R.$$

Example 10. *A particle is projected with speed u so as to strike at right angles a plane through the point of projection inclined at* 30° *to the horizon. Show that the range on this inclined plane is* $4u^2/7g$.   (L.U.)

Let the particle be projected at an angle α to the horizontal.
After time t the components of velocity are

horizontally	$u \cos \alpha,$
vertically downwards	$gt - u \sin \alpha.$

The direction of motion being perpendicular to the inclined plane, we have

$$\frac{gt - u \sin \alpha}{u \cos \alpha} = \sqrt{3},$$

$$t = \frac{u}{g}(\sin \alpha + \sqrt{3} \cos \alpha).$$

When the particle meets the inclined plane we have also

$$x = u \cos \alpha \cdot t,$$

$$y = u \sin \alpha \cdot t - \frac{1}{2}gt^2,$$

$$y = x \tan 30°$$

Hence

$$\frac{u}{\sqrt{3}} \cos \alpha . t = u \sin \alpha . t - \frac{1}{2}gt^2,$$

$$t = \frac{2u}{g}\left(\sin \alpha - \frac{1}{\sqrt{3}} \cos \alpha\right).$$

Equating the two values obtained for t we have

$$\tan \alpha = \frac{5}{\sqrt{3}},$$

$$t = \frac{u \cos \alpha}{g}(\tan \alpha + \sqrt{3}),$$

$$= \frac{8u \cos \alpha}{\sqrt{3}g}.$$

$$x = \frac{8u^2 \cos^2\alpha}{\sqrt{3}g},$$

$$x \sec 30° = \frac{16\,u^2 \cos^2\alpha}{3g}.$$

Now $\cos^2\alpha = \frac{3}{28}$, and hence the range on the inclined plane is $4u^2/7g$.

Example 11. *A particle is projected from a point at a height 3h above a horizontal plane, the direction of projection making an angle α with the horizon. Show that if the greatest height above the point of projection is h, the horizontal distance travelled before striking the plane is 6h cot α.* (L.U.)

Let V be the velocity of projection.

The vertical component of velocity is $v \sin \alpha$, and this is destroyed by a retardation g in a distance h.

Therefore

$$v^2 \sin^2\alpha = 2gh,$$

$$v \sin \alpha = \sqrt{2gh}.$$

The vertical component of velocity is destroyed in time t given by

$$t = \frac{v \sin \alpha}{g},$$

$$= \sqrt{\frac{2h}{g}}.$$

The particle now falls from rest a distance $4h$ under gravity, and the time for this is given by

$$\frac{1}{2}gt^2 = 4h,$$

$$t = \sqrt{\frac{8h}{g}}.$$

Hence, the total time of the motion is $3\sqrt{\frac{2h}{g}}$.

The horizontal velocity is

$$v \cos \alpha = v \sin \alpha \cot \alpha,$$
$$= \sqrt{2gh} \cot \alpha.$$

Hence, the horizontal distance travelled is

$$\sqrt{2gh} \cot \alpha \times 3 \sqrt{\frac{2h}{g}} = 6h \cot \alpha.$$

EXERCISES 14 (b)

1. A bomber plane is moving horizontally in a straight line at 594 km/h pursued by a fighter plane travelling at 720 km/h in the same straight line. When the fighter is 300 metres behind the bomber he fires his guns which are then horizontal. If the bullets have a muzzle velocity of 3,348 km/h relative to the fighter, at what distance below the line of sight, and at what angle, will the bullets hit the bomber? Neglect air resistance and wind effects. (C.S.)

2. If a particle is projected with a velocity whose horizontal and vertical components are u, v, respectively, find expressions for its coordinates at time t referred to horizontal and vertical axes through A, the point of projection. The particle is viewed from a point B on its path against the vertical through A: show that the particle appears to rise along this vertical at a uniform rate $\frac{1}{2}gt_0$, where t_0 is the time taken by the particle to reach B. (O.C.)

3. A bullet is fired from a point O with a velocity whose horizontal and vertical components are u and v respectively; find the direction in which it is moving at time t. If u is 9·81 m/sec, $v = 29·43$ m/sec, prove that at two points the direction of the bullet's motion is at right angles to the line joining the bullet to O; and find the positions of these points.

4. A shell is observed to explode at the level of the gun from which it is fired after an interval of 10 sec; and the sound of the explosion reaches the gun after a further interval of 3 sec. Find the elevation of the gun and the speed with which the shell is fired. (Take the velocity of sound as 334 m/sec.) (O.C.)

5. A projectile is to pass through a point whose angular elevation is γ, and at that point to impinge perpendicularly on an inclined plane of slope β to the horizontal. Show that the angle of elevation α of the gun is given by

$$\tan \alpha = \cot \beta + 2 \tan \gamma. \tag{O.C.}$$

6. A particle is projected from a point in an inclined plane inclined at 2β to the *vertical*, and moves towards the upper part of the plane in the vertical plane through the line of greatest slope; the initial velocity of the particle is $u \cos \beta$, and its initial direction of motion is inclined at β to the *vertical*. Prove that the time of flight of the particle is u/g, its range on the plane is $u^2/2g$, the velocity with which it strikes the plane $u \sin \beta$, and its direction of motion has then turned through a right angle. (O.C.)

7. A particle is projected with a given velocity so that the direction of projection makes an angle α with a plane inclined to the horizontal at an angle β, the motion taking place in a vertical plane through the line of greatest slope of the inclined plane. Find the range on the plane. If the direction of projection is such that the range is a maximum, show that R, this maximum range, and T, the time of flight, are connected by the relation $R = \frac{1}{2}gT^2$. (O.C.)

8. A small object, projected towards a vertical rectangular screen perpendicular to the vertical plane of its path, just clears it at the highest point of its path. The screen is a m in front of the point of projection and its top b m above this point. Find the vertical and horizontal components of the velocity of projection. If the object is projected with the requisite velocity, but the vertical plane through the direction of projection now makes an angle θ with the screen, prove that the object will fail to clear the screen by $b(\operatorname{cosec} \theta - 1)^2$ m.   (O.C.)

9. A particle projected from a point meets the horizontal plane through the point of projection after traversing a horizontal distance a, and attains a greatest height b. Find the horizontal and vertical components of the velocity of projection. Show that when it has described a horizontal distance x it has attained a height

$$\frac{4b(a-x)x}{a^2}.$$ (O.C.)

10. A particle is projected with velocity V and angle of elevation α from a point O. Prove that the equation of its path referred to axes through O is

$$y = x \tan \alpha - \tfrac{1}{2}gx^2/(V \cos \alpha)^2.$$

Prove that if V is given, the particle may be made to pass through any point P inside the parabola

$$V^2(V^2 - 2gy) = g^2x^2$$

by suitable choice of α. Given that P is at a height h above the level of O, and that $OP = d$, prove that the least velocity of projection with which a particle can be projected from O so as to pass through P is $\sqrt{g(h+d)}$.   (O.C.)

11. A balloon is at a horizontal distance a from a gun at O. The balloon is at the maximum height above the level of O at which it can be hit by a shell fired from the gun with velocity V. Prove that in order that the balloon may be hit when in this position, the angle of elevation α of the gun must be $\tan^{-1} V^2/(ga)$. Given that $V = 100$ m/sec, $a = 200$ m and the height of the balloon is 480 m, find whether it is possible for the balloon to be hit.   (O.C.)

12. A particle is projected at elevation $45°$ from a point A on the deck of a ship steaming due east at 18 km/h, and reaches the deck again at B 9·8 m due northeast of A. Find

    (a) the velocity of projection relative to the ship,
    (b) the time of flight,
    (c) the length and direction of the range relative to the surface of the earth.

13. A body is projected at such an angle that the horizontal range is three times the greatest height. Find the angle of projection, and if with this angle the range is 400 m, find the necessary velocity of projection and the time of flight.   (L.U.)

14. Find to the nearest metre the range (*in vacuo*) on a horizontal plane of a rifle-bullet fired at an elevation of $3°$ with a muzzle velocity of 300 m/sec.   (L.U.)

15. A ball is thrown with a velocity whose horizontal component is 12 m/sec from a point 1·5 m above the ground and 6 m away from a vertical wall 5 m high in such a way as just to clear the wall. At what time will it reach the ground?
                    (L.U.)

16. If a particle is projected inside a horizontal tunnel which is 6 m high with a velocity of 30 m/sec, find the greatest possible range.   (L.U.)

17. A body is thrown from the top of a tower 30 m high with a velocity of 20 m/sec at an elevation of $30°$ above the horizontal; find the horizontal distance from the foot of the tower of the point where it hits the ground.   (L.U.)

18. A ball is thrown from a height 1 m above the ground to clear a wall 12 m away horizontally and 6 m high. Show that the velocity of projection must not be less than that acquired by falling under gravity through 9 m, and, when this is the velocity of projection, find how far beyond the wall it will hit the ground.(L.U.)

19. What is the least velocity of projection required to give a horizontal range of 100 m, and what will be the time of flight? (L.U.)

20. Prove that the time of flight T, and the horizontal range X of a projectile are connected by the equation $gT^2 = 2X \tan \alpha$, where α is the angle of elevation. Show that when the maximum horizontal range is 100 km, the time of flight is about 143 sec, and determine the muzzle velocity and the height of the trajectory. (L.U.)

21. A shot projected with velocity v can just reach a certain point on the horizontal plane through the point of projection. Show that in order to hit a mark h ft above the ground at the same point, if the shot is projected at the same elevation the velocity must be increased to $v^2/(v^2-gh)^{\frac{1}{2}}$. (L.U.)

22. If the horizontal range of a particle projected with velocity V is a, show that the greatest height x attained is given by the equation

$$16gx^2 - 8V^2x + ga^2 = 0.$$

Explain why two values of x are to be expected. (L.U.)

23. From a train travelling at 45 km/h an object is projected horizontally and normally to the direction of motion of the train at a height of 3 m above the ground with a velocity of 5 m/sec. Neglecting resistance to motion due to the air, determine the velocity of impact of the object with the ground. (Q.E.)

24. Show that the relative velocity of two bodies moving in any direction under the acceleration of gravity remains constant. A stone is projected horizontally from the top of a tower 60 m high with a velocity of 16 m/sec, and at the same instant another stone is projected in the same vertical plane from the foot of the tower with a velocity of 32 m/sec at an elevation of 60°. Show that the stones will meet, and find the height above the ground and the distance from the tower at the instant of meeting. (L.U.)

25. A projectile is aimed at a mark on a horizontal plane through the point of projection and falls 20 m short when its elevation is 30°, but overshoots the mark by 30 m when its elevation is 45°. Show that the correct elevation is about 33° 26'. (L.U.)

26. A particle projected from A with velocity u at an elevation α hits the horizontal plane through A at B. Show that if a particle is to be projected from A with the same elevation to hit a target at a height h above B, the velocity of projection must be $u^2 \sin \alpha/(u^2 \sin^2\alpha - \frac{1}{2}gh)^{\frac{1}{2}}$. (L.U.)

27. Two particles are projected at the same instant from two points A and B on the same horizontal level where $AB = 28$ m, the motion taking place in a vertical plane through AB. The particle from A has an initial velocity of 39 m/sec at an angle $\sin^{-1}\frac{5}{13}$ with AB, and the particle from B has an initial velocity of 25 m/sec at an angle $\sin^{-1}\frac{3}{5}$ with BA. Show that the particles will collide in mid-air, and find when and where the impact occurs. (L.U.)

28. Two vertical posts, each of height h, stand on a horizontal plane at a distance $3h/2$ apart. A particle is projected from a point on the plane, at an angle of 45° to the horizontal, and just clears the top of each post. Prove that the speed of projection is $3\sqrt{\frac{1}{2}gh}$, and find the horizontal distance of the point of projection from the nearer post. (L.U.)

29. A particle projected from a point O with equal horizontal and vertical components of velocity v strikes a plane through O inclined at an angle θ to the horizontal where $\tan \theta = 3/4$. Find the range on the plane and the angle between the trajectory and the horizontal at the point where the particle strikes the plane.
(L.U.)

30. A particle projected under gravity from a point O passes through two points whose coordinates relative to horizontal and vertical axes through O are (a, a), and $(2a, a)$. Find the angle of projection and show that v, the velocity of projection, is given by

$$v^2 = 13ga/4.$$
(L.U.)

31. A gun can fire shells with speed V at elevations between $30°$ and $60°$. Find the area commanded by the gun on a horizontal plane assuming that the gun can be rotated about a vertical axis so as to point in any desired direction.   (L.U.)

32. A particle is projected with a velocity V so that its range on a horizontal plane is twice the greatest height attained. Show that the range is $\dfrac{4V^2}{5g}$.   (L.U.)

33. A particle is projected from the top of a cliff 50 m high with a velocity of 50 m/sec at an elevation $\tan^{-1} \frac{4}{3}$. Find the distance from the foot of the cliff at which it strikes the sea, and show that its direction of motion then makes an angle of approximately $51°\ 47'$ with the horizontal.   (L.U.)

34. Show that for a given muzzle-velocity there are in general two angles of projection in order that a shot may hit a given point lying in a vertical plane containing the gun-barrel. If the shot is projected from a point on level ground with a speed of 30 m/sec so as just to clear a 5 m vertical wall at a distance of 75 m from the point, and the flatter of two possible trajectories is chosen, prove that it will hit the ground at a distance of 8·7 m beyond the wall.   (L.U.)

35. A particle is projected from a point O with speed V. Find the maximum range on the horizontal plane through O. The particle, when projected so as to attain its maximum range on the horizontal plane through O, passes through this plane at A and meets the ground at B at a depth h below O. If the horizontal distance of B from A is equal to OA, prove that $h = 2v^2/g$.   (L.U.)

36. The horizontal distance between two men, A and B, is 6 m. A cricket ball is thrown by A to B with speed 10 m/sec; B catches it at a point whose vertical height above the point of projection is 2·5 m. Show that there are two directions of projection by means of which this can be effected, and find the time of flight in each case.   (L.U.)

37. A particle is projected with speed u at inclination β to the horizontal from the foot of an inclined plane of inclination α. The motion takes place in a vertical plane which contains the line of greatest slope of the inclined plane. Show that the range on the inclined plane is $2u^2 \sin(\beta - \alpha) \cos \beta / g \cos^2\alpha$. If the particle strikes the plane at right angles and if $\alpha = 20°$, calculate β.   (L.U.)

38. A projectile is fired from a point O with a speed due to a fall of 100 m from rest under gravity, and hits a mark at a depth of 50 m below O and at a distance of 100 m from the vertical through O. Show that there are two possible directions of projection which are perpendicular, and find, to the nearest minute, their inclinations to the horizontal. Determine the time from O to the mark in each case.
(L.U.)

39. Prove that the equation of the path of a particle projected with speed V at an inclination θ is

$$y = x \tan\theta - \frac{gx^2}{2V^2}\sec^2\theta.$$

When at an elevation α, a gun fires a shot to hit a mark P on the horizontal plane through the gun. When the elevation is reduced to 15° the shot falls 100 m short of P, but when the elevation is 45° it falls 400 m beyond P. Show that $\sin 2\alpha = 0·6$ and calculate the distance of P from the gun.   (L.U.)

40. A stone is thrown with initial velocity V at an elevation α to the horizontal. Its range on the horizontal plane through the point of projection is R and the maximum height it attains above the plane is H. For initial velocity $V/\sqrt{2}$ and elevation 2α the corresponding values are R', H' respectively. Prove that

$$\frac{H'}{H} - \frac{R'}{R} = 1.$$

     (L.U.)

41. A mortar stands on a horizontal plane; it fires a bomb with velocity V at a mark on the plane. When the angle of elevation is α the bomb falls a distance a short of the mark; when the elevation is β it falls a distance b beyond the mark. Neglecting air resistance, show that the elevation γ required in order to hit the mark is given by

$$\sin 2\gamma = \frac{a \sin 2\beta + b \sin 2\alpha}{a+b}.$$

Show further that, if the firing is up the line of greatest slope of a plane inclined at an angle θ to the horizontal and the angles α and β are measured from the horizontal and the distances a and b along this plane, the elevation γ required to hit the mark is given by

$$\sin(2\gamma - \theta) = \frac{a \sin(2\beta - \theta) + b \sin(2\alpha - \theta)}{a+b}$$

     (O.C.)

CHAPTER 15

THE LAWS OF MOTION

15.1 Newtonian Mechanics

In previous chapters we have discussed the motion of a body when its acceleration is known; we now discuss the relation between the force acting on a body and its acceleration. This relation is based on the definitions and laws of motion enunciated by Newton in the seventeenth century; these are the foundation of all theoretical work in applied mechanics. Although these laws are incapable of direct proof, they are firmly established by the agreement of predicted results with experience; for example, the time and place of an eclipse can be foretold with accuracy from calculations based on Newton's laws.

15.2 Newton's Laws

Newton's laws of motion, which form the basis of dynamics, may be stated as follows.

(i) Every body perseveres in its state of rest or uniform motion in a straight line except in so far as it is compelled by applied external forces to change that state.

(ii) The rate of change of momentum is proportional to the applied force and is along the line of action of the force.

(iii) Action and reaction are equal and opposite.

The first law gives, in effect, a definition of force as that which changes the state of motion of the body. A state of uniform motion is considered as not differing essentially from a state of rest, since all motion is relative to some frame of reference which may or may not be itself at rest. This law disposed of some pre-Newtonian theories that force was required to keep a body moving.

The third law states that if a body A exerts a certain force on a body B, then the body B exerts an equal and opposite force on A. These equal and opposite forces are called the *reactions* between the bodies. Such reactions occur between the particles that constitute a rigid body and are called the *internal forces* of the body. Since they occur in pairs, equal and opposite, their sum is zero and we shall see that their effect on the motion of the rigid body is nil. Thus change of motion is caused by the *external forces* acting on the body.

It is impossible to verify these principles by designing an experiment in which external forces such as friction which reduce the velocity of a body are completely eliminated. If friction is, however, reduced as much

243

as possible, an approximate verification can be made; it is also evident that a state of rest with respect to surrounding objects will remain unchanged unless a force is applied.

15.3 Newton's Second Law

The *momentum* of a body is defined as the product of its mass and velocity, that is

$$\text{momentum} = mv. \tag{1}$$

Assuming for the moment that for every particle or body there is some constant which is a measure of its mass, we have

$$\text{rate of change of momentum} = \frac{d}{dt}(mv)$$

$$= m\frac{dv}{dt} = ma,$$

where a is the acceleration. Thus Newton's second law states that the product of mass and acceleration is proportional to force. Hence if a force F acts on a particle or body, F is proportional to ma, that is $F = kma$, where k is a constant. By choosing a suitable unit of force it is possible to make the constant k equal to unity and thus we have the fundamental Newtonian equation, in suitable units,

$$F = ma. \tag{2}$$

The mass of a body is usually defined as the quantity of matter that it contains. This is not a very helpful definition but it is easily understood that a small body requires less force to give it a certain acceleration than a more massive one.

We may think of the mass of a body as being a number depending on the size and density of the body such that the equation (2) is satisfied. A standard piece of platinum is kept as a basis for the measurement of mass and its mass is called *one kilogramme* or 1000 grammes. The masses of other bodies are found by comparison with this standard and the comparison is made by weighing. If a certain mass is double the weight of the standard, the force F due to gravity acting on it is double the force acting on the standard and hence, since the acceleration g due to gravity is the same for both, it follows from equation (2) that its mass is two kilogrammes. In the same way the mass of any body can be compared with that of the standard or with other bodies.

We notice here the distinction between the mass of a body and its weight. The weight is a force whereas the mass is a measure of the effect of force. The mass of the standard piece of platinum is unchanged if its latitude is changed, but its weight is altered with its distance from the earth's centre. In the British system the standard of mass is *one pound*, and

$$1 \text{ pound} = 453 \cdot 59 \text{ grammes}$$

approximately. A piece of platinum whose mass is one pound is kept as a standard.

15.4 Units of Force

Having defined masses of one gramme and one pound we next have to consider the units in which the force must be expressed to make the equation $F = ma$ true.

The Système International (SI) takes as its basic units the metre, kilogramme and second. In this system the absolute unit of force is the *newton* (symbol N) defined as the force which will give to a mass of 1 kilogramme an acceleration of 1 metre per second per second. Thus in (2) if m is in kilogrammes and a in metres per second per second, F is in newtons.

Therefore, for example, a force of 8 N will give to a mass of 2 kg an acceleration of 4 m/sec², and to give a mass of 3 kg an acceleration of 7 m/sec² a force of 21 N is required.

A mass of 1 kg falling freely under gravity has acceleration g ($=9 \cdot 81$ m/sec² approximately) and therefore the force acting on it is g newton. This force is the weight of the body and is called 1 kilogramme force (abbreviation kgf) and therefore

$$1 \text{ kgf} = g \text{ N} = 9 \cdot 81 \text{ N, approximately.}$$

Thus to find the acceleration due to a force F kgf we must first bring the force to newtons and write

$$Fg = ma \qquad (3)$$

The kilogramme force is called a *gravitational* force since its magnitude depends on the gravitational constant g whose value varies from one part of the world to another, whereas the newton being independent of local variation of gravity is called an *absolute* unit of force.

Formerly in the metric system the basic absolute unit of force was the *dyne* which is the force required to give a mass of 1 gramme an acceleration of 1 centimetre per second per second; it is obvious that 1 dyne $= 10^{-5}$ newton. In the British system the absolute unit of force is the *poundal* (abbreviation pdl) which will give to a mass of 1 pound an acceleration of 1 foot per second per second. We shall see (§16.10) that 1 pdl $= 0 \cdot 138$ N. The corresponding gravitational unit is the pound force (abbreviation lbf) $= g$ poundals $= 32$ poundals, approximately. The pound force is called the British technical unit of force and has been much used in this country in conjunction with equation (3) written in the form $F = (w/g)a$, the symbol w for mass serving as a reminder that gravitational units are being used.

15.5 Motion of a Rigid Body

If all the particles of a rigid body have the same acceleration a and the force on a particle of mass m_1 of the body is F_1 we have $F_1 = m_1 a$. A similar equation holds for every particle of the body and, adding these equations for all the particles, we have

$$\Sigma F_1 = (\Sigma m_1)a.$$

Here, Σm_1 is the sum of the masses of all the particles and is therefore the mass of the body, which we denote by M. ΣF_1 is the sum of all the forces, both external and internal, which act on particles in the direction of the acceleration. Since the internal forces occur in equal and opposite pairs (by Newton's third law) their sum is zero, and hence ΣF_1, denoted by F, is the sum of the external forces acting on the body. Thus

$$F = Ma, \tag{5}$$

and this basic equation applies to the motion of a rigid body all of whose particles have the same acceleration.

15.6 The Inclined Plane

Consider a particle of mass m kg on a smooth plane inclined at an angle α to the horizontal (Fig. 208). The only forces acting on the particle are its weight, mg newton, and the reaction of the plane on the particle, R newton

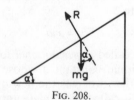

FIG. 208.

(say). These forces combine to give a force $(R - mg \cos \alpha)$ newton perpendicular to the plane and $mg \sin \alpha$ newton down the plane. Since the acceleration perpendicular to the plane is zero we have

$$R - mg \cos \alpha = 0,$$

and, if a is the acceleration down the plane

$$mg \sin \alpha = ma,$$

so that $a = g \sin \alpha$.

If the inclined plane is rough and the coefficient of friction is μ, we have in addition, if we assume the body to be in motion, a frictional force μR acting up the plane. In this case (Fig. 209)

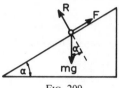

FIG. 209.

$$R - mg \cos \alpha = 0,$$

$$mg \sin \alpha - \mu R = ma,$$

and hence

$$a = g(\sin \alpha - \mu \cos \alpha).$$

If $\mu \cos \alpha$ were greater than $\sin \alpha$, this expression would give a negative acceleration. In fact, the acceleration would be zero, for the friction would not be limiting but only sufficient to prevent motion. Hence, for the particle to slide down the plane we must have $\mu < \tan \alpha$ or, if $\mu = \tan \lambda$ where λ is the angle of friction, $\lambda < \alpha$, that is the angle of friction must be less than the angle of slope of the plane.

In measuring the incline of a road or railway it is usual to speak of a slope of 1 in x, meaning that the ground rises 1 unit in a distance of x units measured along the road or railway.

Thus $\dfrac{1}{x}$ is the *sine* of the angle of slope.

Example 1. *A body is hung from a spring balance suspended from the roof of a lift. When the lift is descending with uniform acceleration 0·9 m/sec², the balance indicates a weight of 10 kg. When the lift is ascending with uniform acceleration x m/sec² the reading is 12 kg. Find the value of x.*

In each case the body moves under the action of two forces, its weight and the pull of the balance shown by the indicated weight.

Thus if m kg be the mass of the body, when descending

$$mg - 10g = m \cdot 0.9,$$

when ascending

$$12g - mg = m \cdot x.$$

From the first equation $m = 11.01$ kg.

and hence

$$x = \frac{12 - 11.01}{11.01} g = 0.882 \text{ m/sec}^2.$$

Example 2. *A train of mass 250 tonnes is travelling at 90 km/h and the frictional resistances to motion are 88 N/tonne. The train slips a carriage of mass 10 tonnes. How far will the carriage go before coming to rest, and what will then be the velocity of the train if the resistance to motion is unaltered?*

The resistance for the 10-tonne carriage will be 880 N and hence if a m/sec^2 be its retardation

$$880 = 10 \times 1000 \times a,$$
$$a = 0{\cdot}088 \text{ m/sec}^2.$$

For its subsequent motion we have

$$u = 25 \text{ m/sec},$$
$$v = 0,$$
$$a = -0{\cdot}088 \text{ m/sec}^2,$$
$$s = ?$$

The formula $v^2 = u^2 + 2as$ gives

$$s = 3550 \text{ m},$$
$$= 3{\cdot}55 \text{ km},$$

and the time is $t = \frac{3550}{12{\cdot}5} = 284$ sec.

When the train is running at the constant speed of 90 km/h the engine pull is equal to the total resistance, therefore when the carriage has been slipped it exceeds the resistance by 880 N, and this is therefore the net accelerating force. We have for the acceleration of the train

$$880 = 240 \times 1000 \times a,$$
$$a = \tfrac{11}{3000} \text{ m/sec}^2.$$

The velocity after 284 sec is given by the formula $v = u + at$, and

$$v = 25 + 3124/3000,$$
$$= 26{\cdot}04 \text{ m/sec},$$
$$= 93{\cdot}75 \text{ km/h}.$$

Example 3. *An engine exerts a force of 35 000 N on a train of mass 240 tonnes and draws it up a slope of 1 in 120 against resistances of 60 N/tonne. Find the acceleration of the train. Find also the braking force that would be required on the return journey to prevent the acceleration exceeding 0·01 m/sec^2.*

The pull of the engine is 35 000 N.

The total resistance is $60 \times 240 = 14\,400$ N.

The component of the train's weight down the slope is $240 \times 10^3 \times g \sin \alpha$, where α is the angle of slope, that is, $\dfrac{24 \times 10^4 \times 9{\cdot}81}{120} = 19\,620$ N.

Therefore, the net accelerating force up the incline is 980 N. If a be the acceleration in m/sec^2, we have

$$980 = 240 \times 1000 \times a,$$
$$a = 0{\cdot}0041 \text{ m/sec}^2.$$

On the return journey let W newton be the braking force when the acceleration is 0.01 m/sec².

We have the component of the weight, $2000g$, down the incline and the resistance, $14\,400$ N, and the braking force up the incline.

Therefore $19\,620 - 14\,400 - W = 240 \times 1000 \times 0.01$,

$$5220 - W = 2400,$$

$$W = 2820 \text{ N}.$$

Example 4. *A lift worked by hand is supported by a rope which passes round the axle of a wheel and axle, a rope around the wheel being pulled from inside the lift. If the lift weighs W newton and a man inside it w N and the ratio of the diameter of the wheel and axle is n, find the least pull the man must exert on the rope to remain stationary. If he increases this pull by w_1 N find the upwards acceleration of the lift.*

If the man's pull on the rope be T N the tension in the rope attached to the axle will be nT, and hence, since the rope exerts an equal and opposite pull T on the man, the total upward force $= (n+1)T$.

The downward force is $(W + w)$ N,
therefore $\hspace{3cm} (n+1)T = W + w,$

$$T = \frac{W+w}{n+1}$$

If the pull is increased by w_1 N the upward force is $(n+1)(T+w_1)$ and hence the net accelerating force upwards is $(n+1)w_1$. The mass accelerated is $W + w$ and hence the upwards acceleration is

$$a = \frac{(n+1)w_1}{W+w}$$

EXERCISES 15 (a)

1. An engine exerting a constant tractive force is pulling seven 10-tonne trucks and giving them an acceleration of 0.1 m/sec² on the level, the frictional and other resistances to motion being 60 N/tonne. If one truck is uncoupled and the engine exerts the same tractive force, show that the acceleration is increased by about 27 per cent.

2. A lift with a mass of $1\,200$ kg is raised from rest by a cable with a tension of $1350g$ N. After a time the tension drops to $1\,000g$ N, and the lift comes to rest at a height of 25 m above its starting point. Find the height at which the tension changes, the greatest speed of the lift and the total time.

3. A lorry travelling on the level at 40 km/h can be stopped by its brakes in a distance of 16 m. Find the speed from which it can be brought to rest in the same distance when descending a hill whose angle of slope is $\sin^{-1}(1/15)$.

4. A plumb-line in a ship is seen to be inclined at an angle of $1° 30'$ to the vertical. Find the acceleration of the ship.

5. A block of wood of mass 120 kg rests on a smooth horizontal plane. On the upper face of the block, which is horizontal, rests a mass of 10 kg. The coefficient of friction between the mass and the block is $\frac{1}{4}$. If the mass is pulled horizontally with a force of $4g$ N, find the accelerations of the mass and the block.

Find also how far the block will have moved when the mass has moved 10 cm along the block.

6. A train travelling uniformly on the level at 72 km/h begins an ascent of 1 in 75. The tractive force which the engine exerts during the ascent is constant and equal to 24·5 kN, the resistance (due to friction, etc.) is constant and equal to 14·7 kN, and the mass of the whole train is 225 tonnes. Show that the train will come to a standstill after climbing for 2·3 km.

7. A train of 180 tonnes starts from rest with an engine pull of 29·4 kN and makes a run of 2 km from one station to rest at the next. At the instant of maximum speed the steam is shut off and the brakes are applied, producing an effective coefficient of friction of $\frac{1}{30}$. Neglecting frictional resistances other than those due to the brakes, prove that the time occupied is about 192 sec and the maximum speed about 75 km/h.

8. Find in N per 1 000 kg the force exerted by the brakes of a train travelling at 60 km/h, which will bring it to rest in half a kilometre, and find the time during which the brakes act.

9. A bullet of mass 30 g is fired into a fixed block of wood with a velocity of 294 metres per second and is brought to rest in $\frac{1}{150}$ sec. Find the resistance exerted by the wood, supposing it to be uniform.   (O.C.)

10. A shell of mass 20 kg is fired horizontally through three screens placed at equal intervals 100 m apart. The velocity of the shell at the first screen is 400 m/sec and the time of flight between the first and second screens is 0·27 sec. Assuming the retardation due to the air resistance to be constant, find the retarding force and the time of flight between the second and third screens.

11. A body whose true weight was 13 N appeared to weigh 12 N when weighed by means of a spring balance in a moving lift. What was the acceleration of the lift at the instant of weighing?   (L.U.)

12. A ship of 10 000 tonnes slows, with engines stopped, from 6 knots to 5 knots in a distance of 300 m; assuming the resistance to be uniform, calculate its value in newtons. (A knot may be assumed to be a speed of 0·515 m/sec.)   (L.U.)

13. A force equal to a weight of 1 000g N acts for 3 sec on a mass of 5 000 kg. Find the velocity produced and the space passed over, stating the units in which the results are measured.   (L.U.)

14. A and B are two railway stations 1 000 m apart on a level track. A train starting from rest at A is uniformly accelerated for one minute and reaches a speed of 36 km/h. This speed is maintained constant until the train is 80 m from B, when, steam being shut off, it is uniformly retarded by the brakes so as to stop at B. Find by means of a speed–time graph, or otherwise, the acceleration and the retardation, and the time for the journey from A to B.

   If the resistances to motion are constant and equal to 97 N per tonne, show that the driving force exerted during acceleration is about half the force exerted by the brakes during retardation.   (C.S.)

15.7 Motion of Connected Particles

We now consider the motion of two or more particles connected by a light inextensible string whose direction is changed by passing over smooth pulleys of negligible mass. The underlying assumption is that the tensile force in such a string remains the same throughout its length.

The accelerations of the particles are related by the fact of their being connected by string, and hence if the equation of motion, $F = ma$, is written down for each particle, it is possible to eliminate the tension in the strings and find the accelerations.

Example 5. *Masses m_1 and m_2 kg ($m_1 > m_2$) are connected by a light inextensible string which passes over a light, smooth, fixed pulley. Find the acceleration of the masses and the tension in the string.*

Let T newton be the tension in the string throughout its length. Then the string exerts an upward force of T newton on each of the masses (Fig. 210).

Let a m/sec² be the downward acceleration of the mass m_1; then a will be the upward acceleration of the mass m_2, since the length of the string connecting the masses is constant.

Writing down the equations of motion for each of the masses, we have

$$m_1 g - T = m_1 a,$$
$$T - m_2 g = m_2 a.$$

Adding, we have

$$(m_1 - m_2)g = (m_1 + m_2)a,$$
$$a = \frac{m_1 - m_2}{m_1 + m_2}g.$$

Substituting for a we have

$$T = m_1(g - a),$$
$$= m_1 g\left(1 - \frac{m_1 - m_2}{m_1 + m_2}\right),$$
$$= \frac{2m_1 m_2}{m_1 + m_2}g.$$

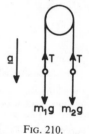

Fig. 210.

It should be noticed that the acceleration of the system depends only on the ratio of the masses.

Thus if $m_1 = 2m_2$, $a = \frac{1}{3}g$, whatever be the magnitudes of the masses or the units in which they are given.

Example 6. *A mass m_1 rests on a rough horizontal table and is connected by a light inextensible string which passes over a smooth light pulley at the edge of the table to a mass m_2 hanging vertically. If the string is initially taut and at right angles to the edge of the table, find the acceleration with which the system begins to move, the tension in the string and the force of the string on the pulley, the coefficient of friction between the mass m_1 and the table being μ.*

If the masses be in kg, let T newton be the tension in the string and a the acceleration of the mass m_2 downwards and of the mass m_1 along the table (Fig. 211). Since the reaction between the mass m_1 and the table is $m_1 g$, the limiting value of the friction

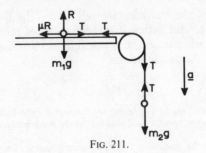

FIG. 211.

opposing its motion is $\mu m_1 g$. Hence we have the equations of motion of the masses

$$m_2 g - T = m_2 a,$$
$$T - \mu m_1 g = m_1 a.$$

Adding we have

$$(m_2 - \mu m_1)g = (m_2 + m_1)a,$$
$$a = \frac{m_2 - \mu m_1}{m_2 + m_1}g.$$

For motion to take place, therefore, we must have $m_2 > \mu m_1$.
Hence

$$T = m_2(g - a),$$
$$= \frac{m_1 m_2 (1 + \mu)}{m_1 + m_2}g.$$

The force exerted by the string on the pulley has equal components T downwards and along the table towards the mass m_1 and hence its value is $T\sqrt{2}$ in a direction making an angle of $45°$ with the downward vertical.

Example 7. *A mass m_1 is connected by a light inextensible string over a light, smooth, fixed pulley to a movable smooth pulley of mass m_2, over which passes a second light inextensible string attached to masses m_3 and m_4 at its ends. Find equations to determine the accelerations of the masses when the system is released, and the tensions in the strings.*

Let the masses be in kg and let T newton be the tension in the first string and T_1

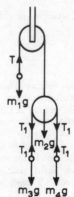

FIG. 212.

newton be the tension in the second string (Fig. 212). Then the forces acting on the masses are:

on m_1, $\quad T - m_1 g,$ $\qquad$ upwards,

on m_2, $\quad 2T_1 + m_2 g - T,$ downwards,

on m_3, $\quad m_3 g - T_1,$ $\qquad$ downwards,

on m_4, $\quad m_4 g - T_1,$ $\qquad$ downwards.

Let a m/sec^2 be the upward acceleration of m_1 and the downward acceleration of the movable pulley. Let a_1 m/sec^2 be the downward acceleration of m_4 with respect to the movable pulley and the upward acceleration of m_3 with respect to the movable pulley. Then the total downward acceleration of m_4 is $a + a_1$, and of m_3, $a - a_1$.

Hence, we have the four equations of motion

$$T - m_1 g = m_1 a,$$
$$2T_1 + m_2 g - T = m_2 a,$$
$$m_3 g - T_1 = m_3(a - a_1),$$
$$m_4 g - T_1 = m_4(a + a_1).$$

These four equations determine the four unknown quantities a, a_1, T, T_1.

Example 8. *One end of a light inextensible string is attached to a mass of 5 kg which rests on a rough horizontal table, the coefficient of friction between the mass and the table being $\frac{1}{3}$. The string at right angles to the edge of the table passes over a smooth fixed pulley at the edge, under a smooth movable pulley of mass 4 kg and over a smooth fixed pulley, and has a mass of 3 kg attached to its other end. Assuming the portions of the string to be vertical between the pulleys, find the accelerations of the masses and the tension in the string.*

Let T newton be the tension in the string (Fig. 213). The forces in newtons acting on the masses are:

on the 5 kg mass $\qquad T - \frac{5}{3}g,$ horizontally,

on the 4 kg mass $\qquad 4g - 2T,$ downwards,

on the 3 kg mass $\qquad 3g - T,$ downwards.

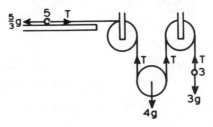

FIG. 213.

If x m be the displacement of the 5 kg mass towards the edge of the table and y m the downward displacement of the 3 kg mass, the length of the string in the loop is increased by $x - y$ and the downward displacement of the 4 kg mass is $\frac{1}{2}(x - y)$. Hence if a_1 and a_2 be the accelerations of the 5 kg and 3 kg masses, horizontally and vertically downwards respectively, the acceleration of the 4 kg mass is $\frac{1}{2}(a_1 - a_2)$ vertically downwards.

The equations of motion of the masses are

$$T - \tfrac{5}{3}g = 5a_1,$$
$$4g - 2T = 4 \times \tfrac{1}{2}(a_1 - a_2),$$
$$3g - T = 3a_2.$$

We have three equations to determine T, a_1 and a_2, giving

$$T = \tfrac{50}{23}g$$
$$a_1 = \tfrac{7}{69}g,$$
$$a_2 = \tfrac{19}{69}g,$$
$$\tfrac{1}{2}(a_1 - a_2) = -\tfrac{2}{23}g.$$

Example 9. *A double inclined plane is in the form of a wedge of weight 10 kg held on the ground with its base horizontal and rough faces inclined at 30° and 45° respectively to the horizontal. A 5 kg particle on the face inclined at 30° is connected by a light, flexible, inextensible string over a smooth pulley at the ridge of the wedge to a 7 kg particle on the other face. If the coefficient of friction between each of the particles and the wedge is $\tfrac{1}{5}$, find the accelerations of the particles and the vertical thrust of the wedge on the ground.*

Let T newton be the tension in the string, R and S newton the reactions between the masses and their respective planes (Fig. 214). Then

$$R = 5g \cos 30°,$$
$$S = 7g \cos 45°,$$

and the frictional forces are $\dfrac{R}{5}$ and $\dfrac{S}{5}$.

Let a be the acceleration of the 7 kg mass down its plane and of the 5 kg mass up its plane.

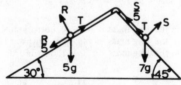

FIG. 214.

The equations of motion of the masses are

$$7g \sin 45° - \tfrac{1}{5}.7g \cos 45° - T = 7a,$$
$$T - 5g \sin 30° - g \cos 30° = 5a,$$

Adding
$$\frac{g}{120}(28\sqrt{2} - 25 - 5\sqrt{3}) = a,$$
$$a = 0.049g,$$
$$= .485 \text{ m/sec}^2,$$
$$T = 3.613g.$$

The forces exerted by the 5 kg mass on the wedge are $5g \cos 30°$ perpendicular to the plane and $g \cos 30°$ up the plane. The component vertically downwards of these forces is

$$5g \cos^2 30° - g \cos 30° \sin 30° = \frac{15 - \sqrt{3}}{4}g.$$

Similarly, the component vertically downwards of the forces exerted by the 7 kg mass on the wedge are

$$7g \cos^2 45° + \tfrac{7}{5}g \sin 45° \cos 45° = \tfrac{21}{5}g.$$

The downward component of the force exerted by the string on the pulley is

$$T \cos 60° + T \cos 45° = 4·36g.$$

Hence, the total downward thrust is

$$10g + 4·36g + 4·2g + \frac{15 - \sqrt{3}}{4}g = 21·88g \text{ newton.}$$

EXERCISES 15 (b)

1. A light inextensible string has one end attached to the under-side of the edge of a smooth table. It passes through a small smooth ring of weight W, and has its other end attached to a weight W' on the table. If the system is held so that the string is taut and then released, prove that W' will move with an acceleration $2Wg/(W + 4W')$. (O.C.)

2. A particle held at rest on a smooth table is attached by a light inextensible string to a second particle, of the same mass as the first, which hangs over the edge of the table, the string being taut and at right angles to the edge. If the particle on the table is released, find the acceleration with which it begins to move. (O.C.)

3. A light inextensible string passing over a small, smooth, fixed pulley, carries at one end a mass of 4 g and at the other two masses, each of 3 g. If the system is allowed to move, find the acceleration with which the mass of 4 g ascends. If one of the 3 g masses falls off after the 4 g mass has ascended 12 cm, how much further will the 4 g mass ascend?

4. A light string $ABCD$ has one end fixed at A, and, passing under a movable pulley of mass M at B and over a fixed pulley at C, carries a mass M' at D. The parts of the string are supposed vertical. Show that M descends with acceleration $(M - 2M')g/(M + 4M')$. (O.C.)

5. A, B are masses of 6 kg and 3 kg respectively resting on two smooth tables, placed with their edges parallel. They are connected by a fine string, which hangs between the tables with its hanging parts vertical and carries in its loop a smooth pulley C of mass 4 kg. The string lies in a vertical plane, and crosses the edges of the tables at right angles to the edges. Find the tension in the string (1) when A and B are held fast, (2) when B is held but A moves, (3) when A and B both move; and show that in the three cases the tensions are in the ratio 21:18:14. (O.C.)

6. Two particles of masses 3 kg and 5 kg respectively are connected by a light inelastic string. Then 3-kg particle lies on a plane inclined at 30° to the horizontal, and the coefficient of friction between the particle and the plane is 1/5. The string lies parallel to a line of greatest slope of the plane, and passes over a smooth pulley at the top, so that the 5-kg mass hangs from a vertical part of the string. Find the tension in the string when the system is released from rest, and the velocity after half a second.

If the string then breaks, find the distance the 3-kg mass travels up the plane before stopping.

7. A particle of mass m_1 is drawn up a smooth inclined plane of height h and length c by a string passing over the top of the plane, and supporting at the other end a mass m_2. If m_1 starts from rest at the bottom of the plane, and m_2 is detached after m_1 has moved a distance x, show that m_1 will just reach the top of the plane if

$$x = \frac{(m_1 + m_2)ch}{m_2(c + h)}.$$ (L.U.)

8. Two particles of mass m and $2m$ are attached to the ends of a taut inextensible string that passes over a smooth pulley at the top of a smooth plane inclined at $30°$ to the horizontal, the particle $2m$ being in contact with the plane, and the particle m hanging freely. Find the time taken for the mass m to fall through 5 m, if its initial velocity is 2 m/sec downwards.

   If the plane is rough, the coefficient of friction being $\frac{1}{3}$, find how far the mass m moves before coming to rest, if its initial velocity is as before.   (L.U.)

9. A particle of mass 6 kg lies on a rough horizontal table, and a taut string attached to the particle passes over a smooth pulley at the edge of the table and carries a particle of mass 10 kg, which hangs freely. If the system starts from rest and each particle has an acceleration 4 m/sec², find the coefficient of friction.   (L.U.)

10. A straight smooth rod AB is fixed at an inclination of $30°$ to the horizontal; a ring of mass $5m$ slides on the rod and is tied to one end of an inextensible string which passes over a smooth pulley fixed at the upper end A of the rod. The other end of the string is tied to a mass $3m$. Initially the mass $3m$ is held vertically below A with the string taut. If it is then released, find the acceleration of the system.   (L.U.)

11. A smooth pulley of mass m is connected with a mass $4m$ by a string which passes over a fixed pulley, and a string carrying masses m and $2m$ at the ends passes over the first pulley. If the system is free to move, find the acceleration of the mass $4m$.   (L.U.)

12. One end of a string is attached to the ceiling. The string passes under a light movable pulley A, then over a light pulley B, and to its free end is attached a mass $4m$. The pulley B is attached by a string to the ceiling at C, and a mass m is attached by a string to the pulley A. Assuming the portions of the strings not round the pulleys to be vertical, find the acceleration of the pulley A during the motion and the pull on the ceiling at C.   (L.U.)

13. One end of a string is attached to a 4-kg mass on a smooth horizontal table. The string passes over the edge of the table, and to its other end is attached a light smooth pulley. Over this pulley passes another string, to the end of which are attached masses of 3 kg and 2 kg respectively. Show that the 4-kg mass moves with an acceleration $6g/11$.   (L.U.)

14. A light string passes over one fixed pulley, under a movable pulley and then over a second fixed pulley. A mass m_1 is attached to one end of the string, a mass m_2 to the other end and a mass M to the movable pulley. Assuming the pulleys to be smooth and light, and the portion of the string not round the pulleys to be vertical, prove that the tension in the string is

$$\frac{4Mm_1m_2g}{M(m_1 + m_2) + 4m_1m_2}.$$ (L.U.)

15. Two bodies, one of mass 536 g and one of mass 445 g, are connected by a long, light string passing over a smooth pulley. Initially they are both at rest and

hanging freely with both parts of the string vertical, the bodies being each 1 metre from the floor. Calculate the time, correct to a tenth of a second, which elapses before the heavier body hits the floor, and also the greatest distance from the floor, correct to the nearest millimetre, reached by the lighter body.

(C.S.)

16. Masses of 200 g and 160 g are connected by a light inextensible string passing over a light smooth pulley. Find the acceleration with which the greater mass descends.

After falling 1 metre from rest the greater mass is brought to rest on reaching the ground. What interval then elapses before the string again becomes taut?

(C.S.)

15.8 Variable Forces

The forces acting on a particle may vary with the time, the distance moved or the velocity. In each case the acceleration of the particle is given according to Newton's second law by the equation $F = ma$, and we have a variable acceleration from which the motion may be found by the graphical methods considered in Chapter 13 or by methods involving calculus, to be considered in Chapter 20.

It has been seen that if the acceleration is plotted against the time, the area beneath the curve for any interval of time give the velocity acquired in that time. Hence, if the force is plotted against the time, since $F = ma$, m being constant, the area under the force–time curve for any interval of time gives the product of the mass, and the velocity acquired in that time, that is, the area under the force–time curve for any interval of time gives the momentum acquired in that time. Units of momentum are units of force × units of time, normally *newton-seconds*.

That is,

$$\int F dt = \text{change of momentum.}$$

If the acceleration is plotted against the distance, the area under the curve gives the change in the quantity $\frac{1}{2}v^2$ over any distance interval. Hence, if the force is plotted against the distance, the area under the curve gives the change in the quantity $\frac{1}{2}mv^2$ over any distance interval. The quantity $\frac{1}{2}mv^2$ is called the *kinetic energy* of the particle, and will be considered in more detail in Chapter 16. Hence we have

$$\int F ds = \text{change of Kinetic Energy.}$$

Units of kinetic energy are units of force × units of distance, normally newton-metres, which are called *Joules*.

Example 10. *The net driving force of a car of mass 1 tonne increases uniformly from 56g N to 84g N in the first 10 sec of its motion; during the next 20 sec it remains constant at 84g N and decreases uniformly to zero in the next 10 sec. Find the velocity acquired in the period of 40 sec.*

The force–time graph consists of three straight lines as shown (Fig. 215), the force in newtons being plotted against the time in seconds.

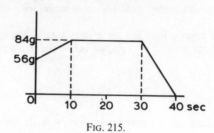

FIG. 215.

The area under the graph is

$$\frac{1}{2}(56g + 84g) \times 10 + 84g \times 20 + \frac{1}{2} \times 84g \times 10,$$

$$= 2800g \text{ newton-sec.}$$

$$= mv, \text{ where } m = 1000 \text{ kg.}$$

Therefore,

$$v = 27 \cdot 5 \text{ m/sec.}$$

Example 11. *A body of mass 8 tonnes is acted on by a variable force of Fg N over a distance of 400 m. The value of F decreases uniformly with the distance, from 2000 to 1400 over the first 100 m, from 1400 to 250 over the next 200 m, and from 250 to 0 over the last 100 m. Find the velocity of the body at the end of 400 m.*

The force–distance graph consists of three straight lines as shown (Fig. 216), the force in newtons being plotted against the distance in metres.

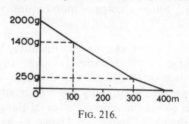

FIG. 216.

The area under the graph is

$$\frac{1}{2}(2000g + 1400g) \times 100 + \frac{1}{2}(1400g + 250g) \times 200 + \frac{1}{2}(250g) \times 100,$$

$$= 347500g \text{ newton-metre or joules,}$$

$$= \frac{1}{2}mv^2, \text{ where } m = 8000 \text{ kg.}$$

Therefore

$$v^2 = \frac{347\,500 \times 9{\cdot}81}{4 \times 1000},$$

$$= 852.$$

$$v = 29{\cdot}2 \text{ m/sec approximately.}$$

EXERCISES 15 (c)

1. A train of mass M kg running at 72 km/h is brought to rest on an upgrade of 1 vertically in 128 along the track by the brakes which can exert a force of $M\left(\dfrac{1}{10}+\dfrac{t}{110}\right)$ N, where t (sec) is measured from the instant when the brakes are applied. Show that the train is brought to rest in 50 sec.

2. The accelerating force of a train of mass 250 tonnes increases uniformly from 15000 N to 50000 N in the first 5 sec; it then increases uniformly to 70000 N in the next 5 sec and remains constant at this value for 10 sec. The force then decreases uniformly to zero in 5 sec. Find the velocity at the end of 25 sec.

3. A horse pulls a wagon of 5000 kg from rest against a constant resistance of 90 N. The pull exerted initially is 600 N, and it decreases uniformly with the distance covered to 400 N at a distance of 15 m from the start. Find the velocity of the wagon at this point.

4. A railway runs up a slope of 1 (vertically) in 50 (along the track) from a point A to a point B 300 m from A. The track is level from B to a point C 100 m from B. An engine-driver shuts off steam at A, applies his brakes at B and comes to rest at C. If the frictional resistances to motion are constant at 60 N/tonne and the braking force is 1200 N/tonne, find the speed of the train as it passes A.

5. The barrel of a gun of mass 2000 kg starts to recoil with a velocity of 15 m/sec. The recoil is taken up by a buffer which exerts a force proportional to the distance recoiled and brings the barrel to rest in a distance of 1 m. Find the maximum force exerted by the buffer.

EXERCISES 15 (d)

1. The engine of a train of mass M tonnes exerts a constant tractive force of F newton, and the track and other resistances amount to R newton per tonne. If $F > MR$, find the time in minutes taken by the train to travel S metres from rest (i) on a level track, (ii) on a down gradient of 1 vertically in 120 along the track.   (L.U.)

2. AD is the vertical diameter of a circle which has A as its highest point, and AB, BC, CD are consecutive sides of a regular hexagon inscribed in the circle. If AB and CD are smooth wires on which small rings can slide freely, show that rings released simultaneously at A to slide down AB, and at C to slide down CD, will reach the circumference of the circle at the same time as a particle simultaneously released to fall freely from A. Find the ratios of the speeds of the three bodies at the instant when they reach the circumference.   (L.U.)

3. A railway carriage runs down an incline of 1 (vertically) in 250 (along the track), and on reaching the foot of the incline runs along the level. Find how far it will run on the level before coming to rest, assuming that the carriage descends the incline with a constant speed of 20 km/h and that the resistance to motion is the same on the incline and on the level.   (L.U.)

4. A man carrying a bag which has a mass of 25 kg steps into a lift. The lift moves upwards a certain distance with constant acceleration and then comes to rest under its own weight after travelling altogether a distance of 60 m. If the man can only exert a force of $75g$ N, find the shortest time in which the ascent can be made if the man holds the bag all the time.   (L.U.)

5. A particle of mass 8 kg moves along a straight line from a point O with a constant speed of 20 m/sec. After 6 sec it is acted upon by a constant force of $\frac{1}{2}$ kgf for 10 sec. This force is then removed and a constant braking force of 1 kgf is brought into action. Draw the velocity–time graph and calculate the distance from O covered by the particle in 20 sec.   (L.U.)

6. Two particles start together from a point O and slide down smooth straight wires inclined at 30°, 60° to the vertical, and in the same vertical plane and on the same side of the vertical through O. Show that the relative acceleration of the second particle with respect to the first is vertical and equal to $\dfrac{g}{2}$.   (L.U.)

7. A vertical shield is made of two plates of wood and iron respectively, the iron being 2 cm and the wood 4 cm thick. A bullet fired horizontally goes through the iron first and then penetrates 2 cm into the wood. A similar bullet fired with the same velocity from the opposite direction goes through the wood first and then penetrates 1 cm into the iron. Compare the average resistance offered by the iron and the wood.   (L.U.)

8. A train of mass 160 tonnes starts from rest at a station, the engine exerting a tractive force of $2\frac{1}{2} \times 10^4$ N in excess of the resistances until a speed of 54 km/h is attained. This speed continues constant until the brakes, causing a retardation of 0·8 m/sec², bring the train to rest 8 km away. Find the time taken (i) during acceleration, (ii) during retardation, (iii) altogether.   (L.U.)

9. An engine which exerts a constant tractive force is hauling a train of $1.2 \times 10^5 g$ N on a line which rises 1 (vertically) in 180 (along the track) against frictional resistances of $0.012g$ N/kg. Six minutes after starting the speed is 60 km/h. Find the acceleration and the pull in the coupling between the engine and the train in newtons.

10. A particle M of mass 5 kg placed on a rough horizontal table, is attached to one end of a string, which passes over a smooth pulley fixed at the edge of the table and carries a mass of 2 kg at its free end. Initially M is 4 m from the pulley and the system is released from rest. After M has moved 3 m the string is cut and M continues to slide until it comes to rest just by the pulley. Show that the acceleration of M before the string is cut is $g/11$.   (L.U.)

11. A mass of $2m$ kg lying on a smooth horizontal table is attached to a light in-extensible string which, passing over the smooth edge of the table, carries a smooth light pulley over which hangs a similar string carrying masses $(m+x)$ kg and $(m-x)$ kg at its ends. Prove that, after the system is released, the acceleration of the mass on the table is $\dfrac{m^2 - x^2}{2m^2 - x^2}g$.   (L.U.)

12. Two particles of masses 2 kg and 3 kg respectively lie side by side on a smooth horizontal table. A light string attached to them at its ends passes in double strand over the edge of the table at right angles to it, and a small smooth ring of mass 4 kg threaded on the string hangs in the overhanging loop of the string. If the system is left free to move and there is no interference between the two

portions of the string, or between the masses on the table, find the tension in the string and the acceleration of the ring while the masses remain on the table.

(L.U.)

13. A double inclined plane is in the form of a wedge with fixed horizontal base and smooth faces inclined at angles 30° to the horizontal. A 3 g particle on the one face is connected by a light, flexible, inextensible string over the smooth ridge of the wedge to a 2 g particle on the other face. If the particles start moving from a position with the string taut, find the direction and magnitude of the velocity of the 2 g particle relative to the 3 g particle 1 sec later, if the string is sufficiently long for the particles still to be one on each face of the wedge. (L.U.)

14. A mass m is drawn up a rough fixed plane, inclined to the horizontal at an angle α, by means of a light inextensible string which passes over a smooth pulley at the top of the plane. The other end of the string carries a mass $3m$, which hangs vertically, and the system is allowed to move from rest. Show that if the coefficient of friction between the mass and the plane is $\tan \alpha$, the tension in the string is $\frac{3}{4}mg(1 + 2\sin \alpha)$. The mass $3m$ reaches the ground after falling a distance h. Show that the mass m moves through a further distance $\dfrac{h(3 - 2\sin \alpha)}{8\sin \alpha}$ before it first comes to instantaneous rest.

(L.U.)

15. Two masses of $\frac{1}{4}$ g and $7\frac{3}{4}$ g, connected by an inextensible string 2 m long, lie on a smooth table 1 m high. The string being straight and perpendicular to the edge of the table, the lighter mass is drawn gently just over the edge and released. Find (i) the time that elapses before the first mass strikes the floor, and (ii) the further time that elapses before the second mass reaches the edge of the table. (L.U.)

16. Two masses 1 kg and 3 kg are connected by a fine string which passes over a small pulley at the vertex of an isosceles right-angled wedge whose base is horizontal. Show that the string slips over the pulley with an acceleration 3·47 m/sec² approximately. The wedge is of mass 1 kg, and rests on a rough horizontal table. Find the vertical pressure on the table, assuming that the wedge does not slide, and show that for this the coefficient of friction between the wedge and the table must exceed 2/9. (O.C.)

17. Masses of 100 g and 60 g are attached to the ends of a fine string which passes over a smooth fixed pulley. Find the accelerations of the masses, and prove that the tension in the string is equal to a weight of 75 g. The pulley whose mass is 50 g is now detached from its fastening and attached by means of another fine string to a mass of 100 g which lies on a smooth table over whose edge the string passes. Prove that the pulley moves as though its original weights were removed and its own mass increased by 150 g. (O.C.)

18. Two pulleys of masses 12 kg and 8 kg are connected by a fine string hanging over a smooth fixed pulley. Over the former is hung a fine string with masses of 3 kg and 6 kg at its ends, and over the latter a fine string with masses 4 kg and x kg. Determine x so that the string over the fixed pulley remains stationary, and find the tension in it. (L.U.)

19. The angle of a smooth wedge of mass M is α. The wedge is placed with one face on a smooth horizontal table and a particle of mass m is allowed to slide down its face. Prove that a horizontal force $mg \sin \alpha \cos \alpha$ must be applied to the wedge to keep it from moving and that the reaction between the wedge and the table is

$$(M + m\cos^2\alpha)g. \qquad \text{(O.C.)}$$

20. In a mountain railway, of uniform inclination 30°, the ascending and descending cars are connected by a rope which passes round a pulley at the top of the incline, and their masses are $\frac{3}{4}M$ and M tonnes, respectively; the resistances due to friction, etc., are $10g$ N per tonne mass of each car, and the brake resistance is Q N per tonne mass. Show that if motion can be prevented by applying the brakes to the descending car alone, Q must be at least 1055. If Q has this value, calculate the retardation when the cars are in motion and the brakes applied in both cars.   (L.U.)

CHAPTER 16

WORK, POWER, ENERGY

16.1 Work Done by a Force

The work done by a force was defined in Chapter 8, and certain theorems concerning work were established there. In the present chapter we are concerned with the relation between work and kinetic energy in dynamics, and we begin with a summary of the principal propositions about the work done by a force.

The work done by a force is defined as the product of the force and the distance moved by its point of application along the line of action of the force. If a constant force P moves its point of application from A to B, where the line AB makes an angle θ with the line of action of the force, the work done is $P \times AB \cos \theta$. If $\cos \theta$ is negative the work done is negative, and work is done against the force.

The work done may be written as the scalar product of the vector $\mathbf{P}$ and the displacement $\mathbf{AB}$ so that the work done is

$$W = \mathbf{P} \cdot \mathbf{AB}.$$

Work being the product of a force and a distance, the units of work will normally be in newton-metres and in the SI system the newton-metre is called a *joule* (symbol J). In the c.g.s. system, the work done by 1 dyne in a displacement of 1 cm is called an *erg*, and, since 1 dyne = 10^{-5} N (see §15.4) and 1 cm = 10^{-2} m, 1 erg = 10^{-7} J. In the British system units of work are the foot-poundal (ft pdl) and the foot-pound (ft lbf) and

$$1 \text{ ft pdl} = 0.042 \text{ J}$$
$$1 \text{ ft lbf} = 1.356 \text{ J}.$$

The work done against gravity in raising a system of particles, or a body, of mass m from one position to another is mgh, where h is the height through which the centre of gravity is raised, and this quantity is independent of the displacement of the system or body relative to its centre of gravity.

The work done in stretching an elastic string is the product of the extension and the mean of the initial and final tensions.

The work done by a couple of constant moment in turning through any angle is the product of the moment of the couple and the angle.

The work done by the resultant of a system of forces in any displacement is equal to the sum of work done by the component forces in that displacement.

Example 1. *A car of mass 1000 kg accelerates uniformly from rest to acquire a velocity of 50 km/h on a level road in a distance of 250 m against frictional and other resistances of 30g N. Find the work done by the engine.*

The constant acceleration a is given by

$$\left(\frac{50 \times 1000}{3600}\right)^2 = 2a \times 250,$$

so that

$$a = 0.386 \text{ m/sec}^2.$$

The force required to give this acceleration is

$$F = 1000 \times 0.386 = 386 \text{ N}.$$

The total force required is therefore $386 + 30 \times 9.81 = 680$ N and the work done is

$$W = 680 \times 250 \text{ newton-metres}$$
$$= 17 \times 10^4 \text{ J}.$$

16.2 Work Done by a Variable Force

Let the point of application of a variable force move along a curved path, so that when the point of application has moved a distance s along the path the force is P in a direction making an angle θ with the tangent to the path at the point. Then, to the first order of small quantities, the work done by the force in moving its point of application a further infinitesimal distance δs is $P \cos \theta . \delta s$.

Hence the work done by the force in moving its point of application from a distance s_0 to a distance s_1 along the path is the sum of such quantities given by the integral

$$\int_{s_0}^{s_1} P \cos \theta \, ds.$$

Since the work done by a force is equal to the work done by its components, if X and Y be the components of the force P parallel to axes of reference, we have for the work done

$$\int_{s_0}^{s_1} P \cos \theta \, ds = \int_{x_0}^{x_1} X \, dx + \int_{y_0}^{y_1} Y \, dy,$$

where (x_0, y_0) and (x_1, y_1) are the points at which s has the values s_0 and s_1, respectively.

In particular, if the displacement of the point of application is along a straight line and the direction of the force P is along this line, we have for the work done in a displacement from x_0 to x_1

$$\int_{x_0}^{x_1} P \, dx.$$

16.3 Forces Which Do No Work

If the direction of a force is perpendicular to the direction of a displacement, the work done by the force is zero. Some examples of forces which do no work are the following:

(i) The tension of an inextensible string with one end fixed.

There is no tension in the string unless it is taut, and if it is taut any infinitesimal displacement of its free end must be perpendicular to the line of the string, and hence the work done by the tension in this displacement is zero. Any finite displacement is the sum of such infinitesimal displacements, and the work done in it will be zero.

(ii) The normal reaction to a surface.

For if the body moves on the surface, any infinitesimal displacement must be perpendicular to the direction of the reaction.

(iii) Internal forces of a rigid body.

The internal forces of a rigid body consist of pairs of equal and opposite forces, and hence in any displacement of the body the total work done by them will be zero.

The reactions between two bodies may be considered as an internal force if the bodies are treated as a unit.

(iv) The reaction at the point of contact of a rolling body.

If the body rolls without sliding on a fixed surface, the point of contact is instantaneously at rest, and hence at any instant the normal reaction and the friction at the point will have zero displacements and do no work. More exactly it may be said that if the body has any infinitesimal displacement by rolling, the displacement of the point of contact is of the second order of small quantities and the work done in a finite displacement is therefore zero to the first order.

16.4 Power

Power is defined as the rate at which work is done. Thus if 30 J of work is done in a time of 2 seconds the average power is 15 J/sec.

In metric units a rate of work of 1 joule per second is called a *watt* (symbol W) and 1000 watts is called a kilowatt (symbol kW).

We have
$$1 \text{ watt} = 1 \text{ joule per second}$$
$$= 10^7 \text{ ergs per second.}$$

In the British system the unit of power is called a *horse-power* (abbreviation h.p.) which is defined as a rate of 550 ft lbf/sec or 33 000 ft lbf/min. This represents a rate of working which a strong horse might be able to maintain, for example, when moving steadily at 10 ft/sec and exerting a tractive force of 55 lbf and 1 h.p. = 746 watts.

If a force F newton is applied to a body at a point which moves along the line of action of the force at a constant speed of v m/sec, the work done per second is Fv joules and the power is Fv watts. If the work is being done by an engine which is working at a rate of n kilowatts, we have

$$n = \frac{Fv}{1000}.$$

Thus the force F can be found if n and v are known and v can be found if n and F are known.

Note that

$$1 \text{ ft pdl} = 421\,386 \text{ ergs},$$

$$550 \text{ ft lbf} = 550 \times 32 \cdot 2 \times 421\,386 \text{ ergs},$$

$$= 746 \times 10^7 \text{ ergs},$$

$$1 \text{ h.p.} = 746 \text{ watts} = 0 \cdot 746 \text{ kilowatts},$$

and 1 kilowatt = 1000 watts = 1·34 h.p.

The French cheval-vapeur (c.v.) raises 75 kg through 1 m in 1 second and is $75 \times 9 \cdot 81 = 735 \cdot 75$ W.

Example 2. *Find the power exerted by a locomotive which keeps a train of 200 tonnes moving at a constant speed of 90 km/h up a slope of 1 in 160 against resistances of 50 N per tonne.*
The resolved part of the weight along the track

$$= 200 \times 1000g/160 = 12\,262 \cdot 5 \text{ N}.$$

The resistances

$$= 50 \times 200 = 10^4 \text{ N}.$$

The total tractive force

$$= 22\,262 \cdot 5 \text{ N}.$$

The work done per second

$$= 22\,262 \cdot 5 \times 25 = 556\,600 \text{ J}.$$

The power

$$= 556 \cdot 6 \text{ kW}.$$

16.5 Efficiency

The power of an engine may be measured in two ways. In a piston engine, for example, the thrust of the expanding gases on the piston end can be measured during its motion and the work done by this thrust calculated. The rate at which this work is done is called the *indicated power* of the engine. There is always a loss of power, due to friction and other causes, between the piston and the rotating parts of the engine, and the power measured at a later stage, for example by a brake on the flywheel, gives what is called the *brake power* of the engine. The *efficiency* of the engine is the ratio of the brake power to the indicated power. The efficiency of any mechanical system may be measured in a similar way as the ratio of the output of work to the input of work. Thus, if a weight w is lifted by a pulley system through a height h, the work done is wh and this is the output of work. The input of work is then the work done in hauling on the rope that causes the system to move and, due to friction, this will usually be somewhat greater than the output.

Example 3. *Find the rate of working in kilowatts of an engine which can fill a cistern 70 m above the level of a river with 1.5×10^5 litres of water in 24 hours, assuming that a litre of water has a mass of 1 kg and that only two-thirds of the work actually done by the engine is available for raising the water.*

The rate at which work is being done in raising 1.5×10^5 kg of water through 70 m in 24 hours is

$$\frac{1.5 \times 10^5 \times 9.81 \times 70}{24 \times 60 \times 60} \text{ J/sec}$$

$$= 1.192 \text{ kilowatts.}$$

Since the efficiency of the system is $\frac{2}{3}$, the power of the engine must be

$$1.192 \times \tfrac{3}{2} = 1.79 \text{ kilowatts.}$$

Example 4. *An engine draws a train of mass 250 tonnes along a level track at a speed of 54 km/h against resistances of 60 N/tonne. Find the power at which it is working. Find the power necessary to draw the train at the same speed up an incline of 1 in 200.*

$$\begin{aligned} \text{The total resistance} &= 60 \times 250, \\ &= 15\,000 \text{ N}, \\ \text{speed} &= 15 \text{ m/sec}, \\ \text{work done per sec} &= 225 \times 10^3 \text{ J/sec}, \\ \text{power} &= 225 \text{ kW.} \end{aligned}$$

The additional force up an incline of 1 in 200 is

$$\frac{250}{200} \times 1000g = 12\,262.5 \text{ N},$$

$$\begin{aligned} \text{the total resistance} &= 27\,262.5 \text{ N}, \\ \text{speed} &= 15 \text{ m/sec}, \\ \text{work done per sec} &= 27\,262.5 \times 15 \text{ J}, \\ \text{power} &= 409 \text{ kW.} \end{aligned}$$

Example 5. *A car of mass 1000 kg tows a second car of equal mass at a uniform speed of 40 km/h on level ground; the resistance to motion of each is $50g$ N. Show that the rate of working is 10·9 kilowatts. The pull of the first car is gradually increased until the tow-rope breaks under a tension of $75g$ N. If the rate of working is then 21·8 kilowatts find how much further the second car then travels before it comes to rest.* (L.U.)

The total pull is $100g$ N when the speed is 40 km/h ($100/9$ m/sec) so that the rate of working is

$$100 \times 9.81 \times \frac{10^2}{9} = 10.9 \text{ kilowatts.}$$

At the instant when the rope breaks the forward pull on each car will be $75g$ N and since the rate of working is then 21.8 kilowatts we have, if v is the speed in m/sec,

$$21.8 \times 10^3 = 150 \times 9.81 \times v,$$

$$v = 1.481 \times 10 \text{ m/sec} = 53.33 \text{ km/h}.$$

The second car is then retarded by the resistance of $50g$ N and the retardation a m/sec² is given by

$$50 \times 9.81 = 1000a,$$

$$a = 0.4905.$$

The distance in which it comes to rest is given by the formula $v^2 = u^2 - 2ax$, and hence

$$\left(\frac{53.33 \times 10^3}{3600}\right)^2 = 0.981x,$$

$$x = 224 \text{ m}.$$

EXERCISES 16 (a)

1. An engine exerting 400 kW draws a train whose mass, including the engine, is 200 tonnes, up a slope of 1 in 80 against resistances of $12g$ N/tonne. Find the maximum speed of the train.

2. A car of mass 2000 kg is travelling at 45 km/h up an incline of $\sin^{-1}(1/14)$, the resistance to motion being $15g$ N. Show that the engine is working at 19.36 kW. The car reaches level ground and the engine continues to work at the same rate. Assuming that the resistance is proportional to the square of the car's speed, find the maximum speed attainable.   (L.U.)

3. A car of mass 2000 kg freewheels down a slope of 1 in 50 with an acceleration of 0.08 m/sec². What power will take the car up the same slope against the same resistances at a steady speed of 54 km/h?

4. The total mass of a train is 220 tonnes, and the resistance to its motion is 60 N per ton. The train acquires a speed of 54 km/h from rest in 5 min when moving on the level. Find the least power of the engine, assuming that the pull of the engine is constant. With this value of the power find the maximum speed of the train up a slope of $\sin^{-1}(\frac{1}{150})$, assuming the resistance remains the same.   (L.U.)

5. A car of mass 1600 kg is climbing a hill which rises 1 (vertically) in 80 (along the road) at a steady speed of 45 km/h. If the engine is then working at 8 kW, calculate the frictional and other resistances. If the car later travels on a level road and the engine is working at 14 kW when the speed is 45 km/h, determine the acceleration at that instant, assuming the resistances to be the same as for the hill.   (L.U.)

6. A locomotive working at 500 kW pulls a train of 200 tonnes (including the locomotive) along a level track, the resistance to motion being 80 N/tonne. When the speed of the train is 45 km/h, determine its acceleration.

   At what steady speed will the locomotive pull the same train up an incline of 1 in 100 with the same expenditure of power against the same resistance?
                                                                                          (L.U.)

7. A lorry of mass 5000 kg moves up a hill with a slope of 1 (vertical) in 20 (horizontal) at a steady speed of 18 km/h. The frictional resistance is equivalent to 400 N. Find the power transmitted by the engine. If the same power is trans-

mitted when the speed is 27 km/h, and the frictional resistance is the same, find the acceleration at this speed on a level road.

8. A locomotive of 668 kW and mass 90 tonnes is drawing a train of mass 120 tonnes up a slope of 1 in 84. The frictional resistances amount to 350 N/tonne. Find the maximum uniform speed at which the train can travel up the incline.
(L.U.)

9. A car of mass 2500 kg is accelerating at 0.6 m/sec^2 up an incline of 1 in 50, the resistance being 300 N. Find the power exerted when the speed is 36 km/h.
(L.U.)

10. A train of total mass 250 tonnes is drawn by an engine working at 418 kW. If at a certain instant the total resistance is 80 N/ton and the speed is 54 km/h, what is the train's acceleration?
(L.U.)

11. A train whose mass is 250 tonnes runs up an incline of 1 in 200 at the uniform rate of 36 km/h; the resistance due to friction etc. is equal to the weight of 3 tonnes. At what power is the engine working?
(L.U.)

12. A car of mass 1000 kg travels at a constant speed of 60 km/h on a level road when the engine works at 15 kW. Prove that the resistance to motion is 900 N. With the same rate of working and the same resistance the car ascends a road inclined at θ to the horizontal at a constant speed of 45 km/h. Find the value of $\sin \theta$.
(L.U.)

13. A car of mass 840 kg freewheels down a slope of $\sin^{-1} (1/14)$ at uniform speed against road resistances. On the level road the engine is switched on and the car accelerates at 2 m/sec^2 from 50 km/h, the road resistances remaining the same. At what rate does the engine work?
(L.U.)

14. An engine draws a train of mass 250 tonnes along a level track at a speed of 54 km/h against resistances which may be taken at 60 N/tonne. Find the power necessary to draw the train at the same speed up an incline of 1 in 160.
(L.U.)

15. It is found that a motor car of mass 1200 kg will run of its own accord with constant speed down a slope of 1 in 120. If the total frictional resistance remains constant, find the power exerted by the engine when the car is driven up the same slope at a constant speed of 54 km/h. If the engine still works at this power and the frictional resistances are the same, find the acceleration of the car directly after it has reached level road at the top of the slope.
(L.U.)

16. A train of 300 tonnes is ascending a track at an inclination of 1 in 200 and the frictional and other resistances are 70 N/tonne. Find the highest speed of the train when the engine is working at 448 kW. If the engine is also working at this rate when the speed is 25 km/h, find the acceleration.
(L.U.)

17. A van of mass 1000 kg free-wheels down a slope of 1 in 14 (i.e. $\sin^{-1} 1/14$) at a uniform speed of 36 km/h. When it reaches level ground at the foot of the slope the engine is switched on and works at 16 kW. At what rate does the van begin to accelerate, assuming the resistance to remain unaltered?
(L.U.)

18. A train of 3×10^5 kg is ascending a track at an inclination of 1 in 250 and the frictional and other resistances are $2000g$ N. Find the highest speed of the train when the engine is working at 500 kW. If the engine is also working at this rate when the speed is 30 km/h, find the acceleration.
(L.U.)

16.6 Kinetic Energy

We have seen (§15.7) that if the force acting on a particle moving in a straight line is plotted against the distance moved, the area under the curve gives the increase of the kinetic energy $\frac{1}{2}mv^2$. Now, the area under the force–distance curve gives the work done during the motion, and hence we have that the change in kinetic energy is equal to the work done. If the force is constant, the work done by a force F moving through a distance s is given by

$$\text{work done} = F \cdot s.$$

The acceleration, which is constant, is given by $F = ma$, where m is the mass, therefore

$$\text{work done} = mas.$$

Also, the initial and final velocities during the motion are given by the formula $v^2 = u^2 + 2as$, therefore

$$\text{work done} = \tfrac{1}{2}mv^2 - \tfrac{1}{2}mu^2,$$

$$= \text{increase in kinetic energy.}$$

The work done may, of course, be negative, causing a decrease of kinetic energy.

The *kinetic energy* of a particle is therefore defined as its capacity for work by virtue of its motion, since it measures the amount of work which it can do against external force before its velocity is destroyed.

The units of kinetic energy are the same as the units of work. Thus for a constant force we have

$$Fs = \tfrac{1}{2}mv^2 - \tfrac{1}{2}mu^2,$$

where the force F is in absolute units, and the units of kinetic energy are absolute units of work such as joules. If the force F is in gravitational units, then in absolute units it is Fg and we have

$$Fgs = \frac{1}{2}mv^2 - \frac{1}{2}mu^2,$$

or

$$Fs = \frac{1}{2}\frac{m}{g}v^2 - \frac{1}{2}\frac{m}{g}u^2.$$

Here, the work done is expressed in gravitational units, and the kinetic energy is also in gravitational units, such as kgf m.

The symbol w is commonly used for the weight of a body and the symbol m for its mass. Thus if, in gravitational units, w is the force with which the earth attracts a mass m, w and m have the same *numerical* value. For example, a body of mass 10 kg is attracted to the earth by a force of 10 kgf.

It has long been customary, particularly in engineering, to write the kinetic energy of a body as $\dfrac{wv^2}{2g}$ when gravitational units are being used, and in theoretical work this serves as a reminder of the type of unit in which the energy is expressed.

Thus we write the kinetic energy as

$$\frac{1}{2}mv^2\ldots\text{in absolute units,}$$

$$\frac{w}{2g}v^2\ldots\text{in gravitational units.}$$

In the same way we may write the force causing a particle of mass m to have an acceleration a as $F = ma$ in absolute units, and $F = \dfrac{w}{g}a$ (where $w = m$) in gravitational units. Momentum may be written as mv in absolute units and $\dfrac{wv}{g}$ in gravitational units.

Example 6. *A bullet of mass 5 g moving with speed 400 m/sec strikes a fixed block of wood and penetrates 15 cm. Find the resistance of the wood, assuming it to be uniform.*

The kinetic energy of the bullet

$$= \tfrac{1}{2} \times 0.005 \times (400)^2,$$

$$= 400 \text{ J.}$$

If the resistance offered by the wood is constant and equal to F newtons, the work done against the bullet in its penetration

$$= F \times 0.15 \text{ joule.}$$

This work changes the kinetic energy from its initial value to zero, therefore

$$0.15F = 400$$

giving

$$F = 2670 \text{ N.}$$

Example 7. *A mass of 4 kilos will compress a spring through 2.5 cm. A model truck, of mass 250 gm, runs into the spring, used as buffer, with a velocity of 90 cm/sec. How far will the spring be compressed before the truck is brought to rest?* (O.C.)

Let the spring be compressed x cm when the truck is brought to rest. The force in the spring will then be $4g \times \dfrac{x}{0.025} = 160gx$ newtons.

The mean of the initial and final compressive forces will be $80gx$ and the work done in compressing the spring $80gx^2$ joules.

The kinetic energy destroyed

$$\tfrac{1}{2}(0.25)(0.9)^2 = 0.10125 \text{ J}$$

Therefore

$$80gx^2 = 0.10125$$

$$x^2 = 0.0001287$$

$$x = 0.0114 \text{ m} = 1.14 \text{ cm.}$$

16.7 Kinetic Energy and Power

In calculating the rate at which an engine is working we have to find the work which it does against resistances or against gravity in a given time, adding the work done in increasing the kinetic energy or deducting the work done against it represented by a decrease of kinetic energy.

Example 8. *Find the power required to pump 500 gal of water per minute from a depth of 40 m, the water being delivered through a circular pipe 10 cm in diameter. (Assume 1 m^3 of water is 220 gal and weighs 1000 kg, and neglect friction.)*

The work done against gravity in 1 min in lifting 500 gal of water through 40 m is

$$\frac{500}{220} \times 10^3 g \times 40 = 8.92 \times 10^5 \text{ J}.$$

500 gal of water passing through a pipe of cross-sectional area 0.0025π in 1 min, must have a speed of $\dfrac{550}{220} \times \dfrac{1}{0.0025\pi} \times \dfrac{1}{60} = 4.82$ m/sec.

Hence, the kinetic energy given to the water passing through the pipe in 1 min is

$$\frac{1}{2} \times \frac{500}{220} \times 10^3 \times (4.82)^2 = 26\,400 \text{ J}.$$

The total work done is therefore

$$9.184 \times 10^5 \text{ J/min}$$

and the power is 15.3 kW.

EXERCISES 16 (b)

1. A train travelling uniformly on the level at the rate of 72 km/h begins an ascent of 1 in 75. The tractive force which the engine exerts during the ascent is constant and equal to 2×10^4 N, the resistance is constant and equal to 1.5×10^4 N and the mass of the whole train is 225 tonnes. Show that the train will come to a standstill after climbing for 1.84 km. At what rate is the engine working (i) just before, (ii) just after, beginning the ascent?

2. An engine in 7 sec has raised a load of 1000 kg through a height of 1 m and has communicated to it a speed of 3.5 m/sec. At what average power has it been working?

3. Find the power of a pump which, in 1 min, raises 1 m^3 of water through 10 m, discharging it at a speed of 4 m/sec.   (O.C.)

4. The area of the cross-section of the nozzle of a hose-pipe is 10 cm^2, and an engine pumps water through it with a velocity of 20 m/sec. Find the weight of water delivered per second and the kinetic energy of this water.

    Determine also the least power of the engine if the nozzle is 5 m above the level of the supply of water.   (L.U.)

5. A car of mass 3000 kg will just run down a slope of angle $\sin^{-1} \frac{1}{20}$ under its own weight. Assuming that the forces resisting its motion remain constant and that the engine exerts a constant tractive force, determine the power developed when a speed of 54 km/h is attained from rest on a level track in a time of 4 min.   (L.U.)

6. The energy due to the *fall* of the water in a waterfall is used to drive a hydraulic plant. If the water reaches the fall with a horizontal velocity of 9 km/h, the height of the fall is 40 m, and the cross-section of the stream is 3 m^2, find the power of the plant. What would be the additional power if the energy of the flowing water could also be used?   (L.U.)

7. A man strikes a block with a 10 kg hammer thirty-three times a minute. If the velocity of the hammer on striking the block is 8 m/sec and the hammer is reduced to rest after each blow, find the average power exerted by the man.
   (L.U.)

8. The pump of a fire-fighting launch throws a jet 6 cm in diameter at a speed of 30 m/sec from the nozzle, which is 3 m above the water-line. Find the power required to drive the pump.

9. A dock 200 m long, 30 m broad and 10 m deep is emptied by a pipe 1 m in diameter in 4 hr. The water is delivered at a point 12 m above the bottom of the dock. Calculate the average power of the pump, assuming its efficiency to be 70 per cent, taking into account the energy of the water issuing from the pipe.

10. An army tank of mass 10000 kg in surmounting an obstacle has its speed reduced from 30 km/h to 15 km/h and its centre of gravity raised through 1·2 m. Find the total loss of energy. (L.U.)

11. A train of mass 100 tonnes acquires uniformly a speed of 54 km/h from rest in 400 m. Assuming a resistance of 30 N per tonne mass of the train, find the tension in the coupling between the engine and the train, and the maximum power at which the engine is working during the run. The mass of the engine may be neglected. (L.U.)

12. A motor car of mass 2000 kg arrives at the bottom of a hill 0·8 km long, which rises 1 in 125, with a speed of 30 km/h, and reaches the top of the hill with a speed of 15 km/h. If there is a retarding force, due to friction, of 14 g N, calculate the work done by the engine in getting the car up the hill. (L.U.)

13. Find the uniform force that will move a 1-kg mass from rest through 1 m in 1 sec. If this force is exerted while the mass moves 100 m from rest, find the work done by the force and the maximum power attained. (L.U.)

14. A jet of water issues from a pipe, of cross-section 20 cm², at the rate of 400 gal per minute. If the whole of its energy could be used, show that it would be doing work at the rate of 3·48 kW nearly, given that 1 m³ of water is 220 gallons.
    (L.U.)

16.8 Potential Energy

The *potential energy* of a particle is the work which the forces acting on it would do if it moved from its given position to some standard position.

Thus if a particle of mass m kg is at a height h m above a table, and we take the surface of the table as the standard position, the force acting on the particle is mg N and the work that would be done by this force as the particle fell to the table would be mgh joules. This is therefore the potential energy of the particle with reference to the surface of the table. If the height above the ground were h_1 m, the potential energy with respect to the ground would be mgh_1 joules. The standard position is not of great importance, and need not usually be specified, since what is of interest is the change of potential energy.

Potential energy due to the force of gravity is the most commonly used form of potential energy, but there are many other forms. For example, a compressed spring, a stretched elastic string, a compressed gas, all have potential energy which is the work the forces in them would do in restoring them to their natural shape.

If the particle of mass m kg falls from a height h m above the table, its velocity when it reaches the table is given by

$$v^2 = 2gh.$$

Hence, its kinetic energy on reaching the table is

$$\tfrac{1}{2}mv^2 = mgh \text{ joules.}$$

This shows that the kinetic energy which the particle acquires in falling to the table is equal to the potential energy which it has lost in changing its position. Thus the total of kinetic and potential energy is unchanged. At any stage during the motion when the particle has fallen x m, its velocity is $\sqrt{2gx}$, and

the kinetic energy $= mgx$ joules,

the potential energy $= mg(h-x)$ joules,

and the total of kinetic and potential energy is unchanged. Thus at any stage the loss of potential energy is equal to the gain of kinetic energy. Since the loss of potential energy is the work done, this example verifies the principle that the increase in kinetic energy is equal to the work done.

16.9 Energy Equation

We have shown that for free motion of a particle in a straight line under gravity the sum of the kinetic and potential energies remains constant. We may extend this principle to forces other than that of gravity by including in the potential energy the work which these forces would do in a displacement to the standard position. The term potential energy is, however, limited to the work that can be done by what are called *conservative* forces, that is, forces such that the work they do as the particle moves from its position to the standard position depends only on its position, and not on the manner in which it moves to the standard position. This excludes forces such as friction which in fact cause an apparent loss of energy by converting mechanical energy into other forms of energy such as heat or sound.

The *energy equation* states that if the forces acting on a particle are conservative, the sum of the kinetic and potential energies remains constant.

If the motion of the particle is two-dimensional, let (x, y) be the co-ordinates of its position, m its mass, and (X, Y) the components of the forces acting on it.

Then $$m\ddot{x} = X, \quad m\ddot{y} = Y.$$

Now

$$\frac{d}{dx}\left(\frac{1}{2}\dot{x}^2\right) = \dot{x}\frac{d\dot{x}}{dx} = \dot{x}\frac{d\dot{x}}{dt}\cdot\frac{dt}{dx} = \ddot{x},$$

$$\frac{d}{dy}\left(\frac{1}{2}\dot{y}^2\right) = \dot{y}\frac{d\dot{y}}{dy} = \dot{y}\frac{d\dot{y}}{dt}\cdot\frac{dt}{dy} = \ddot{y}.$$

Therefore

$$\frac{d}{dx}\left(\frac{1}{2}m\dot{x}^2\right) = X, \quad \frac{d}{dy}\left(\frac{1}{2}m\dot{y}^2\right) = Y.$$

Integrating the first of these equations between the values x_0 and x_1 of x, we have, if $\dot{x}_0$ and $\dot{x}_1$ are the corresponding velocities,

$$\frac{1}{2}m\dot{x}_1{}^2 - \frac{1}{2}m\dot{x}_0{}^2 = \int_{x_0}^{x_1} X\,dx.$$

Similarly, if $\dot{y}_0$ and $\dot{y}_1$ are the velocities for the corresponding values y_0 and y_1 of y, we have

$$\frac{1}{2}m\dot{y}_1{}^2 - \frac{1}{2}m\dot{y}_0{}^2 = \int_{y_0}^{y_1} Y\,dy.$$

Therefore

$$\frac{1}{2}m(\dot{x}_1{}^2 + \dot{y}_1{}^2) - \frac{1}{2}m(\dot{x}_0{}^2 + \dot{y}_0{}^2) = \int_{x_0}^{x_1} X\,dx + \int_{y_0}^{y_1} Y\,dy.$$

That is, if v_0 be the velocity at the point (x_0, y_0) and v_1 the velocity at the point (x_1, y_1), we have

$$v_0{}^2 = \dot{x}_0{}^2 + \dot{y}_0{}^2, \quad v_1{}^2 = \dot{x}_1{}^2 + \dot{y}_1{}^2,$$

and

$$\frac{1}{2}mv_1{}^2 - \frac{1}{2}mv_0{}^2 = \int_{x_0}^{x_1} X\,dx + \int_{y_0}^{y_1} Y\,dy.$$

Hence, the change in kinetic energy is equal to the work done by the forces in the displacement, and, for conservative forces, the sum of the kinetic and potential energies remains constant.

It should be noted that although the energy equation is true only when the forces are conservative, the equation of kinetic energy to work done is universally true. Thus, for example, the work done when a particle slides a distance x down a rough plane inclined at α to the horizontal is

$$(mg \sin \alpha - \mu\, mg \cos \alpha)x,$$

and this is the kinetic energy acquired.

The energy equation applies also to the motion of a rigid body. If the body is moving in a straight line without rotation, its total kinetic energy is the sum of the kinetic energies of its particles, that is $\frac{1}{2}Mv^2$, where M is the total mass. If the body is also rotating, its kinetic energy will include its energy of rotation; this will be considered in a later chapter.

The energy equation is the expression of a very general and fundamental scientific principle known as the Conservation of Energy, which states that the total amount of energy in the universe is constant. It must not, however, be understood that the total *mechanical* energy of a system is constant, since such energy may be converted by non-conservative forces into other forms of energy, such as heat or sound.

In the next chapter we shall see that in any impact of particles or bodies there is a loss of kinetic energy without a corresponding increase in potential energy, due to the conversion of mechanical energy into other forms of energy, and the energy equation cannot be used in such cases. In these cases it is not usually possible to equate the change of kinetic energy to the work done, since bodies are deformed in an impact and the work done is not easily found.

Example 9. *A particle of mass m rests on a smooth plane inclined at an angle α to the horizontal, it is connected by a light inextensible string parallel to the line of greatest slope of the plane, which passes over a smooth pulley at the top of the plane and carries a particle of mass M (> m) hanging vertically. Find the velocity of the particle when it has moved from rest a distance x up the plane.*

When the particle has moved a distance x up the plane (Fig. 217) it has risen through

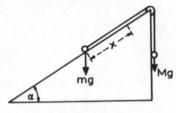

Fig. 217.

$x \sin \alpha$, and its potential energy has increased by $mgx \sin \alpha$. In this displacement the potential energy of the mass M has decreased by Mgx.

Hence, the increase of kinetic energy is equal to the decrease in potential energy, and we have

$$\frac{1}{2}(m+M)v^2 = Mgx - mgx \sin \alpha,$$

$$v = \left\{ \frac{2gx(M - m \sin \alpha)}{M+m} \right\}^{\frac{1}{2}}.$$

Example 10. *A small ring of mass m can slide on a smooth circular wire of radius a, which is fixed in a vertical plane. From a point on the wire at a vertical distance h above its lowest point the ring is given a velocity u along the wire. Find its velocity at the lowest point of the wire and determine whether it will reach the highest point of the wire.*

Since there is no friction, the reaction between the ring and the wire is at any instant perpendicular to the wire, and therefore to the direction of motion of the ring. Hence this force does no work as the ring slides on the wire. Therefore, we may use the energy equation with the potential energy depending only on the height of the ring above the lowest point of the wire.

When the ring starts we have

$$\text{kinetic energy} = \tfrac{1}{2}mu^2,$$

$$\text{potential energy} = mgh,$$
$$\text{total energy} = \tfrac{1}{2}mu^2 + mgh.$$

If v be the velocity at the lowest point of the wire, we have in this position

$$\text{kinetic energy} = \tfrac{1}{2}mv^2,$$
$$\text{potential energy} = 0,$$
$$\text{total energy} = \tfrac{1}{2}mv^2.$$

Therefore

$$\tfrac{1}{2}mv^2 = \tfrac{1}{2}mu^2 + mgh,$$
$$v^2 = \sqrt{(u^2 + 2gh)}.$$

Let w be the velocity at the highest point of the wire; we have in this position

$$\text{kinetic energy} = \tfrac{1}{2}mw^2,$$
$$\text{potential energy} = mg \times 2a,$$
$$\text{total energy} = \tfrac{1}{2}mw^2 + 2mga.$$

Therefore

$$\tfrac{1}{2}mw^2 + 2mga = \tfrac{1}{2}mu^2 + mgh,$$
$$w^2 = u^2 + 2gh - 4ga.$$

If this expression is greater than zero, the ring will reach the highest point, and the condition for this is

$$u^2 \geqslant 2g(2a - h).$$

It should be noted that the direction along the wire of the initial velocity is immaterial to the problem.

Example 11. *A particle of mass M is attached to two particles, each of mass m, by means of two light inextensible strings passing over two small smooth fixed pegs, distant 2c apart at the same level. Show that when the mass M falls from a position in which the strings are each inclined to the vertical at an angle θ, to a position in which they are each inclined to the vertical at an angle φ, there is a loss of potential energy of amount*

$$Mgc(\cot \phi - \cot \theta) - 2mgc(\operatorname{cosec} \phi - \operatorname{cosec} \theta).$$

Deduce that, if there is equilibrium when the strings are each inclined to the vertical at an angle α, and the system is released from a position in which the strings are equally inclined to the vertical at an angle θ, it will next come to instantaneous rest when the inclination is φ, where

$$\tan^2\frac{\alpha}{2} = \tan\frac{\theta}{2}\tan\frac{\phi}{2}. \tag{O.C.}$$

Let A and B be the pegs and C the mid-point of AB, so that $AC = CB = c$ (Fig. 218).

Let D be the position of M when the strings are inclined at θ to the vertical and E the position of M when the inclination is ϕ.

Taking the standard position as that in which M is at C, the potential energy is the position θ is

$$- Mg \, . \, CD + 2mg(AD - AC),$$

since $AD - AC$ is the amount by which each of the masses m is raised.

$$\text{Now, } CD = c \cot \theta,$$

$$AD = c \operatorname{cosec} \theta,$$

therefore the potential energy in the position θ is

$$- Mgc \cot \theta + 2mgc(\operatorname{cosec} \theta - 1).$$

In the position ϕ the potential energy is

$$- Mgc \cot \phi + 2mgc(\operatorname{cosec} \phi - 1).$$

Hence, the loss of potential energy when M moves from D to E is

$$Mgc(\cot \phi - \cot \theta) - 2mgc(\operatorname{cosec} \phi - \operatorname{cosec} \theta).$$

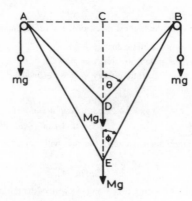

Fig. 218.

In the position of equilibrium, the strings being inclined at α to the vertical, the tension in each string is mg, and we have

$$2mg \cos \alpha = Mg.$$

If the system is released from rest in the position θ and comes to rest in the position ϕ, the kinetic energy in each of these positions is zero, and hence the potential energy has the same value in each position.

That is

$$Mgc(\cot \phi - \cot \theta) - 2mgc(\operatorname{cosec} \phi - \operatorname{cosec} \theta) = 0.$$

Therefore,

$$\cos\alpha(\cot\phi - \cot\theta) = \operatorname{cosec}\phi - \operatorname{cosec}\theta,$$

$$\cos\alpha = 2\cos^2\frac{\alpha}{2} - 1 = \frac{\sin\theta - \sin\phi}{\sin(\theta - \phi)},$$

$$= \frac{2\cos\frac{\theta + \phi}{2}\sin\frac{\theta - \phi}{2}}{2\sin\frac{\theta - \phi}{2}\cos\frac{\theta - \phi}{2}}$$

$$\cos^2\frac{\alpha}{2} = \frac{\cos\frac{\theta}{2}\cos\frac{\phi}{2}}{\cos\frac{\theta - \phi}{2}},$$

$$1 + \tan^2\frac{\alpha}{2} = \frac{\cos\frac{\theta - \phi}{2}}{\cos\frac{\theta}{2}\cos\frac{\phi}{2}},$$

$$\tan^2\frac{\alpha}{2} = \tan\frac{\theta}{2}\tan\frac{\phi}{2}.$$

EXERCISES 16 (c)

1. An engine is raising water from a depth of 20 m and discharging 16 gallons a second with a velocity of 18 m/sec. Taking the mass of a gallon of water to be 4·5 kg, find separately the potential energy and the kinetic energy of the water discharged per second, and find the power at which the engine is working.

2. A small ring of mass m can slide on a smooth circular wire, radius r and centre O, which is fixed in a vertical plane. From a point on the wire at a vertical distance $\frac{1}{2}r$ above O the ring is given a velocity $\sqrt{gr}$ along the downward tangent to the wire. Show that it will just reach the highest point of the wire. (L.U.)

3. A mass of 3 kg is attached to the middle, and masses of 2 kg to the ends of a light inextensible string which is placed over two smooth pegs 4 m apart, the 3-kg mass being held midway between the pegs. If the system is released, find how far the 3-kg mass descends before coming instantaneously to rest.

4. The radii of a wheel and axle of negligible mass running in smooth bearings are a and b respectively. Masses of m and M are attached to light inextensible strings wound round the wheel and axle respectively in opposite senses. Show that when the mass m has fallen through a distance c from rest its velocity is

$$\left\{2gac\frac{am - bM}{a^2m + b^2M}\right\}^{\frac{1}{2}}.$$

5. An elastic string can be stretched 1 m by a mass of m kg. Show that the potential energy of the string when it has been stretched a metre is $\frac{1}{2}mga^2$ J. One end of the string is fixed, and a mass of M kg is attached to the other end below the point of suspension with the string taut but unstretched and then let go. Show that the mass will come to rest again after falling through a distance $2M/m$.

6. Three equal masses are attached to the middle and ends of a light cord which is placed over two smooth pulleys at the same level, so that the central mass

hangs symmetrically between the pulleys and the others hang vertically. If the central mass is pulled down until its connecting cord makes angles of 50° with the horizontal, and then let go, find what the angles will be when next the masses come to momentary rest. (L.U.)

7. A particle of mass 1 kg is hung on a light elastic string and is found to stretch it 30 cm. Show that the increase of potential energy of the system when the mass is pulled down a further x cm is $gx^2/6000$ J. If the mass is pulled down 4·5 cm below its equilibrium position and released, find its velocity as it passes through the equilibrium position.

8. A light inextensible string with one end fixed passes under a movable pulley of mass m and over a fixed smooth pulley and carries a mass $M(> \frac{1}{2}m)$ at its free end, the parts of the string being vertical. If the system is released from rest, show that the velocity of the mass M when it has fallen through a distance c is

$$\left\{ \frac{4gc(2M-m)}{4M+m} \right\}^{\frac{1}{2}}.$$

9. Two masses M and M' $(M > M')$ are connected by a light inextensible string which passes over a small, smooth, fixed pulley. M' hangs freely and M is on a smooth plane inclined to the horizontal at an angle α. Prove that, if the pulley is at a height h vertically above a point of the plane and the string from the pulley to M is inclined at an angle θ to the plane, both portions of the string being in a vertical plane through a line of greatest slope of the plane, the potential energy of the system differs by a constant from

$$h(M'g \operatorname{cosec} \theta - Mg \sin \alpha \cot \theta) \cos \alpha.$$

If this is not the equilibrium position and the system is held in this position and then released, show that in the subsequent motion the system will first come to instantaneous rest when θ has changed to θ', where $\tan \dfrac{\theta}{2} \tan \dfrac{\theta'}{2} = \tan^2 \dfrac{\beta}{2}$, β being the value of θ in the equilibrium position. (O.C.)

16.10 Units and Dimensions

The *fundamental units* used in dynamics are those of length, mass and time which are denoted by L, M and T respectively and the units of any quantity used in dynamics are expressible in terms of these basic units. Thus velocity is a unit of length divided by a unit of time, that is L/T or LT^{-1}, and may be in metres per second, miles per hour, etc. The following table gives the fundamental units of various quantities used in dynamics and the expression of a quantity in terms of these units is called its *dimensions*.

DIMENSIONS

Velocity LT^{-1}
Acceleration LT^{-2}
Force (absolute units) MLT^{-2}
Force (gravitational units) M
Energy (absolute units) ML^2T^{-2}

Energy (gravitational units) ML
Momentum (absolute units) MLT^{-1}
Momentum (gravitational units) MT
Power (absolute units) ML^2T^{-3}
Power (gravitational units) MLT^{-1}
Pressure (absolute units) $ML^{-1}T^{-2}$
Pressure (gravitational units) ML^{-2}

To change the units of a quantity the dimensions must be considered. Thus since force (in absolute units) has dimension MLT^{-2} and 1 lb = 0·4536 kg, 1 ft = 0·3048 m,

$$\frac{1 \text{ poundal}}{1 \text{ newton}} = \frac{(1 \text{ lb}) (1 \text{ ft}) (1 \text{ sec})^{-2}}{(1 \text{ kg}) (1 \text{ m}) (1 \text{ sec})^{-2}}$$
$$= 0·4536 \times 0·3048 = 0·1383$$

and 1 poundal = 0·1383 newton.

16.11 SI Units

In 1960 the Conférence Générale des Poids et Mesures, the international body which aims at maintaining standards of measurements, formally approved the use of SI units (Système International d'Unités) and the use of these units is being actively encouraged in this country and elsewhere. The main features of this system for use in dynamics are:
1. The basic units of length, mass and time are respectively the metre (symbol m), the kilogramme (symbol kg) and the second (symbol s).
2. The unit of force is the newton (symbol N), which is an absolute unit giving to a mass of 1 kg an acceleration 1 m/s^2.
3. The unit of energy is the joule (symbol J), which is the product of a newton and a metre, and the unit of power is the watt (symbol W) which is 1 joule per second.
4. Some other derived SI units are:

Quantity	General units	SI units	Symbol
Area	L^2	square metres	m^2
Volume	L^3	cubic metres	m^3
Density	ML^{-3}	kg per cubic metre	kg/m^3
Velocity	LT^{-1}	metres per second	m/s
Acceleration	LT^{-2}	metres per second per second	m/s^2
Angular velocity	T^{-1}	radians per second	rad/s
Pressure	$ML^{-1}T^{-2}$	newton per square metre	N/m^2

A complete change from Imperial Units to SI units will have to wait upon the installation of metric machinery and equipment. In the interim period such units as the poundal, the pound per square inch and the horse-power will be less and less used.

16.12 Conversion Table to SI Units

Length

1 inch = 0·0254 metre
1 foot = 0·3048 metre
1 mile = 1609·34 metre
1 sea mile = 1853·18 metre

Velocity

1 foot/sec = 0·3048 metre/second
1 mile/hour = 0·44704 metre/second
1 knot = 0·51477 metre/second
1 km/hour = 0·2778 metre/second

Mass

1 pound = 0·45359 kilogramme
1 ton = 1016·05 kilogramme
1 slug = 14·594 kilogramme
1 tonne = 1000 kilogramme

Force

1 poundal = 0·138255 newton
1 lb force = 4·44822 newton
1 ton force = 9964·013 newton
1 dyne = 10^{-5} newton
1 kg force = 9·8067 newton

Energy, Work

1 ft pdl = 0·042140 joule
1 ft lbf = 1·35582 joule
1 erg = 10^{-7} joule
1 metre kgf = 9·8067 joule

Density

1 lb/in^3 = 27680 $kg/(metre)^3$
1 lb/ft^3 = 16·0185 $kg/(metre)^3$

Pressure

1 lbf/in^2 = 6894·76 $newton/(metre)^2$
1 gmf/cm^2 = 9806·7 $newton/(metre)^2$
1 millibar = 100 $newton/(metre)^2$

Power

1 horse power = 745·70 watt
1 metric h.p.
(cheval vapeur) = 735·48 watt

The following prefixes are used to denote multiples of the standard units

10	deka	da	10^2	hecto	h	10^3	kilo	k
10^6	mega	M	10^9	giga	G	10^{12}	terra	T
10^{-1}	deci	d	10^{-2}	centi	c	10^{-3}	milli	m
10^{-6}	micro	μ	10^{-9}	nano	n	10^{-12}	pico	p
10^{-15}	femto	f	10^{-18}	atto	a			

EXERCISES 16 (d)

1. Given that 1 cm = 0·3937 in, and 1 kilo = 2·205 lb, find the number of dynes in a poundal. (L.U.)

2. If a second be the unit of time, the acceleration due to gravity (981 in c.g.s. units) the unit of acceleration, and a kilogram the unit of mass, find the unit of energy in ergs. (L.U.)

3. If m is the mass of a body in lb, V its velocity in ft/sec, in what units is its kinetic energy expressed when we say that this energy is measured by $\frac{1}{2}mV^2$?

    If the units of length and mass be each multiplied by 10 and the unit of time divided by 10, how will the following units be affected, (a) acceleration, (b) energy, (c) force, (d) power? (L.U.)

4. Given that 1 kilo = 2·204 lb, 1 metre = 3·281 ft, 1 h.p. = 33,000 ft lb/min, g = 981 cm/sec², show that 3 h.p. is approximately $2·24 \times 10^4$ ergs/sec. (L.U.)

5. Define a foot-poundal and a joule. Find the number of joules in a foot-poundal, given that 1 metre = 3·281 ft, 1 kilo = 2·205 lb. Find also the weight of 1 oz in dynes. (L.U.)

6. Assuming that 1 metre = 39·37 in and that 1 oz = 28·35 gm, calculate the force in *poundals* required to produce an acceleration of 10 metres/sec² in a mass of 1 kilo. Determine also the number of foot-poundals in one million ergs. (L.U.)

7. Given that 1 oz = 28·3 gm and that 1 in = 2·54 cm, g = 32·2 ft/sec², determine
    (i) the number of gm wt in 1 poundal,
    (ii) the number of kilowatts in 1 horse-power. (L.U.)

8. Find the ratio of (i) the momenta, (ii) the kinetic energies, of a mass of 8 oz moving at $1\frac{1}{2}$ miles a minute, and a mass of 10 kilo moving at 2 metres/sec. (1 lb = 454 gm, 1 ft = 30·5 cm.) (L.U.)

EXERCISES 16 (e)

1. A particle is set moving with kinetic energy E straight up a rough inclined plane, of inclination α and coefficient of friction μ. Prove that the work done against friction before the particle comes to rest is $\dfrac{E\mu \cos \alpha}{\sin \alpha + \mu \cos \alpha}$. (L.U.)

2. A man with his bicycle has a total mass of 100 kg. He begins to ascend an incline of 1 in 10, with a speed of 25 km/h, and with uniform retardation. He has to dismount when his speed is not greater than 5 km/h. If he works at an average of 0·15 kW, how far will he ascend? How far would he have ascended if he had not worked at all? (L.U.)

3. A train is running at 45 km/h when it is at a distance of 500 m from a station. Power is then shut off, and the train runs against a uniform resistance equal to $\frac{1}{100}$ of the weight of the train. If the uniform brake force that can be exerted on the train provides an additional resistance equal to $\frac{1}{10}$ of the weight of the train, find how far from the station the brake must be applied so that the train may stop there. (L.U.)

4. A man lifts a stone of mass 1 kg from the ground to a height of 2 m, and throws it away horizontally with a velocity of 10 m/sec. How many joules of work has to be done on the stone? If he does this 20 times a minute, find the average rate at which he is working, neglecting the work he does in moving himself. (L.U.)

5. Assuming that the resistances to the motion of a train are 10 kgf/tonne, if a route ascends 100 m in 10 km, and then descends through the same height in the same distance, show that if a detour on the level would not exceed in total distance 30 km, there would be economy in running, supposing that in descent steam is shut off. (1 tonne = 1000 kg.) (L.U.)

6. The diameter of the low-pressure cylinder of a marine engine is 116 cm, the average speed of the piston is 270 m/min and the average pressure of the steam on the piston is $2·2 \times 10^5$ N/m². What is the indicated power of the engine? (L.U.)

7. A cyclist and his machine together have a mass of 100 kg. Riding along a certain road he observes that, when he is free-wheeling down a slope of 1 in 40, his speed, when it has become uniform, is 20 km/h, and is 30 km/h when he is free-wheeling down a slope of 1 in 20. If the air-resistance varies as the square of the speed, and other resistances remain constant, find in watts the rate at which he must work to maintain a speed of 15 km/h on the level.

8. A train of total mass 400 tonnes is travelling on the level at 90 km/h, the engine working at 600 kW. If the resistances, apart from air resistance, are 50 N/tonne, find the magnitude of the air resistance. If air resistance varies as the square of the speed, find the rate at which the engine is working when drawing the same train up a gradient of 1 in 200 at a steady rate of 45 km/h; and find the acceleration which the train would have on this gradient at this speed if the engine were working at 600 kW.

9. A locomotive of 20 tonnes drawing a train of 180 tonnes, climbs an incline of 1 in 160 at a uniform speed of 45 km/h. Steam is shut off at the top of the incline, and the train descends an incline of 1 in 200 at the same uniform speed. Find the

initial acceleration of the train if power is turned on again as it descends the second incline. Find the rate of working of the locomotive on the first incline. Assuming that the locomotive develops the same power and that frictional forces are proportional to the speed, find the maximum speed of the train on the level.

10. A body slides down a rough plane ($\mu = \frac{1}{4}$) a distance of 100 m, the inclination of the plane being 28°. It then runs over a short curved piece and up an equally rough plane inclined at 35° to the horizontal. Find how far it runs up this plane.

11. A motor car of mass 1800 kg starts up an incline at 18 km/h. The road rises 100 m in 1 km, and at the end of that distance the speed of the car has been reduced to 9 km/h. If the frictional resistances are 300 N, find the average power exerted, the time for the mile being 5 min.

12. A 10-tonne tram-car arrives at the foot of an incline of 1 in 15 at a speed of 27 km/h and commences to climb with a constant tractive effort of 10^4 N, the frictional resistance being 800 N. Find the speed of the car and the effective power after 30 sec.

13. A train travelling uniformly on the level at 90 km/h begins an ascent of 1 in 50. The tractive force due to adhesion has a maximum value of 3×10^4 N, the resistances due to friction, etc., are 1.5×10^4 N, and the mass of the whole train is 200 tonnes. Show that it cannot surmount the incline if this exceeds 2.58 km in length, and find the power exerted by the engine, (i) just before beginning the ascent, (ii) just after. (L.U.)

14. It is found that to drive a car at a uniform speed of (i) 10, (ii) 20, (iii) 30 m/sec on a level road the engine must work at (i) 2, (ii) 5, (iii) 10 kW. Show that these facts are consistent with the assumption that the forces which retard the motion of a car are a constant force together with a force proportional to the square of the speed.

Regarding this assumption as correct, find the power for a speed of 90 km/h.

15. A car is of mass 1500 kg, and the greatest driving force which can be exerted on it is 1000 N. The resistance due to friction is $200 + v^2/10$ N, where v is the speed in km per hour. Calculate (i) the greatest speed at which the car can be driven up a slope of 1 in 40, (ii) the power developed when running at a steady speed of 72 km/h on the level. (L.U.)

16. A car has a maximum speed of 90 km/h on the level and the engine is then working at 60 kW. Calculate the total resistance to motion. If the mass of the car is 1000 kg and the tractive force remains unaltered, and if the resistance varies as the square of the speed, find, in degrees and minutes, the greatest slope up which a speed of 72 km/h could be maintained. (L.U.)

17. The total mass of a train is 600 tonnes. Find the greatest power the engine can develop on the level if the greatest speed attainable on a horizontal track is 72 km/h and the resistances to motion are 50 N/tonne. Find also the maximum speed, v km/h, attainable up a slope of 1 vertically to 80 along the slope, if the power then developed is the power on the level multiplied by

$$\left(1 - \frac{v}{20}\right).$$ (L.U.)

18. An electric tram-car of mass 2×10^4 kg, driven by two motors, is travelling on a horizontal road at 27 km/h and accelerating at 0.2 m/sec². The total forces resisting motion amount to 1800 N. If the power drawn from each electric wire is 30 kW, calculate the efficiency of the motors at this speed. (L.U.)

19. A vehicle has an engine which can exert a maximum propulsive power of 6 kW. Friction and wind resistance to the motion of the vehicle may be taken as a force of $(100 + 0.05V^2)$ N, where V is its velocity in m/sec. Show that its maximum speed on a level road is a little more than 36 m/s, assuming the propulsive power to be at its greatest.

20. A body of mass 10 kg, initially at rest, is acted on by a force which varies linearly with the distance the body has moved. The force is initially 200 N and falls to zero when the body has moved 5 m. A constant force of 50 N also acts opposing the motion of the body throughout the 5 m.

    Determine the final velocity of the body and the work done by the propulsive force. Sketch the form of the velocity–distance curve and determine whether the maximum propulsive power acts before or after the maximum velocity occurs.

21. A body of mass 50 kg is acted on by a variable force which has during 16 sec the values given in the following table:

Force (N)	10·0	11·6	13·0	14·4	15·2
Time (sec)	0	2	4	6	8
Force (N)	12·6	8·4	5·6	4·0	
Time (sec)	10	12	14	16	

    Initially the body is at rest and during motion there is a constant resisting force of 8 N. Determine the distance moved in 16 sec, and the rate at which the applied force is doing work at the end of 8 sec.   (Q.E.)

22. The frictional resistance to motion of a car of mass 1000 kg, when travelling on a level road, is given by $a + bV^2$ N, V being the speed in km per hour.

    With a power supply of 36 kW the car can travel at a constant speed of 54 km/h up a hill of slope 1 in 10. At 27 km/h on the level, with a supply of 25 kW, the acceleration of the car is 2 m/sec². Find the values of the constants a and b.   (Q.E.)

CHAPTER 17

IMPULSE, IMPACT

17.1 Impulse

When a constant force F acts on a particle of mass m for time t and increases its velocity from u to v along the line of action of the force, we have

$$F = ma,$$

$$Ft = m(v - u),$$

$$= mv - mu,$$

$$= \text{change of momentum.}$$

If the force F is a force of variable magnitude, we have

$$F = ma,$$

$$= m\frac{dv}{dt}.$$

$$\int_0^t F\,dt = \int_0^t m\frac{dv}{dt}.\,dt,$$

$$= mv - mu,$$

$$= \text{change of momentum.}$$

These formulae measure the change in momentum of the particle along the line of action of the force and, as was seen in §15.7, give the area under the force–time curve. The formulae are valid for all values of t for which the force is defined and apply to the change of momentum of a rigid body all of whose particles have the same velocity, F being the external force acting on the body.

The quantity $\int_0^t F\,dt$, (or Ft, if F is constant), is called the *impulse* acting on the particle or body. An impulse is not a force, but is a product of force and time. If F is in newtons and the time in seconds, the units of impulse are *newton-seconds*, that is, the same as the absolute units of momentum. If the force F is in kilogrammes weight, it is convenient to write the momentum in gravitational units, and we have

$$\int_0^t F\,dt = \frac{w}{g}v - \frac{w}{g}u,$$

and in this case the units of impulse are kgf seconds.

The concept of an impulse is particularly useful when dealing with a large force acting for a very short time, as, for example, when a bat strikes a ball or a charge of ammunition is ignited. In such cases it is usually impossible to measure either the magnitude of the force at any instant or the time during which it acts, but it is possible to measure the change of momentum which it causes, and therefore the impulse.

Since momentum is a vector, impulse is also a vector. Thus an impulse I acting in a direction making an angle α with a direction OX is equivalent to an impulse $I \cos \alpha$ along OX and $I \sin \alpha$ in a perpendicular direction, and $I \cos \alpha$ and $I \sin \alpha$ are the changes in momentum along and perpendicular to OX.

17.2 Recoil of Guns

When the explosive charge in a gun is ignited, the gases formed exert a very high pressure on the base of the shot and give to the shot a certain momentum. The gases exert an equal and opposite pressure backwards on the barrel of the gun, and therefore give to the barrel a momentum equal to that given to the shell in the opposite direction, if the forward momentum of the moving gases be neglected. In modern guns the barrel recoils along its axis, and this recoil is taken up by a spring or buffer against the gun-carriage which remains almost stationary. Only in certain large guns on railway mountings is the carriage allowed to recoil. A gun is designed so that the recoiling part has as large a part of the total mass as possible, so that, since its momentum is that of the shot, its recoiling velocity is small. Thus if the recoil is taken up by a piston compressing a spring, the piston is held stationary, and the spring and the cylinder containing it are fixed to and recoil with the barrel.

Where the whole gun is allowed to recoil on a horizontal or inclined plane, the momentum which it acquires is the component in the direction of recoil of the impulse causing the momentum of the shot. The component of the impulse in the perpendicular direction is cancelled by an impulsive reaction of the ground.

The force on a spring or buffer during recoil may be found by equating the kinetic energy of the recoiling part to the work done by this force over the length of the recoil. A good approximation is obtained by assuming that the recoil spring does not begin to act until the shot has left the barrel, so that the recoiling part may have the same momentum as the shot.

Let M be the mass of the recoiling parts,
   V the initial velocity of recoil,
   m the mass of the shot,
   v the muzzle velocity of the shot,
   l the length of recoil,
   F the force resisting recoil (assumed constant).

Then the impulse is

$$MV = mv,$$

and

$$V = \frac{m}{M}v.$$

The work done against the recoil is

$$Fl = \frac{1}{2}MV^2,$$

$$= \frac{1}{2}\frac{m^2v^2}{M}.$$

Example 1. *A shell of mass 120 kg is fired from a piece of mass 3584 kg with a velocity of 1250 m/sec. Find the impulse of the explosion and the velocity of recoil (assuming the recoil to be free) at the instant when the shell leaves the muzzle. If the recoil is taken up by a constant force in a distance of 1 m, find this force.*

The momentum given to the shell is

$$120 \times 1250 \text{ N sec},$$

$$= 15 \times 10^4 \text{ N sec}.$$

This is therefore the impulse.

If V m/sec be the velocity of recoil, this is caused by the same impulse and we have

$$3584V = 15 \times 10^4,$$

$$V = 41 \cdot 85 \text{ m/sec}.$$

The kinetic energy of recoil is

$$\tfrac{1}{2} \times 3584 \times (41 \cdot 85)^2 = 3 \cdot 14 \times 10^6 \text{ N m}$$

If the force resisting recoil be F newton, the work done in a recoil of 1 metre is F N m. This is equal to the kinetic energy destroyed, therefore

$$F = 3 \cdot 14 \times 10^6 \text{ N}$$

17.3 Impact of Water-jets

If a jet of water is played on a fixed surface at right angles to the jet, the momentum of a certain quantity of water is destroyed in each second, and this momentum destroyed measures the impulse on the surface. Now the duration of the impulse is one second, therefore we can find the average thrust on the surface during that second.

Example 2. *Water issues from a circular pipe 5 cm in diameter with a velocity of 14 m/sec and strikes a fixed plane at right angles. Find the thrust of the water on the plane.*

The volume of water discharged per second is

$$\pi\tfrac{2 \cdot 5}{4} \times 10^{-4} \times 14 \text{ m}^3 = 2 \cdot 75 \times 10^{-2} \text{ m}^3.$$

The mass of this volume of water is

$$27 \cdot 5 \text{ kg}.$$

The momentum of this water is

$$27 \cdot 5 \times 14 = 385 \text{ N sec.}$$

This momentum is destroyed by a force F newton in 1 sec, therefore

$$Ft = 385$$

where $t = 1$.
Hence, $F = 385$ N.

If a jet of water with velocity v impinges at right angles on a surface which is moving with velocity u, a column of water of length $v - u$ strikes the surface in each second, and this water has its velocity reduced from v to u in one sec, hence if A be the cross-sectional area of the jet and ρ the density of the water, the thrust of the jet is

$$F = A(v - u)\rho(v - u).$$

17.4 Impact of Two Particles

If two particles moving in the same straight line collide there is a short period of contact, during which each particle exerts on the other a certain force, which may vary during the period of contact. At any instant the forces exerted by each body on the other are equal and opposite, by Newton's third law, and hence the *impulses* exerted by each particle on the other are equal and opposite. It follows that the momentum given to one particle is equal and opposite to that given to the other.

Let m_1, m_2 be the masses of the particles,
         u_1, u_2 their velocities before impact,
         v_1, v_2 their velocities after impact;

all velocities being measured in the same direction; then the loss of momentum of one is the increase of momentum of the other, that is

$$m_1(u_1 - v_1) = m_2(v_2 - u_2),$$
$$m_1 u_1 + m_2 u_2 = m_1 v_1 + m_2 v_2.$$

Hence, the total momentum of the two particles is unaltered by the impact. It is assumed that during the short period of contact of the particles the effect of any other external forces which act on the particles is negligible.

Here we have the *Principle of Conservation of Linear Momentum*, which states that the total momentum of a system of particles in any direction is unaltered by collisions between the particles of the system.

In the collision of two particles moving in any directions the line of action of the mutual impulse between them is the relative path of the particles. If there is no frictional impulse perpendicular to this path, the momentum of *each* particle perpendicular to the path is unaltered, while along the path the *total* momentum is unaltered.

The principle of conservation of linear momentum applies to the linear momentum of rigid bodies during collision, the line of the impulse being the normal to the common tangent plane of the bodies during the impact. If after impact two bodies are joined together, or move on with the same velocity, we may find this velocity.

Let m_1, m_2 be the masses and u_1, u_2 the velocities of the bodies before impact, and v their common velocity after impact, all velocities being measured in the same direction. Then by the principle of conservation of momentum

$$(m_1 + m_2)v = m_1 u_1 + m_2 u_2,$$

$$v = \frac{m_1 u_1 + m_2 u_2}{m_1 + m_2}.$$

In this case the loss of kinetic energy during the impact is

$$\frac{1}{2}m_1 u_1^2 + \frac{1}{2}m_2 u_2^2 - \frac{1}{2}(m_1 + m_2)v^2$$

$$= \frac{1}{2}\left\{ m_1 u_1^2 + m_2 u_2^2 - \frac{(m_1 u_1 + m_2 u_2)^2}{m_1 + m_2} \right\},$$

$$= \frac{1}{2(m_1 + m_2)}\{ m_1 m_2 u_1^2 - 2m_1 m_2 u_1 u_2 + m_1 m_2 u_2^2 \},$$

$$= \frac{m_1 m_2}{2(m_1 + m_2)}(u_1 - u_2)^2.$$

This quantity must always be positive, and hence there is a definite loss of kinetic energy.

The principle of conservation of linear momentum also applies to bodies connected by an inextensible string when the string suddenly becomes taut. There is an impulsive tension along the line of the string which imparts to one body the momentum which it takes from the other. If the string remains taut in the subsequent motion, the velocities of the bodies following the impulse must be equal.

Example 3. *A railway truck of mass 8000 kg running at 6 km/h is overtaken by a truck of mass 12 000 kg running at 10 km/h. After impact the trucks begin to separate at 1 km/h. Find the speed of the trucks after impact and the loss of kinetic energy in the impact.*

Let v km/h be the speed of the heavier truck after impact, then the speed of the lighter truck will be $v + 1$ km/h. The total momentum after impact will be the same as that before and, since no other quantities are involved, we may write the momentum with the mass in thousands of kilogrammes (tonnes) and the velocity in kilometres per hour, giving

$$12v + 8(v + 1) = 12 \times 10 + 8 \times 6,$$

so that

$$v = 8 \text{ km/h},$$

$$v + 1 = 9 \text{ km/h}.$$

The loss of kinetic energy is

$$\{\tfrac{1}{2} \times 12 \times 10^3(10^2 - 8^2) + \tfrac{1}{2} \times 8 \times 10^3(6^2 - 9^2)\}\left(\frac{10^3}{3600}\right)^2$$

$$= \frac{10^5}{36 \times 36}\{(6 \times 18 \times 2) - (4 \times 15 \times 3)\}$$

$$= 2780 \text{ J}.$$

Example 4. *A bullet of mass 30 g is fired horizontally into a small block of wood of mass 8 kg which is suspended by a string 2 m long. The bullet remains embedded in the wood and the block rises until the string makes an angle of 30° with the vertical. Find the velocity of the bullet.*

This is an example of a ballistic pendulum such as were at one time used to find the velocities of bullets and shells. Let V m/sec be the velocity of the bullet before impact and v m/sec the velocity of the bullet and block after impact. The momentum equation gives

$$30 \times V = 8030 \times v,$$

so that

$$v = \frac{3}{803}V.$$

Thus the velocity to be measured, that of the block, is considerably smaller than that of the bullet before impact. When the string turns through 30° the block rises a height $(2 - 2 \cos 30°)$ m, and the work done against gravity is

$$8 \cdot 03g \times 2(1 - \cos 30°) = 21 \cdot 11 \text{ N m}.$$

The kinetic energy of the block has been destroyed by this work, so that

$$\frac{1}{2} \times 8 \cdot 03\left(\frac{3V}{803}\right)^2 = 21 \cdot 11,$$

giving

$$V = 614 \text{ m/sec}.$$

Example 5. *A and B are two particles, of mass 4 kg and 8 kg respectively, lying in contact on a smooth horizontal table, and connected by a string 3 m long. B is 7 m from the smooth edge of the table and is connected by a taut string passing over the edge to a particle C of mass 4 kg hanging freely. If the system be released from rest, find the speed with which A begins to move.* (L.U.)

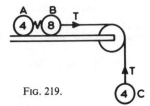

Fig. 219.

When B (Fig. 219) is in motion and less than 3 m from A, its acceleration is given by the equations

$$4g - T = 4a,$$

$$T = 8a,$$

where T is the tension in the string, and hence

$$a = \tfrac{1}{3}g = 3\cdot27 \text{ m/sec}^2.$$

Hence, when B has moved 3 m its velocity is given by

$$v^2 = 2 \times \tfrac{9\cdot81}{3} \times 3,$$

$$v = 4\cdot43 \text{ m/sec},$$

and this will also be the velocity of the mass C hanging vertically.

The impulse in the string joining B to C when the string AB becomes taut will give a certain horizontal momentum to B and take away the same amount of vertical momentum from C. Hence, we may use the conservation of momentum as if all three particles were moving in the same straight line. If v m/sec be their common velocity after A has been brought into motion, we have

$$(4+8+4)v = (8+4)4\cdot43,$$

$$v = 3\cdot32 \text{ m/sec}.$$

This is therefore the speed with which A begins to move.

Example 6. *A shell of mass m is fired from a gun of mass M which can recoil freely on a horizontal base, and the elevation of the gun is* α. *Prove that the initial inclination of the path of the shell to the horizon is* $tan^{-1}\{(1 + m/M)tan\,\alpha\}$. *Prove also that the energy of the shell on leaving the gun is to that of the gun as* $\{M^2 + (M+m)^2\,tan^2\alpha\}: Mm$, *assuming that none of the energy of the explosion is lost.*   (L.U.)

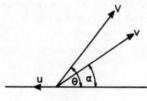

FIG. 220.

Let v be the velocity of the shell relative to the barrel and u the backwards velocity of the gun (Fig. 220). Then if the actual velocity of the shell be V in a direction inclined at θ to the horizontal, we have

$$V \sin \theta = v \sin \alpha \tag{1}$$

$$V \cos \theta = v \cos \alpha - u \tag{2}$$

The horizontal component of the impulse causing the shot to move is $mV \cos \theta$ and this component gives the backward momentum Mu to the gun.

Therefore

$$mV \cos \theta = Mu \tag{3}$$

From (2) and (3)

$$mv \cos \alpha = (M + m)u,$$

from (1) and (3)

$$\tan \theta = \frac{mv \sin \alpha}{Mu},$$

$$= \frac{M+m}{M} \tan \alpha,$$

$$\theta = \tan^{-1}\{(1 + m/M) \tan \alpha\}.$$

The ratio of the energies of the shell and gun is

$$\frac{\frac{1}{2}mV^2}{\frac{1}{2}Mu^2} = \frac{M}{m} \sec^2\theta, \text{ from (3)},$$

$$= \frac{M}{m}\left\{1 + \left(\frac{M+m}{M}\tan \alpha\right)^2\right\},$$

$$= \frac{M^2 + (M+m)^2 \tan^2\alpha}{Mm}.$$

Example 7. *An inelastic pile of weight W N is driven a metres into the ground by a hammer of weight w N falling h metres before hitting the pile. Show that the resistance of the ground, supposed uniform is* $W + w + \dfrac{w^2h}{(W+w)a}$. (L.U.)

The hammer falling h m acquires a velocity $\sqrt{(2gh)}$ m/sec, and after impact with the pile we have for the common velocity V of the hammer and pile

$$(W + w)V = w\sqrt{(2gh)}.$$

Hence the kinetic energy of the hammer and pile is

$$\frac{1}{2}\frac{W+w}{g}V^2 = \frac{1}{2}\frac{W+w}{g}\cdot\frac{w^2 \cdot 2gh}{(W+w)^2},$$

$$= \frac{w^2h}{W+w}.$$

This kinetic energy is destroyed in a distance a by the resistance of the ground, R, less the weight $W + w$.

Therefore $(R - W - w)a = \dfrac{w^2h}{W+w}$,

$$R = W + w + \frac{w^2h}{(W+w)a} \text{ kg}.$$

EXERCISES 17 (a)

1. If the coefficient of friction between the tyres of a car and the road surface is 2/3, find the time in which a car can be brought to rest with all wheels locked from speed of (a) 36, (b) 72 km/h. Find the stopping distance in each case.
2. A ball of mass 100 gm and moving at 8 m/sec is struck by a bat and rebounds with a velocity of 20 m/sec. Find the work done on the ball, and the average pressure on the bat, assuming the bat and ball to be in contact for 0·1 sec.

3. A bullet of mass 30 g is fired into a fixed block of wood with a velocity of 294 metres/sec and is brought to rest in $\frac{1}{150}$ sec. Find the resistance exerted by the wood supposing it to be uniform.   (O.C.)

4. A body of weight W N moving due north at u m/sec, is suddenly caused to move north-west at v m/sec. What is the impulse it has received? If the change in velocity had been gradual under a constant force and had taken a time T, find what would have been the acceleration.   (L.U.)

5. Two trucks, with masses of respectively 5 tonnes and 3 tonnes, are standing on the same level set of rails. If the heavier truck impinges on the lighter, which is at rest, with a speed of 5 m/sec, and the velocity of the lighter relative to the heavier after they separate is 3 m/sec, find the actual speeds of the two trucks after they separate and the kinetic energy lost by the impact.   (O.C.)

6. A truck, of mass 5 tonnes, is moving on level rails at 5 m/sec and impinges on a second truck, of mass 10 tonnes, which is standing on the same rails. If after the impact the second truck moves on at the rate of 2 m/sec, find the speed of the first truck and the kinetic energy lost by the impact.   (O.C.)

7. A small block of mass M is moving with velocity V when it is struck by a bullet of mass m moving with velocity v in the same direction. If the bullet becomes embedded in the block, show that there is a loss of kinetic energy $\dfrac{Mm(V-v)^2}{2(M+m)}$, and find the impulse on the block.   (L.U.)

8. A bullet of mass m is fired into a block of mass M which is free to move on a smooth horizontal table. If the bullet penetrates to a depth d, show that the distance moved by the block during penetration is $md/(M+m)$, assuming the resisting force is constant.   (L.U.)

9. A railway truck of mass 12 000 kg moving at 6 m/sec strikes an empty truck of mass 2000 kg which is at rest against a buffer in a fixed frame. The buffer is in the form of a spring of natural length 1 m. The two trucks are brought instantaneously to rest when the spring is compressed to 50 cm. Find the force which would hold the buffer compressed by 25 cm.   (L.U.)

10. A wooden ball of mass 250 g is moving horizontally at 10 m/sec at a height of 50 m above the ground when it is struck centrally by a bullet of mass 20 g moving vertically upwards at 500 m/sec. If the bullet emerges vertically with its speed halved, find the magnitude and direction of the velocity of the ball after impact and the time before it reaches the ground, assuming the penetration to be instantaneous.   (L.U.)

11. If a gun of mass M fires horizontally a shot of mass m, find the ratio of the energy of recoil of the gun to the energy of the shot. If a $\frac{1}{2}$-tonne gun discharges a 50-kg shot with a velocity of 1000 m/sec, find the uniform resistance necessary to stop the recoil in 50 cm.   (L.U.)

12. A bullet of mass 10 g, when fired from a gun weighing 20 **kg has** a muzzle velocity of 800 m/sec. What is the velocity of recoil of the **gun and** the total energy of the gun and bullet?

    If the same bullet were fired from a gun weighing 10 kg, and if the total energy were the same as in the previous case, show that the muzzle velocity of the bullet would be not more than 0·5 m/sec less than before.   (L.U.)

13. A shot of mass 10 kg is fired horizontally from a gun whose mass is 500 kg. If the muzzle velocity of the shot is 600 m/sec, calculate that of the gun. Calculate the **total kinetic** energy produced (in the shot and gun) and if the **distance travelled**

along the bore of the gun is 2 m, prove that the average force applied to the shot is about 9.2×10^5 N. How far will the gun have moved when the shot leaves the muzzle?   (O.C.)

14. A machine gun firing 20 g bullets with velocity 800 m/sec at the rate of 500 rounds per min is mounted on a car and fired straight ahead. Find the average thrust of the gun on the car while firing.

15. A shot of mass m is fired from a gun of mass M placed on a smooth horizontal plane and inclined at an angle α to the horizontal. If v is the velocity of the gun's recoil at the instant when the shot leaves it, prove that the horizontal component at right angles to the gun's length is $mv \sin \alpha$. Prove that the initial direction of the shot's motion is inclined at $\tan^{-1}\left\{\left(1+\dfrac{m}{M}\right)\tan \alpha\right\}$ to the horizontal.   (O.C.)

16. A rifle, of mass 4 kg, is suspended by cords with its bore horizontal. It fires a 20 g bullet, and in recoiling rises 40 cm. Find the muzzle velocity of the bullet. If the accelerations of the rifle and bullet are taken as constant, and the bore is 60 cm long, show that the time of the bullet in the bore is about $\frac{1}{467}$ sec and that in this time the rifle will only have moved about 0·6 cm.

17. Water issues from a circular pipe of 8 cm diameter with a velocity of 5 m/sec; find the weight of water discharged per minute. If the water impinges directly on a plane and its momentum is thereby wholly destroyed, what is the pressure of the jet on the plane?   (L.U.)

18. A jet of water of cross-section 25 cm^2 and velocity 15 m/sec impinges normally on a plane inelastic wall, so that the velocity of the water is destroyed on reaching the wall. Calculate the thrust on the wall.   (L.U.)

19. Prove that if a horizontal jet of water could be made to issue through a nozzle of 10 sq cm orifice at the rate of 5 m^3/min, it would exert a force about equal to the weight of 708 kg against any obstacle placed in its path; and find the power required to produce the jet.   (L.U.)

20. Waves are striking against a vertical sea-wall with a speed of 16 m/sec. Taking the specific gravity of sea-water as 1·025, show that the pressure on the wall, due to the destruction of the momentum of the waves is very approximately 2.6×10^5 N/m^2.

21. A pipe of internal diameter 5 cm delivers 1000 kg of water per min. It bends to one side through a right angle, and 1 m farther on bends back to its original direction. Find the force exerted by the water at each bend; show that these forces form a couple and find its moment.

22. A 2-tonne mass is raised to a height of 3 m above the top of a pile of mass 1 tonne. It is let fall and drives the pile 15 cm into the ground, the weight remaining on top of the pile. Assuming the resistance of the ground to be uniform, find

    (i) the resistance of the ground,
    (ii) the time in sec during which the pile moves.

What is the loss of kinetic energy?   (L.U.)

23. An inelastic vertical pile of mass $\frac{1}{2}$ tonne is driven 60 cm into the ground by 30 blows of a hammer, of mass 2 tonnes, falling through 1·5 m. Show that the resistance of the ground, supposed uniform, is 1.42×10^6 N.   (L.U.)

24. A pile-driver is to fall 2 m on to a pile of mass 2000 kg and drive it 4 cm into the ground against resistance 10^6 N. Find a suitable mass for the driver and the energy lost by each fall.

25. A bullet of mass m kg is fired horizontally with a velocity of v m/sec into a block of wood of mass M kg suspended by a light cord. It is noticed that the wood and embedded bullet swing until a height of h m above the original position is reached. Show that $mv = (M+m)\sqrt{(2gh)}$, it being given that the whole motion takes place in a vertical plane.   (O.C.)

26. A train of trucks is being started from rest, and just before the last coupling becomes taut, the front part has acquired a velocity of 36 km/h. If the front portion of the train has a mass of 72 tonnes and the last truck has a mass of 6 tonnes, find the jerk in the coupling.   (L.U.)

27. A launch of mass 10 tonnes which is moving ahead at 3 m/sec takes in tow a boat of mass 4 tonnes which is drifting in the direction in which the launch is moving at 1 m/sec. Find the common speed when the towing rope becomes taut.

   If the launch can exert an effective power of 20 kW, and on accelerating with the boat in tow reaches a maximum speed of 6 m/sec, find the total resistance to the motion of the two boats at this speed.

   If the resistance to each boat is proportional to its mass and varies directly as the speed, show that the resistance to the launch when travelling by itself at V m/sec is approximately 397 V newton.   (C.S.)

28. A body of mass 30 kg moving in a straight line at 24 m/sec strikes another body of mass 9 kg moving in the same straight line in the same direction at 10 m/sec. After the impact the velocity of the heavier body is 18 m/sec. Calculate the velocity of the lighter body.

   Find the kinetic energy gained by the lighter body, and lost by the heavier body owing to the impact. Find also what fraction of the sum of the kinetic energies of the two bodies before the impact has been lost during it.   (C.S.)

29. A string passes over a light pulley which can rotate without friction about a fixed horizontal axis. To one end of the string is attached a 2 kg mass, and to the other a pan of mass $\frac{1}{2}$ kg, the 2 kg mass resting on the ground and the pan hanging freely. A 1 kg mass is allowed to fall from a height of 1 m into the pan, which it strikes without bouncing. Assuming the string to be light and inextensible, determine how high the 2 kg mass will rise from the ground.   (Q.E.)

30. A motor-driven pump raises 1 m³ of water per minute through a height of 12 m, and delivers it at the upper level in a jet with a velocity of 10 m/sec.

   (a) If 40 per cent of the energy output from the motor is transferred to the water in the jet as kinetic and potential energy, find the power output of the motor.

   (b) If the jet is directed normal to a flat surface, what force will it apply to that surface, assuming the water does not rebound?   (Q.E.)

31. A railway truck of mass 15 tonnes, moving at 15 km/h, runs into a stationary truck of mass 10 tonnes, and the two trucks move on with a common velocity. Determine this common velocity.

   If, instead of moving on together, the trucks separate, the buffer springs restoring one-third of the energy absorbed by them, determine the velocities of the trucks.

   Throughout the problem neglect all resistance to motion of the trucks. (Q.E.)

32. A rectangular block of wood of mass 60 kg is supported by four vertical strings, each of length 1 m, attached to the corners of the upper, horizontal, face. A bullet of mass 0·1 kg, travelling horizontally, strikes the block centrally and remains embedded in it, and the block consequently swings so that the strings make a maximum angle of 30° with the vertical. Find the velocity of the bullet.   (Q.E.)

33. A block of mass 40 kg is allowed to fall a distance of 1 m on to a vertical pile of mass 80 kg. The block does not bounce, and the pile is driven into the ground a distance of 20 cm. Determine the magnitude of the force resisting the penetration of the pile assuming this force to be constant.   (Q.E.)

34. A force F acts for 20 sec upon a body of mass 20 kg originally at rest and varies with time according to the following table:

Time (sec)	0	4	8	10	12	16	20
F (N)	5·0	6·5	7·6	6·4	4·2	2·0	1·2

If there is a constant force of 3·0 N resisting the motion, find the greatest velocity of the body and its velocity at the end of the 20 sec.   (Q.E.)

17.5 Elasticity of Bodies

When a body strikes a fixed surface there is a period of impact during which the momentum of the body is destroyed. During this period the body undergoes some compression and its shape is altered. This period of compression is followed by a period of restitution during which the body regains its shape and some of its momentum. The ratio of the restoring impulse to the destroying impulse, that is, of the momentum after impact to the momentum before impact, is called the *coefficient of restitution* (or elasticity) and denoted by the letter e. That is

$$\frac{\text{momentum after impact}}{\text{momentum before impact}} = e.$$

The momentum after impact is, of course, in the opposite direction to that before impact. Thus, the mass being unaltered during the impact, if we measure the velocities before and after impact *in the same direction* we have

$$\frac{\text{velocity after impact}}{\text{velocity before impact}} = -e.$$

If e is zero the body is said to be *inelastic*, and if $e = 1$ it is *perfectly elastic* in the impact with the given surface.

This theory is most easily applicable to the impact of spheres on smooth surfaces or on each other, so that the impulse during compression and restitution is normal to the surface.

The theory has its origin in experimental work carried out by Newton, which led him to formulate the law for the impact of spheres, namely, *the relative velocity of the spheres along the line of centres immediately after impact is $-e$ times the relative velocity before impact.*
Fairly consistent values of e are found for impact between spheres of a given material; thus for impact between glass spheres a value of e of about 0·94 is found.

17.6 Impact of a Sphere on a Smooth Fixed Surface

The impact is said to be direct when it is normal to the surface, indirect when it is not.

For direct impact, if u is the velocity before impact and e the coefficient of restitution, we have for the velocity v after impact measured in the same direction

$$v = -eu.$$

Thus, if a sphere falls from a height h on to a smooth horizontal fixed plane, the velocity before impact is

$$u = \sqrt{(2gh)}.$$

Therefore the velocity after impact measured *upwards* is

$$eu = \sqrt{(2ghe^2)}.$$

This velocity is destroyed by gravity when the sphere has risen to a height h', therefore

$$\sqrt{(2gh')} = \sqrt{(2ghe^2)},$$

$$\frac{h'}{h} = e^2,$$

$$e = \sqrt{(h'/h)}.$$

Thus the value of e is easily found experimentally by measuring the height of rebound.

If the impact of a sphere on a surface is indirect, let u be the velocity before impact in a direction inclined at an angle α to the surface.

Let v be the velocity after impact in a direction making an angle β with the surface (Fig. 221).

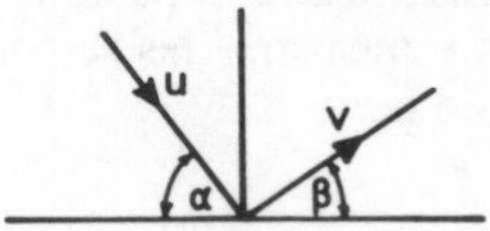

FIG. 221.

The velocity before impact parallel to the surface is $u \cos \alpha$, and since the impulse is along the normal, this component of the velocity is unchanged by the impact.

That is, $u \cos \alpha = v \cos \beta.$

The components of velocity along the normal before and after impact are respectively $u \sin \alpha$ and $v \sin \beta$.

Therefore $v \sin \beta = eu \sin \alpha.$

Hence, $v^2 \cos^2 \beta + v^2 \sin^2 \beta = u^2(\cos^2\alpha + e^2 \sin^2\alpha),$

$$v = u\sqrt{(\cos^2\alpha + e^2 \sin^2\alpha)},$$

$$\tan \beta = e \tan \alpha.$$

We have also $u^2 - v^2 = u^2(1 - e^2) \sin^2\alpha,$

and hence the loss of kinetic energy due to the impact is

$$\tfrac{1}{2}mu^2 - \tfrac{1}{2}mv^2 = \tfrac{1}{2}mu^2(1-e^2)\sin^2\alpha,$$

and the proportional loss of kinetic energy is $(1-e^2)\sin^2\alpha$.

17.7 Parabolic Motion

If a sphere is projected with velocity V from a point on a fixed horizontal plane, in a direction making an angle α with the plane, the coefficient of restitution being e, we have a series of parabolas described by the sphere between successive impacts.

If x_1 be the horizontal range and t_1 the time of flight for the first parabola we have (§14.6)

$$x_1 = \frac{V^2}{g}\sin 2\alpha,$$

$$t_1 = \frac{2V\sin\alpha}{g}.$$

The velocity just before the first impact is V in a direction making an angle α with the surface, therefore after impact the horizontal velocity is $V\cos\alpha$ and the vertical velocity $eV\sin\alpha$.

Therefore, if x_2 be the horizontal range and t_2 the time of flight for the second parabola, we have

$$t_2 = \frac{2eV\sin\alpha}{g},$$

$$x_2 = \frac{2eV\sin\alpha}{g}V\cos\alpha = \frac{eV^2}{g}\sin 2\alpha.$$

Similarly, the time of flight and horizontal range for the third parabola are

$$t_3 = \frac{2e^2V\sin\alpha}{g},$$

$$x_3 = e^2\frac{V^2}{g}\sin 2\alpha.$$

Hence the total horizontal range is

$$X = x_1 + x_2 + x_3 + \ldots,$$

$$= \frac{V^2\sin 2\alpha}{g}(1 + e + e^2 + \ldots),$$

$$= \frac{V^2\sin 2\alpha}{g(1-e)}.$$

The total time of flight is

$$T = \frac{2V \sin \alpha}{g}(1 + e + e^2 + \ldots),$$

$$= \frac{2V \sin \alpha}{g(1 - e)}.$$

17.8 Impact on a Moving Plane

If a sphere impinges on a plane which is moving away from it with velocity V, let u be the normal component of the velocity of the sphere before impact and v the normal component of its velocity after impact, both velocities being measured in the same direction as the velocity of the plane.

Then, assuming that the impact causes a negligible change in the velocity of the plane, the relative velocities of the sphere with respect to the plane are

before impact $u - V$,
after impact $v - V$.

Hence, by Newton's experimental law

$$\frac{v - V}{u - V} = -e,$$

$$v = -eu + V(1 + e).$$

Example 8. *A body slides from rest down a smooth plane of length l and inclination α, and at the bottom impinges on a smooth horizontal plane; show that the range on the horizontal plane after the first rebound is 2el sin α sin 2α, where e is the coefficient of restitution between the body and the horizontal plane.* (L.U.)

The velocity after sliding a distance l down the inclined plane with acceleration $g \sin \alpha$ is $\sqrt{(2gl \sin \alpha)}$.

The vertical component of this velocity is $\sin \alpha \sqrt{(2gl \sin \alpha)}$ downwards, and the horizontal component is $\cos \alpha \sqrt{(2gl \sin \alpha)}$.

The vertical component of velocity after impact, in an upward direction, is

$$e \sin \alpha \sqrt{(2gl \sin \alpha)}.$$

This velocity is destroyed by gravity in time

$$\frac{e \sin \alpha}{g} \sqrt{(2gl \sin \alpha)}.$$

Hence the total time of flight is

$$\frac{2e \sin \alpha}{g} \sqrt{(2gl \sin \alpha)}.$$

The range on the horizontal plane is therefore

$$\frac{2e \sin \alpha}{g} \sqrt{(2gl \sin \alpha)} \times \cos \alpha \sqrt{(2gl \sin \alpha)},$$

$$= 4el \sin^2\alpha \cos \alpha,$$

$$= 2el \sin \alpha \sin 2\alpha.$$

EXERCISES 17 (b)

1. A marble dropped on a stone floor from a height of 3 m is found to rebound to a height of 2·5 m. Find the coefficient of restitution to the nearest hundredth.
(L.U.)

2. A ball dropped to the ground from a height of 10 m rebounds to a height of 8 m. Find the height to which it rebounds after a second impact and the time between the second and third impacts.
(O.C.)

3. A small sphere hangs freely by a light inextensible string from a point on a smooth vertical plane. It is drawn aside so that the string is taut and makes an angle of 60° with the plane and released to strike the plane at right angles. After impact the sphere rises until the string makes an angle of 30° with the plane. Find the coefficient of restitution between the sphere and the plane.

4. A sphere falls from a height h to strike a smooth horizontal plane. Show that, if e is the coefficient of restitution, the total distance moved by the sphere while it bounces is $\frac{1+e^2}{1-e^2}h$.

5. A sphere of mass m moving with velocity u impinges on a fixed smooth plane, the direction of motion making an angle α with the plane. If e is the coefficient of restitution between the sphere and the plane, find (i) the magnitude and direction of the velocity v of the sphere after impact; (ii) the loss of momentum; (iii) the loss of kinetic energy.
(L.U.)

6. If sheets of paper are placed on a table, the coefficient of restitution is reduced by an amount proportional to the thickness of the paper. When a ball is dropped on the bare table it rises after impact to three-quarters of the height of fall. When the thickness of paper is 1 cm it rises to only one-half of the height of the fall. What thickness of paper is required in order that the rebound shall be one-quarter of the height of fall?
(L.U.)

7. A billiard ball of mass 200 gm strikes a smooth cushion when moving at 3m/sec in a direction inclined at 30° to the cushion. If the coefficient of restitution is 7/8, find the loss of kinetic energy due to the impact.
(L.U.)

8. A billiard table is 2 m by 8/3 m. Find the position of a point in the shorter side and the direction of projection, such that a ball thus struck off will describe a rectangle and return to the same spot after rebounding at each of the other three cushions, the ball being smooth and the coefficient of elasticity being 4/9.
(L.U.)

9. A particle is projected from a point on a horizontal plane with velocity 10 m/sec at an elevation 30° and rebounds from the plane after each impact. Find the total horizontal distance travelled by the particle before coming to rest if the coefficient of restitution between the plane and the particle is $\frac{1}{2}$.

10. A particle is dropped from a height of 4 m on to an elastic horizontal plane, and just before the third impact with the plane it has described a total distance of 6·5 m. Calculate the coefficient of restitution.   (L.U.)

11. Hailstones are observed to strike the surface of a frozen pond when moving in a direction inclined at 30° to the vertical and to rebound in a direction inclined at 60° to the vertical. Assuming the contact to be smooth, calculate the coefficient of restitution. Calculate the speed of impact if the hailstones rise to a vertical height of 30 cm after striking the ice.   (L.U.)

12. A particle is projected with velocity V and inclination α from a point on a horizontal plane. If the coefficient of restitution between the particle and the plane is e, prove that the total range on the plane of the particle while moving as a projectile is $V^2 \sin 2\alpha / g(1-e)$. If $V = 20$ m/sec, $\alpha = 30°$ and $e = 2/3$, find the height of the particle when it has travelled 80 m horizontally.   (L.U.)

13. Each step of a flight of smooth steps has width a and depth d. A marble is projected from a point on the highest step with a velocity whose horizontal and vertical components are u and v respectively. After time t it rebounds from the next highest step with a velocity whose vertical component is also v. If e is the coefficient of restitution between the marble and a step, show that

$$\text{(i) } v^2 = \frac{2gde^2}{1-e^2}; \quad \text{(ii) } t = \frac{v(1+e)}{ge}.$$

Show that the marble will continue to strike each successive step at the corresponding place if v^2 has the above value and if, in addition,

$$u^2 = \frac{ga^2(1-e)}{2d(1+e)}. \tag{L.U.}$$

14. A particle is travelling horizontally with speed v in a vertical plane containing the line of greatest slope of a fixed smooth plane inclined at an angle α to the horizontal. The coefficient of restitution between the particle and the plane is e. Given that $e < \cot^2\alpha$, prove that the distance between the first and second points at which the particle meets the plane is

$$2ev^2 \sin \alpha(1 - e \tan^2\alpha)/g.$$

Prove that if the particle is travelling horizontally the second time it meets the plane, then $e(2 \sec^2\alpha - 1) = 1$.   (O.C.)

15. A particle is projected with velocity V from a point of a plane inclined to the horizontal at an angle α, in a vertical plane through the line of greatest slope. The direction of projection is up the plane and makes an angle β with the plane. The coefficient of restitution between the plane and the particle is e. Prove that the range of the particle on the plane at the moment of its second impact is greatest when $\cot 2\beta = (1+e)\tan \alpha$, and that this greatest range is

$$V^2(1+e)\tan \beta/(g \cos \alpha),$$

where β has the value given by the first equation.   (O.C.)

16. A ball, mass 120 g, is released when at relative rest from a position 2 m above the floor of a lift which is descending with a uniform acceleration of 1 m/sec². Prove that if the ball rises to the same position after striking the floor, the impulse on the floor at impact is nearly 1·43 N sec, and find the times of ascent and descent of the ball relative to the lift.   (O.C.)

17.9 Direct Impact of Spheres

If two spheres of masses m_1 and m_2 collide when moving in the same straight line, let u_1 and u_2 be their respective velocities before impact, and v_1 and v_2 their velocities after impact, *all velocities being measured in the same direction* (Fig. 222).

Consider the sphere of mass m_1. The relative velocity of m_1 with respect to m_2 before impact is $u_1 - u_2$, and after impact it is $v_1 - v_2$. Hence if e be the coefficient of restitution we have

$$\frac{v_1 - v_2}{u_1 - u_2} = -e. \qquad (4)$$

We have also by the principle of conservation of momentum, that the total momentum of the pair of spheres is unaltered by the impact. Therefore

$$m_1 v_1 + m_2 v_2 = m_1 u_1 + m_2 u_2 \qquad (5)$$

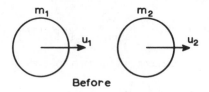

Before

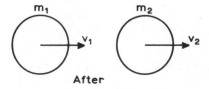

After

FIG. 222.

These two equations determine the values of v_1 and v_2. Multiplying (4) by m_2 we have

$$m_2 v_1 - m_2 v_2 = -m_2 e u_1 + m_2 e u_2.$$

Hence $(m_1 + m_2)v_1 = (m_1 - em_2)u_1 + m_2(1 + e)u_2.$

Similarly $(m_1 + m_2)v_2 = m_1(1 + e)u_1 + (m_2 - em_1)u_2.$

In particular, if $m_1 = m_2,$

$$v_1 = \frac{1-e}{2}u_1 + \frac{1+e}{2}u_2,$$

$$v_2 = \frac{1+e}{2}u_1 + \frac{1-e}{2}u_2.$$

17.10 Loss of Kinetic Energy

From the equation of conservation of momentum we have that the velocity V of the centre of mass of the two spheres is unchanged by the impact, and

$$V = \frac{m_1 u_1 + m_2 u_2}{m_1 + m_2} = \frac{m_1 v_1 + m_2 v_2}{m_1 + m_2}.$$

The kinetic energy of the two spheres before impact is

$$\frac{1}{2}m_1 u_1{}^2 + \frac{1}{2}m_2 u_2{}^2,$$

$$= \frac{1}{2(m_1 + m_2)}\{m_1{}^2 u_1{}^2 + m_2{}^2 u_2{}^2 + m_1 m_2(u_1{}^2 + u_2{}^2)\},$$

$$= \frac{1}{2(m_1 + m_2)}\{(m_1 u_1 + m_2 u_2)^2 + m_1 m_2(u_1 - u_2)^2\},$$

$$= \frac{1}{2}(m_1 + m_2)V^2 + \frac{m_1 m_2}{2(m_1 + m_2)}(u_1 - u_2)^2.$$

Similarly, the kinetic energy of the two spheres after impact, is

$$\frac{1}{2}m_1 v_1{}^2 + \frac{1}{2}m_2 v_2{}^2,$$

$$= \frac{1}{2}(m_1 + m_2)V^2 + \frac{m_1 m_2}{2(m_1 + m_2)}(v_1 - v_2)^2.$$

Hence, the loss of kinetic energy in the impact is

$$\frac{m_1 m_2}{2(m_1 + m_2)}\{(u_1 - u_2)^2 - (v_1 - v_2)^2\},$$

$$= \frac{m_1 m_2}{2(m_1 + m_2)}(1 - e^2)(u_1 - u_2)^2.$$

This expression is greater than zero if $e < 1$, and hence for $e < 1$ there is always a loss of kinetic energy.

17.11 Indirect Impact of Spheres

Let the spheres have masses m_1, m_2. Let their velocities before impact be u_1, u_2 in directions making angles α_1 and α_2 with the line of centres, and after impact let their velocities be v_1 and v_2 in directions making angles β_1 and β_2 with the line of centres (Fig. 223), all angles being measured in the same sense.

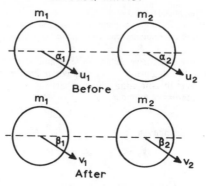

m_1 m_2
α_1 α_2
u_1 u_2

Before

m_1 m_2
β_1 β_2
v_1 v_2

After

FIG. 223.

The impact is along the line of centres, and therefore the velocities of the spheres perpendicular to the line of centres are unchanged.
That is

$$u_1 \sin \alpha_1 = v_1 \sin \beta_1 \tag{6}$$

$$u_2 \sin \alpha_2 = v_2 \sin \beta_2 \tag{7}$$

Along the line of centres, the velocities of the spheres are $u_1 \cos \alpha_1$, $u_2 \cos \alpha_2$ before impact, $v_1 \cos \beta_1$, $v_2 \cos \beta_2$ after impact.

Therefore, if e be the coefficient of restitution, we have

$$m_1 v_1 \cos \beta_1 + m_2 v_2 \cos \beta_2 = m_1 u_1 \cos \alpha_1 + m_2 u_2 \cos \alpha_2 \tag{8}$$

$$v_1 \cos \beta_1 - v_2 \cos \beta_2 = -e(u_1 \cos \alpha_1 - u_2 \cos \alpha_2) \tag{9}$$

Hence, as in §17.9, we have

$$(m_1 + m_2)v_1 \cos \beta_1$$
$$= (m_1 - em_2)u_1 \cos \alpha_1 + m_2(1 + e)u_2 \cos \alpha_2 \tag{10}$$

$$(m_1 + m_2)v_2 \cos \beta_2$$
$$= m_1(1 + e)u_1 \cos \alpha_1 + (m_2 - em_1)u_2 \cos \alpha_2 \tag{11}$$

The equations (6), (7), (10), (11) determine v_1, v_2, β_1, β_2.

The kinetic energy of each sphere is the sum of its kinetic energy due to its velocity along the line of centres and its kinetic energy due to its velocity perpendicular to the line of centres. Hence, the loss of kinetic energy in the impact may be found by considering only the change of velocity along the line of centres.

Hence, as in §17.10, we have for the loss of kinetic energy

$$\frac{m_1 m_2}{2(m_1 + m_2)}(1 - e^2)(u_1 \cos \alpha_1 - u_2 \cos \alpha_2)^2.$$

Example 9. *Two spheres of masses 20 and 30 gm are moving in their line of centres towards each other with velocities of 8 m/sec and 10 m/sec, and their coefficient of restitution is $\frac{3}{4}$. Find their velocities after impact and the amount of kinetic energy transformed in the collision.* (L.U.)

Let v_1 and v_2 m/sec be the velocities of the 20 and 30 gm masses after impact in the direction in which the 20 gm mass is moving before impact. The velocity of the 30 gm mass is -10 m/sec in this direction before impact.

We have the equation of momentum

$$20v_1 + 30v_2 = -130.$$

The equation of elasticity is

$$v_1 - v_2 = -\tfrac{3}{4}(8+10) = -13\cdot5.$$

Hence

$$v_1 = -10\cdot7 \text{ m/sec},$$

$$v_2 = +2\cdot8 \text{ m/sec}.$$

Thus the velocities of both spheres are reversed by the impact.
The loss of kinetic energy

$$= \tfrac{1}{2}\{20(8^2 - 10\cdot7^2) + 30(10^2 - 2\cdot8^2)\} \times 10^{-3} = 0\cdot873 \text{ J}.$$

Example 10. *Two smooth equal balls A and B lie on a smooth table, their line of centres being perpendicular to a smooth vertical wall. The coefficient of restitution between the balls is $\frac{3}{4}$ and between a sphere and the wall is $\frac{1}{2}$. If the ball A, farther from the wall, is given a velocity of 16 m/sec towards the centre of the other ball B, find the velocity of each ball after their second impact, and show that there will be no more impacts between the balls.*

Let the balls be of unit mass, and let v_1 and v_2 be the velocities of A and B towards the vertical plane after their first impact.

Then

$$v_1 + v_2 = 16,$$

$$v_1 - v_2 = -\tfrac{3}{4} \times 16 = -12,,$$

$$v_1 = 2 \text{ m/sec},$$

$$v_2 = 14 \text{ m/sec}.$$

After impact with the vertical plane, B has a velocity 7 m/sec away from the wall.
Let w_1 and w_2 be the velocities of A and B away from the wall after their second impact.

Then

$$w_2 + w_1 = 7 - 2 = 5,$$

$$w_2 - w_1 = -\tfrac{3}{4} \times (7+2) = -6\cdot75,$$

$$w_2 = -0\cdot875 \text{ m/sec},$$

$$w_1 = 5\cdot875 \text{ m/sec}.$$

Subsequently, the ball B will hit the wall again and rebound with velocity $0\cdot4375$ m/sec but will not overhaul A.

Example 11. *A billiard ball is at rest, and another equal ball is aimed at the first so that the direction of motion of the centre just touches the first; if the coefficient of restitution is 4/5, find the directions in which the balls travel after impact, and prove that the amount of kinetic energy transferred to the first ball is about 0·61 of the energy of the other before impact, while the other has about 0·26 of its original energy left.* (L.U.)

Let the velocity given to the second ball be u (Fig. 224); since the direction of this velocity is that of a tangent to the first ball when the balls meet, it makes angle of 30°

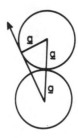

FIG. 224.

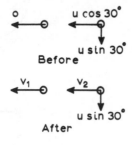

FIG. 225.

with the line of centres. Hence, before impact the velocity of the second ball along the line of centres is $u \cos 30°$, and perpendicular to this line it is $u \sin 30°$ (Fig. 225).

Let v_1 and v_2 be the velocities of the first and second balls along the line of centres after impact,

Then
$$v_2 + v_1 = u \cos 30°,$$
$$v_2 - v_1 = -\tfrac{4}{5}u \cos 30°,$$
$$v_1 = \tfrac{9}{10}u \cos 30°,$$
$$v_2 = \tfrac{1}{10}u \cos 30°.$$

The direction of motion of the first ball after impact is along the line of centres; the second ball has velocities $\tfrac{1}{10}u \cos 30°$ along the line of centres and $u \sin 30°$ in a perpendicular direction, therefore its direction of motion makes an angle $\tan^{-1}(10 \tan 30°)$ with the line of centres.

The kinetic energy of the first ball after impact
$$= \tfrac{1}{2}m(\tfrac{9}{10}u \cos 30°)^2,$$
$$= 0.6075 \times \tfrac{1}{2}mu^2.$$

The kinetic energy of the second ball after impact
$$= \tfrac{1}{2}m(u^2 \sin^2 30° + \tfrac{1}{100} \times u^2 \cos^2 30°),$$
$$= 0.2575 \times \tfrac{1}{2}mu^2.$$

Example 12. *A smooth, inelastic sphere of mass M lies on a smooth horizontal plane; a second smooth, inelastic sphere of mass m falls on it. At the moment of impact the line of centres makes an angle α with the vertical, and the velocity of the falling sphere is U. Prove that the subsequent velocity of the lower sphere is* $\dfrac{mU \sin \alpha \cos \alpha}{M + m \sin^2 \alpha}$. (O.C.)

Before impact, the sphere of mass m has velocity $U \cos \alpha$ along the line of centres and $U \sin \alpha$ in a perpendicular direction (Fig. 226). This latter velocity is unchanged by the impact.

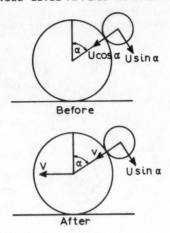

FIG. 226.

After impact let V be the horizontal velocity of the sphere of mass M and v the velocity along the line of centres of the sphere of mass m.

The spheres are inelastic, therefore their relative velocity along the line of centres after impact is zero.

That is $v = V \sin \alpha$.

As well as the impact between the spheres, there is a vertical impulse between the ground and the sphere of mass M, but this does not alter the total momentum of the two spheres in a horizontal direction, which is zero before impact.

Therefore, $MV + mv \sin \alpha - mU \sin \alpha \cos \alpha = 0$.

Hence $(M + m \sin^2 \alpha) V = mU \sin \alpha \cos \alpha$,

$$V = \frac{mU \sin \alpha \cos \alpha}{M + m \sin^2 \alpha}.$$

EXERCISES 17 (c)

1. Two particles each of mass m and moving in opposite directions with speeds of 6 m/sec and 3 m/sec collide directly. Prove that, if $e = 2/3$, the kinetic energy of the two particles before impact is twice their kinetic energy after impact. (O.C.)

2. Two particles of masses m_1, m_2 lie at rest on a smooth horizontal table connected by a light flexible inelastic string of length a. Initially the string is taut and a blow J is given to m_1 in the direction to make it hit m_2. If the coefficient of restitution is e, find the time which elapses before the string is again taut and the common velocity of the particles at this instant.   (L.U.)

3. Two particles of masses $2m$ and m, moving with speeds u and $2u$ respectively in opposite directions, collide directly. If K_1 and K_2 denote the sums of the kinetic energies of the two particles before and after impact respectively, prove that the coefficient of restitution is $\sqrt{(K_2/K_1)}$.   (O.C.)

4. A particle is projected inside a smooth straight tube of length a which lies at rest on a smooth horizontal table, and is closed at the ends. The mass of the tube is twice that of the particle; the coefficient of restitution is $\frac{1}{2}$. Show that between the first and second impacts and between the second and third the distances traversed by the tube are both a, and that five-eighths of the kinetic energy is destroyed by the first two impacts. (O.C.)

5. A smooth sphere of mass m_1, moving with speed u on a smooth horizontal table, impinges directly on an equal sphere of mass m_2 which is at rest, the coefficient of restitution between the spheres being e. Prove that the kinetic energy after impact is

$$\frac{m_1(m_1 + m_2 e^2)u^2}{2(m_1 + m_2)}.$$

If half the kinetic energy is lost, prove that e is not greater than $\frac{1}{2}\sqrt{2}$. (L.U.)

6. Two beads A, B, of equal mass are threaded on a smooth circular wire, fixed in a horizontal plane. The bead A is projected with speed u towards the bead B, which is at rest. If the coefficient of restitution is e, find the speeds of the beads after impact, and show that after the second impact (when B catches up with A) the velocities of A and B are respectively $\frac{1}{2}u(1 + e^2)$ and $\frac{1}{2}u(1 - e^2)$. (L.U.)

7. Two smooth spheres of equal mass rest in a smooth horizontal circular groove, at opposite ends of a diameter. One sphere is projected along the groove, and collides with the other after time t. Prove that there is a second impact after a further time $2t/e$, where e is the coefficient of restitution between the spheres. (L.U.)

8. A sphere of mass m and velocity $2u$ impinges directly on a sphere of mass $2m$ and velocity u, moving in the same direction. Prove that whatever the value of the coefficient of restitution e, the second sphere must have its velocity increased. Find e if the velocity of the sphere of mass m is halved by the impact. (L.U.)

9. Three balls, A, B, C, of mass $3m$, $2m$, $2m$, and of equal radii, lie on a smooth table with their centres in a straight line. Their coefficient of restitution is $\frac{1}{4}$; show that, if A is projected with velocity V to strike B, there are three impacts and that the final velocities are $(50, 57, 60)V/128$. (O.C.)

10. A, B, C are three exactly similar small spheres at rest in a smooth, horizontal, straight tube. A is set in motion and impinges on B. Show that A will impinge on B again after B has impinged on C, and show that there will be no more impacts if e, the coefficient of restitution, in not less than $3 - \sqrt{8}$. (O.C.)

11. Three small exactly similar spheres, A, B, C, are at rest in a smooth, horizontal, straight tube. The coefficient of restitution between any two of the spheres is 0.5. A is projected towards B with a velocity u. Determine the velocities of the three spheres after B has impinged on C and A has impinged a second time on B, and show that there will be no more impacts. (O.C.)

12. Three spheres, A, B, C, of equal radius but of respective masses $2m$, $3m$, $4m$ rest in that order in a straight, smooth, horizontal groove. A is projected with speed u so as to strike B, which subsequently impinges on C. If for A and B the coefficient of restitution is $\frac{2}{3}$, and for B, and C it is $\frac{1}{2}$, find the speed acquired by C. (L.U.)

13. Three spheres, A, B, C, of mass m, $2m$, $4m$ respectively, rest on a smooth table with their centres collinear, B lying between A and C, and the coefficient of restitution between A and B being equal to that between B and C. A is projected directly towards B with velocity u, and C moves with velocity $\frac{u}{4}$ after it has been

struck by B. Prove that A and B are reduced to rest, and find the coefficient of restitution. (L.U.)

14. A ball A impinges on an equal ball B, which is at rest. If the direction of A before and after impact makes angles θ, θ' respectively with the line of centres of the balls, find θ' in terms of θ and e, the coefficient of restitution between the balls. Show that when the deviation of A is greatest $\theta + \theta' = 90°$. (O.C.)

15. A smooth sphere impinges on an equal smooth sphere moving in a perpendicular direction with the same speed u, the line of centres at the instant of impact being perpendicular to the direction of motion of the second sphere. If e is the coefficient of restitution, find the speed of each sphere after impact, and prove that the direction of motion of the second sphere is turned through an angle $\tan^{-1} \dfrac{1+e}{2}$. (L.U.)

16. A uniform rod of mass 2 kg lies on a horizontal table. A particle of mass 250 gm moving on the table with speed 10 m/sec strikes the centre of the rod at an angle of 60° to the rod. If the coefficient of restitution is 0·8, determine the speed and direction of motion of the particle after impact, friction being ignored. (L.U.)

17. A smooth sphere impinges obliquely upon another sphere at rest. If θ, ϕ are the angles made by the direction of motion of the second sphere after impact with those of the first sphere before and after impact respectively, show that

$$(1-e)\tan \phi = 2\tan \theta,$$

where e is the coefficient of restitution between the spheres. (L.U.)

18. Two identical smooth spheres impinge obliquely, the coefficient of restitution being unity. If α, α' are the angles which their initial directions of motion make with their line of centres, and β, β' are the corresponding angles after impact (all angles being measured in the same sense), prove that $\tan \alpha \tan \alpha' = \tan \beta \tan \beta'$. (L.U.)

19. A smooth sphere A of mass m moving with velocity v impinges on a smooth sphere B of mass $2m$ which is at rest, the direction of motion of A making an angle of 30° with the line of centres. After impact, the direction of motion of A is perpendicular to its original direction. Find the velocity of each sphere after impact and the coefficient of restitution between them. (L.U.)

20. Two equal spheres lie at rest and in contact on a smooth horizontal table, when they are struck simultaneously by a third equal sphere moving at right angles to their line of centres along the table. If this last sphere is brought to rest by the impact and all the spheres are smooth, prove that the coefficient of restitution is $\frac{2}{3}$.

Determine the fraction of the original kinetic energy which is lost. (L.U.)

CHAPTER 18

MOTION IN A CIRCLE

18.1 Normal Acceleration

If there are no forces acting on a particle, or if the resultant of the forces acting on it is zero, the particle will remain at rest or move with uniform velocity in a straight line. This follows from Newton's first law of motion. Hence, if a particle moves in a circle with uniform speed, there must be some force constraining it to do so. Thus if a weight on a smooth horizontal table is whirled around with uniform speed in a horizontal circle at the end of a string, the force of tension in the string constrains it to move in a circle. This force acting towards the centre of the circle gives the particle a certain acceleration towards the centre of the circle. We shall prove that this acceleration is $\dfrac{v^2}{r}$, where v is the speed of the particle and r the radius of the circle, and hence that the tension in the string is $\dfrac{mv^2}{r}$.

Let the particle move in a circle of centre O and radius r with uniform

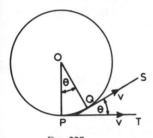

FIG. 227.

speed v. Let P and Q (Fig. 227) be two positions of the particle on the circle, and let the angle POQ be θ. Let PT be the tangent to the circle at P and QS the tangent at Q. The angle between the tangents PT and QS is θ. The velocity of the particle at P is of magnitude v and its direction is along the tangent PT. The velocity of the particle at Q is also of magnitude v, but is along the tangent QS.

Resolving the velocity of the particle at Q parallel to and perpendicular to PT, we have the components of velocity at Q,

$$v \cos \theta, \quad \text{parallel to } PT,$$
$$v \sin \theta, \quad \text{perpendicular to } PT.$$

Hence, the change of velocity while the particle moves from P to Q is

$$v \cos \theta - v, \quad \text{parallel to } PT,$$
$$v \sin \theta, \quad \text{perpendicular to } PT.$$

Since the particle is moving in a circle with uniform speed v and the length of the arc PQ is $r\theta$, the time taken for the particle to move from P to Q is $r\theta/v$.

311

Hence, the average acceleration of the particle in this time is

$$\frac{v^2}{r}\frac{\cos\theta-1}{\theta}, \text{ parallel to } PT,$$

$$\frac{v^2}{r}\frac{\sin\theta}{\theta}, \text{ perpendicular to } PT.$$

The limiting values of these quantities as θ tends to zero are the components along and perpendicular to the tangent at P of the acceleration at P.

Now $$\frac{\cos\theta-1}{\theta} = -\frac{\sin^2\frac{1}{2}\theta}{\frac{1}{2}\theta},$$

$$= -\frac{\sin\frac{1}{2}\theta}{\frac{1}{2}\theta} \times \sin\frac{1}{2}\theta.$$

The limiting value of $\dfrac{\sin\frac{1}{2}\theta}{\frac{1}{2}\theta}$ as θ tends to zero is 1, and the limiting value of $\sin\frac{1}{2}\theta$ is zero, and therefore

$$\lim_{\theta\to0}\frac{\cos\theta-1}{\theta} = 0.$$

Hence, the component of acceleration along the tangent at P is zero. The component of acceleration perpendicular to the tangent at P is

$$\frac{v^2}{r} \times \lim_{\theta\to0}\frac{\sin\theta}{\theta} = \frac{v^2}{r}.$$

Hence, the acceleration of the particle at any point of its path is $\dfrac{v^2}{r}$ towards the centre of the circle.

If ω be the uniform *angular* velocity with which the particle describes the circle, we have $v = r\omega$, and hence the acceleration towards the centre is $r\omega^2$.

It should be noted that the dimensions of v^2/r or $r\omega^2$ are LT^{-2}, which are the dimensions of an acceleration.

18.2 Effective Normal Force

The term *effective force* is used to denote the product of the mass and acceleration of a particle. Thus if a particle of mass m has an acceleration a in a certain direction, we say that it has an effective force ma in that direction. If P be the resultant of the forces acting on the particle, then the force P has the same magnitude and direction as the effective force ma.

When a particle of mass m is moving in a circle of radius r with uniform speed v, its effective force is $\dfrac{mv^2}{r}$ towards the centre of the circle.

When the particle is describing the circle on a smooth horizontal table at the end of a string attached at the centre of the circle, we have for the tension T in the string, in absolute units of force,

$$T = \frac{mv^2}{r}.$$

If the particle is describing the circle under the action of a more complex system of forces, the forces acting on the particle and the effective force may be shown on two diagrams. Thus if the particle is describing a

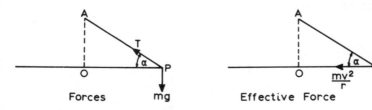

Forces   mg   Effective Force

FIG. 228.

horizontal circle of radius r at the end of a string of length l attached at a point A above the centre of the circle O, the forces acting on the particle are the tension in the string T and the weight of the particle. The diagrams (Fig. 228) show the forces and the effective force acting on the particle when it is at a point P of the circle. Thus if the angle APO be denoted by α, we have $\cos \alpha = \dfrac{r}{l}$, and since the resultant of T and mg must be equivalent to the effective force

$$T \sin \alpha = mg,$$

$$T \cos \alpha = \frac{mv^2}{r}.$$

Hence
$$T = mgl/\sqrt{(l^2 - r^2)},$$
$$v^2 = gr \cot \alpha = gr^2/\sqrt{(l^2 - r^2)}.$$

Thus the velocity v with which the circle can be described is related to the radius in this way.

18.3 Reversed Effective Force

If the *reversed* effective force be shown on the same diagram as the real forces, we have a static balance between the forces and the reversed effective forces. Thus if a force P acting on a particle of mass m gives it an acceleration a, the effective force is ma in the same direction as the force P.

The reversed effective force will be ma in the opposite direction to P, and the particle may be considered as being in equilibrium under forces P and ma in opposite directions.

In problems involving uniform motion in a circle it is convenient to show the reversed effective force $\dfrac{mv^2}{r}$ on the same diagram as the forces, and then to balance the forces as in a statical problem.

Thus, for a particle of mass m describing a horizontal circle of radius r with speed v at the end of a string of length l attached at a point A above the centre of the circle O, we may show the forces and the reversed effective normal force on the same diagram as in Fig. 229.

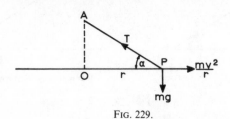

FIG. 229.

Then the problem may be treated as one of statical equilibrium and we have

$$T \cos \alpha = \frac{mv^2}{r},$$

$$T \sin \alpha = mg,$$

where $\cos \alpha = \dfrac{r}{l}$, leading to the same results as in the previous section.

The reversed effective force which balances the other forces in uniform motion in a circle is always in a direction *away from the centre* of the circle.

Example 1. *Two equal particles are connected by a string passing through a hole in a smooth table, one particle being on the table, the other underneath. How many revolutions per minute would the particle on the table have to perform in a circle of radius 15 cm, in order to keep the other particle at rest?* (L.U.)

Let m kg be the mass of each particle and ω rad/sec the angular velocity with which the circle is described.

Then the tension in the string is mg newton and the effective normal force is $m \times 0.15 \times \omega^2$ newton.

Therefore

$$mg = 0.15m\omega^2,$$

$$\omega^2 = \frac{981}{15} = 65.4,$$

$$\omega = 8.09 \text{ rad/sec}.$$

One revolution, or 2π radians, is described in $2\pi/\omega$ sec and therefore the particle makes $\dfrac{60 \times \omega}{2\pi} = \dfrac{243}{\pi}$ revolutions per minute.

18.4 Conical Pendulum

An arrangement by which a particle attached by a string to a fixed point describes a horizontal circle below the fixed point is called a conical pendulum. As the particle describes the circle the string traces out a cone whose semi-vertical angle is the inclination of the string to the vertical.

Let the mass of the particle be m, h the height of the cone and α its semi-vertical angle (Fig. 230). The speed of revolution and the tension in the string may be found in terms of h and α.

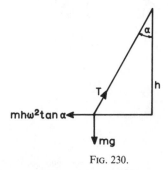

Fig. 230.

Let ω be the angular velocity with which the circle is described and T the tension in the string. The radius of the circle is $h \tan \alpha$ and the reversed effective force is $mh\omega^2 \tan \alpha$ away from the centre of the circle. The particle may be considered as in equilibrium under the forces T, mg and $mh\omega^2 \tan \alpha$.

We have

$$T \sin \alpha = mh\omega^2 \tan \alpha,$$

$$T \cos \alpha = mg.$$

Therefore

$$\omega^2 = g/h,$$

$$T = mg \sec \alpha.$$

If ω is in rad/sec, the time of a complete revolution is $\dfrac{2\pi}{\omega}$ sec, and the number of r.p.m. is

$$\frac{30\omega}{\pi} = \frac{30}{\pi}\sqrt{g/h}.$$

Example 2. *A mass of 10 kg rests on a rough horizontal table with coefficient of friction $\frac{1}{2}$. It is attached to one end of a light inextensible string which passes through a smooth hole in a table and carries a mass of 4 kg at its free end. If the mass of 4 kg describes a horizontal* *circle with a uniform velocity of 8 m/sec and the mass on the table is on the point of slipping, find the radius of the circle and the length of string below the table.*

Since the 10-kg mass is on the point of slipping the tension in the string must be 5*g* N.

Let *a* m be the radius of the circle and θ the angle made by the string with the horizontal (Fig. 231).

The reversed effective force is $\dfrac{4 \times 8^2}{a}$ N away from the centre of the circle, and the

4-kg mass may be considered as in equilibrium under the forces 5*g*, 4*g* and $\dfrac{256}{a}$ N.

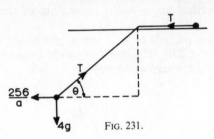

Fig. 231.

Then

$$5g \cos \theta = \frac{256}{a},$$

$$5g \sin \theta = 4g,$$

$$\sin \theta = \frac{4}{5},$$

$$\cos \theta = \frac{3}{5} = \frac{256}{5 \times 9 \cdot 81 \times a},$$

$$a = \frac{256}{29 \cdot 43} = 8 \cdot 7.$$

The length of string below the table is

$$a \sec \theta = \frac{5}{3} a = 14 \cdot 5 \text{ m}.$$

Example 3. *A string 8 m long has its ends attached to two points A and B, A being 4 m vertically above B. A small heavy ring C is threaded on the string and slides on it without friction. If the ring is made to describe a horizontal circle, find the speed of rotation when the radius of the circle is 3 m.*

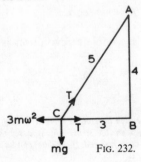

Fig. 232.

Let ω rad/sec be the speed of rotation, m kg the mass of the ring.

To describe a circle of radius 3 m with the string taut, the ring must be level with B (Fig. 232).

Let T newton be the tension in the string.

The reversed effective force is $3m\omega^2$ newton, and this must balance the tensions in the two portions of the string and the weight of the ring.

Therefore
$$T \cos CAB = mg,$$
$$T(1 + \sin CAB) = 3m\omega^2.$$
$$T = \frac{5}{4}mg.$$
$$\frac{5}{4}mg\left(1 + \frac{3}{5}\right) = 3m\omega^2,$$
$$\omega^2 = \frac{2g}{3},$$
$$\omega = 2 \cdot 56 \text{ rad/sec},$$
$$\frac{30\omega}{\pi} = 24 \cdot 4.$$

Therefore the ring makes 24·4 r.p.m.

18.5 Governors

A governor is a device attached to a rotating shaft of a steam engine to ensure that the engine does not run faster than a certain speed. It usually consists of two heavy balls attached to the shaft and rotating with it. The balls describe a circle, and if their speed increases, the forces in the framework joining them to the shaft increase, and cause a collar on the shaft to move; this opens a valve and decreases the speed.

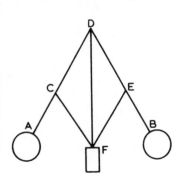

FIG. 233.

The framework is commonly as shown in Fig. 233. It consists of four light rods, AD, BD, CF and EF, freely jointed at C and E, hinged to a fixed point of the shaft at D and to a collar which slides on the shaft at F. The collar at F, whose lifting opens the valve, may have its movement restricted by a weight or spring. In the mathematical treatment we shall assume that the members of the framework are of negligible weight and that the balls may be treated as particles.

Example 4. *In a simple governor four equal, light, smoothly jointed links form a rhombus ABCD of side 30 cm. Two balls each of mass 6 kg are attached at B and D. The point A is fixed on a vertical rotating shaft, and at C there is a collar of mass 40 kg which can slide freely on the shaft. Find the speed of the shaft at which the balls will rotate in a circle of radius 15 cm. If the speed is increased by 10 r.p.m. find the amount by which the collar rises.*

When the radius of the circle in which the balls rotate is 15 cm the angle $BAC = 30°$ (Fig. 234).

Let ω rad/sec be the speed of rotation, T_1 and T the tensions in the upper and lower links.

The reversed effective force on each ball is $0.15 \times 6 \times \omega^2 = 0.9\omega^2$ N.

Considering the equilibrium of the collar, we have

$$T \cos 30° = 20g.$$

Considering the equilibrium of the ball at B, we have

$$T_1 \cos 30° = 6g + T \cos 30° = 26g.$$
$$T_1 \sin 30° + T \sin 30° = 0.9\omega^2.$$

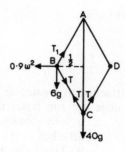

Fig. 234.

Therefore

$$0.9\omega^2 = \frac{1}{2}(20g + 26g) \sec 30°,$$

$$\omega^2 = \frac{46 \times 9.81 \times 2}{2 \times 0.9 \times \sqrt{3}} = 289,$$

$$\omega = 17 \text{ rad/sec},$$

$$\frac{30\omega}{\pi} = 162.$$

Therefore the shaft is rotating at 162 r.p.m.

10 r.p.m. is equivalent to an angular velocity of 1.05 rad/sec, and hence the new speed of rotation is

$$\omega_1 = 18.05 \text{ rad/sec}.$$

Let α be the new value of the angle BAC. The reserved effective force is now $1 \cdot 8\omega_1^2 \sin \alpha$, and we have

$$T \cos \alpha = 20g,$$

$$T_1 \cos \alpha = 26g,$$

$$(T + T_1) \sin \alpha = 1 \cdot 8\omega_1^2 \sin \alpha.$$

Therefore,

$$\sec \alpha = \frac{1 \cdot 8\omega_1^2}{46g} = 1 \cdot 30,$$

$$\alpha = 39° \, 43',$$

$$0 \cdot 3 \times 2 \cos \alpha = 0 \cdot 4615,$$

$$0 \cdot 3 \times 2 \cos 30° = 0 \cdot 5196,$$

$$\text{rise of collar} = 0 \cdot 0581 \text{ m} = 5 \cdot 81 \text{ cm}.$$

18.6 Relative Equilibrium of a Rotating Particle

If a particle rests in contact with a rotating body so that it describes a circle with uniform speed, we may study the relative equilibrium of the particle with respect to the body by the methods of statics, including among the forces to be balanced the reversed effective force due to rotation.

For example, if a particle is inside a smooth hemispherical bowl of radius r which is rotating with its rim horizontal and uppermost about a vertical axis through the centre, let m be the mass of the particle, α the inclination to the vertical of the radius from the centre of the bowl to the particle and ω the angular velocity of rotation (Fig. 235). The particle is describing a circle of radius $r \sin \alpha$, and the reversed effective force is $mr\omega^2 \sin \alpha$ horizontally, away from the axis of rotation.

We have therefore

$$R \sin \alpha = mr\omega^2 \sin \alpha,$$

$$R \cos \alpha = mg,$$

and hence,

$$R = mg \sec \alpha,$$

$$\omega^2 = \frac{g}{r} \sec \alpha.$$

Thus the position at which the particle can rest depends on the speed of rotation.

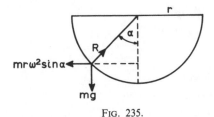

FIG. 235.

FIG. 236.

A body of mass m which is at rest relative to the earth in latitude λ is rotating with the earth in a circle of radius $a \cos \lambda$, where a is the earth's radius (assuming the earth to be spherical) (Fig. 236). The reversed effective force on the body is $ma \cos \lambda \Omega^2$, where Ω is the angular velocity of the earth.

Now

$$a = 21 \cdot 16 \times 10^6 \text{ ft} = 6 \cdot 45 \times 10^6 \text{ m}$$

$$\Omega = 7 \cdot 29 \times 10^{-5} \text{ rad/sec, approximately.}$$

Hence if $m = 1$ kg, the reversed effective force is

$$a\Omega^2 \cos \lambda = 0 \cdot 0343 \cos \lambda \text{ N.}$$

At the equator where $\cos \lambda = 1$ this is about $\frac{1}{260}$ of the weight of the body. This proportion, therefore, of the earth's attraction of a body on the equator is causing the body to move in a circle, and the remainder of the earth's attraction is the apparent weight of the body.

Example 5. *A hollow cone with its vertex downwards and its axis vertical, revolves about its axis with a speed of 120 r.p.m. The inner surface of the cone is rough, and carries round a particle in horizontal circles. If the semi-vertical angle of the cone is 30° and the coefficient of friction $\frac{1}{4}$, find the greatest and least distances from the vertex at which the particle can be carried round in this way.*

Let m be the mass of the particle and R the normal reaction. Let l be the greatest distance from the vertex with friction μR acting towards the vertex (Fig. 237). The angular velocity is 4π rad/sec and the reversed effective force is $ml \sin 30° (4\pi)^2 = 8ml\pi^2$.

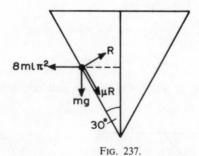

Fig. 237.

Resolving horizontally and vertically we have

$$8ml\pi^2 = R \cos 30° + \mu R \sin 30°,$$

$$mg = R \sin 30° - \mu R \cos 30°.$$

Hence

$$l = \frac{g}{8\pi^2} \cdot \frac{\sqrt{3}+\mu}{1-\mu\sqrt{3}},$$

$$= 0\cdot124 \frac{1\cdot732+0\cdot25}{1-0\cdot433},$$

$$= 0\cdot435 \text{ m}.$$

The least distance to the vertex is found by assuming the friction to act away from the vertex. This may be done by changing the sign of μ, giving

$$l' = 0\cdot124 \frac{1\cdot732-0\cdot25}{1+0\cdot433},$$

$$= 0\cdot129 \text{ m}.$$

EXERCISES 18 (a)

1. A rough horizontal circular disc is rotating with uniform angular velocity ω about a fixed vertical axis through its centre. Two particles of masses M, m lie on the disc and are at rest relative to it, being on the same radius and at distances a and $2a$ respectively from the centre. They are connected by a light inextensible string of length a, and μ is the coefficient of friction between either particle and the disc. Show that both particles are on the point of slipping outwards if $\omega^2 = \dfrac{\mu g(M+m)}{a(M+2m)}$ and find an expression for the corresponding tension in the string. (L.U.)

2. A particle of mass m lies on a smooth horizontal table, and is attached, by an inextensible string which passes through a smooth hole in the table, to a particle of mass $2m$ which hangs freely below the table. The particle of mass m describes a circle of radius 1 m on the table with such uniform speed that the particle of mass $2m$ remains at rest. Calculate the speed required. (L.U.)

3. One end of a light inextensible string is attached to a mass of $7\frac{1}{2}$ kg which is at rest on a rough horizontal table, the coefficient of friction being $\frac{1}{3}$. The string passes through a small hole in the table, and supports at its other end a mass of 2 kg which is revolving in a horizontal circle of radius 20 cm. Find the number of revolutions made per minute if the mass on the table is on the point of slipping. (L.U.)

4. Three equal particles each of mass 1 kg are at the vertices of an equilateral triangle whose sides are taut inextensible strings of length 12 cm. If the figure is on a smooth horizontal plane and revolves uniformly about its centre at a rate of 5 revolutions per second, find the tensions in the strings. (L.U.)

5. A particle of mass 4 kg is whirled round at the end of a string 50 cm long, so as to describe a horizontal circle, making 60 revolutions per minute; calculate the tension in the string and prove that the fixed end of the string is a little less than 25 cm above the centre of the circle. (O.C.)

6. A particle suspended by a fine string from a fixed point describes a circle uniformly in a horizontal plane. If it makes three complete revolutions every 2 sec, show that its vertical depth below the fixed point is 10·8 cm approximately. (O.C.)

7. A particle attached to a fixed point by a string 1 m long describes a circle in a horizontal plane. The string can only support a tension equal to fifteen times the

weight of the particle; show that the greatest possible number of revolutions per second is just over two.   (O.C.)

8. A plane horizontal circular disc is constrained to rotate uniformly about its centre, describing two complete revolutions per second. Show that the greatest distance from the centre of the disc at which a small object can be placed so as to stay on the disc is very approximately $6 \cdot 17\mu$ cm, where μ is the coefficient of friction between the object and the disc.   (O.C.)

9. A particle attached by a light inextensible string to a fixed point describes a horizontal circle with uniform angular velocity ω, the plane of the circle being at a distance h below the fixed point. Prove that $g = h\omega^2$.

   If the length of the string is 8 cm, and it is inclined at an angle of 60° to the vertical, and the weight of the particle is 30 g, find the tension in the string and the number of revolutions per minute that the particle is making.   (O.C.)

10. A particle of mass 6 kg is fastened by a string 125 cm long to a point 75 cm above the level of a horizontal smooth table. How many r.p.m. must the particle make in horizontal circles so as just to keep clear of the table? Calculate the thrust between the particle and the table if this speed is reduced to 25 r.p.m.

11. A particle of mass m is attached to a fixed point by a light inextensible string of length l, and is attached also by another such string of length l to a ring of mass m which can slide on a smooth vertical wire passing through the fixed point. The particle is describing a horizontal circle with uniform angular velocity ω. Prove that the depth of the ring below the fixed point is $6g/\omega^2$, and find the expressions for the tensions in each string in terms of m, ω and l.

12. A particle P of mass 6 kg is attached by two strings, PQ, and PR, of lengths 75 cm and 125 cm respectively, to two points Q and R, of which R is 1 m vertically above Q. If the particle describes a horizontal circle with a speed of 10 m/sec, both strings being taut, find the tension in each string. Find the minimum speed of the particle in order that both strings may be taut.   (L.U.)

13. A heavy particle B is supported by two light rods, AB, BC, whose extremities A and C are smoothly hinged to fixed points in a vertical line AC (A above C), BC being horizontal. The configuration rotates uniformly about the vertical axis AC, so that B traces a horizontal circle of radius BC. If there is a tension S in BC when the system rotates with angular velocity ω_1, and a thrust S in BC when the system rotates with angular velocity ω_2, prove that

$$\omega_1{}^2 + \omega_2{}^2 = 2g/AC. \qquad \text{(L.U.)}$$

14. A small ring of mass m, free to slide on a thin, smooth, vertical rod, is attached by a light inelastic string of length $2a$ to a point on the rod. A particle of equal mass is fixed to the mid-point of the string. Prove that the system can rotate in steady motion about an axis coinciding with the rod, with each part of the string inclined to the rod, provided the angular velocity exceeds $\sqrt{(3g/a)}$.   (L.U.)

15. A steam governor consists of four equal light rods, AB, BC, CD, DA, of length 25 cm, freely hinged at their ends and rotating about a vertical axis to which it is hinged at the fixed point A and on which it slides without friction on a light collar attached to the rods at C below A. It carries masses of 6 kg at B and D, and is kept in position by a spring at C. Find the number of revolutions being made per minute if the force exerted by the spring is 10 N downwards and AC equals 30 cm.   (L.U.)

16. Particles of masses $3m$ and $5m$ are attached to the ends of a light string of length a which passes through a fixed smooth ring at O. The lighter particle describes a

horizontal circle about the heavier particle (which remains stationary) as centre. Prove that the two particles lie in a horizontal plane at a distance $3a/8$ below O, and that the time of a complete revolution is $\pi\sqrt{(3a/2g)}$. (O.C.)

17. Two small masses, of 60 g and 30 g respectively, are connected by a light inextensible string, 30 cm long, which passes through a small smooth fixed ring. The 60 g mass hangs at a distance 22·5 cm below the ring, while the 30 g mass describes a horizontal circle. Show that the plane of this circle is 3·75 cm below the ring, and show also that the 30 g mass makes very approximately 153 r.p.m. (O.C.)

18. Two equal particles A and B are connected by a light inextensible string of length a, and A is attached to a fixed point by a light inextensible string of length b. The particles describe horizontal circles with the same uniform angular velocity, the string joining A to the fixed point making an angle of 45° with the vertical, and the string joining A to B making an angle of 60° with the vertical. Find the ratio of b to a. (O.C.)

19. The ends of a light string of length $2a$ are attached to two points in the same vertical distance $2c$ apart, and the string passes through a smooth ring of weight w. Show that if the ring revolves in a horizontal circle at the level of the lower point of attachment its velocity is $\{(a^2-c^2)g/c\}^{\frac{1}{2}}$ and the tension in the string is $\frac{1}{2}w(a^2+c^2)/ac$. (O.C.)

20. The smooth inside surface of a bowl is a segment of a sphere of radius 8 cm, the height of the segment being 4 cm. The bowl has its axis fixed and vertical, and it is rotated about the axis. Find the greatest permissible angular velocity of the bowl, in revolutions per minute, if a particle placed in it can remain at rest relative to the bowl just within the rim. (L.U.)

18.7 Vehicles Moving in a Circle

When a vehicle is moving in a circle with constant speed we may examine the forces acting on it by the methods of statics by introducing the reversed effective normal force.

Let a vehicle of mass M be moving in a circle of centre O with constant angular velocity ω (Fig. 238). The effective normal force for an element

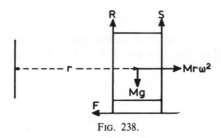

FIG. 238.

of mass m distant x from O is $mx\omega^2$, hence for the whole body it is $\Sigma mx\omega^2 = Mr\omega^2$, where r is the distance of the centre of gravity of the body from O. Hence the reversed effective force is $Mr\omega^2$ acting at the centre of gravity of the body away from O. Let R and S be the reactions at the wheels of the ground, assumed horizontal. It is evident that there cannot be a balance of forces unless there is also some force F acting towards the centre of the circle. This force is due to friction between the tyres of the vehicle and the road, or, in the case of railway stock, to the pressure of the outer track on the flange of the outer wheels. Let h be the height of the centre of gravity of the vehicle and $2a$ the width of its track, so that its centre of gravity is at a horizontal distance a from each of the points of contact of the wheels.

We have

$$R + S = Mg,$$

$$F = Mr\omega^2,$$

and, taking moments about the centre of gravity,

$$Sa - Ra = Fh.$$

Hence,

$$R = \frac{1}{2}M\left(g - \frac{h}{a}r\omega^2\right),$$

$$S = \frac{1}{2}M\left(g + \frac{h}{a}r\omega^2\right).$$

The vehicle may skid if the friction between the tyres and the road is insufficient, that is, since the maximum force of friction is $\mu(R + S)$, where μ is the coefficient of friction, if

$$\mu Mg < Mr\omega^2,$$

that is,

$$\omega^2 > \frac{\mu g}{r},$$

or, if $v = r\omega$,

$$v > \sqrt{(\mu g r)}.$$

The vehicle is on the point of overturning when the reaction at the inner wheels vanishes, that is, when $R = 0$, and this gives

$$g = \frac{h}{a}r\omega^2,$$

$$v = \sqrt{\left(\frac{a}{h}gr\right)}.$$

If $v > \sqrt{\left(\frac{a}{h}gr\right)}$, the overturning moment of the forces about the point of contact of the outer wheel is

$$hMrw\omega^2 - Mga,$$

$$= \frac{Mh}{r}\left(v^2 - \frac{agr}{h}\right),$$

and this quantity, being greater than zero, will cause the vehicle to overturn · about the outer wheels.

18.8 Banking

A road or railway is frequently banked at corners, that is, the road is inclined downwards towards the centre of the curve, and on railways the outer track is placed higher than the inner.

Let α (Fig. 239) be the inclination of a road towards the centre of the

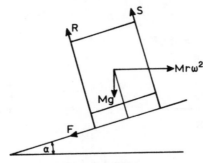

FIG. 239.

circle. Then, taking R and S as the normal reactions, F the friction, and $Mr\omega^2$ the reversed effective force, which is horizontal, we have

$$R + S = Mg\cos\alpha + Mr\omega^2\sin\alpha,$$

$$F = -Mg\sin\alpha + Mr\omega^2\cos\alpha,$$

and, taking moments about the centre of gravity,

$$Sa - Ra = Fh.$$

From these equations we have the values of F, R, and S as before.
If $F = 0$ we have

$$\tan\alpha = \frac{r\omega^2}{g} = \frac{v^2}{gr},$$

and this gives the ideal angle of banking for a given speed on a given circle.

For overturning, we have $R = 0$, and hence

$$a(Mg \cos \alpha + Mr\omega^2 \sin \alpha) = h(Mr\omega^2 \cos \alpha - Mg \sin \alpha),$$

$$v^2 = r^2\omega^2 = gr\frac{a + h \tan \alpha}{h - a \tan \alpha}.$$

This gives the overturning speed when the angle of banking is α.

18.9 Bicycles Moving in a Circle

A bicycle cannot be ridden in a circle if the centre of gravity of the bicycle and rider is vertically above the wheels (Fig. 240); for a certain friction F would be necessary to balance the reversed effective force, and there would be no other moment to counteract the turning moment of the force F about the centre of gravity.

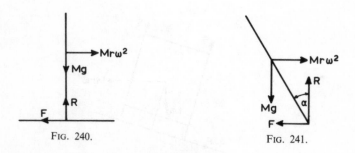

FIG. 240.   FIG. 241.

The bicycle has therefore to be inclined inwards towards the centre of the circle. Let α be the inclination of the plane through the centre of gravity and the points of contact of the wheels to the vertical (Fig. 241).

The forces acting are the vertical reaction R and the friction F at the point of contact A, the weight Mg and the reversed effective force $Mr\omega^2$ at the centre of gravity G.

We have

$$F = Mr\omega^2,$$

$$R = Mg.$$

Also, taking moments about A,

$$Mr\omega^2 \times AG \cos \alpha = Mg \times AG \sin \alpha,$$

$$\tan \alpha = \frac{r\omega^2}{g},$$

$$= \frac{v^2}{gr}, \text{ where } v = r\omega.$$

This angle is the same as the ideal banking angle found for vehicles.

If the road is banked at an angle β, let α be the inclination of the plane of the bicycle to the plane through the points of contact perpendicular to the road.

The forces (Fig. 242) are R and F perpendicular to and along the road,

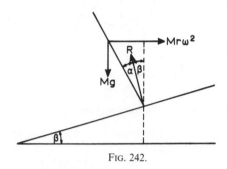

FIG. 242.

$Mr\omega^2$ and Mg horizontally and vertically through the centre of gravity G. Moments about the point of contact A gives

$$Mr\omega^2 \times AG \cos(\alpha+\beta) = Mg \times AG \sin(\alpha+\beta),$$

$$\tan(\alpha+\beta) = \frac{r\omega^2}{g} = \frac{v^2}{gr}.$$

Hence $$\alpha = \tan^{-1}\left(\frac{v^2}{gr}\right) - \beta.$$

Example 6. *A road is banked at an angle of* 15° *to the horizontal round a curve of* 100 m *radius. At what speed can a car go round with no tendency to skid?*

What is the maximum speed with which a car, whose track is 135 cm *wide, and whose centre of gravity is central and* 75 cm *from the ground can take this curve without overturning, and what coefficient of friction will keep it from skidding at this speed?*

The components of the weight of the car and of the reversed effective force parallel to the road are $Mg \sin 15°$ and $M\dfrac{v^2}{r} \cos 15°$ respectively. If there is no tendency to to skid these components must balance and we have

$$v^2 = gr \tan 15°,$$
$$= 100 \times 9.81 \times 0.2679,$$
$$= 262.8,$$
$$v = 16.21 \text{ m/sec} = 58.4 \text{ km/h}.$$

If v_1 be the overturning speed, the reaction at the inner wheels is zero at this speed, and we have the reaction S at the outer wheels and the friction F to balance the weight Mg and the reversed normal effective force $m\dfrac{v_1^{\,2}}{r}$ (Fig. 243).

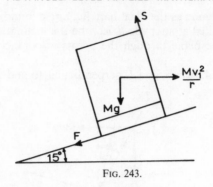

FIG. 243.

Taking moments about the outer wheel we have

$$Mg(67 \cdot 5 \cos 15° + 75 \sin 15°) = M\frac{v_1^2}{r}(75 \cos 15° - 67 \cdot 5 \sin 15°),$$

$$v_1^2 = gr\frac{27 + 30 \tan 15°}{30 - 27 \tan 15°},$$

$$= 981 \times 1 \cdot 539,$$

$$v_1 = 38 \cdot 86 \text{ m/sec} = 140 \text{ km/h}.$$

We have also at this speed from moments about the centre of gravity.

$$75 F = 67 \cdot 5 S,$$

$$\frac{F}{S} = 0 \cdot 9.$$

Hence, the coefficient of friction necessary to avoid skidding at this speed is 0·9.

Example 7. *The sleepers of a railway line at a point where the curve of the track has a radius of 60 m have such a slope that a train moving at 45 km/h exerts no lateral force on the rails. What lateral force would an engine of mass 100 tonnes exert on the rails (i) if it were at rest, (ii) if it were travelling at 90 km/h?*

Let α be the angle of inclination of the sleepers. The weight Mg and the reversed effective force $M\frac{v^2}{r}$ are inclined at angles α and $90° - \alpha$ respectively to the perpendicular to the track (Fig. 244).

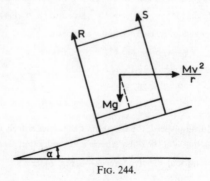

FIG. 244.

There is no lateral thrust of the rails, therefore,

$$Mg \sin \alpha = M\frac{v^2}{r} \cos \alpha,$$

$$\tan \alpha = \frac{v^2}{gr},$$

$$= \frac{12\cdot5 \times 12\cdot5}{9\cdot81 \times 60},$$

$$= 0\cdot2655,$$

$$\alpha = 14° 52'.$$

If the velocity is zero, there is no normal effective force, and hence the component of the weight $Mg \sin \alpha$ must be balanced by the lateral thrust of the inner rail on the flanges of the wheels.

Therefore,

$$\text{lateral thrust} = Mg \sin \alpha,$$

$$= 100\,000 \times 0\cdot2565 \times g,$$

$$= 2\cdot52 \times 10^5 \text{ N}.$$

If the velocity is 90 km/h the reversed normal effective force is four times what it was at 45 km/h, and its component parallel to the sleepers is $4Mg \sin \alpha$. Hence the lateral thrust exerted by the outer rail on the flanges of the wheels must be $3Mg \sin \alpha$, that is

$$\text{lateral thrust} = 7\cdot56 \times 10^5 \text{ N}.$$

EXERCISES 18 (b)

1. A vehicle whose wheel track is 1·7 m wide and whose centre of gravity is 1 m above the road and central between the wheels takes a curve whose radius is 50 m on a level road. Find the speed at which the inner wheels would leave the road. Show that if the centre of gravity were displaced 0·5 m towards the inner wheels the overturning speed would be increased by about 25 per cent.
2. A cyclist turns a corner on a curve of radius 30 m on a level road at a speed of 30 km/h. Find the angle at which he leans from the vertical and the coefficient of friction between the tyres and the road necessary to prevent skidding.
3. A humpback bridge as the shape of an arc of a circle of 40 m radius. Find the greatest speed at which a cyclist can cross the bridge without leaving the road.
4. The width of the track of a car is 115 cm and the centre of gravity is 60 cm above the road and 7·5 cm to the right of the centre line of the car. The road bends, first to the right and then to the left, the radius of each curve being 40 m. If the coefficient of friction between the tyres and the road is 0·9, show that if the car were driven too fast it would skid at the first bend and overturn at the second.
5. A two-wheeled vehicle has its wheels 183 cm apart and its centre of gravity at a height of 135 cm. If it is travelling round a curve of radius 110 m on a level road at 27 km/h, find the ratio of the normal reactions on its inner and outer wheels.
6. A cyclist rounds a curve of 30 m radius on a road which is banked at an angle of 20° to the horizontal. If the coefficient of friction between the tyres and the road is $\frac{1}{2}$, find the greatest speed at which he can ride without skidding and his inclination to the vertical at this speed.

7. A car is moving round a curve of 24 m radius on a level road. If the outer wheels do not slip, find the speed at which the inner wheels will leave the ground. Assume that the centre of gravity of the car is 70 cm from the ground and that the width of the wheelbase is 1·5 m.   (L.U.)

8. A railway carriage, of mass 20 tonnes, moves round a curve of radius 300 m with a speed of 6 m/sec. The distance between the rails is 1·5 m, and the outer rail is raised to such a height above the inner that there is no thrust on the flanges of the wheels. Calculate this height. Find the thrust on the flanges when the speed is increased to 9 m/sec.   (L.U.)

9. A train of mass 250 tonnes is moving at a speed of 45 km/h round a curve of radius 1120 m. If the track is level, find the lateral thrust on the rails. If the width of the track is 1·5 m, find the height to which the outer rail must be raised above the inner if there is to be no lateral thrust on the rails at a speed of 63 km/h. (L.U.)

10. A bicyclist is describing a curve of 20 m radius at a speed of 18 km/h; find the inclination to the vertical of the plane of the bicycle. What is the least coefficient of friction between the bicycle and the road, that the bicycle may not side-slip?   (O.C.)

11. The shape of a cycle-track at a corner is that of an arc of a circle whose radius is 100 m. Find the angle at which the track should be inclined to the horizontal, so that a rider can take the corner at 54 km/h without any lateral reaction between his bicycle and the track. If a motor-cyclist can take the corner safely at 90 km/h, find the least possible value of the coefficient of friction between the track and his tyres.

12. A curve on a railway line is banked up so that the lateral thrust on the inner rail due to a truck moving with speed v_1 is equal to the thrust on the outer rail when the truck is moving with speed $v_2(v_2 > v_1)$. Show that there will be no lateral thrust on either rail when the truck is moving with speed $\{\frac{1}{2}(v_1{}^2 + v_2{}^2)\}^{\frac{1}{2}}$. (O.C.)

13. The gauge of a railway is 1·5 m, and the line runs along an arc of a circle of radius 800 m. The average speed of the train on the line is 63 km/h; what should be the height of the outer rail above the inner rail?   (L.U.)

14. A vehicle travels round a curved track of radius 300 m at a speed of 90 km/h. The track is banked at an angle of 10° to the horizontal. Determine the ratio of the normal component of the reaction between the wheels and the track to the component of that reaction along the line of greatest slope of the track. For what speed would this latter component be zero?   (Q.E.)

15. A motor track describes a curve of 75 m radius and is sloping downwards towards the inside of the curve at an angle $\tan^{-1} 1/5$. At what speed must a car run along it so that there should be no tendency to side-slip?   (N.U.)

18.10 Circle Described with Variable Velocity

When a particle moves in a circle of radius r with varying velocity v, the acceleration towards the centre of the circle is $\dfrac{v^2}{r}$ as before, but there is in addition an acceleration $\dfrac{dv}{dt}$ along the tangent to the circle.

Let P and Q be two positions of the particle on the circle and let the angle subtended by PQ at the centre be the small angle $\delta\theta$. Let PT be the tangent at P, QS the tangent at Q, the angle between the tangents being also $\delta\theta$ (Fig. 245).

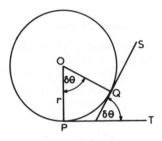

FIG. 245.

Let the velocity of the particle at P be v along PT, and at Q, $v + \delta v$ along QS.

The components of the velocity at Q parallel to and perpendicular to PT are $(v + \delta v) \cos \delta\theta$ and $(v + \delta v) \sin \delta\theta$ respectively. The change of velocity while the particle moves from P to Q is therefore

$$(v + \delta v) \cos \delta\theta - v, \quad \text{parallel to } PT,$$

$$(v + \delta v) \sin \delta\theta, \quad \text{perpendicular to } PT.$$

The time in which the arc PQ of length $r\delta\theta$ is described is $r\delta\theta/v$ to the first order of small quantities.

Hence the acceleration is

$$\frac{v}{r\delta\theta}\{v(\cos \delta\theta - 1) + \delta v \cos \delta\theta\}, \quad \text{parallel to } PT,$$

$$\frac{v(v + \delta v)}{r\delta\theta} \sin \delta\theta, \quad \text{perpendicular to } PT.$$

Now

$$\lim_{\delta\theta \to 0} \frac{\cos \delta\theta - 1}{\delta\theta} = 0,$$

$$\lim_{\delta\theta \to 0} \frac{v}{r} \frac{\delta v}{\delta\theta} \cos \delta\theta = \frac{v}{r} \frac{dv}{d\theta} = \frac{v}{r\theta} \frac{dv}{dt} = \frac{dv}{dt},$$

$$\lim_{\delta\theta \to 0} \frac{v(v + \delta v)}{r} \frac{\sin \delta\theta}{\delta\theta} = \frac{v^2}{r}.$$

Hence, the acceleration of the particle at P is $\dfrac{v^2}{r}$ towards the centre of the circle and $\dfrac{dv}{dt}$ along the tangent.

18.11 Motion in a Vertical Circle

If a particle describes a vertical circle swinging at the end of an inextensible string or sliding on a smooth surface we may use the energy equation to determine its velocity at any point.

If a particle of mass m is started on its motion with velocity v_0 along a tangent at height h_0 above the lowest point of the circle (Fig. 246), its

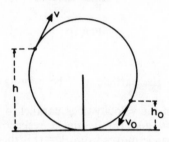

Fig. 246.

initial kinetic energy is $\tfrac{1}{2}mv_0{}^2$, and its initial potential energy is mgh_0. If in a subsequent position at height h above the lowest point of the circle the velocity of the particle is v, its kinetic energy is $\tfrac{1}{2}mv^2$ and its potential energy mgh.

Therefore, by the principle of conservation of energy we have

$$\tfrac{1}{2}mv^2 + mgh = \tfrac{1}{2}mv_0{}^2 + mgh_0,$$

and

$$v^2 = v_0{}^2 - 2g(h - h_0).$$

Thus the velocity at any point of the path may be determined.

We have assumed that the forces other than that of gravity which act on the particle are along the radius of the circle at any point, and hence, since the displacement is along the tangent, do no work.

18.12 Normal Balance of Forces

The reversed effective forces on a particle moving in a circle with variable velocity v are $\dfrac{mv^2}{r}$ away from the centre of the circle and $m\dfrac{dv}{dt}$ along the tangent in the direction opposite to that in which the particle is moving. Taking the reversed effective forces with the other forces acting on the particle, we may equate to zero the sum of the components in two directions. To find the force on the particle along the radius of the circle we may balance the forces in that direction only without bringing in the reversed effective force along the tangent.

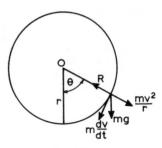

FIG. 247.

Let a particle of mass m be moving in a vertical circle of radius r, and let v be the velocity at any point and R the force acting on it along the radius to the centre (Fig. 247). We shall assume that the only other force is that of gravity.

Let θ be the angle which the radius to the particle makes with the downward vertical through the centre.

The normal balance of forces and effective forces gives

$$R = mg \cos \theta + \frac{mv^2}{r}.$$

The velocity v being determined by the energy equation, this equation gives the value of R at any point. R may, of course, be negative, that is, acting away from the centre.

Example 8. *Particle on smooth wire ring.*

If a particle slides on a smooth wire in the form of a vertical circle of radius r and its velocity at the lowest point of the circle is v_0, its velocity when the radius to it makes an angle θ with the downward vertical from the centre (Fig. 247) is given by

$$v^2 = v_0{}^2 - 2gr(1 - \cos \theta).$$

The normal reaction is

$$R = \frac{mv^2}{r} + mg \cos \theta,$$

$$= \frac{mv_0{}^2}{r} - mg(2 - 3 \cos \theta).$$

If the reaction R is zero we have

$$\frac{v_0{}^2}{gr} = 2 - 3 \cos \theta,$$

$$\cos \theta = \frac{2gr - v_0{}^2}{3gr}.$$

If this equation gives a value of $\cos \theta$ numerically greater than unity there is no real value of θ at which the reaction is zero and the reaction does not change sign during the motion.

The condition that the particle should reach the highest point of the circle is obtained from the energy equation, and is

$$v_0{}^2 > 4gr.$$

If $v_0{}^2 = 4gr$, the particle will come to rest at the highest point of the wire.

Example 9. *Particle suspended by a string.*

Let a particle of mass m suspended from a fixed point by a light inextensible string of length r describe a vertical circle about the point. Let v_0 be the velocity at the lowest point and let v be the velocity and T the tension in the string when the string makes an angle θ with the downward vertical.

Then, as in the previous example,

$$v^2 = v_0{}^2 - 2gr(1 - \cos \theta),$$

$$T = \frac{mv_0{}^2}{r} - mg(2 - 3 \cos \theta).$$

In this case the particle will not describe a complete circle unless the tension in the string remains positive. This tension is least when $\theta = \pi$, that is, at the highest point of the circle, and the condition that the particle should describe a complete circle is

$$\frac{mv_0{}^2}{r} > mg(2 - 3 \cos \pi),$$

that is,

$$\frac{mv_0{}^2}{r} > 5mg,$$

$$v_0{}^2 > 5gr.$$

If v_0 has a value less than $5gr$, the particle will leave the circle at the point where the tension becomes zero given by

$$\cos \theta = \frac{2gr - v_0{}^2}{3gr}.$$

When $\cos \theta$ has this value the velocity is

$$v^2 = v_0{}^2 - 2gr\left(1 - \frac{2gr - v_0{}^2}{3gr}\right),$$

$$= \frac{1}{3}(v_0{}^2 - 2gr).$$

Hence, if $v_0{}^2 < 2gr$ there is an imaginary value for the velocity where the string becomes slack and the particle will not rise to this point. If $v_0{}^2 < 2gr$ the particle will not rise above the centre of the circle, and thus the string cannot become slack in the lower half of the circle.

Example 10. *Particle on the outside of a smooth sphere.*

Let a particle of mass m slide on the outside of a fixed smooth sphere of radius r, starting from the highest point of the sphere with horizontal velocity v_0. We assume, in the first instance, that it remains in contact with the sphere, and that its velocity is v when the radius to the particle makes an angle θ with the upward vertical (Fig. 248). Let R be the normal reaction between the particle and the sphere, acting outwards from the centre.

From the energy equation we have

$$v^2 = v_0{}^2 + 2gr(1 - \cos \theta).$$

From the normal balance of forces

$$R + \frac{mv^2}{r} = mg \cos \theta.$$

Hence

$$R = mg(3\cos\theta - 2) - \frac{mv_0^2}{r}.$$

R is positive to start with if $v_0^2 < gr$.

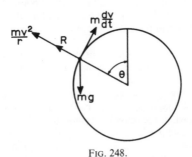

FIG. 248.

The particle will leave the sphere at the point where R vanishes, that is, at the point where

$$\cos\theta = \frac{v_0^2 + 2gr}{3gr}.$$

The velocity with which it leaves the sphere is given by

$$v^2 = v_0^2 + 2gr\left(1 - \frac{v_0^2 + 2gr}{3gr}\right),$$

$$= \frac{1}{3}(v_0^2 + 2gr).$$

The direction of this velocity is at angle $\sin^{-1}\left(\dfrac{v_0^2 + 2gr}{3gr}\right)$ with the downward vertical and the subsequent motion of the particle is a parabola.

EXERCISES 18 (c)

1. A small ring of mass m can slide on a smooth circular wire, radius r and centre O, which is fixed in a vertical plane. From a point on the wire at a vertical distance $r/2$ above O the ring is given a velocity $\sqrt{gr}$ along the downward tangent to the wire. Show that it will just reach the highest point of the wire. Find the reaction between the ring and the wire when the ring is at a vertical distance $r/2$ below O.
(L.U.)

2. A heavy particle of mass M attached to a fixed point by a light rod describes a vertical circle. If the speeds of the particle at the highest and lowest points are u and $3u$ respectively, prove that the tension in the rod when its inclination to the downward vertical is θ is $Mg(3\cos\theta + 2.5)$. If the length of the rod is 20 cm, determine the speed of the particle when $\theta = 60°$.
(L.U.)

3. A heavy particle in a smooth circular tube, fixed in a vertical plane, is slightly disturbed from rest at the top of the tube. Find the ratio of the thrusts on the

particle in the two positions where its vertical distance above and below the
centre of the tube is half a radius.   (L.U.)

4. A smooth hemispherical bowl of radius r, whose lowest point is A, is fixed with
   its rim uppermost and horizontal. A particle of mass m is projected along the
   inner surface of the bowl with a speed $\sqrt{(gr)}$ towards A, from a point at a vertical
   height $r/2$ above A, so that its motion is in a vertical plane through A. Show that
   the particle will just reach the top of the bowl, and find the reaction between the
   particle and the bowl when the particle is at a vertical height $r/3$ above A.
                                                                                        (L.U.)

5. A heavy particle, of mass m, oscillates through $180°$ on the inside of a smooth
   circular hoop of radius a fixed in a vertical plane. Prove that the pressure on
   the hoop at any point is $3mv^2/2a$.   (O.C.)

6. A mass of 1 g, hanging by a string 1 metre long, is swinging as a pendulum
   through an arc of total magnitude 1 radian. Find the central acceleration and the
   tension in the string when the mass is passing through its lowest point.   (L.U.)

7. A stone of mass 1 kg is whirled round on a smooth horizontal table with constant
   speed in a circle of radius 1 m, at the end of a string 1 m long, whose other end is
   fixed. If the string can only bear a tension of 49 N, find the maximum speed the
   stone can have, and how many revolutions per second it makes in that case.

   If the same stone is whirled round in a vertical circle, of radius 1 m, find the
   greatest speed the stone can have at the highest point of its path in order that the
   whole circle can be described without the string breaking.   (L.U.)

8. A heavy particle is attached to a fixed point O by a light inextensible string of
   length a. When at rest vertically below O, the particle is projected horizontally
   with speed u. Prove that it will describe a complete circle if $u^2 > 5ga$. Show
   further that if the string is replaced by a light rod of the same length, free to turn
   about O, the above inequality is replaced by $u^2 > 4ga$. Explain very briefly what
   happens in the former case if $u^2 = 4ga$.   (L.U.)

9. A mass m hangs at one end of a string of length a, the other end of which is fixed.
   If the mass be given a horizontal velocity of $\sqrt{(7ga/2)}$, show that the string will
   be about to become slack when it makes an angle of $60°$ with the upward vertical.
   Find the tension in the string when it makes an angle of $60°$ with the downward
   vertical.   (L.U.)

10. A heavy particle, hanging from a fixed point by a light inextensible string of
    length l, is projected horizontally with speed $(gl)^{\frac{1}{2}}$. Find the speed of the particle
    and the inclination of the string to the vertical at the instant of the motion when
    the tension in the string equals the weight of the particle.   (L.U.)

11. A ball of mass 200 g is attached to one end of a thread, 80 cm long, which can
    just support a weight of 900 g without breaking; the other end of the thread is
    fixed. The ball is held with the string taut and at a height of 40 cm above the
    level of the fixed point, and is started at right angles to the string with a velocity
    of 2 m/sec. Show that the string will break when the ball is directly below the
    starting point.   (O.C.)

12. A mass of 250 g is attached to two fixed points A, B, which are 90 cm apart and
    in the same horizontal line, by means of two strings each 75 cm in length.
    The mass is held with the strings taut in the horizontal plane through AB, and
    is then released. Find the tension in a string when the mass is in the vertical
    plane through AB.   (O.C.)

13. Show that the velocity with which a particle hanging from a fixed point by a
    string of length a must be started so as to describe a complete vertical circle must

not be less than $\sqrt{5ga}$. The particle is started with velocity $2\sqrt{ga}$, and when the string is horizontal it is held at such a point that the particle just completes the circle. At what distance from the particle is the string held?   (L.U.)

14. A particle slides from rest at the top down the outside smooth surface of a fixed sphere of radius a. Show that it leaves the surface when the radius to the particle makes an angle $\cos^{-1} 2/3$ with the upward vertical. Find the initial horizontal velocity to be imparted to the particle at the top if it leaves the surface at a point whose vertical height above the centre of the sphere is $3a/4$.   (L.U.)

15. A heavy particle is held at a point P on the outside of a smooth circular hoop of radius a, fixed in a vertical plane, the radius through P making an angle α with the upward vertical; the particle is released from rest, and it leaves the hoop at a point Q such that the radius through Q makes an angle $90° - \alpha$ with the upward vertical. Prove that $\tan \alpha = 2/3$.   (O.C.)

16. A particle is attached by a light inextensible string of length a to a fixed point, and is projected horizontally from its position of equilibrium with velocity u. Show that, if $5ga > u^2 > 2ga$, the string will go slack in the subsequent motion.

  If the particle is held with the string stretched and making an acute angle α with the upward drawn vertical and is then released, show that after the string tightens it will never go slack again and the particle will not rise to the level of the fixed end of the string if $\alpha < \frac{1}{4}\pi$, but that if $\alpha > \frac{1}{4}\pi$, the particle will rise above this level and the string will go slack again, when the particle is at a height $-\frac{2}{3}a \cos \alpha \cos 2\alpha$ above this level.   (O.C.)

17. A particle, suspended from a fixed point by a string of length a, is projected horizontally so as to describe part of a circle in a vertical plane; show that if the parabolic path of the particle after the string becomes slack passes through the original point of projection, the velocity of projection is $\sqrt{(7ga/2)}$. Show that in the subsequent motion the particle oscillates between two points at a vertical height $a/16$ above its original position.   (O.C.)

CHAPTER 19

VARIABLE ACCELERATION; SIMPLE HARMONIC MOTION

19.1 Variable Acceleration

If a particle moves in a straight line so that its distance from a fixed point O in the straight line is x after time t, then its velocity v at time t is $\dfrac{dx}{dt}$ along the straight line away from O, that is in the direction of x increasing. Its acceleration a at time t in the same direction is $\dfrac{dv}{dt}$, and we have (§ 13.4)

$$\frac{dv}{dt} = \frac{d^2x}{dt^2} = v\frac{dv}{dx} \tag{1}$$

If the distance x is given as a function of the time, or the velocity v as a function of the distance or the time, we may find the acceleration in terms of x or t by differentiation.

If the acceleration has a constant value a we may integrate the equations (1) and obtain the equations for constant acceleration (see §13.9)

$$\left.\begin{array}{c} v = u + at \\ v^2 = u^2 + 2as \\ x = ut + \tfrac{1}{2}at^2 \end{array}\right\} \tag{2}$$

If the acceleration is variable, the equations (2) no longer apply, and when the acceleration is given as a function of the time, velocity or distance, we must equate the function to one of the above expressions for the acceleration and find the velocity and the distance by integration.

For example, given that the acceleration at any instant has the value $4t$, we have

$$\frac{dv}{dt} = 4t,$$

$$v = \frac{dx}{dt} = 2t^2 + c, \text{ where } c \text{ is a constant,}$$

$$x = \frac{2}{3}t^3 + ct + d, \text{ where } d \text{ is a constant.}$$

The values of x and v depend on their initial values, and if these initial values are known, the constants of integration c and d may be found and v and x completely determined.

Thus if when $t = 0$, $x = 5$ and $v = 2$,

we have $\qquad 2 = 2 \times 0 + c, \qquad c = 2,$

$\qquad\qquad\qquad 5 = 0 + 0 + d, \qquad d = 5,$

and hence $\qquad v = 2t^2 + 2,$

$\qquad\qquad\qquad x = \tfrac{2}{3}t^3 + 2t + 5.$

It is evident that when the distance is obtained by integration from the acceleration in this way there must always be two constants of integration to be determined, since the distance depends not only on the acceleration but also on the initial distance and velocity.

19.2 Simple Harmonic Motion

When a particle moves in a straight line in such a way that its acceleration is always directed towards a fixed point of the line and is proportional to its distance from that point, the particle is said to move with simple harmonic motion.

Let O be the fixed point on the straight line $X'OX$, and let x be the distance of the particle from O at time t, x being positive if the particle is to the right of O (Fig. 249). Then we may take the acceleration of the

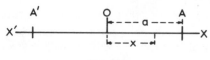

Fig. 249.

particle along OX as $-\omega^2 x$, where ω^2 is a constant which is positive. If x is positive, this acceleration is directed towards O, and if x is negative, it is also directed towards O.

If v be the velocity at time t, the acceleration is $v\dfrac{dv}{dx}$ in the direction OX and we have the differential relation

$$v\frac{dv}{dx} = -\omega^2 x,$$

that is, $\qquad\qquad \dfrac{d}{dx}\left(\dfrac{1}{2}v^2\right) = -\omega^2 x,$

Therefore $\qquad\qquad \tfrac{1}{2}v^2 = -\tfrac{1}{2}\omega^2 x^2 + c \text{ (a constant).}$

Suppose the particle starts from rest at a point A, distant a from O, so that when $t = 0$, $x = a$ and $v = 0$.

We have
$$0 = \tfrac{1}{2}\omega^2 a^2 + c,$$

and hence
$$v^2 = \omega^2(a^2 - x^2),$$

$$v = \pm\omega\sqrt{(a^2 - x^2)}.$$

In the initial stage of the motion v is negative as the particle is moving towards O.
Therefore

$$\frac{dx}{dt} = -\omega\sqrt{(a^2 - x^2)},$$

$$\frac{dt}{dx} = -\frac{1}{\omega\sqrt{(a^2 - x^2)}},$$

$$\omega t = \cos^{-1}\frac{x}{a} + d \text{ (a constant)}.$$

When $t = 0$, $x = a$, and $\cos^{-1} 1 = 0$, hence $d = 0$ and we have

$$\omega t = \cos^{-1}\frac{x}{a},$$

$$x = a\cos\omega t,$$

and
$$v = -a\omega\sin\omega t.$$

When $\omega t = \dfrac{\pi}{2}$, $\cos\omega t = 0$, thus the particle starting from A moves towards O, arriving at O in time $\dfrac{\pi}{2\omega}$ with velocity $-a\omega$. It continues along the straight line, and its velocity is zero when $\omega t = \pi$ and $x = -a$. It then returns towards O, arriving at O when $\omega t = \dfrac{3}{2}\pi$ with velocity $a\omega$, and reaches A in time $\dfrac{2\pi}{\omega}$ with zero velocity. The motion is then repeated, and continues indefinitely unless it is destroyed by a frictional force of some kind.

This type of oscillatory motion is of very common occurrence, and is encountered in every branch of science. Many rather complicated types of oscillation approximate to simple harmonic motion and can be treated as such. The term simple harmonic motion is not limited to motion in a straight line, and can be applied to the variation of any variable quantity which satisfies a differential relation of the type considered.

The length a is called the *amplitude* of the motion and is the distance of the extreme points from the centre of the oscillation.

The time $\frac{2\pi}{\omega}$ is called the *period* of the oscillation and is the time of a complete oscillation from one extreme point to the other and back again. Since both x and v are unchanged if t is increased by $\frac{2\pi}{\omega}$ this is also the time in which the particle completes an oscillation from any point so that it returns to the point with the same velocity in the same direction.

The *frequency* is the number of complete oscillations made per unit time. Thus if n be the frequency and the period $\frac{2\pi}{\omega}$, we have

$$n = \frac{\omega}{2\pi}.$$

If the period and amplitude of the motion are known the motion is completely determined. The period may be written down at once if the magnitude of the acceleration for some value of x is known. The amplitude is determined by the initial displacement.

19.3 Other Initial Conditions

If the motion is started by giving the particle a velocity v_0 when its distance from O is x_0, the type of motion is unchanged and we can regard the time as being measured from this instant instead of from the instant when $x = a$. Then the value of x at any instant is given by

$$x = a \cos(\omega t + \epsilon),$$

where ϵ is a constant.

Now $x = x_0$ when $t = 0$, therefore

$$x_0 = a \cos \epsilon.$$

Also $\frac{dx}{dt} = v_0$ when $t = 0$, therefore

$$v_0 = -a\omega \sin \epsilon.$$

Then

$$a = \sqrt{\left(x_0^2 + \frac{v_0^2}{\omega^2}\right)},$$

$$\epsilon = \tan^{-1}\left(-\frac{v_0}{\omega x_0}\right).$$

The quantity ϵ is called the *epoch* of the motion. The *phase* of the motion at time t is the time which has elapsed since the particle was at the positive end of its path, thus the phase is $t + \frac{\epsilon}{\omega}$, less a multiple of the period.

Also
$$x = a \cos \omega t \cos \epsilon - a \sin \omega t \sin \epsilon,$$

$$= x_0 \cos \omega t + \frac{v_0}{\omega} \sin \omega t.$$

In particular, if $x_0 = 0$, that is, if the particle starts from O,

$$x = \frac{v_0}{\omega} \sin \omega t,$$

and the amplitude is $\frac{v_0}{\omega}$.

Since the acceleration at any instant is $\frac{d^2 x}{dt^2}$, usually written as $\ddot{x}$, the equation

$$\ddot{x} = -\omega^2 x$$

is characteristic of simple harmonic motion and its solution

$$x = a \cos (\omega t + \epsilon)$$

may be written down at once if the amplitude and epoch are known. The graph of distance against time is as shown in Fig. 250.

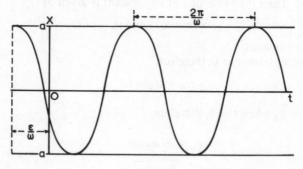

Fig. 250.

19.4 Relation to Uniform Motion in a Circle

If a particle is describing a circle of radius a with uniform angular velocity ω, its orthogonal projection on a diameter of the circle moves on the diameter in simple harmonic motion of amplitude a and period $\frac{2\pi}{\omega}$.

Let ϵ be the angle which the radius to the particle makes with a diameter $X'OX$ initially (Fig. 251). Then after time t the angle made by the radius

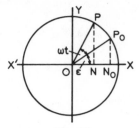

FIG. 251.

to the particle is $\omega t + \epsilon$. Hence, if P be the position of the particle at time t and N the foot of the perpendicular from P on OX, we have

$$ON = a \cos(\omega t + \epsilon),$$

and the point N moves with simple harmonic motion of amplitude a and period $\dfrac{2\pi}{\omega}$.

Example 1. *A particle moves with simple harmonic motion in a straight line; find the time of a complete oscillation if the acceleration is 4 m/sec² when the distance from the centre of oscillation is 2 m. If the velocity with which the particle passes through the centre of oscillation is 8 m/sec, find the amplitude.*

If the acceleration is of magnitude $\omega^2 x$ at distance x m from the centre of oscillation, we have

$$\omega^2 \times 2 = 4,$$
$$\omega = \sqrt{2}.$$

Hence the period is

$$\frac{2\pi}{\omega} = \pi\sqrt{2} \text{ sec}.$$

If the phase is zero when $t = 0$ we have

$$x = a \cos \omega t,$$

where a is the amplitude.

Then

$$v = -a\omega \sin \omega t,$$

and the value of v at the centre of oscillation is $\pm a\omega$.

Therefore

$$a\omega = 8 \text{ m/sec},$$
$$a = 4\sqrt{2} \text{ m}.$$

Example 2. *A particle is moving with simple harmonic motion of period 4π about a centre O. It passes through a point distant 4 m from O with the velocity 4 m/sec away from O. Find the time which elapses before it next passes through this point.*

Since the period is $\dfrac{2\pi}{\omega}$ we have $\omega = \dfrac{1}{2}$.

Also since

$$v^2 = \omega^2(a^2 - x^2),$$
$$4^2 = \frac{1}{4}(a^2 - 4^2),$$

$$a^2 = 80,$$
$$a = 4\sqrt{5} \text{ m.}$$

Therefore we have

$$x = 4\sqrt{5}\cos\frac{t}{2},$$

and when $x = 4$

$$\cos\frac{t}{2} = \frac{1}{\sqrt{5}},$$

$$\frac{t}{2} = 2n\pi \pm \cos^{-1}\left(\frac{1}{\sqrt{5}}\right).$$

where $n = 0, 1, 2\ldots$ etc.

Hence, the shortest time between instants when the particle is in this position is given by

$$\frac{t}{2} = 2\cos^{-1}\frac{1}{\sqrt{5}}, \qquad\qquad t = 4\cos^{-1}\frac{1}{\sqrt{5}}.$$

Example 3. *The velocity v m/sec of a particle moving in a straight line is related to its distance x m from a fixed point O of the line by the equation*

$$v^2 + 4x^2 - 2x - 6 = 0.$$

Show that the motion is simple harmonic and find the distance of the centre of oscillation from O, the amplitude and the period.

We have

$$v^2 = -4x^2 + 2x + 6,$$
$$= -4\left(x - \frac{1}{4}\right)^2 + \left(\frac{5}{2}\right)^2,$$
$$= 4\left\{\left(\frac{5}{4}\right)^2 - \left(x - \frac{1}{4}\right)^2\right\},$$
$$v\frac{dv}{dx} = -4\left(x - \frac{1}{4}\right).$$

The acceleration is directed towards the point $x = \frac{1}{4}$, and is proportional to the distance from this point, therefore the motion is simple harmonic and its centre is $\frac{1}{4}$ m from O.

Also

$$\omega^2 = 4,$$
$$\omega = 2.$$

and the period is $\frac{2\pi}{\omega} = \pi$ sec.

The velocity is zero when $x - \frac{1}{4} = \pm\frac{5}{4}$, hence the amplitude is $1\frac{1}{4}$ m.

EXERCISES 19 (a)

1. A particle moves in a straight line, with simple harmonic motion, making seven complete oscillations in 11 sec. The velocity of the particle is 1·2 m/sec when its distance from the centre of oscillation is 12·5 cm. Find the amplitude of the motion, the maximum velocity and the maximum acceleration. (L.U.)
2. A particle moving with simple harmonic motion in a straight line has a speed of 6 m/sec when 4 m from the centre of oscillation, and a speed of 8 m/sec when 3m

from the centre. Find the amplitude of the oscillation and the shortest time taken by the particle in moving from an extreme position to a point midway between this position and the centre. (L.U.)

3. A particle moves in a straight line with simple harmonic motion, the centre of oscillation being A. When the particle is 45 cm from A its velocity is 1·2 m/sec and its acceleration is 1·8 m/sec^2. Find the amplitude and period of the motion, and the maximum velocity attained. (L.U.)

4. A piston moving with simple harmonic motion performs three complete oscillations per minute, and its maximum speed is 5 cm/sec. Find the amplitude of the motion, the velocity when the displacement from the centre of motion is 7·5 cm, and the maximum acceleration. (L.U.)

5. A particle moving with simple harmonic motion performs ten complete oscillations per minute and its speed, when at a distance of 20 cm from the centre of oscillation, is $\frac{3}{5}$ of its maximum speed. Find the amplitude, the maximum acceleration and the speed of the particle when it is 15 cm from the centre of oscillation. (L.U.)

6. The displacement of a particle at time t is given by $x = a \cos(\omega t + \epsilon)$, where a, ω, ϵ are constants. Find the acceleration of the particle in terms of its displacement, describe the motion and find its periodic time.

   Two particles moving in simple harmonic motion pass through their centres of oscillation at the same instant. They *next* reach their greatest distances from their centres of oscillation after 2 sec, 3 sec respectively, having been at the same distance from these centres after 1 sec. Find the ratio of their amplitudes. (L.U.)

7. A point P moves with simple harmonic motion along a straight line from A to A', points equidistant from O. The acceleration of P when at A is 1·2 m/sec^2, and when at B, between A and O is 0·6 m/sec^2. It moves from B to A' in 3 sec. Find the time P takes to move from A to A' and its velocity as it passes B. (L.U.)

8. Calculate the amplitude and periodic time of a simple harmonic motion if the velocity is 48 m/sec when the displacement from the mean position is 7 m, and 40 m/sec when the displacement is 15 m. (L.U.)

9. A particle moving with simple harmonic motion passes through two points A and B, 55 cm apart, with the same velocity, having occupied 2 sec in passing from A to B; after another 2 sec it returns to B. Find the period and amplitude of the oscillation. (L.U.)

10. If the period of a simple harmonic motion is 8 sec, and the amplitude 4 m, find the maximum velocity and also the velocity when the particle is 2 m from the central position. (L.U.)

11. A point is moving in a straight line with simple harmonic motion about a fixed point O. The point has velocity v_1 when its displacement from O is x_1, and velocity v_2 when its distance from O is x_2. Show that the period of its motion is

$$2\pi \sqrt{\frac{x_1{}^2 - x_2{}^2}{v_2{}^2 - v_1{}^2}}. \qquad \text{(L.U.)}$$

12. A particle is performing a simple harmonic motion of period T about a centre O, and its passes through a point P with velocity v in the direction OP. Prove that the time which elapses before its return to P is

$$\frac{T}{\pi} \tan^{-1} \frac{vT}{2\pi \cdot OP}. \qquad \text{(L.U.)}$$

13. A circle of radius a rolls with uniform angular speed on the inside of a fixed circle of radius $2a$. Prove that any point on the circumference of the moving circle describes a straight line with simple harmonic motion. (L.U.)

14. If a be the amplitude and n the frequency in a simple harmonic motion, find the velocity in any position in terms of (i) the distance from the centre, and (ii) the time that has elapsed since the particle was at rest. Show that the time that elapses as the particle moves from the position of maximum velocity to the position in which the velocity is half the maximum is $\dfrac{1}{6n}$ sec. (L.U.)

15. A particle moving with acceleration $-\mu x$ has coordinates x_1 and x_2 and velocities v_1 and v_2 at any two moments. At the moment midway in time between them its coordinate and velocity are $\bar{x}$ and $\bar{v}$.

Show that $$\frac{x_1-x_2}{v_2-v_1} = \frac{\bar{v}}{\mu\bar{x}}, \qquad \frac{x_1+x_2}{v_1+v_2} = \frac{\bar{x}}{\bar{v}}.$$ (O.C.)

16. A horizontal platform moves up and down with simple harmonic motion through a distance of 25 cm. Show that a small body lying on the platform will not leave it if the periodic time is 1 sec. If the periodic time is halved, show that the particle will leave the platform at about 18·75 cm above its lowest position.

17. A particle rests on a horizontal plane which is displaced up and down with simple harmonic motion of frequency 50 hertz (vibrations/sec). Determine the maximum amplitude of the motion for the particle to remain in contact with the plane. If the amplitude of the motion is half this value, up to what value can the frequency of vibration be increased, the particle still remaining in contact with the plane? (Q.E.)

18. A heavy smoked glass plate is dropped past the end of a vibrating tuning-fork, making n complete simple harmonic oscillations per second, and by means of a light style attached to the fork a rippling trace is obtained on the plate. The vertical length of a certain ten consecutive ripples is found to be l cm, and of the next 10 is found to be l' cm. Deduce that the value of g is $(l'-l)n^2/100$ cm/sec². (L.U.)

19.5 Forces Causing Simple Harmonic Motion

If the acceleration of a particle of mass m at a distance x from a fixed point O is $\omega^2 x$ towards O, the force acting on the particle must be $m\omega^2 x$ towards O, and hence the force must be proportional to the distance from O. Thus simple harmonic motion is caused by forces whose magnitude varies with distance. Simple examples of such forces are the force in a spring, which is proportional to the increase or decrease of its length from its natural length, and the force of tension in an elastic string.

If a particle of mass m rests on a smooth horizontal table attached to the end of a spring of natural length l and modulus λ, and the particle is displaced a distance x from its equilibrium position O, along the axis of the spring, the force in the spring is $\lambda\dfrac{x}{l}$ towards O and we have

$$m\frac{d^2x}{dt^2} = -\frac{\lambda x}{l}, \qquad \frac{d^2x}{dt^2} = -\left(\frac{\lambda}{ml}\right)x.$$

Hence, the particle oscillates about its equilibrium position with period $\frac{2\pi}{\omega}$, where $\omega^2 = \frac{\lambda}{ml}$.

If the spring is suspended from a fixed point with the particle attached to its free end, its extension c in the equilibrium position is given by

$$mg = \frac{\lambda}{l}c.$$

If the particle is given a *further* displacement x vertically downwards, the force in the spring is $\frac{\lambda}{l}(c+x)$ upwards and the weight of the particle is mg downwards, therefore the resultant force on the particle is $\frac{\lambda}{l}x$ upwards.

Thus we have

$$m\frac{d^2x}{dt^2} = -\frac{\lambda x}{l},$$

as before, and the motion is simple harmonic with the same period, the centre of the oscillation being the position of equilibrium. The simple harmonic motion is always about the position of equilibrium, and it is best to measure the displacement x from this position.

If x were measured from the position where the spring is unstretched we would have

$$m\frac{d^2x}{dt^2} = -\frac{\lambda}{l}x + mg,$$

$$= -\frac{\lambda}{l}(x-c).$$

If $z = x - c$, this gives

$$m\frac{d^2z}{dt^2} = \frac{\lambda}{l}z,$$

and the solution is of the form

$$z = a\cos(\omega t + \epsilon),$$

or
$$x - c = a\cos(\omega t + \epsilon)$$

where $\omega^2 = \frac{\lambda}{ml}$ and a and ϵ are constants depending on the initial displacement and velocity.

19.6 Suspension by an Elastic String

If a particle is suspended by an elastic string and displaced from the equilibrium position, the motion is simple harmonic, just as in the case of the spring, provided that the string does not return to its natural length during the motion; if this happens the string will become slack and the particle begin to move freely under gravity. Hence, the amplitude of the simple harmonic motion must be less than the extension of the string in the equilibrium position.

The elasticity of an elastic string is usually given by stating how much a certain weight stretches it. Thus if a mass m, attached to the end of an elastic string, stretches it a distance a, we have, if l be the natural length and λ the modulus of elasticity,

$$mg = \frac{\lambda}{l}a,$$

$$\frac{\lambda}{l} = \frac{mg}{a}.$$

Then if a particle of mass M hangs freely at the end of the string and is given a small vertical displacement x from its equilibrium position we have

$$M\frac{d^2x}{dt^2} = -\frac{mg}{a}x,$$

$$\frac{d^2x}{dt^2} = -\frac{mg}{Ma}x,$$

and the period is $\qquad 2\pi\sqrt{\left|\frac{Ma}{mg}\right|}.$

Example 4. *One end of an elastic string of length 24 cm is fixed and to the other end a mass of 5 kg is attached, which when in equilibrium stretches the string 4 cm. The mass is pulled down a distance of 3 cm below its equilibrium position and then released. Find the period of oscillation and the maximum kinetic energy of the mass.*

If λ be the modulus of elasticity of the string, we have

$$5g = \frac{\lambda \times 4}{24},$$

$$\lambda = 30g \text{ N}.$$

For a displacement x m from the equilibrium position we have

$$5\frac{d^2x}{dt^2} = -\frac{30g}{0 \cdot 24}x,$$

$$\frac{d^2x}{dt^2} = -25gx.$$

Hence $\omega^2 = 25g$, $\omega = 15\cdot66$, and the period is $0\cdot4$ sec.
The amplitude is 3 cm, and since the epoch is zero,

$$x = 0\cdot03 \cos 15\cdot66t,$$

$$\frac{dx}{dt} = v = -0\cdot47 \sin 15\cdot66t.$$

The maximum velocity is therefore $0\cdot47$ m/sec, and the corresponding kinetic energy

$$\tfrac{1}{2} \times 5 \times 0\cdot47^2 = 0\cdot552 \text{ J.}$$

Example 5. *A spiral spring supports a carrier weighing 2 kg, and when a 10-kg weight is placed in the carrier the spring extends 5 cm. The carrier with its load is then pulled down another 7·5 cm and let go. How high does it rise and what is the period of its oscillation?*   (L.U.)
If λ N be the modulus and l m the unstretched length of the spring we have

$$10g = \frac{\lambda}{l} \times 0\cdot05,$$

$$\frac{\lambda}{l} = 200g.$$

Hence, when the mass is 12 kg in a displacement x downwards from the equilibrium position we have

$$12\frac{d^2x}{dt^2} = -200gx,$$

$$\frac{d^2x}{dt^2} = -\frac{50g}{3}x.$$

Hence, $$\omega^2 = 50g/3 = 163\cdot5,$$

$$\omega = 12\cdot79,$$

and the period is $$\frac{2\pi}{\omega} = 0\cdot49 \text{ sec.}$$

The amplitude of the motion is 7·5 cm and hence if the 10-kg weight is fixed in the carrier, it will rise in all 15 cm.

When $x = -6$ cm, the carrier and the weight have an acceleration g downwards. Above this level the downward acceleration will be greater than this, and the weight may leave the carrier.

When $x = -0\cdot06$, the velocity is $\omega\{0\cdot075^2 - 0\cdot06^2\}^{\frac{1}{2}} = 0\cdot576$ m/sec, and hence the weight may rise a further distance $(0\cdot576)^2/2g = 0\cdot0169$ m.

Hence, the weight may rise $0\cdot06 + 0\cdot017$ m $= 7\cdot7$ cm above the equilibrium position, that is, 15·2 cm above its lowest position.

Example 6. *If a particle could move freely along any chord of the earth, show that it would move with simple harmonic motion (about the mid-point of the chord). Taking the radius of the earth as 6400 km, show that a particle released at one end of the chord would reach the other end in about $42\frac{1}{2}$ min.*

For a particle inside the earth the acceleration due to the earth's attraction is proportional to its distance from the earth's centre and directed towards the earth's centre. Therefore, at distance r from the earth's centre it is kr, if $r < R$, the earth's radius.

On the surface this acceleration is g, therefore $kR = g$ and $k = \dfrac{g}{R}$.

Let O be the earth's centre, AB any chord and C its mid-point. Let P be any point on the chord and let $CP = x$ (Fig. 252).

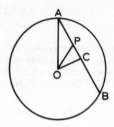

FIG. 252.

The acceleration of a particle at P towards O is $\dfrac{g}{R} \times OP$. The component of this acceleration along AB is $\dfrac{g}{R} \times OP \cos OPC = \dfrac{gx}{R}$ towards C.

Hence the particle moves with simple harmonic motion about C.

The period is $\dfrac{2\pi}{\omega}$, where $\omega^2 = \dfrac{g}{R}$; the time from A to B is therefore $\pi\sqrt{\dfrac{R}{g}}$.

$$R = 64 \times 10^5 \text{ m},$$
$$g = 9{\cdot}81 \text{ m/sec}^2,$$
$$\frac{R}{g} = 66 \times 10^4,$$
$$\sqrt{\frac{R}{g}} = 812{\cdot}4,$$
$$\pi\sqrt{\frac{R}{g}} = 2552 \text{ sec},$$
$$= 42{\cdot}5 \text{ min approximately.}$$

EXERCISES 19 (b)

1. A body of mass 12 kg is suspended by a spring and makes three complete oscillations per second. Find how far the string would be stretched by a load of 10 kg hanging at rest. (L.U.)

2. A spiral spring is found to extend 9·81 cm for each additional kilogramme of loading. It is hung up carrying a mass of 4 kg, and put in vibration. Find the period. (L.U.)

3. A particle is suspended from a fixed point by a spiral spring and set in vertical

motion. Show that the period of an oscillation is $2\pi\sqrt{\dfrac{a}{g}}$, where a is the extension of the spring produced by the weight of the attached mass.   (L.U.)

4. A spring loaded with a certain mass is extended 4 cm when in equilibrium. Find the time of oscillation if the mass is pulled down through a further distance of 2 cm and then let go. Find also the velocity and acceleration when the mass is at a distance 1 cm below its equilibrium position.   (L.U.)

5. A particle of mass 1 kg is acted upon by a variable force which makes it move with simple harmonic motion. The maximum speed attained is 5 m/sec and the period is 2 sec. Find (a) the amplitude of the motion, and (b) the maximum rate at which the applied force does work.   (L.U.)

6. An elastic string of natural length $2a$ can just support a certain weight when it is stretched till its whole length is $3a$. One end of the string is now attached to a point on a smooth horizontal table, and the same weight is attached to the other end and can move on the table. Prove that if the weight is pulled out to

any distance and let go, the string will become slack again after a time $\dfrac{\pi}{2}\sqrt{\dfrac{a}{g}}$.
                    (L.U.)

7. A light elastic string of natural length 2 m and modulus of elasticity 19·6 N is attached to two points A and B, 3 m apart on a smooth horizontal table. To the middle point of the string is attached a mass of 500 g which is drawn aside towards A and released from rest when 1 m from A. Show that the resulting motion is simple harmonic, find the period of oscillation and the greatest speed of the mass during motion.   (L.U.)

8. A mass of 2 kg hangs from one end of an elastic string of length 4 m, the other end of which is fixed, and in the equilibrium position the extension is 40 cm. When in this position a further mass of 3 kg is attached and the combined mass then released. Show that the subsequent motion is simple harmonic. Find the period, the greatest extension of the string during the motion and the speed with which the mass passes through the centre of oscillation.   (L.U.)

9. A light elastic string of unstretched length l is suspended from a fixed point, and a particle of mass m hangs at rest from the free end, the extension being $l/5$. The particle is pulled down a further distance $l/5$ and released from rest. Prove that its motion is simple harmonic, and find (i) the period of the oscillation, (ii) the maximum speed of the particle.   (L.U.)

10. One end of an elastic string of natural length 2 m is fixed, and to the other end a particle of 4 kg is attached which, when in equilibrium, stretches the string 50 cm. The particle is pulled down a further 25 cm and released. Show that the motion is simple harmonic and find the period of oscillation. Find also the maximum kinetic energy of the particle.   (L.U.)

11. A particle of mass 5 kg hangs in equilibrium on the end of a light spring, the extension of which is found to be 15 cm. The mass is then pulled down a further 5 cm and released from rest. Find the period of the subsequent oscillations and the kinetic energy of the particle as it passes through its equilibrium position.
                    (L.U.)

12. One end of a light elastic string of natural length a and modulus mg is attached to a particle of mass m. The other end is attached to a fixed point O. The particle is released from rest at a point $a/2$ below O. Prove that it returns to its initial position

after a time $(\frac{3}{2}\pi+2)\sqrt{(a/g)}$. Prove also that the greatest speed attained is $\sqrt{(2ag)}$.
(O.C.)

13. Define simple harmonic motion and prove that, with the usual notation, the speed v is given by the formula $v^2 = \omega^2(a^2 - x^2)$. A rough horizontal table moves horizontally in simple harmonic motion, the period being 3 sec and the maximum speed of 4 m/sec. A small heavy mass is placed on the table. Find the least coefficient of friction if the mass does not slide on the table throughout the motion.

14. A light spring has a natural length of 10 cm, and a force of 9·81 mN applied to one end with the other end held fixed, gives it an extension of 1 cm. One end of the spring is attached to a fixed point from which the spring hangs freely with a scale pan of mass 1 g attached to the other. A mass of 1 g is now held in the scale pan just touching it and is then released. Find the extension of the spring at any time t after release up to the time t_1 of maximum extension, and find t_1.
(L.U.)

15. A particle of 100 g is suspended from a fixed point by a light elastic string and is found to extend it by 3 cm. If the mass is pulled down a further 1 cm from the equilibrium position and then released from rest, find the period of the subsequent oscillations and the kinetic energy of the mass as it passes through the equilibrium position.
(L.U.)

16. Prove that the speed v of a particle describing simple harmonic motion is given by $v^2 = 4\pi^2 f^2(a^2 - x^2)$, where a is the amplitude, x the distance of the particle from the mean position, and f the frequency of oscillation. A light elastic string is stretched between two points A and B, distant $2l$ apart, on a smooth horizontal table, the tension in the string being T. A particle, of mass m, attached to the middle point of the string, is displaced a small distance perpendicular to AB and then released. Show that the periodic time of an oscillation is approximately

$2\pi\sqrt{\dfrac{ml}{2T}}$. (The tension T may be supposed constant throughout and the approximation $\sin\theta = \tan\theta$, where θ is small, may be assumed.)
(L.U.)

19.7 The Simple Pendulum

The simple pendulum consists of a heavy particle attached by a light inextensible string to a fixed point and moving in a circle in a vertical plane.

Let O be the centre of the circle, l the length of the string, θ the angle which it makes at any instant with the downward vertical OA, and m the mass of the particle (Fig. 253).

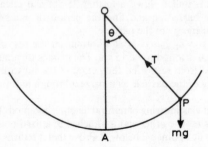

FIG. 253.

The angular velocity at any instant is $\dfrac{d\theta}{dt} = \dot{\theta}$, and the velocity along the tangent to the circle is $l\dot{\theta}$.

The energy equation states that the sum of the kinetic and potential energies of the particle is constant, therefore

$$\tfrac{1}{2}ml^2\dot{\theta}^2 + mg(l - l\cos\theta) = \text{constant,}$$

that is

$$\tfrac{1}{2}l\dot{\theta}^2 - g\cos\theta = \text{constant.}$$

Differentiating this equation with respect to the time we have

$$l\dot{\theta}\ddot{\theta} + g\dot{\theta}\sin\theta = 0.$$

Therefore,

$$l\ddot{\theta} = -g\sin\theta.$$

When θ is small, writing $\sin\theta = \theta$, we have

$$l\ddot{\theta} = -g\theta.$$

This is an equation of simple harmonic motion of period $2\pi\sqrt{\dfrac{l}{g}}$, and this is therefore the time of one complete oscillation from one side of the vertical to the other and back again.

If the amplitude of θ is α, that is, if the pendulum swings from an angle α on one side of the vertical to an angle α on the other side, θ is given in terms of the time by the equation

$$\theta = \alpha\cos\sqrt{\dfrac{g}{l}}t,$$

the time being measured from the highest point of the swing.

The motion of a pendulum is only approximately simple harmonic when θ is small, and the period of the motion depends in fact on the value of α. An approximate value of the period taking account of the amplitude of the motion is $2\pi\sqrt{l/g}\left\{1 + \dfrac{\alpha^2}{16}\right\}$.

19.8 The Seconds Pendulum

The seconds pendulum is a simple pendulum whose period is 2 sec, and whose half-period is 1 sec.

That is,

$$\pi\sqrt{\dfrac{l}{g}} = 1,$$

$$l = \dfrac{g}{\pi^2}.$$

Taking $g = 9.81$ m/sec^2, and $\pi^2 = 9.870$ we have

$$l = 0.994 \text{ m}$$
$$= 99.4 \text{ cm.}$$
$$= 39.12 \text{ in.}$$

The time of a beat of a pendulum may vary if the length varies or if the value of g varies. Also if the point of suspension is given a certain acceleration in any direction, the acceleration of gravity on the bob of the pendulum is decreased by this acceleration.

If a seconds pendulum is found to lose x sec per day when moved to a new locality, we may find the ratio of the values of g in the two places.

In the first place $\sqrt{g} = \pi\sqrt{l}.$

In the second place it makes $86{,}400 - x$ beats in $86{,}400$ sec, therefore its half-period is $\dfrac{86{,}400}{86{,}400 - x}$ sec. Hence, if g' be the acceleration due to gravity

$$\sqrt{g'} = \frac{86{,}400 - x}{86{,}400}\pi\sqrt{l}.$$

Hence $\dfrac{g'}{g} = \left(\dfrac{86{,}400 - x}{86{,}400}\right)^2,$

$$= \left(1 - \frac{x}{86{,}400}\right)^2,$$

$$= 1 - \frac{x}{43{,}200} \text{ approximately.}$$

Thus, if the pendulum *gains* 30 sec in a new locality, we have

$$\frac{g'}{g} = 1 + \frac{30}{43{,}200} = \frac{1441}{1440}.$$

Example 7. *A pendulum, supposed to beat seconds, is found to lose 50 sec a day. By what percentage must it be shortened so as to beat seconds accurately?*

The time of a beat is $\dfrac{86{,}400}{86{,}400 - 50}$ sec and hence if l be its length

$$\pi\sqrt{\frac{l}{g}} = \frac{86{,}400}{86{,}400 - 50}.$$

If l' be the corrected length

$$\pi\sqrt{\frac{l'}{g}} = 1.$$

Hence,
$$\frac{l'}{l} = \left(1 - \frac{50}{86,400}\right)^2,$$
$$= 1 - \frac{1}{864} \text{ approximately,}$$
$$= 0.9988.$$

Hence the pendulum must be shortened by 0·12 per cent.

Example 8. *A pendulum beats seconds at sea level. How many seconds per day will it lose if taken to the top of a nearby mountain 1 kilometre high?*

If g be the earth's attraction at sea level, its value g' at height h above sea level is proportional to the inverse square of the distance of the point from the centre of the earth. Therefore, if R be the earth's radius

$$\frac{g'}{g} = \frac{R^2}{(R+h)^2}.$$

The ratio of the half-periods in the two places is

$$\pi\sqrt{\frac{l}{g}} \div \pi\sqrt{\frac{l}{g'}} = \sqrt{\frac{g'}{g}} = \frac{R}{R+h}.$$

If the pendulum loses x sec per day on the mountain, its half-period there is $\dfrac{86,400}{86,400-x}$.

Hence
$$\frac{R+h}{R} = \frac{86,400}{86,400-x},$$
$$86,400h - (R+h)x = 0,$$
$$x = \frac{86,400h}{R+h}.$$

Taking
$$R = 6400 \text{ km}, R+h = 6401 \text{ km}.$$
$$x = \frac{86\,400}{6401},$$
$$= 13.5 \text{ sec}.$$

Example 9. *A seconds pendulum is placed in a lift which ascends with an acceleration of 2 cm/sec². Find the rate at which it gains.*

In the lift the relative acceleration is $g+2$ cm/sec² downwards on the bob of the pendulum. Hence, if l be the length of the pendulum and x the number of sec per day at which it is gaining

$$\pi\sqrt{\left(\frac{l}{g+2}\right)} = \frac{86,400}{86,400+x},$$

and

$$\pi\sqrt{\frac{l}{g}} = 1.$$

Therefore
$$\left(1 + \frac{x}{86,400}\right) = \sqrt{\frac{g+2}{g}},$$
$$= \sqrt{(1.0020)},$$
$$= 1.010,$$
$$x = 864 \text{ sec}.$$

Hence, the pendulum gains at the rate of 864 sec per day, or about 0·6 sec per minute.

EXERCISES 19 (c)

1. A clock regulated by a seconds pendulum (i.e. a pendulum whose period should be 2 seconds) loses 10 seconds per day. Find by what percentage the length of the pendulum should be altered in order that the clock should keep correct time, and state whether it should be lengthened or shortened.   (L.U.)

2. Calculate the length of a simple pendulum to beat time to a march of 100 paces per minute. In what ratio would the length have to be decreased if the march quickened to 150 paces per minute?   (L.U.)

3. A pendulum which beats seconds at a place where $g = 9.81$ m/sec^2 is taken to a place where it loses 210 seconds a day. Find the value of g at the latter place.
         (L.U.)

4. The period of a simple pendulum at a place A is T, and at a second place B is $T + t$, where t is small compared with T. Prove that the ratio of the value of g at B to that at A is approximately $T - 2t : T$.   (L.U.)

5. A clock is regulated by a pendulum whose period is supposed to be two seconds. The clock is found to gain 40 seconds in 24 hours. In order that the clock may keep correct time, should the pendulum be lengthened or shortened, and by what per cent?   (L.U.)

6. A balloon ascending vertically with constant acceleration from rest on the ground reaches a height of 371 m in 1 minute. It carries a pendulum clock which keeps correct time on the ground. Show that it will gain about 37 seconds an hour.
         (L.U.)

7. A pendulum clock beats seconds correctly at a place where $g = 981$ cm/sec^2. How many seconds will it gain or lose in 24 hours, if taken to a place where $g = 984.3$ cm/sec^2?   (L.U.)

8. A pendulum beats seconds accurately at a place where the acceleration of gravity is 32 ft/sec^2. It taken to a place where this acceleration is 32.2 ft/sec^2, will it gain or lose, and how many seconds in 24 hours?   (L.U.)

9. Prove that if a pendulum swings from rest to rest n times per second, then $g = n^2\pi^2 l$, where l is the length of the pendulum. In old French measure, the length of the seconds pendulum (for which $n = 1$) at Paris is 3.06 French feet. Calculate the value of g in these units.   (L.U.)

10. Calculate the length of a seconds pendulum at a place where $g = 981$ cm/sec^2. If a pendulum clock loses 9 minutes per week, find what change is required in the length of the pendulum in order that the clock may keep correct time.   (L.U.)

11. A simple pendulum is suspended from the roof of a railway carriage which is being accelerated horizontally at 0.3 m/sec^2. Show the period of the pendulum is decreased by about 0.025 per cent.

12. A seconds pendulum at the bottom of a mine, 1 km deep, loses 8 seconds a day; at the top of a mountain 1 km high, show that it will lose about 14.75 seconds a day, assuming the radius of the earth is 6400 km.

    (Inside the earth the weight of a body varies directly as its distance from the centre; outside the earth it varies inversely as the square of its distance from the centre.)   (L.U.)

19.9 Acceleration as a Function of the Distance

There are many types of motion, other than simple harmonic motion, in which the acceleration of a particle is related in some way to its distance from a fixed point. If the acceleration is a known function of the distance x from a fixed point, by equating $v\dfrac{dv}{dx}$ to the acceleration we have a differential relation between velocity and distance. If the velocity is obtained in terms of the distance by integration, we may write $v = \dfrac{dx}{dt}$, giving a differential relation between distance and time which may in its turn be integrated.

The universal law of gravitation states that the mutual attraction between two bodies is inversely proportional to the square of the distance between them. Thus if a particle be outside the earth at a distance x from the earth's centre, its acceleration towards the earth is $\dfrac{c}{x^2}$, where c is a constant. On the earth's surface $x = R$, the radius of the earth, and the acceleration is g, hence $\dfrac{c}{R^2} = g$, and the acceleration at distance x from the earth's centre is $\dfrac{gR^2}{x^2}$.

Example 10. *A particle is let fall from a height h above the earth. Neglecting air resistance, find the velocity with which it reaches the earth.*

If x be the distance, measured vertically upwards from the centre of the earth, the acceleration $v\dfrac{dv}{dx}$ is in the same direction and we have

$$v\frac{dv}{dx} = -\frac{gR^2}{x^2},$$

$$\frac{d(\frac{1}{2}v^2)}{dx} = -\frac{gR^2}{x^2},$$

$$\frac{1}{2}v^2 = \frac{gR^2}{x} + c \text{ (a constant).}$$

When $x = R + h$, $v = 0$, therefore

$$c = -\frac{gR^2}{R+h},$$

and hence,

$$v^2 = 2gR^2\left(\frac{1}{x} - \frac{1}{R+h}\right).$$

Hence, the velocity at the earth's surface, when $x = R$, is

$$\left\{\frac{2ghR}{R+h}\right\}^{\frac{1}{2}}.$$

Example 11. *The acceleration of a particle moving in a straight line is $x + \dfrac{1}{x^3}$ towards a fixed point O, where x is its distance from O. If it starts from rest where $x = 1$, find its velocity when $x = \frac{1}{2}$ and show that it reaches the point O in time $\dfrac{\pi}{4}$.*

We have

$$v\frac{dv}{dx} = \frac{d}{dx}(\tfrac{1}{2}v^2) = -x - \frac{1}{x^3},$$

$$\frac{1}{2}v^2 = -\frac{1}{2}x^2 + \frac{1}{2}\frac{1}{x^2} + c \text{ (a constant)}.$$

Since $v = 0$ when $x = 1$, we have $c = 0$ and

$$v^2 = \frac{1}{x^2} - x^2.$$

When $x = \frac{1}{2}$,

$$v^2 = 4 - \frac{1}{4},$$

$$v = \frac{1}{2}\sqrt{15}.$$

We have

$$v = \frac{dx}{dt} = -\frac{(1-x^4)^{\frac{1}{2}}}{x},$$

since $\frac{dx}{dt}$ is the velocity away from O.

$$\frac{dt}{dx} = -\frac{x}{(1-x^4)^{\frac{1}{2}}},$$

$$t = -\int \frac{x\,dx}{(1-x^4)^{\frac{1}{2}}}.$$

Let $x^2 = \sin\theta$, then $2x\,dx = \cos\theta\,d\theta$,

$$(1-x^4)^{\frac{1}{2}} = \cos\theta,$$

$$t = -\frac{1}{2}\int d\theta,$$

$$= -\frac{1}{2}\theta + d \text{ (a constant)}.$$

$$= -\frac{1}{2}\sin^{-1}x^2 + d.$$

We have $t = 0$ when $x = 1$, therefore $d = \frac{1}{2}\sin^{-1}1 = \frac{\pi}{4}$.

Hence

$$t = \frac{\pi}{4} - \frac{1}{2}\sin^{-1}x^2,$$

and when $x = 0$, $t = \pi/4$.

19.10 Acceleration as a Function of the Velocity

When a body moves through the air, the resistance of the air to its motion varies with its velocity, and hence the retardation which it causes is a function of the velocity. For low velocities the retardation may be proportional to the velocity (Stoke's Law), and for greater velocities below the speed of sound it may be proportional to the square of the velocity (Newton's Law) for bodies of regular shape.

In either of these cases we may find a relation between velocity and time by equating $\dfrac{dv}{dt}$ to the acceleration, and a relation between velocity and distance by equating $v\dfrac{dv}{dx}$ to the acceleration.

Example 12. *A particle is projected vertically upwards with velocity V and the retardation due to the air's resistance is kv, where k is a constant. Find the height to which it rises, and the time to reach this height.*

The acceleration is $g + kv$ downwards. If the distance x be measured upwards the acceleration $\dfrac{dv}{dt} = v\dfrac{dv}{dx}$ is upwards and we have

$$\frac{dv}{dt} = -g - kv,$$

$$-\frac{dt}{dv} = \frac{1}{g + kv},$$

$$-t = \frac{1}{k}\ln(g + kv) + c \text{ (a constant)}.$$

When $t = 0$, $v = V$, and hence $c = -\dfrac{1}{k}\ln(g + kV)$.

Therefore,

$$-kt = \ln\frac{g + kv}{g + kV},$$

$$v = -\frac{g}{k} + \left(\frac{g}{k} + V\right)e^{-kt}.$$

Let T be the time to the highest point, where $v = 0$, then

$$\frac{g}{k} = \left(\frac{g}{k} + V\right)e^{-kT},$$

$$T = \frac{1}{k}\ln\left(1 + \frac{kV}{g}\right).$$

The distance risen may be obtained by integrating the equation for the velocity in terms of the time.

We have

$$v = \frac{dx}{dt} = -\frac{g}{k} + \left(\frac{g}{k} + V\right)e^{-kt},$$

$$x = -\frac{g}{k}t - \frac{1}{k}\left(\frac{g}{k} + V\right)e^{-kt} + d \text{ (a constant)}.$$

Since $x = 0$ when $t = 0$ we have $d = \dfrac{1}{k}\left(\dfrac{g}{k} + V\right)$, and hence

$$x = -\frac{g}{k}t + \frac{1}{k}\left(\frac{g}{k} + V\right)(1 - e^{-kt}).$$

When $t = T = \dfrac{1}{k}\ln\left(1 + \dfrac{kV}{g}\right)$, we have for the greatest height X,

$$X = -\frac{g}{k^2}\ln\left(1 + \frac{kV}{g}\right) + \frac{V}{k}.$$

Alternatively, we have

$$v\frac{dv}{dx} = -g-kv,$$

$$\frac{dx}{dv} = -\frac{v}{g+kv},$$

$$= \frac{1}{k}\cdot\frac{g}{kv+g}-\frac{1}{k},$$

$$x = \frac{g}{k^2}\ln(kv+g)-\frac{v}{k}+b \text{ (a constant).}$$

When $x = 0$, $v = V$, and hence $b = \frac{V}{k}-\frac{g}{k^2}\ln(kV+g)$,

and

$$x = \frac{V-v}{k}+\frac{g}{k^2}\ln\frac{g+kv}{g+kV}.$$

Now $x = X$ when $v = 0$, and we have as before

$$X = \frac{V}{k}-\frac{g}{k^2}\ln\left(1+\frac{kV}{g}\right).$$

Example 13. *A particle falls from rest at a height h above the ground and the retardation due to the air's resistance is kv^2, where k is a constant. Find the velocity with which it reaches the ground and its velocity after it has fallen for time t.*

Let the distance x be measured downwards; the acceleration in this direction is $g-kv^2$.

We have

$$v\frac{dv}{dx} = g-kv^2,$$

$$\frac{dx}{dv} = \frac{v}{g-kv^2},$$

$$x = -\frac{1}{2k}\ln(g-kv^2)+c \text{ (a constant).}$$

When $x = 0$, $v = 0$, and hence $c = \frac{1}{2k}\ln g$, and

$$x = -\frac{1}{2k}\ln\left(1-\frac{k}{g}v^2\right),$$

$$v^2 = \frac{g}{k}(1-e^{-2kx}).$$

Thus as x increases the velocity increases and ultimately approaches the value $\sqrt{(g/k)}$. This is known as the terminal velocity, and is the velocity at which the acceleration is zero.

The velocity with which the particle reaches the ground is

$$v = \sqrt{\frac{g}{k}}(1-e^{-2kh})^{\frac{1}{2}}.$$

Writing

$$\frac{dv}{dt} = g - kv^2,$$

$$\frac{dt}{dv} = \frac{1}{g - kv^2},$$

$$= \frac{1}{k(a^2 - v^2)}, \text{ where } a^2 = \frac{g}{k},$$

$$t = \frac{1}{2ak} \ln \frac{a+v}{a-v} + d \text{ (a constant)}.$$

Since $v = 0$ when $t = 0$, the constant d is zero.
Hence

$$t = \frac{1}{2ak} \ln \frac{a+v}{a-v},$$

$$v = a\frac{1 - e^{-2akt}}{1 + e^{-2akt}}.$$

EXERCISES 19 (d)

1. A particle moves in a straight line in such a way that at the end of t sec its distance (s m) from a fixed point of the line is given by the equation $s = 7t + 2\cos 3t$; find its acceleration at any instant. Prove that the velocity of the particle never changes in direction, but that its acceleration vanishes whenever its velocity is equal to 13 m/sec or to 1 m/sec. (O.C.)

2. A particle of mass M starts at time $t = 0$ to move along the axis of x from the origin, under the action of a variable force of such magnitude that the distance travelled in time t is $2a(2t - \sin 2t)$, where a is a constant. Prove that (i) the magnitude of the force is $8Ma \sin 2t$, (ii) the work done by the force from starting until time t is $32Ma^2 \sin^4 t$, (iii) the power exerted by the force at time t is $128Ma^2 \sin^3 t \cos t$. (O.C.)

3. The kinetic energy of a particle moving in a straight line is proportional to the time. Prove that the distance x moved in time t is proportional to $t^{\frac{3}{2}}$, and that the force acting on the particle along the straight line is inversely proportional to the cube root of x.

4. A particle moves in a straight line with an acceleration $4t^2$ m/sec^2 away from a point O in the straight line. Initially the particle is passing through the point O with velocity 2 m/sec. Find its velocity and the distance it has moved after 3 sec.

5. The acceleration of a particle moving in a straight line when at a distance x from a fixed point O is k^2x away from O, k being a constant. If the particle starts from rest at a distance a from O, show that its velocity at any instant is $v = k(x^2 - a^2)^{\frac{1}{2}}$, after time t given by $t = \frac{1}{k} \ln (x + \sqrt{(x^2 - a^2)})/a$.

6. The velocity v and the distance x moved by a body in a straight line are connected by the relation $x = a + \dfrac{b}{v}$, where a and b are constants. Show that the retardation of the body is proportional to the cube of the velocity. If the initial

velocity of the particle was V, show that the relation between distance and time is $t = \dfrac{(x-a)^2}{2b} - \dfrac{b}{2V^2}$.

7. Show that if work is being done on a particle at a constant rate, the force on the particle is inversely proportional to its velocity.

Two particles, moving in straight lines, the first acted on by a constant force, the second acted on by a force doing work at a constant rate, each have their velocities increased from V to $2V$ after traversing a distance a. Show that the time taken by the second is $\frac{27}{28}$ of that taken by the first. Show also that the velocity acquired by the second after traversing a distance x, less than a, is greater than that acquired by the first after traversing the same distance.   (O.C.)

8. A particle is projected with a horizontal velocity of 80 m/sec in a medium which causes a retardation $\dfrac{v}{100}$ m/sec^2 when the velocity is v m/sec. Find the distance gone in 100 sec and the velocity after 100 sec.

9. A particle is projected vertically upwards with a velocity of 80 m/sec and the retardation due to air resistance is $\dfrac{v}{100}$ m/sec^2, when v is the velocity in m/sec. Find the height to which it rises given that $\ln 1 \cdot 081 = 0 \cdot 0780$.

10. The resistance to the motion of a train is $50g$ N per tonne at all speeds. It is moving on the level with uniform speed V, and comes to an incline of 1 in 100. The engine continues to work at the same rate as before; prove that if v is the velocity, and x the distance described up the incline in time t, then

$$v^2 = V^2 - \frac{g}{50}(6x - 5Vt).$$ (O.C.)

11. A train of mass M tonnes running at 34·36 km/h is brought to rest on an upgrade of 1 (vertically) in 120 (along the track) by the brakes which exert a force of $M\left(\dfrac{1}{10} + \dfrac{t}{110}\right)$ N, where t (seconds) is measured from the instant when the brakes are applied. Show that the train is brought to rest in 30 sec, and find the distance that it travels in this time.   (L.U.)

12. If the retardation caused by the resistances to the motion of a train is $a + bv^2$, where v is the velocity, show that it will come to rest from velocity V in a distance $\dfrac{1}{2b}\ln\left(1 + \dfrac{bV^2}{a}\right)$.

13. The resistances to motion of a train of 300 tonnes are $(900 + 7v^2)100$ N when the speed is v m/sec. Find the distance travelled in slowing from 90 km/h to 54 km/h with steam cut off.

CHAPTER 20

MOTION ABOUT A FIXED AXIS

20.1 Kinetic Energy of Rotation

If a rigid body is rotating about a fixed axis with angular velocity $\dot{\theta}$, its kinetic energy in absolute units is $\frac{1}{2}I\dot{\theta}^2$, where I is the moment of inertia of the body about the axis.

Let P be a point of the body (Fig. 254) and let the perpendicular from P to the axis of rotation meet the axis in O. Let $OP = r$. The point P is moving in a circle about O with angular velocity $\dot{\theta}$, and hence its velocity is $r\dot{\theta}$. Therefore, the kinetic energy of a particle of mass m of the body at P is $\frac{1}{2}mr^2\dot{\theta}^2$. Considering the rigid body to be made up of such particles, all with the same angular velocity $\dot{\theta}$, we have for the total kinetic energy T of the body,

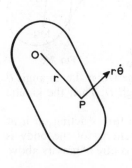

FIG. 254.

$$T = \tfrac{1}{2}\Sigma mr^2\dot{\theta}^2,$$
$$= \tfrac{1}{2}\dot{\theta}^2\Sigma mr^2,$$
$$= \tfrac{1}{2}I\,\dot{\theta}^2,$$

where I is the moment of inertia of the body about O. The units of the kinetic energy of the constituent particles and of the whole are absolute units of energy or work.

If k be the radius of gyration of the body about O, we have $I = Mk^2$ where M is the mass of the body, and hence

$$T = \tfrac{1}{2}Mk^2\dot{\theta}^2.$$

Hence, the kinetic energy of the body is the same as that of a particle of mass equal to the mass of the body, placed at a distance k from the axis and turning about the axis with the same angular velocity as the body.

Example 1. *Find the kinetic energy of a solid cylindrical flywheel of mass 200 kg and radius 75 cm, rotating at 1200 revolutions per minute.*

The moment of inertia of the flywheel about its axis is $\frac{1}{2}Ma^2$, where $M = 200$ and $a = 75$ cm. The angular velocity is $20 \times 2\pi$ radians per second, and the kinetic energy is therefore given by

$$T = \tfrac{1}{2} \times 200 \times \tfrac{1}{2} \times (0.75)^2 \times (40\pi)^2,$$
$$= 4.44 \times 10^5 \text{ J}.$$

20.2 Energy Equation

If a rigid body is rotating about a fixed axis, the increase of kinetic energy of any particle of the body is equal to the work done by the forces, both internal and external, which act on the particle. Hence, the increase of kinetic energy of the body in any displacement is the total work done by all the forces in that displacement. Since the internal forces of the body consist of pairs of equal and opposite forces, their total work will be zero in any displacement. Hence, the increase of kinetic energy of the body is the total work done by the external forces acting on the body in that displacement. If the forces acting on the body are conservative, the work done by the external forces is equal to the loss of potential energy, and we have that the sum of the kinetic and potential energy is constant.

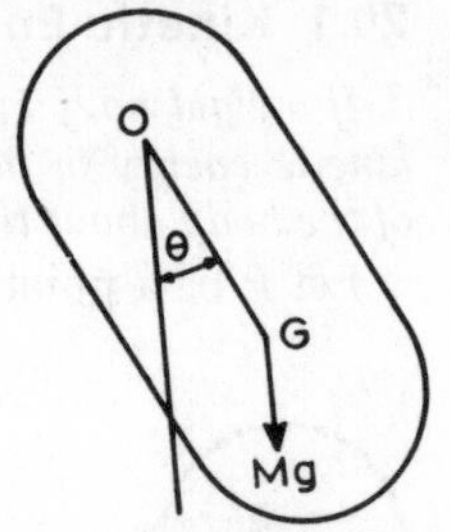

FIG. 255.

Let a body of mass M have radius of gyration k about a fixed axis through a point O (Fig. 255), and let G, the centre of gravity of the body, be distant h from the axis of rotation at O. Let the line OG make an angle θ at any instant with the downward vertical through O. Then the kinetic energy of the body is $\frac{1}{2}Mk^2\dot{\theta}^2$.

If the body can turn freely about the axis, the forces acting on it at O do no work as it rotates, and the potential energy of the body is $Mgh(1-\cos\theta)$, since $h-h\cos\theta$ is the height of the centre of gravity above its lowest position.

Therefore we have

$$\frac{1}{2}Mk^2\dot{\theta}^2 + Mgh(1-\cos\theta) = \text{constant.} \qquad (1)$$

In particular if the body is released from rest in a position in which $\theta = \alpha$, $\dot{\theta}$ is initially zero and we have

$$\frac{1}{2}Mk^2\dot{\theta}^2 + Mgh(1-\cos\theta) = Mgh(1-\cos\alpha),$$

$$\dot{\theta}^2 = \frac{2gh}{k^2}(\cos\theta - \cos\alpha). \qquad (2)$$

More generally, if the resultant of the external forces acting on the body has a moment G about O, the work done by the resultant as the angle changes from θ to $\theta+\delta\theta$ is $G\,\delta\theta$ (see § 8.5). If at the same time the kinetic energy increases from T to $T+\delta T$ we have, on equating the increase in kinetic energy to the work done

$$\delta T = G\,\delta\theta,$$

and in the limit as $\delta\theta$ tends to zero

$$\frac{dT}{d\theta} = G.$$

Writing $T = \frac{1}{2}Mk^2\dot\theta^2$ we have, since

$$\frac{d\dot\theta^2}{d\theta} = \frac{d\dot\theta^2}{d\dot\theta}\frac{d\dot\theta}{dt}\frac{dt}{d\theta} = 2\dot\theta . \ddot\theta . 1/\dot\theta = 2\ddot\theta,$$

$$Mk^2\ddot\theta = G. \tag{3}$$

The quantity $Mk^2\dot\theta$ is called the *angular momentum* of the body about the axis of rotation and equation (3) states that *the rate of change of angular momentum about the axis of rotation is equal to the moment of the external forces about this axis.*

Here G is the moment about O of the external forces in the sense of increasing θ. In this case we have $G = -Mgh\sin\theta$, giving

$$Mk^2\ddot\theta = -Mgh\sin\theta,$$

$$\ddot\theta = -\frac{gh}{k^2}\sin\theta. \tag{4}$$

If, in addition, there is a frictional couple of moment G_1, at the axis, we have

$$Mk^2\ddot\theta = -Mgh\sin\theta - G_1 \tag{5}$$

giving, on multiplying by $\dot\theta$ and integrating, in an angular displacement from θ_1 to θ_2

$$\frac{1}{2}Mk^2\dot\theta_2{}^2 - \frac{1}{2}Mk^2\dot\theta_1{}^2 = Mgh(\cos\theta_2 - \cos\theta_1) - \int_{\theta_1}^{\theta_2} G_1\,d\theta.$$

If G_1 is constant the latter integral is $G_1(\theta_2 - \theta_1)$. This equation holds only when θ is increasing, if θ is decreasing the sign of G_1 must be reversed.

Example 2. *A uniform circular disc of mass 10 kg and radius 1 m is free to turn in a vertical plane about a horizontal axis. A particle of mass 2 kg is attached to the highest point of the disc and given a small displacement. Find the greatest angular velocity of the disc in the subsequent motion.*

The moment of inertia of the disc about its axis is $10 \times 1^2/2$, and that of the 2-kg weight about the same axis is 2×1^2. Hence the total moment of inertia is 7 kg m^2.

If $\dot\theta$ be the angular velocity when the disc has turned through an angle θ, the loss of potential energy in this position is $2g(1 - 1\cos\theta)$ and we have

$$\frac{1}{2} \times 7\dot\theta^2 = 2g(1 - 1\cos\theta).$$

Hence, the velocity when $\theta = \pi$ is given by

$$\dot\theta^2 = \frac{8g}{7} = \frac{8 \times 9\cdot81}{7},$$

$$\dot\theta = 3\cdot19 \text{ rad/sec.}$$

Example 3. *A uniform rod of length 4 m and mass 2 kg is free to turn about a horizontal axis through the rod at a point 1 m from one end. The rod is held in a horizontal position and released; what should be its angular velocity when it becomes vertical?*

If there is a constant frictional couple at the axis of rotation, and the rod after passing through the vertical position rises only until it is inclined at 60° to the vertical, find the frictional couple and the angular velocity when it first reached the vertical position.

The moment of inertia about the centre of the rod

$$= 2 \times \frac{2^2}{3} = \frac{8}{3} \text{ kg m}^2.$$

The moment of inertia about the axis of rotation

$$= 2\left(\frac{2^2}{3} + 1\right) = \frac{14}{3} \text{ kg m}^2.$$

The kinetic energy when the angular velocity is $\dot\theta$ rad/sec

$$= \frac{7}{3}\dot\theta^2 \text{ J}.$$

The work done by gravity as the rod falls to the vertical position

$$= 2g \times 1 \text{ J}.$$

Therefore

$$\frac{7}{3}\dot\theta^2 = 2g,$$

$$\theta = 2 \cdot 9 \text{ rad/sec}.$$

If the rod comes to rest inclined at 60° to the vertical the loss of potential energy

$$= 2g \times \cos 60°,$$

$$= 9 \cdot 81 \text{ J}.$$

This is therefore the work done by the frictional couple in the rotation through 150° or $\frac{5}{6}\pi$ radians.

Hence, if G N m be the moment of the frictional couple

$$G \times \frac{5\pi}{6} = 9 \cdot 81,$$

$$G = 3 \cdot 74.$$

With this couple, the velocity in the vertical position was $\dot\theta$, where

$$\frac{7}{3}\dot\theta^2 = 2g - \frac{\pi}{2}G,$$

$$= 19 \cdot 62 - 5 \cdot 89$$

$$\dot\theta^2 = 13 \cdot 73,$$

$$\dot\theta = 3 \cdot 70 \text{ rad/sec}.$$

Example 4. *Masses of 4 kg and 6 kg are attached to the ends of a light inextensible string passing over a rough pulley mounted on a smooth horizontal axle. The pulley is approximately a circular cylinder of mass 5 kg and radius 4 cm. If the masses are released from rest find their acceleration and the tension in the two parts of the string.*

When the pulley has turned through an angle θ, the masses have each moved a distance 4θ cm and the loss of potential energy is

$$6g \times 4\theta - 4g \times 4\theta = 8g\theta.$$

If $\dot\theta$ is then the angular velocity, the kinetic energies of the two masses and of the pulley are

$$\tfrac{1}{2}.4(4\dot\theta)^2 + \tfrac{1}{2}.6(4\dot\theta)^2 + \tfrac{1}{2}.\tfrac{5}{2}(4)^2\dot\theta^2 = 100\dot\theta^2.$$

Therefore

$$100\dot\theta^2 = 8g\theta,$$

giving

$$\dot\theta^2 = \tfrac{2}{25}g\theta.$$

If we differentiate this equation with respect to t we find

$$2\dot\theta\ddot\theta = \tfrac{2}{25}g\dot\theta,$$

so that $\ddot\theta = \tfrac{1}{25}g$ and hence $4\ddot\theta = \tfrac{4}{25}g$.

This is the acceleration of each of the masses. The tensions T_1 and T_2 in the two parts of the string are easily found from the equations of motion of the masses, namely

$$6g - T_1 = 6 \times 4\ddot\theta = \tfrac{24}{25}g,$$

$$T_2 - 4g = 4 \times 4\ddot\theta = \tfrac{16}{25}g,$$

whence $T_1 = \tfrac{126}{25}g$, $T_2 = \tfrac{116}{25}g$.

20.3 Wheel Turned by a Falling Weight

Consider the motion of a wheel driven by a weight hanging freely at the end of a light inextensible string which passes round the wheel (Fig. 256).

Let M be the mass of the wheel, r its radius and k its radius of gyration about its axis. Let m be the mass of the weight hanging freely. The mass of the wheel is taken to include that of the axle, and the wheel is assumed to be free to turn about its axis.

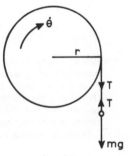

Let $\dot\theta$ be the angular velocity of the wheel when it has turned from rest through an angle θ. Then the kinetic energy of the wheel and the weight is

$$\tfrac{1}{2}Mk^2\dot\theta^2 + \tfrac{1}{2}mr^2\dot\theta^2,$$

Fig. 256.

since the speed with which the weight descends is $r\dot\theta$. The work done by the weight in descending a distance $r\theta$ is $mgr\theta$, and we have

$$(\tfrac{1}{2}Mk^2 + \tfrac{1}{2}mr^2)\dot\theta^2 = mgr\theta.$$

This gives the velocity for any value of θ. Differentiating with respect to θ we have

$$(Mk^2 + mr^2)\ddot{\theta} = mgr, \tag{6}$$

and this equation shows that the angular acceleration is constant.

The tension in the string T may be found by considering the work done on the hanging weight, and we have

$$\tfrac{1}{2}mr^2\dot{\theta}^2 = (mg - T)r\theta.$$

If the bearings are *not* smooth and a frictional couple of constant magnitude G is assumed to act on the axle, the work done by this couple in the displacement is $G\theta$, and we have

$$(\tfrac{1}{2}Mk^2 + \tfrac{1}{2}mr^2)\dot{\theta}^2 = mgr\theta - G\theta.$$

Hence, by measuring the velocity for a given value of θ the value of G may be found.

Example 5. *A flywheel is mounted on a horizontal axle 2 centimetres in diameter. A mass of 10 kg attached to a light string wrapped around the axle falls 3 m from rest in 10 seconds. Assuming the bearings are frictionless, find the moment of inertia of the flywheel and axle.*

Equation (6) shows that the angular acceleration of the wheel is constant and hence that the acceleration of the falling mass is constant. Since it falls 300 cm from rest in 10 seconds we have, from the formula $x = \tfrac{1}{2}at^2$, $300 = 50a$, so that $a = 6$ cm/sec^2. Hence, since the radius of the axle is 1 centimetre,

$$\ddot{\theta} = 6 \text{ rad/sec}^2.$$

From equation (6)

$$6 = g\frac{10}{Mk^2 + 10},$$

giving

$$Mk^2 + 10 = \frac{10g}{6} = 1635,$$

so that $Mk^2 = 1625$ kg cm^2.

Example 6. *A uniform cylindrical wheel of mass 100 kg and radius 2 m is fixed on a light horizontal axle of radius 50 cm, which turns in frictionless bearings. A fine string wrapped round the axle carries a weight of 10 kg at its free end, and a similar string wrapped round the wheel in the opposite sense carries a mass of 12 kg at its free end. If the system is released from rest, find the velocity of the 12 kg wt when it has fallen through 6 m, and the tension in the string from which it hangs.*

When the angular velocity is $\dot{\theta}$ we have for the kinetic energy

of the wheel $\qquad \tfrac{1}{2} \times 100 \times \dfrac{2^2}{2} \times \dot{\theta}^2 = 100\,\dot{\theta}^2,$

of the 10 kg mass $\qquad \tfrac{1}{2} \times 10 \times \left(\dfrac{1}{2}\dot{\theta}\right)^2 = \dfrac{5}{4}\dot{\theta}^2,$

of the 12 kg mass $\qquad \tfrac{1}{2} \times 12 \times (2\dot{\theta})^2 = 24\,\dot{\theta}^2.$

Hence, the total kinetic energy is $125\cdot25\,\dot\theta^2$. The loss of potential energy when the 12 kg mass descends 6 m and the 10 kg mass rises 1·5 m is

$$12g \times 6 - 10g \times 1\cdot5 = 57g.$$

Therefore, at this point

$$125\cdot25\,\dot\theta^2 = 57 \times 9\cdot81,$$

$$\dot\theta^2 = 4\cdot39.$$

The velocity required is $2\dot\theta = 4\cdot19$ m/sec approximately.
The kinetic energy of the 12 kg mass

$$= 24\,\dot\theta^2,$$

$$= 24 \times 4\cdot39 = 105\cdot4 \text{ J}.$$

If the tension in the string be T N the work done on the 12 kg wt

$$= (12g - T) \times 6 \text{ J}.$$

Therefore $12g - T = 17\cdot57,$

$$T = 100 \text{ N approximately.}$$

EXERCISES 20 (a)

1. A uniform straight rod AB of length $2a$ is smoothly jointed at A to a horizontal table and is allowed to fall, in a vertical plane through A, from rest when AB makes an angle α with the vertical. Prove that when the angle which AB makes with the vertical is θ, then

$$2a\dot\theta^2 = 3g(\cos\alpha - \cos\theta).$$

Find also the angular acceleration of the rod just before it becomes horizontal.
                                                                                (O.C.)

2. A uniform circular disc of mass 12 kg and radius 10 cm is free to rotate about a horizontal axis through its centre perpendicular to its plane. A particle of mass 3 kg is attached to the highest point of the rim of the disc and the equilibrium of the system slightly disturbed. Find the angular velocity of the particle, in revolutions per minute, when the particle is passing through its lowest point.
                                                                                (L.U.)

3. A uniform thin rod of length $6a$ and mass m is suspended so as to rotate freely about a fixed axis perpendicular to the rod and through a point of trisection. It is allowed to rotate freely from the horizontal position. What should be its greatest angular velocity? If there is a constant frictional couple, so that the rod turns through an angle of 60° beyond the vertical before coming to instantaneous rest, show that the greatest angular velocity is $\sqrt{\dfrac{7g}{20a}}$.

4. From the expression $\frac{1}{2}mv^2$ for the kinetic energy of a particle of mass m moving with speed v, deduce the kinetic energy of a uniform rigid disc of mass M and radius a rotating with angular velocity ω about an axis through its centre perpendicular to its plane. Prove that if it rotates about a parallel axis at distance $a/\sqrt{2}$ from its centre, with the same angular velocity, its kinetic energy will be twice its previous value.
                                                                                (L.U.)

5. A heavy circular disc of mass 20 kg and radius 1 m is capable of rotating about its centre in a vertical plane. A mass of 10 kg is attached to the rim at the highest

point, and the whole slightly displaced. Find the angular velocity when the mass of 10 kg is at the lowest point. (L.U.)

6. A flywheel, 2 m in diameter and weighing 20 kg, is keyed on to a shaft of 50 cm diameter, which can turn freely in smooth horizontal bearings; a long fine chain is attached to and wrapped round the axle and carries at its other end a mass of 16 kg.

The wheel is turned till it acquires a speed of 480 revolutions per minute, and is then left running. Prove that it will come to rest after about 107 more revolutions. (Neglect the masses of the axle and chain and assume the mass of the wheel to be concentrated in and uniformly distributed round its rim.)

(O.C.)

7. A wheel has a diameter of 2 m and a mass of 50 kg which may be regarded as distributed uniformly round the rim. Calculate the energy stored in the wheel when it is making 600 revolutions per minute. If the wheel is to be stopped in 50 sec by a brake pressing on the rim, calculate the pressure required, assuming that the coefficient of friction is 0·1 between the brake block and the rim. (O.C.)

8. A wheel has a cord of length 10 m coiled round its axle; the cord is pulled with a constant force of 100 N, and when the cord leaves the axle, the wheel is rotating five times a second. Calculate the moment of inertia of the wheel and axle. (L.U.)

9. A torpedo is driven by expending the energy stored in a flywheel, initially rotating at 10 000 r.p.m. If the mass of the flywheel is 200 kg and it is regarded as a uniform circular disc of diameter 60 cm, show that it will be rotating at half the initial rate after about 925 m run at 54 km/h, assuming that the average power necessary for this speed is 50 kW. (L.U.)

10. Three equal uniform rods, each of length l and mass m, form the sides of an equilateral triangle ABC. The triangular frame is attached to a smooth hinge at A, about which it can rotate in a vertical plane. The frame is held, with AB horizontal and C below AB, and then let go from rest. Find the maximum angular velocity of the triangle in the subsequent motion. (L.U.)

11. A bucket of mass m hangs at the end of a light rope which is coiled round a wheel of mass M. If the wheel can rotate freely about its axis, which is horizontal, and if its entire mass is supposed concentrated in its rim, find the speed of the bucket when it has fallen x ft from rest. (L.U.)

12. Masses M_1 and M_2 ($M_1 > M_2$) are attached to the ends of a string which passes over a pulley, of radius a and mass M, with its axis horizontal and rotating in frictionless bearings; the pulley is sufficiently rough to prevent the string from slipping. Initially the masses hang vertically. Prove that when the masses are released from rest the angular acceleration of the pulley is

$$2(M_1 - M_2)g/(M + 2M_1 + 2M_2)a.$$

The tensions in the strings are T_1 and T_2. Prove that

$$\frac{T_1}{T_2} = \frac{M_1(M + 4M_2)}{M_2(M + 4M_1)}.$$

(O.C.)

13. A flywheel whose moment of inertia is 5400 kg m^2 is rotating at 100 r.p.m. Find its kinetic energy. During ten revolutions the kinetic energy decreases by 10 per cent, find the average retarding torque. Find how long it would take this torque to bring the flywheel to rest from 200 r.p.m., assuming it to be constant.

14. A flywheel on a horizontal axis 6 cm in diameter is set in motion by weights attached to a cord round the axle and allowed to fall vertically. The time to fall 3 m from rest for weights of 10 kg and 20 kg are 9·5 and 5·5 sec respectively. Show that the moment of inertia of the flywheel is approximately 0·22 kg m² and determine the frictional torque in the bearings.   (L.U.)

15. Two bodies of equal mass are attached to the ends of an inextensible string which passes over a pulley, which may be regarded as a uniform circular disc, whose plane is perpendicular to the edge of a rough horizontal table, coefficient of friction $\frac{1}{2}$. One body rests on the table and the other hangs vertically, and the mass of the pulley is equal to the mass of each of the bodies. Assuming that the string does not slip on the pulley and that the part of the string over the table is parallel to the table, determine the acceleration of the system and prove that the ratio of the tensions in the string on the two sides of the pulley is 7:8.   (L.U.)

16. A solid flywheel 25 cm in diameter is mounted on a horizontal axle 5 cm in diameter running in frictionless bearings. The mass of the wheel is 44 kg and of the axle 8·8 kg. One end of a string is fixed to the axle and twenty turns of the string are wound round it and a mass of 30 kg is hung from the free end. If the system is released from rest, find the angular velocity when the string is just unwound.

17. Two particles each of mass m are joined by a light inextensible string of length πa which passes over a uniform rough circular cylinder of radius a and mass $2m$. The cylinder is free to rotate about its axis which is horizontal. Initially the particles are in equilibrium at opposite ends of a horizontal diameter of the cylinder. One particle then receives a small displacement vertically downwards. When the second particle reaches the top of the cylinder, the first particle strikes the floor and remains there. Find the velocity of the first particle on striking the floor, and prove that the second particle leaves the cylinder when it has travelled a further distance

$$a \cos^{-1}\{\tfrac{1}{6}(\pi+1)\}. \qquad \text{(O.C.)}$$

18. A uniform circular disc of radius a and mass M with a rough edge is mounted on a horizontal axis. A string is passed over the disc and carries masses m_1 and m_2 $(m_1 > m_2)$ at its ends. The system starts from rest, and the string does not slip on the disc. Show that the velocity v of each weight is expressible in terms of the distance x each has moved by the equation

$$(M+2m_1+2m_2)v^2 = 4(m_1-m_2)gx.$$

Find the acceleration if $m_1 = 4$ kg, $m_2 = 2$ kg and $M = 12$ kg.   (L.U.)

19. A flywheel is carried on a shaft of radius 3 cm, mounted horizontally in frictionless bearings. A thin cord has one end attached to the shaft and is then wound round it, a weight of 40 kg being attached to the other end, which leaves the shaft vertically.

On releasing the weight it is found that it takes 2 sec to fall 3 m. Find the moment of inertia of the flywheel and shaft about their axis, and the tension in the cord during the motion.   (Q.E.)

20. A light string passes round the circumference of a circular disc of radius r and carries masses M and m hanging freely at its ends. If the axis of the disc is horizontal and the moment of inertia of the disc about the axis is I, find an expression for the acceleration of the masses, assuming that the string does not slip and that $M > m$.   (Q.E.)

21. A wheel and axle having a moment of inertia of 4 kg m^2 is free to rotate about a horizontal axis. A mass of 3 kg is fixed to the wheel at a distance of 1 m from its axis. A mass of 18 kg is suspended from a light string wound round the axle which is 6 cm in diameter. The 3 kg mass is held level with the axis of the axle and released, thus causing the 18-kg mass to be wound up. What is the greatest angular velocity of the wheel and axle in the subsequent motion? (Q.E.)

20.4 Compound Pendulum

A rigid body oscillating about a horizontal axis is called a compound pendulum. If k be the radius of gyration of the body about the axis of rotation and h the distance of its centre of gravity from the axis, we have found (§20.2) for the angular acceleration the equation

$$\ddot{\theta} = -\frac{gh}{k^2}\sin\theta,$$

that is

$$\frac{k^2}{h}\ddot{\theta} = -g\sin\theta.$$

For a simple pendulum of length l we have the equation

$$l\ddot{\theta} = -g\sin\theta,$$

and for small oscillations about the equilibrium position, the motion is approximately simple harmonic of period $2\pi\sqrt{\dfrac{l}{g}}$.

The equation of motion for the compound pendulum is exactly the same as that for a simple pendulum of length k^2/h, and the quantity k^2/h is known as the *length of the equivalent simple pendulum*.

The period for small oscillations about the equilibrium position is

$$2\pi\sqrt{\frac{k^2}{gh}}.$$

Example 7. *A uniform rod of length a oscillates in a vertical plane about an axis through one end of the rod. Find the period of small oscillations.*

The radius of gyration about the axis $= \sqrt{\dfrac{a^2}{3}}$.

The distance of the centre of gravity from the axis $= \dfrac{a}{2}$.

The length of the equivalent simple pendulum $= \dfrac{2}{3}a$.

The period $= 2\pi\sqrt{\dfrac{2a}{3g}}$.

Example 8. *A uniform piece of wire of length 4a is bent into two equal portions at right angles to each other. It oscillates in a vertical plane about an axis through one end of the wire. Find the period of its small oscillations.*

Let $2m$ be the mass of the wire, A the axis of rotation and AB and BC (Fig. 257) the two portions. The moment of inertia of AB about the axis is $\frac{4}{3}ma^2$. The moment of inertia of BC about an axis through its centre is $m\frac{a^2}{3}$, about the axis through A it is $m\left(\frac{a^2}{3}+5a^2\right)$.

Total moment of inertia about the axis $= \frac{20ma^2}{3}$.

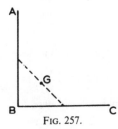

FIG. 257.

The distance of the centre of gravity from A is $\frac{3}{2}a$ along AB and $\frac{a}{2}$ perpendicular to AB, that is, $\frac{1}{2}\sqrt{10}a$ from A.

Hence, the length of the equivalent simple pendulum is

$$= \frac{10a^2}{3} \div \frac{\sqrt{10}}{2}a,$$

$$= \frac{2}{3}\sqrt{10}a,$$

and the period $= 2\pi\sqrt{\frac{l}{g}}.$

Example 9. *A compound pendulum consists of a uniform rod of length 6 m attached to the rim of a uniform disc of diameter 3 m, the rod lying in the plane of the disc and the centre of the disc in the line of the rod produced. If the mass of the disc is four times that of the rod and the pendulum oscillates in the plane of the disc about an axis through the other end of the rod, find the length of the equivalent simple pendulum.*

If the mass of the rod be m lb, its moment of inertia about the axis of rotation (Fig. 258)

$$= \tfrac{4}{3}m \times 3^2 = 12m \text{ kg m}^2.$$

The moment of inertia of the disc about a parallel axis through its centre is $4m \times \frac{3^2}{8}$, and about the axis of rotation it is

$$4m\left(\frac{9}{8}+\left(\frac{15}{2}\right)^2\right) = \frac{459}{2}m \text{ kg m}^2.$$

The total moment of inertia $= \frac{483}{2}m \text{ kg m}^2.$

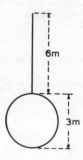

FIG. 258.

The distance of the centre of gravity from the axis

$$= \left(m \times 3 + 4m \times \frac{15}{2} \right) \bigg/ 5m = \frac{33}{5} \text{ m.}$$

The length of the equivalent simple pendulum

$$= \frac{483}{10} \div \frac{33}{5},$$

$$= \frac{483}{66},$$

$$= 7 \cdot 32 \text{ m.}$$

Example 10. *A uniform rod of mass 3m and length 2 m can turn freely in a vertical plane about a horizontal axis through one end. Find at what distance from the axis of rotation a particle of mass 4m must be attached to the rod so that the period of small oscillations of the combined mass shall be a minimum, and find this period.*

Let the particle be x m from the axis of rotation.

The total moment of inertia about the axis

$$= 3m \times \frac{4}{3} + 4mx^2,$$

$$= 4m(x^2 + 1).$$

The distance of the centre of gravity from the axis

$$= (3m \times 1 + 4mx)/7m,$$

$$= \frac{4x + 3}{7}.$$

The length of the equivalent simple pendulum is

$$l = \frac{4(x^2 + 1)}{7} \div \frac{4x + 3}{7},$$

$$= \frac{4(x^2 + 1)}{4x + 3},$$

$$= x - \frac{3}{4} + \frac{25}{4(4x + 3)}.$$

This length has to be a minimum, and we have

$$\frac{dl}{dx} = 1 - \frac{25}{(4x+3)^2},$$

$$\frac{d^2l}{dx^2} = \frac{200}{(4x+3)^3}.$$

For a turning value, $\qquad 4x+3 = \pm 5,$

$$x = \frac{1}{2} \text{ or } -2.$$

When $x = \frac{1}{2}$, $\frac{d^2l}{dx^2}$ is positive and l is a minimum.

Hence, the particle must be attached at 0·5 m from the axis and the corresponding value of l is

$$l = \frac{1}{2} - \frac{3}{4} + \frac{5}{4}$$

$$= 1 \text{ m.}$$

The period is $\qquad 2\pi\sqrt{\frac{1}{g}} = \frac{2\pi}{\sqrt{(9·81)}},$

$$= 2 \text{ sec.}$$

20.5 Centre of Oscillation

Let GO (Fig. 259) be the perpendicular from the centre of gravity to the axis of rotation of a compound pendulum, so that $OG = h$, and the radius of gyration of the body about the axis through O is k.

Let O' be a point on OG produced, such that $OO' = k^2/h$, the length of the equivalent simple pendulum. Then the radius of gyration squared about an axis parallel to the axis of rotation through G is

$$k^2 - h^2.$$

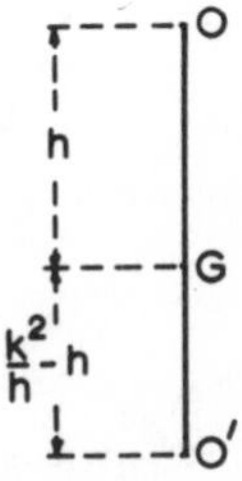

About a parallel axis through O' it is

$$k^2 - h^2 + \left(\frac{k^2}{h} - h\right)^2,$$

$$= \left(\frac{k^2}{h} - h\right)\left(h + \frac{k^2}{h} - h\right),$$

$$= \frac{k^2}{h}\left(\frac{k^2}{h} - h\right).$$

Fig. 259.

But the length $O'G$ is $\frac{k^2}{h} - h$, therefore if the body should oscillate about the axis through O', the length of the equivalent simple pendulum is again k^2/h. The point O' is called the *centre of oscillation* of the pendulum.

This property of an alternative point of suspension with the same period is used in Kater's pendulum to determine the value of g. This pendulum has two points of suspension, whose distance apart is accurately known, and a movable mass is adjusted until the time of oscillation about the two points is the same. Then if l be their distance apart, the period is $2\pi\sqrt{l/g}$, and by measuring the period g may be found. Thus the quantity to be measured in determining g is a time which may be found accurately from a number of oscillations.

20.6 Thrust on the Axis of Rotation

Since a particle P of mass m, distant r from the axis of rotation, is moving in a circle of radius r with velocity $r\dot\theta$, it has an acceleration $r\dot\theta^2$ towards the centre of the circle and an acceleration $r\ddot\theta$ in a perpendicular direction in the direction of θ increasing.

Let the radius OP (Fig. 260) make an angle α with the line OG joining the centre of gravity to the axis of rotation. The effective force acting on the particle has components $mr\dot\theta^2$ along PO and $mr\ddot\theta$ perpendicular to OP.

Resolving these components along and perpendicular to GO, we have for the effective force on the particle

$$mr\dot\theta^2 \cos\alpha + mr\ddot\theta \sin\alpha, \text{ parallel to } GO,$$

$$mr\ddot\theta \cos\alpha - mr\dot\theta^2 \sin\alpha, \text{ perpendicular to } GO.$$

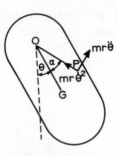

Fig. 260.

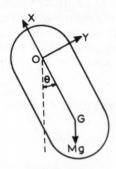

Fig. 261.

If the summation is taken over all the particles of the body, since these sums determine the position of the centre of gravity with respect to O,

$$\Sigma mr \cos\alpha = Mh,$$

$$\Sigma mr \sin\alpha = 0,$$

M being the total mass of the body.

Hence, the total effective force for the body is

$$Mh\dot\theta^2, \text{ along } GO,$$

$$Mh\ddot\theta, \text{ perpendicular to } GO.$$

Let X and Y be the components of the thrust of the axis of rotation on the body, along and perpendicular to OG (Fig. 261). If the only other force acting on the body be the weight acting at G we have

$$X - Mg \cos \theta = Mh\dot\theta^2,$$

$$Y - Mg \sin \theta = Mh\ddot\theta.$$

If the body is rotating freely, so that

$$\dot\theta^2 = \frac{2gh}{k^2}(\cos\theta - \cos\beta),$$

$$\ddot\theta = -\frac{gh}{k^2}\sin\theta,$$

the components X and Y are

$$X = Mg\left(1 + \frac{2h^2}{k^2}\right)\cos\theta - 2Mg\frac{h^2}{k^2}\cos\beta,$$

$$Y = Mg\left(1 - \frac{h^2}{k^2}\right)\sin\theta.$$

Example 11. *A rod of length 2a and mass m has a particle of mass m attached to one end and oscillates freely about a horizontal axis through the other end. If the rod oscillates through an angle of 60° each side of the vertical, find the vertical thrust on the axis of suspension when the rod is vertical.*

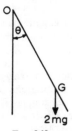

Fig. 262.

The moment of inertia about the axis of rotation (Fig. 262)

$$= \frac{4}{3}ma^2 + 4ma^2,$$

$$= \frac{16}{3}ma^2.$$

The distance of the centre of gravity from the axis

$$= \frac{3}{2}a.$$

The difference in the potential energy of the rod in the vertical and extreme position

$$= 3mga(1 - \cos 60°),$$
$$= \frac{3}{2}mga.$$

If the angular velocity in the vertical position be $\dot\theta$ we have

$$\frac{1}{2} \times \frac{16}{3}ma^2\dot\theta^2 = \frac{3}{2}mga,$$
$$\dot\theta^2 = \frac{9}{16}\frac{g}{a}.$$

The reversed effective normal force in the vertical position

$$= 2m \times \frac{3}{2}a^2\dot\theta^2,$$
$$= \frac{27}{16}mg.$$

The weight of the body being $2mg$, the total thrust on the axis

$$= \frac{59}{16}mg.$$

EXERCISES 20 (b)

1. A heavy uniform rod AB of length $2a$ and mass M has a mass m attached to it at B. The whole oscillates about a horizontal axis through A. Prove that the time of a small oscillation is

$$4\pi\sqrt{\left\{\frac{(M+3m)a}{3(M+2m)g}\right\}}.$$
(L.U.)

2. A rod AB of length l and negligible mass has two equal masses m attached to the end B and to a point M distant $l/3$ from B. Find the period of small oscillations about a horizontal axis through A. (L.U.)

3. A uniform circular disc has a particle of equal mass attached to a point A of the circumference. If the whole can turn freely about a horizontal axis perpendicular to the plane of the disc and through the other end of the diameter through A, find the length of the equivalent simple pendulum. (L.U.)

4. A uniform rectangular plate $ABCD$ is free to turn about a smooth horizontal axis coinciding with the edge AB. If $BC = 2b$, show that the time of a small oscillation about the position of equilibrium is $2\pi\sqrt{(4b/3g)}$. Find the position of another horizontal axis, parallel to AB, about which the time of a small oscillation would be equal to that about AB.

5. A uniform wire of mass M and length $4a$ is bent in the form of a square. It is hung by one corner over a smooth horizontal nail and released from rest from the position in which the sides are horizontal and vertical and the centre of gravity is at a lower level than the nail. Find the angular velocity with which it

passes through the position in which the diagonals are horizontal and vertical, and the reaction on the nail as it passes through this position.   (L.U.)

6. A cylindrical rod 60 cm long and 5 cm in radius is free to swing about a horizontal axis at right angles to its geometrical axis and intersecting it. Find the position of the axis of suspension if the length of the equivalent simple pendulum is a minimum.   (L.U.)

7. A uniform circular disc of radius a has a particle of mass equal to that of the disc fixed to its circumference. The disc can turn freely about a fixed horizontal axis through its centre at right angles to its plane. Assuming that the radius of gyration of the disc about this axis is $a/\sqrt{2}$, show that the length of the equivalent simple pendulum for small oscillations of the system about its position of stable equilibrium is $3a/2$.   (O.C.)

8. A rigid body is free to turn about a smooth fixed horizontal axis. Show how to find the period of its small oscillations about its position of stable equilibrium. If the body consists of a uniform rod, 4 m long, with a particle of weight equal to that of the rod attached to the middle point of the rod, and the axis passes through an extremity of the rod, calculate this period.   (O.C.)

9. Calculate the period of small oscillations of a uniform rod, 2 m long, about a horizontal axis through one end, when a particle of weight equal to that of the rod is attached to its middle point.

10. A fine circular hoop of weight W is free to move about a fixed horizontal tangent. It falls over from a position in which it is vertical, so that its centre describes a circle in a vertical plane perpendicular to the tangent. Show that in the positions when the hoop is vertical the stress on the support is $\frac{11}{3} W$ or W.   (O.C.)

11. An equilateral triangular frame ABC formed of three uniform equal rods, each of mass m and length l, is free to rotate about a horizontal axis coinciding with the rod AC. If a particle of mass $2m$ is attached to the point B, show that the length of the equivalent simple pendulum is $\dfrac{4\sqrt{3}l}{9}$. (Neglect the inertia of AC.)

12. A central hole of radius $\dfrac{r}{2}$ is bored through a disc of uniform thickness and radius r, and the disc oscillates on a knife-edge through the hole. If the periodic time of a small oscillation is $\dfrac{\pi}{2}$ sec, find the value of r.

13. A thin uniform rod of length $4a$ and mass m has a uniform disc of mass m and radius a attached to one end, the centre being in line with the rod. If the body oscillates as a pendulum about an axis through the end of the rod perpendicular to the plane of the disc, find the period.   (L.U.)

14. A straight uniform thin rod of mass $3m$ and length $2a$ has a particle of mass m attached to one end. It swings under gravity in a vertical plane about a horizontal axis through a point on it. Find all possible positions of the axis for which the length of the equivalent simple pendulum is $5a/3$.   (L.U.)

15. A circular washer of uniform material has internal radius a and external radius b. Find the period of small oscillations in the plane of the washer about a knife-edge in contact with the inner surface.   (L.U.)

16. A uniform circular disc of radius r oscillates as a compound pendulum about an axis perpendicular to its plane through a point on its circumference. Find the period of the oscillation.

    If the mass of the disc be M, show that the effect of removing a mass m by drilling a circular hole through the centre of the disc is to increase the period in the ratio $\sqrt{\left|\dfrac{3M+m}{3M}\right|}$. (L.U.)

17. A thin uniform rod of mass m and length $2a$ can turn freely about one end which is fixed. A uniform bar, whose mass is $8m/9$ and length $3a$, can be clamped to the rod so that its centre occupies any position on the rod. Show that the length of the simple equivalent pendulum for oscillations in which the bar and the rod remain in a vertical plane lies between $3a/2$ and $2a$. (O.C.)

18. A uniform rod of length 90 cm and mass m is rigidly attached to a thin uniform disc of diameter 60 cm and mass $4m$. The rod is in the plane of the disc and lies along a radius produced. The rod and the disc are suspended freely from the outer end of the rod. Determine the periodic time of small oscillations in the plane of the disc. (Q.E.)

19. A pendulum consists of a thin uniform rod 150 cm long pivoted 30 cm below its upper end. If it is released from a position $2°$ from vertical, calculate its inclination 20 sec later, assuming successive swings all have the same amplitude. (Q.E.)

20. A symmetrical bicycle wheel has a moment of inertia of 1 kg m² about its axis. It is supported in frictionless horizontal bearings, and a concentrated mass of 2 kg is rigidly attached to its rim, 30 cm from its axis.

(a) If it is released from the position in which the mass is as high as possible and the equilibrium is just disturbed, find the greatest angular velocity the wheel will have during its subsequent motion.

(b) What is the period of small oscillations of the wheel and weight about their position of stable equilibrium? (Q.E.)

20.7 Impulses

If an impulse J acts on a rigid body, free to rotate about a fixed axis, it sets up a set of internal impulses in the body between the constituent particles, and these internal impulses cause the changes in momentum of the particles.

Let the impulse J change the angular velocity of the body from $\dot{\theta}_0$ to $\dot{\theta}_1$.

Let X be the component of impulse, on a particle of mass m distant r from the axis of rotation, perpendicular to the radius from the particle to the axis.

The change of momentum of the particle is $mr\dot{\theta}_1 - mr\dot{\theta}_0$ and we have

$$X = mr(\dot{\theta}_1 - \dot{\theta}_0),$$

and $$Xr = mr^2(\dot{\theta}_1 - \dot{\theta}_0).$$

Summing over the whole body we have

$$\Sigma Xr = \Sigma mr^2(\dot{\theta}_1 - \dot{\theta}_0).$$

Now, Σmr^2 is the moment of inertia Mk^2 about the axis of rotation, and the right-hand side of the equation is $Mk^2(\dot{\theta}_1 - \dot{\theta}_0)$.

ΣXr is the sum of the moments of all the impulses about the axis of rotation. In this sum the moments of the internal impulses cancel out and hence the sum is the moment of the external impulse J about the axis of rotation.

Hence the moment of the impulse J about the axis of rotation

$$= Mk^2(\dot{\theta}_1 - \dot{\theta}_0).$$

The quantity $Mk^2\dot{\theta}$ is called the *angular momentum* of the body about the axis of rotation, and we have that the moment of impulse about the axis of rotation is the change of angular momentum about the same axis.

Example 12. *A uniform rod of mass m and length l is free to turn about a horizontal axis through one end of the rod. When the rod is at rest in its position of stable equilibrium it receives a blow J perpendicular to the rod and to the axis of rotation at the lower end of the rod. If the rod subsequently turns through an angle of 60° before coming to rest, show that*

$$J = m\sqrt{\left(\frac{gl}{6}\right)}.$$

The moment of inertia of the rod about the axis is $m\dfrac{l^2}{3}$. If $\dot{\theta}$ be the angular velocity imparted by the blow, the angular momentum of the rod is $m\dfrac{l^2}{3}\dot{\theta}$.

The moment of the blow about the axis is Jl and we have

$$m\frac{l^2}{3}\dot{\theta} = Jl,$$

$$l\dot{\theta} = \frac{3J}{m}.$$

The kinetic energy of the rod

$$= \frac{1}{2}m\frac{l^2}{3}\dot{\theta}^2,$$

$$= \frac{m}{6}\left(\frac{3J}{m}\right)^2,$$

$$= \frac{3J^2}{2m}.$$

The gain of potential energy as it turns through 60°

$$= mg\frac{l}{2}(1 - \cos 60°),$$

$$= mg\frac{l}{4}.$$

Therefore

$$\frac{3J^2}{2m} = mg\frac{l}{4},$$

$$J = m\sqrt{\left(\frac{gl}{6}\right)}.$$

20.8 Energy of a Rolling Body

The displacement of a rigid body moving in a vertical plane may be described as a displacement of its centre of gravity and a rotational displacement of the body in the vertical plane about its centre of gravity. In the same way, the velocity of the body at any instant may be described in terms of the velocity of the centre of gravity and the angular velocity about the centre of gravity.

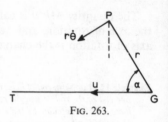

FIG. 263.

If u be the velocity of the centre of gravity G, in the direction GT, and $\dot{\theta}$ the angular velocity, a particle of mass m at P, distant r from G, has the velocity u of the centre of gravity and a velocity $r\dot{\theta}$ with respect to the centre of gravity (Fig. 263). If the direction GP makes an angle α with the line GT, the particle at P has components of velocity $u + r\dot{\theta} \sin \alpha$ and $r\dot{\theta} \cos \alpha$ along and perpendicular to the direction GT. Hence the kinetic energy of the particle at P

$$= \tfrac{1}{2}m\{(u + r\dot{\theta} \sin \alpha)^2 + (r\dot{\theta} \cos \alpha)^2\},$$
$$= \tfrac{1}{2}mu^2 + \tfrac{1}{2}mr^2\dot{\theta}^2 + mur\dot{\theta} \sin \alpha.$$

Hence the total kinetic energy of the body is

$$T = \tfrac{1}{2}u^2 \, \Sigma m + \tfrac{1}{2}\dot{\theta}^2 \, \Sigma mr^2 + u\dot{\theta} \, \Sigma mr \sin \alpha.$$

If M be the mass of the body, $\Sigma m = M$, and $\dfrac{1}{M} \Sigma mr \sin \alpha$ gives the distance of the centre of gravity from the line GT and is therefore zero. Also, $\Sigma mr^2 = Mk^2$, the moment of inertia about an axis through the centre of gravity perpendicular to the plane of motion.

Therefore

$$T = \tfrac{1}{2}Mu^2 + \tfrac{1}{2}Mk^2\dot{\theta}^2.$$

Thus the kinetic energy of the body consists of two parts, the kinetic energy of translation $\tfrac{1}{2}Mu^2$, and the kinetic energy of rotation $\tfrac{1}{2}Mk^2\dot{\theta}^2$.

If a spherical or cylindrical shaped body is rolling on a plane surface (Fig. 264), the point P of the body in contact with the surface at any instant is instantaneously at rest, and the velocity of the centre of gravity G is perpendicular to GP. If r be the distance GP, the point P has the velocity u of the centre of gravity and, in the opposite direction, the velocity $r\dot{\theta}$ with respect to the centre of gravity.

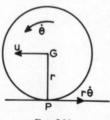

FIG. 264.

Therefore $\quad u = r\dot{\theta}.$

Hence, if M be the mass of the body and k its radius of gyration about the axis of rotation through its centre of gravity, we have for the kinetic energy

$$T = \tfrac{1}{2}Mu^2 + \tfrac{1}{2}Mk^2\dot\theta^2,$$
$$= \tfrac{1}{2}M(r^2 + k^2)\dot\theta^2.$$

Since the moment of inertia of the body about a parallel axis through P is $M(r^2 + k^2)$, the same value may be found for the kinetic energy by considering the body as rotating about the point P with angular velocity $\dot\theta$.

When a body is rolling on a surface, the forces at the point of contact do no work (see § 16.3), and hence the change of kinetic energy of the body may be equated to the work done by the other forces acting on the body.

Example 13. *A uniform solid sphere of radius a rolls a complete revolution from rest down a rough plane inclined at an angle α to the horizontal. Find the velocity of its centre of gravity at this point and the time taken.*

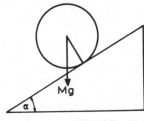

FIG. 265.

The moment of inertia of the sphere (Fig. 265) is $\tfrac{2}{5}Ma^2$ about a diameter, and hence $M\left(\tfrac{2}{5}a^2 + a^2\right)$ about a parallel axis through the point of contact.

Hence if $\dot\theta$ be the angular velocity when the sphere has turned through an angle θ, the kinetic energy is $\tfrac{1}{2} \times \tfrac{7}{5}Ma^2\dot\theta^2$.

The work done by gravity when the centre of gravity moves a distance $a\theta$ down the plane is $Mg \sin \alpha \times a\theta$.

Hence, we have

$$\frac{7}{10}Ma^2\dot\theta^2 = Mga \sin \alpha \times \theta.$$

When $\theta = 2\pi$ $a\dot\theta = \sqrt{(20\pi ga \sin \alpha/7)}$, and this is the velocity of the centre of gravity.

Differentiating the energy equation with respect to θ, since $\dfrac{d\dot\theta^2}{d\theta} = 2\ddot\theta$, we have

$$a\ddot\theta = \frac{5}{7}g \sin \alpha.$$

Hence, the acceleration is constant and the time to move a distance $2\pi a$ from rest is given by

$$2\pi a = \frac{1}{2} \times \frac{5}{7}g \sin \alpha . t^2,$$

$$t = \sqrt{\left(\frac{28\pi a}{5g \sin \alpha}\right)}.$$

EXERCISES 20 (c)

1. A uniform solid flywheel of mass 25 kg and diameter 40 cm is set in motion by a pull on a rope wrapped round the wheel. If the impulsive tension in the rope is 50 N sec, find the kinetic energy imparted to the flywheel.

2. A uniform solid flywheel of mass 10 kg and diameter 36 cm is rotating at 1200 r.p.m. A particle of mass 1 kg which is at rest becomes attached to a point on the rim of the wheel. Find the loss of speed of the wheel.

3. A uniform rod of length $2a$ and mass m can turn freely about a horizontal axis through one end. The rod is released from a horizontal position, and when it is vertical it strikes a particle of mass m which becomes attached to the extremity of the rod. Find the angle through which the rod turns from the vertical before coming to instantaneous rest.

4. A uniform rod of length 60 cm and mass 1 kg is free to oscillate about a horizontal axis through one end. When the rod is hanging vertically it receives a blow in a direction perpendicular to the rod and to the axis of rotation at the mid-point of the rod. Subsequently the rod turns through a right angle before coming to rest. Find the magnitude of the blow.

5. A flywheel whose moment of inertia is 240 kg m^2 is rotating at 1000 r.p.m. when it is suddenly put into gear with a stationary wheel whose moment of inertia is 75 kg m^2. Find the rate at which the two wheels rotate and the loss of kinetic energy.

6. A uniform square steel plate of side 1 m and mass 80 kg can turn freely about one side which is horizontal. When the plate is hanging vertically a bullet of mass 60 g moving horizontally strikes the plate at a distance of 60 cm from the axis of rotation and the plate turns through an angle of 30°. If the momentum of the bullet is destroyed by the impact, find the velocity with which it strikes the plate.

7. A uniform solid circular cylinder rolls from rest a distance of 10 m down a plane inclined at 30° to the horizontal. Find the velocity of its centre of gravity and the time taken.

8. A uniform solid sphere rolls from rest a distance of 10 m down a plane inclined at 30° to the horizontal. Find the velocity of its centre of gravity and the time taken.

9. A wheel whose mass may be regarded as distributed uniformly round its rim rolls from rest a distance of 10 m down a plane inclined at 30° to the horizontal. Find the velocity of its centre and the time taken.

10. A wheel of radius a is formed of a thin uniform rim of mass M and n uniform spokes of length $a-b$, each of mass m, which are fastened to the rim and to an axle of radius b and mass m'. The wheel rolls down an inclined plane of angle α. Find the acceleration of its centre.   (O.C.)

11. The total mass of a railway truck was 2000 kg. It had two pairs of wheels, each
    pair with the attached axle having a mass of 240 kg. The radius of gyration of
    each wheel was 28 cm, and the distance from the centre of the axle to the rail
    was 40 cm. Calculate the kinetic energy of the truck when travelling at 20 m/sec.
    If it can be brought to rest by the brakes in 80 sec, without slipping of the wheels
    on the rails, find the retarding force, supposed constant, exerted by the rails.
                                                                                (L.U.)
12. A girder is being pushed horizontally on three rollers at a speed of 5 cm/sec, the
    diameter of each roller being 15 cm; find the speed of their forward motion if
    there is no slipping. If the girder has a mass of 1 tonne and each roller 100 kg
    find the kinetic energy of the system.   (L.U.)
13. A wheel of diameter 1 m and mass 40 kg, which may be regarded as distributed
    uniformly round the rim is rolling along a horizontal road at a speed of 18 km/h.
    Calculate the energy stored in the wheel. If it comes to a hill rising 1 m in 5 m
    along the road how far will it go before it stops?   (O.C.)
14. Find the moment of inertia of a uniform circular cylinder 30 cm in diameter, and
    weighing 20 kg, about its axis. A roller of the above dimensions rolls down a
    plane inclined at 30° to the horizontal, and rough enough to prevent slipping.
    The handle of the roller, whose mass may be neglected, is parallel to the plane,
    and is attached by a cord also parallel to the plane which passes over a smooth
    fixed pulley attached to the highest point of the plane and carries a weight of
    5 kg at its other end. Find the acceleration of the weight as the roller rolls down
    the plane.   (O.C.)
15. A locomotive with six wheels, each of diameter 150 cm and mass 1000 kg, alto-
    gether weighs 55 tonnes. Find its total kinetic energy when moving at 54 km/h,
    taking into account the rotational energy of the wheels, each of which may be
    considered as a solid disc of uniform thickness. In calculating the distance in
    which a braking force would stop the locomotive, find by what percentage the
    distance would be underestimated if the rotational energy were not taken into
    account.
16. A flywheel in the form of a circular disc of diameter 2 m and thickness 15 cm is of
    uniform density 250 kg/m³. The flywheel is mounted on a shaft of negligible
    inertia on which it is rotating at a speed of 100 r.p.m. on bearings with negligible
    friction. A brake is applied to the wheel producing a constant tangential force
    of 100 N at a radius of 1 m. Determine the time to bring the wheel to rest.
                                                                                (Q.E.)
17. A rectangular door 2 m × 1 m of mass 30 kg is hinged about a longer edge which
    is vertical. The door is controlled by a spring which exerts a closing couple
    proportional to the angle the door is open, its value when the door is open 90°
    being 3 N m. The door is released from this position. Determine the angular
    velocity of the door as it reaches the closed position.   (Q.E.)
18. A flywheel of mass 100 kg is rotating about its axis at 150 r.p.m., and it is acted
    on by a constant frictional couple, so that after 10 sec it is rotating at 100 r.p.m.
    Find how many more revolutions it will make before it is brought to rest. If the
    value of the couple is 55 N m, find the radius of gyration of the wheel.   (N.U.)

CHAPTER 21

MATHEMATICAL METHODS

21.1 Introductory

The present chapter deals with the applications of mathematics to simple physical situations. This involves making a selection of data and setting up algebraic and differential equations which fit a problem, using the calculus method of small increments and making suitable approximations, as well as solving the equations obtained.

The chapter comprises four sections each with its set of worked examples and exercises, the exercises being usually worded in such a way as to help the student in the formulation of the problem. In the first section the problems are of a general nature, some involving the use of inequalities and others the solution of simple differential equations. In the second section the emphasis is on problems familiar to students of Physics and Chemistry. The third section deals with problems in statics, the topics going slightly beyond those treated earlier in the book, while in the fourth section, on dynamics, the opportunity has been taken to give a brief treatment of the motion of a rocket and the use of polar and tangential-normal components of acceleration.

21.2 Problems of a General Nature

Example 1. *If the equations $x + y = k$, $2y - 3x + 5 = 0$, $5y - x - 9 = 0$ are consistent find the value of k. Find the values of k for which it is possible to satisfy the inequalities $2y - 3x + 5 < 0$ and $5y - x - 9 > 0$, with $x + y = k$.*

Solving the equations $2y - 3x + 5 = 0$, $5y - x - 9 = 0$ in the usual way we find $x = 3\frac{4}{13}$, $y = 2\frac{6}{13}$. Hence $x + y = 5\frac{10}{13}$, and this must be the value of k if the third equation is satisfied.

Writing the two inequalities in similar ways, remembering that multiplication by -1 changes an inequality sign from $<$ to $>$ or from $>$ to $<$ (or alternatively, that we must change the sign of quantities taken across the inequality sign) we have

$$2y - 3x + 5 < 0,$$

$$x - 5y + 9 < 0.$$

Multiplying the first inequality by 5, the second by 2 (both positive numbers) and adding we have

$$-13x + 43 < 0, \text{ that is } x > 3\tfrac{4}{13}.$$

Multiplying the second inequality by 3 and adding to the first we have

$$-13y + 32 < 0, \text{ that is } y > 2\tfrac{6}{13}.$$

Hence, since $k = x + y$, we have $k > 5\frac{10}{13}$.

A graphical solution of this problem may be found by the method suggested in Exercise 21 (a) 2.

Example 2. *With OX as the initial line and OY perpendicular sketch the curve $r = 4 + 3 \cos \theta$. A cam is cut in this shape pivoted at O and with its axis of symmetry initially along OX. A light rod BC is along OY with its end B in contact with the cam and is free to move within guides along OY. If the cam now rotates in an anti-clockwise direction with uniform angular velocity ω find the greatest velocity and acceleration of the rod.*

The curve is as shown in Fig. 266. After time t the line OQ will be along OX and angle $QOX = \omega t$. The perpendicular OP will be along OY and angle $XOP = \frac{1}{2}\pi - \omega t$.

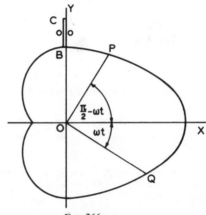

Therefore

$$OP = 4 + 3 \cos(\tfrac{1}{2}\pi - \omega t),$$

$$= 4 + 3 \sin \omega t,$$

and this will be the distance z of B from O at time t.

Hence

$$\frac{dz}{dt} = 3\omega \cos \omega t,$$

$$\frac{d^2z}{dt^2} = -3\omega^2 \sin \omega t,$$

giving greatest velocity 3ω and greatest acceleration $3\omega^2$.

Fig. 266.

Example 3. *A hemi-spherical bowl of radius a is filled with water. Water can escape from the bowl through a hole in the bottom of effective cross-sectional area C. The velocity of the escaping water at any instant is $\sqrt{(2gx)}$, where x is the depth of water remaining in the bowl. Find the time taken to empty the bowl.*

Let x be the depth of the water at time t and y the radius of the free surface, so that $(a-x)^2 + y^2 = a^2$, that is $y^2 = 2ax - x^2$.

The increase in volume δV corresponding to a small increase δx of x is given by

$$\delta V = \pi y^2 \delta x = \pi(2ax - x^2)\delta x.$$

The quantity emerging through the hole in time δt is $C\sqrt{(2gx)}\delta t$ and this is the *decrease* in volume so that

$$-\pi(2ax - x^2)\delta x = C\sqrt{(2gx)}\delta t,$$

whence

$$\frac{dx}{dt} = -\frac{C\sqrt{2g}}{\pi} \frac{\sqrt{(x)}}{2ax - x^2}.$$

Hence if T is the time when the bowl is empty

$$\int_a^0 (x^{\frac{3}{2}} - 2ax^{\frac{1}{2}})dx = \int_0^T \frac{C\sqrt{2g}}{\pi}dt,$$

that is

$$\frac{4}{3}a^{\frac{5}{2}} - \frac{2}{5}a^{\frac{5}{2}} = \frac{C\sqrt{(2g)}T}{\pi},$$

$$T = \frac{14\pi a^{\frac{5}{2}}}{15C\sqrt{(2g)}}.$$

Example 4. *O is the origin and $P(x, y)$ is a point on a curve which passes through the point (a, O). The tangent to the curve at P makes an angle of $\frac{1}{4}\pi$ with OP. Prove that the curve is the spiral whose equation in polar coordinates is $r = ae^\theta$.*

If $OP(= r)$ makes an angle θ with OX then ψ, the inclination of the tangent to the horizontal, is given by

$$\psi = \theta + \tfrac{1}{4}\pi, \text{ and } \tan \psi = \frac{1+\tan\theta}{1-\tan\theta}.$$

Therefore

$$\frac{dy}{dx} = \frac{1+\tan\theta}{1-\tan\theta} = \frac{\cos\theta+\sin\theta}{\cos\theta-\sin\theta} \qquad (1)$$

Now since $x = r\cos\theta, y = r\sin\theta$

$$\frac{dy}{dx} = \frac{dy/d\theta}{dx/d\theta} = \frac{\dfrac{dr}{d\theta}\sin\theta + r\cos\theta}{\dfrac{dr}{d\theta}\cos\theta - r\sin\theta} \qquad (2)$$

From (1) and (2) $\dfrac{dr}{d\theta} = r$, whence $r = Ae^\theta$ and, since $r = a$ when $\theta = O$,

$$r = ae^\theta.$$

EXERCISES 21 (a)

1. If there were no emigration, the population x of a certain country would increase at a constant rate of k per cent per annum. By emigration the country loses population at a constant rate of n people per annum. When the time t is measured in years, express dx/dt in terms of x, k and n. If initially the population is N people, find the population after t years. Deduce that, if $N < 100n/k$, the country will become completely depopulated in a finite time.   (O.C.)

2. If the equations $y + x = k$, $y - 4x + 8 = 0$, $2y - x - 5 = 0$ are consistent, i.e. if there are numbers x and y which satisfy all three equations simultaneously, find the value of k.

    Draw the straight lines $y - 4x + 8 = 0$ and $2y - x - 5 = 0$ on the same diagram and shade distinctively the regions in which (a) $y - 4x + 8 < 0$, (b) $2y - x - 5 > 0$. For what values of k is it possible to find numbers satisfying the inequalities (a) and (b) and also the equation $y + x = k$?   (O.C.)

3. A square garden of side a is surrounded by a high wall of height h above eye level. A tower of height H above eye level is built outside the garden. If Cartesian axes are taken along two sides of the square with the origin at the corner most distant from the tower the coordinates of the foot of the tower are (b, c). Prove that, if $bh > aH$ or $ch > aH$, the top of the tower is not visible from the garden. Prove also that, if $1 < b/a < H/h$ and $1 < c/a < H/h$, the top of the tower is visible from anywhere in the garden within a rectangle of area

$$(Ha - hb)(Ha - hc)/(H - h)^2. \qquad \text{(O.C.)}$$

4. A rectangular classroom of length x m, width y m and ceiling height 3 m is to be built with a floor area of at most 40 m^2. It is to be longer than it is wide and one end wall will have a blackboard 3 m long by 2 m high mounted on it. One side wall is to have a window 2 m high running the whole of its length and the

door is to be 2·5 m high and 1 m wide. Find the inequalities which x, y must satisfy and, in a sketch, indicate the region of the x, y-plane which satisfies these conditions.

The acoustic specialists recommend that for such a classroom at least 70 m² of acoustic tiling should be used on the walls (excluding door, window and blackboard). Find the limitations imposed on the length of the room if this minimum area of acoustic tiling is used.

It is finally decided that the greatest possible area of acoustic tiling should be used on the walls; find the dimensions for the room.   (O.C.)

5. The rate of installing washing machines in a country is proportional to the number of households in the country which do not possess washing machines; the rate of scrapping of installed washing machines is proportional to the total number W remaining installed. No household has more than one washing machine installed. If H is the number of households in the country, prove that $dW/dt = kH - (k + k_1)W$, where k, k_1 are positive constants.

The number of households is growing at a steady rate, so that $H = a + bt$, where a, b are positive. Solve for W in terms of a, b, t, k, k_1 and an arbitrary constant c by finding constants α, β and μ such that

$$W = \alpha + \beta t + ce^{\mu t}$$

satisfies the differential equation. Find the proportion of households ultimately possessing washing machines.   (O.C.)

6. Water is poured into a fixed spherical bowl of radius 20 cm, at the rate of 150 cm³/sec. Calculate the rate at which the depth of water in the bowl is rising when the depth is 10 cm.   (O.C.)

7. It is known that a physical quantity P can be expressed as a function of the time t by the formula

$$P = k + a \sin(nt + c),$$

where k, a, n, c are constants. Determine the 4 constants so as to satisfy the following conditions:
   (a) the greatest and least values of P are 21 and 5,
   (b) $P = 21$ when $t = 0$,
   (c) the period of P is 4.   (O.C.)

8. A tracking station T observes a satellite S and wishes to observe its velocity V (assumed constant) and its least distance $TH(= h)$. Instruments can determine at every instant the values of the two quantities ω and z; ω is $d\theta/dt$, where θ is the inclination of TS to TH, and z (determined from apparent radio frequency) is the rate of change of the resolved part of V along TS. Prove that $\omega = V\cos^2\theta/h$ and $z = V^2\cos^3\theta/h$. If ω_1 and z_1 are the recorded maximum values of ω and z, show that $V = z_1/\omega_1$, $h = z_1/\omega_1^2$.   (O.C.)

9. A cylinder of radius a and height $h(> 2a)$ is filled with water and stands upright. It is then tilted very slowly at a uniform rate. Find an expression for the volume of water poured out when the axis is inclined at an angle θ to the vertical. Show that when $\theta = 45°$ water is being poured out twice as fast as it was initially.

10. In a rectangular channel of width a and depth h the velocity of flow at depth x below the surface is $v(1 - x^2/h^2)$, v being a constant. Show that the volume of water flowing past a given section in unit time is $\frac{2}{3}ahv$.

11. Oil is flowing inside a straight pipe of internal radius a and elements move in straight lines parallel to the axis of the pipe with speed $v(1 - r^2/a^2)$, where v is

constant and r is the distance from the central axis. Find the volume of oil flowing past a section in unit time.

12. The water level in a tank is at height h above an orifice. The cross-sectional area of the free surface is A and the effective cross-sectional area of the orifice is a and the water emerges with velocity v.

    (i) Show by equating the loss of potential energy in time δt to the gain in kinetic energy (the pressure on the free surface of the liquid being the same) that $v^2 = 2gh$.

    (ii) Show by equating the loss of volume of the water in the tank to the quantity emerging in time δt that $dh/dt = -av/A$.

Deduce that the time taken by a cylindrical tank of height H to empty itself through a hole in its base is $(2A/a)\sqrt{(H/2g)}$.

13. The rate of increase of the size of a culture is proportional to its size; after time t the size is a and after time $2t$ the size is b. Show that after time λt the size is

$$\frac{a^2}{b}\left(\frac{b}{a}\right)^{\lambda}.$$

14. O is the origin and P is the point (x, y) on a curve. The tangent to the curve at P meets OX at T and TN is drawn perpendicular to OP to meet OY in N. Show that if ON is a constant length a for all positions of P

$$\frac{dy}{dx} = \frac{xy}{x^2 - ay}.$$

Verify that a solution of this equation is

$$\frac{2ay - x^2}{y^2} = \text{constant},$$

and hence show that the curve is an ellipse or a hyperbola.

15. O is the origin and P is the point (x, y) on a curve; OP is inclined at an angle θ to the x-axis and the tangent at P is inclined at an angle ψ. Given that $\psi = \frac{1}{2}\theta$, prove that

$$\frac{dy}{dx} = \frac{\sqrt{(x^2 + y^2)} - x}{y}.$$

Prove that if $y = xz$,

$$x\frac{dz}{dx} = \frac{\sqrt{(1 + z^2)} - (1 + z^2)}{z}.$$

Integrating this equation, show that

$$x\{1 - \sqrt{(1 + z^2)}\} = -2a \text{ (a constant)},$$

and hence show that the curve is the parabola with focus at O

$$y^2 = 4a(x + a).$$

Deduce that the normal to the curve at P besets the angle between OP and the parallel to the x-axis through P.

16. A mathematical model for the *steady* motion of a sailing boat sailing in the same direction as the wind takes v as the boat's speed relative to the water, w as the wind speed relative to the boat, A as the effective stopping area which boat and

sail present to the wind and ρ as the density of the air. By either a dynamical or a dimensional method, derive a formula for the wind force F in terms of ρ, A and w. If a similar type of expression holds for water resistance, derive a relationship between w and v for a given vessel (so long as full sail can be carried).

In fact as w rises beyond a certain value the area A must be reduced to keep F within safe limits. We can obtain a relationship between top speeds of boats of identical design, but various sizes, by assuming F_{max} to be proportional to the weight of the boat. Derive the form of relation between v_{max} and, say, the length l of the boat.   (O.C.)

17. A time T is allowed for a journey of length a. The travelling speed decreases from its initial value at such a rate that if at any time t after the start the speed became constant at the value it then had the journey would be completed in half the remaining time available. Form a differential equation relating x, the distance travelled, and t, the time. Solve this equation and show that the journey will be completed in the time allowed.

21.3 Pressure Altitude Equation for Atmosphere

Consider a vertical column of air of unit cross-sectional area in equilibrium. Let p be the pressure at height h and $p + \delta p$ the pressure at height $h + \delta h$ (Fig. 267). Then p exceeds $p + \delta p$ by the weight of the column of air between the two levels, so that if ρ be the density

$$-\delta p = \rho \delta h$$

and in the limit $\dfrac{dp}{dh} = -\rho.$ (1)

Taking v as the volume which has unit mass, so that $\rho v = 1$, this equation may also be written as

$$\frac{dh}{dp} = -v.$$ (2)

Alternatively, using the gas equation $pv = RT$ (T being the temperature in degrees Centigrade absolute), we may write

$$\frac{dh}{dp} = -\frac{RT}{p}.$$ (3)

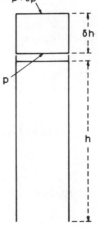

Fig. 267.

No progress can be made in the solution of this differential equation without making some assumption as to the relation between temperature and pressure. Three different assumptions are made :—

(a) *The isothermal assumption*, that T is constant.

Then (3) gives

$$\int_0^h dh = -RT \int_{p_0}^p \frac{dp}{p},$$

p_0 being the pressure when $h = 0$, so that

$$h = -RT \ln(p/p_0),$$
$$p = p_0 \exp(-h/RT).$$

(b) *The adiabatic assumption*, that $pv^\gamma = p_0 v_0^\gamma$, where γ is a constant $= 1.41$ approximately.

Then (2) gives

$$\int_0^h dh = -\int_{p_0}^p v\,dp = -v_0 p_0^{1/\gamma} \int_{p_0}^p p^{-1/\gamma} dp,$$

$$h = -\frac{\gamma}{\gamma-1} v_0 p_0^{1/\gamma} \{p^{1-1/\gamma} - p_0^{1-1/\gamma}\},$$

and hence

$$p = p_0 \left\{ 1 - \frac{\gamma-1}{\gamma} \cdot \frac{h}{p_0 v_0} \right\}^{\gamma/(\gamma-1)}$$

(c) *The lapse rate assumption*, that the temperature decreases with height according to the formula $T = T_0 - ah$, where $a = 0.00198$ and $T_0 = 288°$.

Then (3) gives

$$\frac{dh}{dp} = -\frac{R(T_0 - ah)}{p},$$

so that

$$-\int_0^h \frac{a\,dh}{T_0 - ah} = aR \int_{p_0}^p \frac{dp}{p},$$

and

$$\ln \frac{T_0 - ah}{T_0} = aR \ln \frac{p}{p_0},$$

$$p = p_0 \left(1 - \frac{a}{T_0} h \right)^{1/aR}$$

21.4 Loss of Heat

Example 5. *A body is heated so that its temperature T increases at a rate ct, while at the same time its temperature decreases at a rate $k(T-T_0)$, where T_0 is the temperature of the surrounding medium, show that*

$$\frac{dT}{dt} + k(T-T_0) = ct,$$

and show that if $T = T_1$ when $t = 0$

$$T - T_0 = (T_1 - T_0 + c/k^2)e^{-kt} + (c/k^2)(kt-1).$$

Newton's law of cooling states the rate of loss of the surface heat of a sphere is proportional to the difference of heat between the surface and the surrounding medium, that is $\frac{dT}{dt} = -k(T-T_0)$.

In this case the temperature is also being increased at a rate ct so that

$$\frac{dT}{dt} = -k(T-T_0) + ct.$$

This differential equation is more easily solved by taking $T-T_0$ as the dependent variable and writing

$$\frac{d}{dt}(T-T_0) + k(T-T_0) = ct.$$

Multiplying by the integrating factor e^{kt} we have

$$\frac{d}{dt}(T-T_0)e^{kt} = e^{kt}ct$$

so that

$$(T-T_0)e^{kt} = \int e^{kt}ct\,dt,$$

$$= \frac{c}{k}e^{kt}t - \frac{c}{k^2}e^{kt} + A \text{ (a constant)}.$$

Since $T = T_1$ when $t = 0$ we have

$$(T_1 - T_0) = -\frac{c}{k^2} + A,$$

and on substituting for A and dividing by e^{kt} we have

$$T - T_0 = (T_1 - T_0 + c/k^2)e^{-kt} + (c/k^2)(kt-1).$$

This shows that, since e^{-kt} becomes negligible for large values of t, the rate of *increase* of temperature eventually approximates to c/k.

21.5 Potential of a Disc

Example 6. *The potential at a point O of an element of mass δm at a point P is defined as $k\delta m/OP$. Find the potential of a uniform circular disc of radius a and mass m per unit area at a point O on a central axis perpendicular to the disc and distant p from the disc.*

Consider (Fig. 268) an annulus of the disc of radius r and width δr which has mass $2\pi r m \delta r$ and is all (to the first order of small quantities) distant $\sqrt{(r^2 + p^2)}$ from O. The potential at O of the element is

$$\frac{k 2\pi r m \delta r}{\sqrt{(r^2 + p^2)}}$$

and hence the potential at O of the disc is

$$2\pi m k \int_0^a \frac{r\,dr}{\sqrt{(r^2 + p^2)}}$$
$$= 2\pi m k \{\sqrt{(a^2 + p^2)} - p\}.$$

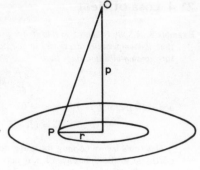

FIG. 268.

21.6 Chemical Reactions

Example 7. *The amounts x, y, z of three substances A, B, C satisfy the equation*

$$\frac{dx}{dt} = -px, \quad \frac{dy}{dt} = px - qy, \quad \frac{dz}{dt} = qy$$

and initially, when $t = O$, $x = a$ and $y = z = O$. Solve these equations and show that, if $p \neq q$, y is a maximum when $t = (\ln p - \ln q)/(p - q)$. Find the amount of B at this instant.

The first equation gives on separating the variables $dx/x = -p\,dt$, so that

$$\ln x = -pt + \ln a,$$

giving

$$x = ae^{-pt}.$$

Substituting for x in the second equation we have

$$\frac{dy}{dt} + qy = ape^{-pt}.$$

Here e^{qt} is an integrating factor for the left hand side and we have

$$e^{qt}\frac{dy}{dt} + qe^{qt}y = ape^{-(p-q)t},$$

that is

$$\frac{d}{dt}e^{qt}y = ape^{(q-p)t},$$

$$ye^{qt} = \frac{ap}{q-p}e^{(q-p)t} + A,$$

and from the initial condition $A = -ap/(q-p)$ so that

$$y = \frac{ap}{q-p}(e^{-pt} - e^{-qt}).$$

Adding the three differential equations we find

$$\frac{dx}{dt} + \frac{dy}{dt} + \frac{dz}{dt} = 0,$$

so that

$$x + y + z = \text{constant} = a,$$

and hence

$$z = \frac{a}{q-p}\left\{q(1 - e^{-pt}) - p(1 - e^{-qt})\right\}.$$

Now

$$\frac{dy}{dt} = \frac{ap}{q-p}(-pe^{-pt} + qe^{-qt}),$$

and this quantity is zero when

$$e^{(p-q)t} = \frac{p}{q},$$

$$t = \frac{\ln p - \ln q}{p - q}.$$

For this value of t, $\dfrac{d^2y}{dt^2} = \dfrac{ap}{q-p}\left\{p^2 e^{-pt} - q^2 e^{-qt}\right\} = -apqe^{-qt} < 0.$

This value of t therefore gives a maximum value of y which is

$$y = \frac{ap}{q-p}\left\{\left(\frac{p}{q}\right)^{p/(q-p)} - \left(\frac{p}{q}\right)^{q/(q-p)}\right\},$$

$$= \frac{ap}{q-p}\left(\frac{p}{q}\right)^{p/(q-p)}\left\{1 - p/q\right\},$$

$$= a\frac{p}{q}\left(\frac{p}{q}\right)^{p/(q-p)} = a\left(\frac{p}{q}\right)^{q/(q-p)}$$

EXERCISES 21 (b)

1. The rate of decay of a substance is kx, where x is the amount of the substance remaining and k is a constant. Show that the half-life (the time in which the amount is halved) of the substance is $(1/k)\ln 2$. (O.C.)

2. A radioactive substance A decays at a rate (in g per sec) equal to λ times the amount present (in g). The decay of A produces an equal mass of substance B which in turn decays at a rate equal to μ times the amount of B present into a third substance. Taking x g to be the mass of A and y g to be the mass of B at any time t and considering changes that occur in a further time interval δt, find expressions for dx/dt and dy/dt in terms of x and y and deduce that, if initially $x = 1$ and $y = 0$, then $x = e^{-\lambda t}$ and y is of the form $pe^{-\lambda t} + qe^{-\mu t}$ where p and q are constants to be determined. (O.C.)

3. The decrease of the intensity I of a beam of light passing through a medium in a distance δx is $\mu I \delta x$, where μ is the absorbtion coefficient. If $\mu = ae^{-bx}$, form the differential equation for the intensity at distance x and show that $I = I_0 \exp \{a(e^{-bx} - 1)/b\}$, where I_0 is the intensity at $x = 0$.

4. By Newton's law of cooling the rate of change at time t of the surface temperature T of a sphere in an atmosphere of constant temperature T_0 is proportional to the difference of these temperatures. Form a differential equation for T and show that, if $T = 3T_0$ when $t = 0$ and $T = 2T_0$ when $t = 1$,

$$T = T_0(1 + 2^{1-t}). \qquad \text{(O.C.)}$$

5. It is found that when quantities of two liquids A and B are boiling in the same container the ratio of the rates of vaporization of the two liquids being vaporized at any instant is a fixed multiple of the ratio of the amounts remaining. If x and y are the respective amounts of A and B remaining at any instant show that $b^k x = a y^k$, where k is a constant and a and b are the initial values of x and y.

(O.C.)

6. The pressure p, the density ρ, and the temperature T of the atmosphere at height y above ground level are connected by the relations

$$(1) \ RT\rho = p, \quad (2) \ \frac{dp}{dy} = -g\rho,$$

where R is a constant and g is the acceleration due to gravity which may be taken as constant in the range considered.

(a) Explain briefly the meaning of the relation (2).

(b) If T_0 and p_0 denote the values of T and p at ground level and $T = T_0 - \beta y$, where β is a constant, show that

$$p = p_0 \left(\frac{T_0 - \beta y}{T_0} \right)^{g/R\beta}$$

(c) Show, by differentiating the relation (1) or otherwise, that, if the density does not alter with height, then the temperature changes with height at a constant rate, and find that rate.

(O.C.)

7. The pressure at height h and at ground level in the atmosphere are p and p_0 respectively and v and v_0 are the corresponding volumes per unit mass. Given that, if δp is the infinitesimal increase in pressure due to an increase δh in height,

$$\delta p = -(1/v)\delta h,$$

show that, if the adiabatic relation $pv^\gamma = p_0 v_0^\gamma$ holds, than

$$dh/dp = -v_0 (p_0/p)^{1/\gamma}.$$

Solve this differential equation to find an expression for the pressure at height h.

(O.C.)

8. Show that the pressure p at height h in the atmosphere satisfies the relation

$$\delta p = -(1/v)\delta h$$

where v is the volume per unit mass. Deduce that in an isothermal layer in which $pv = RT$, R and T being constants,

$$p = p_0 \exp \{h/(RT)\},$$

where p_0 is the pressure for $h = 0$.

(O.C.)

9. A chemical dissolved in a fixed volume of solvent exists in two forms, type A and type B, each of which is of the same density when dry. The rate at which type A changes into type B is proportional to the concentration x of type A in the solution and similarly the rate at which type B changes into type A is proportional to the concentration y of type B in the solution. Prove that $dx/dt = -kx + k'y$, where k, k' are constants and find a similar differential equation for dy/dt.

Hence prove that x satisfies the differential equation

$$\frac{d^2 x}{dt^2} + (k+k')\frac{dx}{dt} = 0.$$

Solve this equation for $\dfrac{dx}{dt}$ and hence for x, given that the initial concentration

of type A is 1 part in 20 and that its final concentration is half this.   (O.C.)

10. The potential at a point P, polar coordinates r, θ, of a small magnet at O with its axis along the line $\theta = O$ is $\mu \cos \theta / r^2$ where μ is constant. The work done in moving the pole at P through a small distance is equal to the change in the potential of the magnet in the displacement. By considering the displacements δr and $r\delta\theta$ show that the force exerted on the unit pole at P by the magnet is $(\mu/r^3)(1 + 3\cos^2\theta)^{\frac{1}{2}}$.

11. Defining the potential at a point O of an element of mass δm at a point P as $k\delta m/OP$, show that the potential of a uniform thin rod of length $2l$ and mass m per unit length at a point O on a perpendicular bisector of the rod distant r from the rod is $2km \ln \{l + \sqrt{(l^2 + r^2)}\}/r$.

12. In a reversible chemical reaction the yield x at time t satisfies the differential equation

$$\frac{dx}{dt} = k_1(a-x)(b-x) - k_2 x^2,$$

and $x = 0$ when $t = 0$. If $b = 2a$ and $k_2 = 3k_1$, $(k_1 > 0)$ find x in terms of t and show that the equilibrium value of x is $a/2$.

13. In successive irreversible chemical reactions $A \rightarrow B \rightarrow C...$, the velocities of the first two reactions are given by the equations

$$\frac{dx}{dt} = -kx, \quad \frac{dy}{dt} = 2k(b+a-x-y),$$

where x is the concentration of A, and y the amount of B transformed by the second reaction, at time t, and a, b, and k are constants. Solve these equations given that $x = a$ and $y = 0$ initially.

14. A tank, at time t, contains a volume v of a solution at a concentration c of a given reagent, and a solution of constant concentration c_0 flows into the tank at a (variable) rate q (litres per minute), while solution is removed by an outlet pipe at the constant rate q_0. The solution in the tank is continually stirred so that the concentration c of the reagent is uniform throughout the tank except in a very small region round the inlet. Prove that

$$\frac{d}{dt}\left\{(c-c_0)v\right\} + (c-c_0)q_0 = 0,$$

and hence show how to obtain the concentration at any instant from data giving v as a function of t.

If initially $c = 0$ and if $v = v_0 + q_0 t$, find the concentration c at any time t.

15. The velocity of a reversible chemical reaction is given by

$$\frac{dx}{dt} = k_1(3-x)(4-x) - k_2 x(1+x),$$

where k_1 and k_2 are positive constants. If $x = 0$ at $t = 0$, show, graphically or otherwise, that x increases steadily up to an equilibrium value which is between 0 and 3.

If $k_1 = 3$, $k_2 = 1$, solve the differential equation, and show that x reaches nine-tenths of its equilibrium value in a time $t = 0.149$ approximately.

16. In a chemical reaction a substance A forms a substance B which in turn forms a substance C. The respective concentrations of A, B, C at time t are x, y, z and when $t = 0$, $x = a$, $y = z = 0$. The reaction velocity of A is k_1 times the amount of A remaining; that of C is $k_2 y$. Prove that at time t

$$x = ae^{-k_1 t}, \quad y = \{ak_1/(k_2-k_1)\}(e^{-k_1 t} - e^{-k_2 t}),$$
$$z = \{a/(k_2-k_1)\}\{k_2(1-e^{-k_1 t}) - k_1(1-e^{-k_2 t})\}.$$

21.7 Friction on a Rope

Example 8. *A rope of weight w per unit length hangs over a fixed horizontal cylinder of radius a and the coefficient of friction between the rope and the cylinder is μ. T_1 is the vertical tension on the rope where it leaves the cylinder at one side and T_0 the vertical tension where it leaves the cylinder at the other end and $T_0 < T_1$. Find the relation between T_1 and T_0 if the rope is on the point of slipping.*

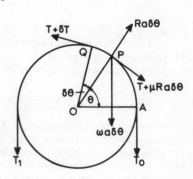

FIG. 269.

Let P (Fig. 269) be a point on the cylinder such that OP is inclined at an angle θ to the horizontal OA and let Q be an adjacent point with $QOA = \theta + \delta\theta$. The element of rope PQ is of length $a\delta\theta$ and mass $wa\delta\theta$; if T and $T + \delta T$ be the tensions at P and Q their directions will be inclined at angles θ and $\theta + \delta\theta$ to the horizontal. Then there is a reaction R per unit length, giving a reaction $Ra\delta\theta$ on the element and the friction will be $\mu Ra\delta\theta$ in the direction of T. Equating to zero the resolved parts of these forces along and perpendicular to the tangent at P we have, to the first order of small quantities,

$$\delta T - \mu Ra\delta\theta - wa\cos\theta\,\delta\theta = 0,$$
$$T\delta\theta - Ra\delta\theta + wa\sin\theta\,\delta\theta = 0.$$

Eliminating R and letting $\delta\theta$ tend to zero we have

$$\frac{dT}{d\theta} - \mu T = wa(\cos\theta + \mu\sin\theta).$$

The integrating factor is $e^{-\mu\theta}$ and multiplying by this quantity we have

$$e^{-\mu\theta}\frac{dT}{d\theta} - \mu e^{-\mu\theta}T = \frac{d}{d\theta}e^{-\mu\theta}T,$$
$$= wae^{-\mu\theta}(\cos\theta + \mu\sin\theta).$$

Hence

$$Te^{-\mu\theta} = wa\int e^{-\mu\theta}(\cos\theta + \mu\sin\theta)d\theta.$$

Now

$$\int e^{-\mu\theta}\cos\theta\,d\theta = \frac{e^{-\mu\theta}}{1+\mu^2}(\sin\theta - \mu\cos\theta),$$

$$\int e^{-\mu\theta} \sin\theta d\theta = \frac{e^{-\mu\theta}}{1+\mu^2}(-\cos\theta - \mu\sin\theta),$$

so that

$$Te^{-\mu\theta} = \frac{wae^{-\mu\theta}}{1+\mu^2}\left\{(1-\mu^2)\sin\theta - 2\mu\cos\theta\right\} + \text{constant.}$$

Since $T = T_0$ when $\theta = 0$, the constant $= T_0 + \dfrac{2\mu wa}{1+\mu^2}$, and we have

$$T = \{wa/(1+\mu^2)\}\{(1-\mu^2)\sin\theta - 2\mu\cos\theta\} + \{T_0 + 2\mu wa/(1+\mu^2)\}e^{\mu\theta},$$

and hence, since $T = T_1$ when $\theta = \pi$,

$$T_1 = T_0e^{\mu\pi} + \{2\mu wa/(1+\mu^2)\}(1+e^{\mu\pi}).$$

21.8 Work Done in a Small Displacement

Example 9. *A symmetrical framework ACEDB (Fig. 270) consists of four uniform rods each of weight w per unit length. AC and BD are each of length 2l, DE and EC are each of length l and O is the mid-point of AC. The rods are pin-jointed at O, D, E and C and the frame rests in a vertical plane with A and B connected by a light string and resting on smooth horizontal ground. At each of the four joints there can be a frictional torque of magnitude $\frac{1}{2}wl^2$ resisting turning. When the angle $CAB = \theta$, find the work done by the weight, the frictional torque and the tension T in the string when θ is increased by $\delta\theta$.*

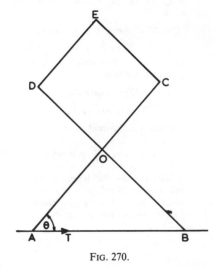

FIG. 270.

The lower pair of rods weigh $4wl$ and their centre of gravity is at height $l\sin\theta$. It is raised to height $l\sin(\theta + \delta\theta)$ and the work done against gravity is

$$4wl^2\{\sin(\theta + \delta\theta) - \sin\theta\}$$

$$= 4wl^2\cos\theta d\theta,$$

to the first order of small quantities. The upper pair of rods weigh $2wl$ and their centre of gravity is at height $\frac{5}{2}l\sin\theta$, therefore the work done against gravity when θ is increased by $\delta\theta$ is

$$5wl^2\{\sin(\theta + \delta\theta) - \sin\theta\}$$

$$= 5wl^2\cos\theta d\theta.$$

Thus the total work done by gravity is $-9wl^2\cos\theta\,\delta\theta$. The angle AOD is 2θ and when θ is increased by $\delta\theta$ the relative angular displacement of the rods is $2\delta\theta$. This is the same for each of the four joints, so the total work done against friction is

$$4 \times \tfrac{1}{2}wl^2 \times 2\delta\theta = 4wl^2\delta\theta.$$

The length AB is $2l \cos \theta$ and when θ is increased by $\delta\theta$ this length is increased by $2l\{\cos(\theta + \delta\theta) - \cos\theta\} = -2l \sin\theta \, \delta\theta$. In this displacement the work done by the tension in the string is

$$T \, 2l \sin\theta \, \delta\theta.$$

The total work done in the displacement is therefore

$$T \, 2l \sin\theta \, \delta\theta + 4wl^2 \delta\theta - 9wl^2 \cos\theta \, \delta\theta.$$

The principle of virtual work states that when the forces are in equilibrium the total work done in an infinitesimal displacement is zero, and in this case shows that

$$T \, 2l \sin\theta + 4wl^2 - 9wl^2 \cos\theta = 0,$$

$$T = wl \frac{9\cos\theta - 4}{2\sin\theta}.$$

21.9 Catenary of Uniform Strength

Example 10. *A cable of varying cross-section hangs in a loop between two points in such a way that the stress at any point has a constant value f. Find the equation of the curve in which the cable hangs and the manner in which its cross-section varies along its length. This curve is known as the catenary of uniform strength.*

Let T_0 be the tension at the lowest point O, T the tension at a point P distant s from O at which the tangent makes an angle ψ with the horizontal and let w be the weight per unit length of the cable at P. If A be the cross-sectional area at P then $T = Af$.

Consider the equilibrium of a small element of cable of length δs between P and adjacent point Q, and let the tangent at Q be inclined at $\psi + \delta\psi$ to the horizontal (Fig. 271). If $T + \delta T$ be the tension at Q we have

$$(T + \delta T) \cos\delta\psi - T = w\delta s \sin\psi,$$

$$(T + \delta T) \sin\delta\psi = w\delta s \cos\psi,$$

so that to the first order of small quantities we have

$$\delta T = w \sin\psi \, \delta s,$$

$$T\delta\psi = w \cos\psi \, \delta s,$$

and hence in the limit

$$\frac{dT}{ds} = w \sin\psi, \quad T\frac{d\psi}{ds} = w \cos\psi.$$

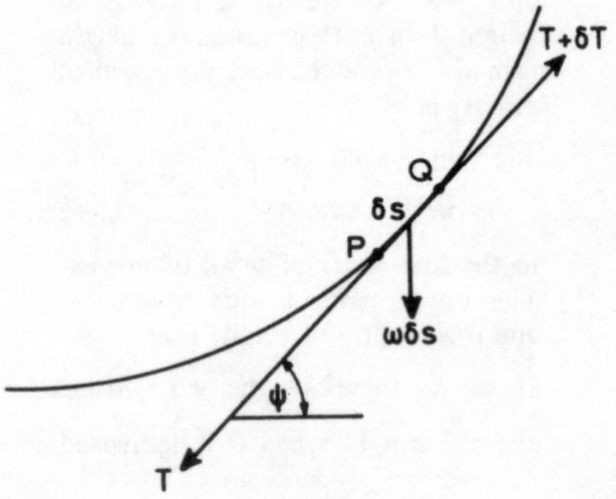

FIG. 271.

Now if ρ be the density of the material in N/m², $w = A\rho$ and, since $T = Af$, $T = (f/\rho)w$, therefore the second equation gives

(1)

$$\frac{d\psi}{ds} = \frac{w}{T}\cos\psi = \frac{\rho}{f}\cos\psi,$$

$$\int \sec\psi \, d\psi = \frac{\rho}{f}\int ds,$$

$$s = \frac{f}{\rho}\ln(\sec\psi + \tan\psi). \qquad (2)$$

The additive constant is zero since $s = 0$ when $\psi = 0$ and so we have the instrinsic equation of the curve.

To find the equation in terms of cartesian coordinates with origin at the lowest point of the curve we use the relations $dx/ds = \cos \psi$, $dy/ds = \sin \psi$, giving

$$\frac{dx}{d\psi} = \frac{dx}{ds} \frac{ds}{d\psi} = (\cos \psi)\left(\frac{f}{\rho} \sec \psi\right) = \frac{f}{\rho},$$

and

$$x = (f/\rho)\psi.$$

$$\frac{dy}{d\psi} = \frac{dy}{ds} \frac{ds}{d\psi} = \frac{f}{\rho} \tan \psi,$$

and

$$y = (f/\rho) \log_e \sec \psi,$$

so that

$$y = (f/\rho) \log_e \sec (\rho x/f).$$

We have also from the differential equation (1)

$$\frac{1}{T} \frac{dT}{d\psi} = \tan \psi,$$

giving on integration

$$\ln (T/T_0) = \ln \sec \psi,$$

$$T = T_0 \sec \psi,$$

and hence

$$A = A_0 \sec \psi.$$

From (2)

$$e^{\rho s/f} = \sec \psi + \tan \psi,$$

$$e^{-\rho s/f} = \sec \psi - \tan \psi,$$

$$\sec \psi = \cosh \rho s/f,$$

so that

$$A = A_0 \cosh \rho s/f.$$

EXERCISES 21 (c)

1. Determine the work done when the force $(3i + 4j)$ N moves its point of application along the curve $(1 + 3 \cos \theta)i + (2 + 3 \sin \theta)j$ from the point $A(\theta = 0)$ to the point $B(\theta = 2\pi/3)$ the unit of distance being a metre. What is the work done if the force now moves its point of application from B to A along the straight line BA?

2. A thin disc of radius a spins, totally immersed in fluid, about its axis with angular velocity ω. The resistance of the fluid to motion on an element of area δA moving with speed v is $kv\delta A$, where k is constant. Find the retarding torque on the disc.

3. In winding up a clock spring a torque $a + b\theta$ must be exerted when the key has turned through an angle θ. Find the work done in n complete turns of the key.

4. A rope passes round a cylindrical surface with coefficient of friction μ. Show that the change in tension δT in a distance in which the direction of the pull changes by $\delta\theta$ is $\mu T \delta\theta$. Hence show that if the tension at the slacker end where the rope meets the surface is T_0, the tension where the direction of pull has changed by θ is $T_0 e^{\mu\theta}$

5. A cyclist exerts a vertical thrust on the forward pedal which is proportional to the horizontal distance of the pedal pin from the crank centre; the maximum thrust is

P and the crank length is a. Find the work done on the pedals in one complete revolution. If during this revolution the bicycle moves forward a distance c with uniform speed against a resistance Q, find the value of Q.

6. A chain of weight w per unit length hangs freely under gravity with its ends fixed to separate points. Prove that, if s is the distance measured along the chain from the lowest point to a point P and T is the tension at P and ψ the inclination of the tangent to the curve to the horizontal at P,

$$T \sin \psi = ws, \quad T \cos \psi = \text{constant}.$$

Deduce the intrinsic equation of the catenary in the form $s = c \tan \psi$.

By using the relations $dx/ds = \cos \psi$, $dy/ds = \sin \psi$ show that the equation can be written in the parametric form

$$y = c \sec \psi, \quad x = c \ln (\sec \psi + \tan \psi).$$

7. The vertical cable of length l holding a captive balloon tapers so that the stress across any cross-section has the same value f. By considering the equilibrium of a length of the cable between heights h and $h + \delta h$, with radii r and $r + \delta r$ at the lower and upper ends, show that, if w is the weight per unit volume of the material, to the first order of small quantities,

$$f \pi (r^2 + 2r\delta r) = f \pi r^2 + w \pi r^2 \delta h.$$

Deduce that $r = r_0 \exp (wh/2f)$ and show that the total weight of cable is

$$\pi r_0^2 f \{ \exp(wl/f) - 1 \}$$

8. A belt of mass m per unit length runs with constant speed v over a pulley of radius a and μ is the coefficient of friction between the belt and the pulley. By considering the motion of a length $a\delta\theta$ of the belt with tensions T and $T + \delta T$ at its ends, show that, if R is the normal reaction on a unit length of the element,

$$\delta T = \mu R a \delta \theta, \quad ma\delta\theta(v^2/a) = T\delta\theta - Ra\delta\theta,$$

and hence that

$$\frac{dT}{d\theta} = \mu(T - mv^2).$$

Deduce that if T_1 and T_2 are the tensions at the points where the belt clears the pulley, πa apart,

$$T_1 - mv^2 = (T_2 - mv^2)e^{\mu\pi}.$$

21.10 Motion with Varying Mass

Consider firstly the case of a body which increases its mass as it moves along. Let m be the mass, v the velocity and P the force acting on the body at time t, and let $m + \delta m$ and $v + \delta v$ be the mass and velocity at time $t + \delta t$. Further, let v_1 be the velocity, measured in the same direction as v, of the mass δm at time t.

The momenta of the masses before and after impact are:

$$before \quad mv + \delta m \cdot v_1$$

$$after \quad (m + \delta m)(v + \delta v).$$

The change in momentum is caused by the force P in time δt, so that

$$P\delta t = (m+\delta m)(v+\delta v)-mv-\delta m \,.\, v_1,$$
$$= m\delta v+(v-v_1)\delta m_1+\delta m \,.\, \delta v,$$

and hence in the limit as δt tends to zero

$$P = m\frac{dv}{dt}+(v-v_1)\frac{dm}{dt}. \tag{1}$$

In the particular case in which $v_1 = 0$, as for example in the case of a chain being continuously drawn into motion from rest, we have

$$P = m\frac{dv}{dt}+v\frac{dm}{dt} = \frac{d}{dt}(mv),$$

and in this case the rate of change of momentum is equal to the applied force.

Consider secondly the case of a body, such as a rocket, which is continuously losing mass. Let m be the mass, v the velocity and P the force acting on the body at time t. Let Δm be the *loss* of mass at time $t+\delta t$ and $v+\delta v$ the velocity and let v_1 be the velocity of Δm in the same direction as v.

The momenta of the masses at time t and $t+\delta t$ are:

$$\begin{aligned} &\textit{before} \quad mv, \\ &\textit{after} \quad (m-\Delta m)(v+\delta v)+v_1\Delta m. \end{aligned}$$

The change in momentum is caused by the force P in time δt so that

$$P\delta t = (m-\Delta m)(v+\delta v)+v_1\Delta m-mv,$$
$$= m\delta v-(v-v_1)\Delta m-\Delta m \,.\, \delta v,$$
$$P = m\frac{\delta v}{\delta t}-(v-v_1)\frac{\Delta m}{\delta t}-\frac{\Delta m}{\delta t}\,.\,\delta v.$$

In the limit as t tends to zero $\Delta m/\delta t$ becomes the rate of *loss* of matter. dm/dt is formally the rate of *increase* of m and is $-\lim \Delta m/\Delta t$. Hence we have

$$P = m\frac{dv}{dt}+(v-v_1)\frac{dm}{dt}, \tag{2}$$

as before. It is usual to write $v-v_1 = u$, so that u is the relative velocity backwards of the mass discarded, and the rocket equation is written as

$$m\frac{dv}{dt}+u\frac{dm}{dt} = P. \tag{3}$$

Example 11. *The mass of a rocket after burning for time t is m(5−3t) and burning ceases when t = 1. If the burnt matter is ejected backwards with relative velocity u while the rocket moves upwards from rest under gravity find the maximum velocity attained and the height when t = 1.*

From equation (3) we have

$$m(5-3t)\frac{dv}{dt} - 3mu = -m(5-3t)g,$$

$$\int dv = -\int g\,dt + \int \frac{3u}{5-3t}dt,$$

$$v = -gt - u\ln(5-3t) + A,$$

and, since $v = 0$ when $t = 0$, $A = u\ln 5$. Therefore when $t = 1$

$$v_{max} = -g + u\ln 2{\cdot}5.$$

Also, if $v = dy/dt$,

$$y = -\tfrac{1}{2}gt^2 - u\int \ln(1-3t/5)dt,$$

$$= -\tfrac{1}{2}gt^2 - u(t-5/3)\ln(1-3t/5) + ut,$$

giving when $t = 1$

$$y = u - \tfrac{1}{2}g - \tfrac{2}{3}u\ln 5/2.$$

21.11 Central Forces

When the resultant force acting on a particle passes through a fixed point O it is convenient to write the equations of motion in terms of polar coordinates with origin at O. It has been shown (§ 1.16) that the components of acceleration in polar coordinates are respectively

$$\frac{d^2r}{dt^2} - r\left(\frac{d\theta}{dt}\right)^2 \quad \text{and} \quad \frac{1}{r}\frac{d}{dt}\left(r^2\frac{d\theta}{dt}\right),$$

along and perpendicular to the radius vector. If the force acts along the radius vector and is a function of r, $F(r)$ say, we have the equations

$$m\left\{\frac{d^2r}{dt^2} - r\left(\frac{d\theta}{dt}\right)^2\right\} = F(r), \qquad (1)$$

$$\frac{m}{r}\frac{d}{dt}\left(r^2\frac{d\theta}{dt}\right) = O. \qquad (2)$$

The second equation shows that $r^2 d\theta/dt$ is a constant, usually denoted by h, so that $d\theta/dt = h/r^2$, and on substituting in equation (1) we have

$$\frac{d^2r}{dt^2} - \frac{h^2}{r^3} = \frac{1}{m}F(r), \qquad (3)$$

an equation involving only r and t. Multiplying by dr/dt and integrating with respect to t we have

$$\frac{1}{2}\left(\frac{dr}{dt}\right)^2 + \frac{h^2}{2r^2} = \frac{1}{m}\int F(r)\frac{dr}{dt}dt,$$

that is

$$\left(\frac{dr}{dt}\right)^2 = -\frac{h^2}{r^2} + \frac{2}{m}\int F(r)dr, \tag{4}$$

A second integration of this equation will give a solution connecting r and t.

Alternatively, dividing the left-hand side of equation (4) by $(d\theta/dt)^2$ and the right-hand side by the equal quantity h^4/r^4 we find

$$\left(\frac{dr}{d\theta}\right)^2 = -r^2 + \frac{2}{m}\frac{r^4}{h^2}\int F(r)dr, \tag{5}$$

and integration of this equation gives a relation between r and θ which is the equation of the path of the particle.

Example 12. *A planet of mass m is attracted towards the sun's centre by a force mc/r^2 when at a distance r. (This is the inverse square law and $c = \gamma(M+m)$, M being the mass of the sun and γ the gravitational constant). Find the equation of the path of the planet in terms of polar coordinates with origin at the sun.*

The equation of motion is (§21.11 (3)), noting that the force mc/r^2 is backwards towards the origin,

$$\frac{d^2r}{dt^2} - \frac{h^2}{r^3} = -\frac{c}{r^2},$$

and hence,

$$\left(\frac{dr}{dt}\right)^2 = -\frac{h^2}{r^2} + \frac{2c}{r} + d \text{ (a constant).}$$

Writing $d = -c/a$ where a is a constant, (5) gives

$$\left(\frac{dr}{d\theta}\right)^2 = -r^2 + \frac{2c}{h^2}r^3 - \frac{2c}{h^2a}r^4.$$

The solution of this last equation is, as may be verified,

$$\frac{l}{r} = 1 + e\cos(\theta + \alpha),$$

where $l = h^2/c$, $e^2 = 1 - h^2/ac$ and α is an arbitrary constant. This is the equation in polar coordinates of an ellipse whose major and minor axes are a and $(la)^{\frac{1}{2}}$.

21.12 Tangential and Normal Acceleration

When the resultant force acting on a particle is given in terms of components along and perpendicular to the tangent to its path it is convenient to write the equations of motion in terms of intrinsic coordinates s and ψ using the expressions found in § 1.16 namely

$$\frac{d^2s}{dt^2}\left(=\frac{dv}{dt}\right) \text{ and } v\frac{d\psi}{dt}\left(=\frac{v^2}{\rho}\right),$$

along and perpendicular to the tangent. The method is illustrated in the following example.

Example 13. *A particle of mass m is projected with velocity V at an angle of elevation α. The air resistance is mkv, where v is the velocity at any instant, opposing motion. Find the velocity of the particle at the highest point of its trajectory·*

The equations of motion are (Fig. 272)

$$m\frac{dv}{dt} = -mkv - mg\sin\psi,$$

$$mv\frac{d\psi}{dt} = -mg\cos\psi.$$

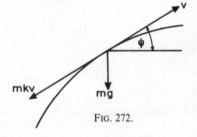

Dividing the second equation by the first we have

$$\frac{1}{v}\frac{dv}{d\psi} = \tan\psi + \frac{k}{g}v\sec\psi, \qquad (1)$$

Fig. 272.

that is

$$-\frac{1}{v^2}\sec\psi\frac{dv}{d\psi} + \frac{1}{v}\sec\psi\tan\psi = -\frac{k}{g}\sec^2\psi.$$

In this last equation the left hand side is the derivative of $\sec\psi/v$ and we have

$$\frac{d}{d\psi}\frac{\sec\psi}{v} = -\frac{k}{g}\sec^2\psi,$$

$$\frac{\sec\psi}{v} = -\frac{k}{g}\tan\psi + \frac{\sec\alpha}{V} + \frac{k}{g}\tan\alpha,$$

and hence

$$v = \frac{V\cos\alpha}{\cos\psi + (Vk/g)\sin(\alpha-\psi)}. \qquad (2)$$

At the highest point $\psi = 0$ and we have for the remaining velocity

$$v = \frac{V\cos\alpha}{1 + \dfrac{Vk}{g}\sin\alpha}.$$

A further integration can be carried out by replacing v by $-g\cos\psi\dfrac{dt}{d\psi}$ in (2).

EXERCISES 21 (d)

1. A string is wound round the axle of a flywheel and is pulled off with increasing force Px/a, where x is the length of string unwound. The radius of the axle is a and the moment of inertia of the wheel and axle is I. Find the angular velocity imparted to the flywheel when n complete turns have been pulled off.

2. Stokes' law states that the resistance to the motion of a sphere of radius a moving with speed v in a fluid of viscosity μ is $6\pi\mu av$. Show that when a sphere of mass m falls under gravity in the fluid through a distance x from rest the equation of motion is $v\,dv/dx = \lambda(v_0 - v)$, where v_0 is the terminal velocity and $\lambda = 6\pi\mu a/m$. Show also that the sphere reaches a velocity which is half of its terminal velocity after falling a distance $v_0(\ln 2 - \tfrac{1}{2})/\lambda$.

3. A locomotive of mass M lb works at a constant rate H ft lb per sec and the resistance to its motion is Mkv/g lbf, where v is the velocity at time t and k is a constant. Derive the equation of motion

$$\frac{dv}{dt} = k(\alpha^2 - v^2)/v,$$

where $\alpha^2 = Hg/(Mk)$.

Prove that, if the locomotive starts from rest and acquires a velocity v in a distance x,

$$v = \alpha(1 - e^{-2kt})^{1/2},$$

$$x = \frac{\alpha}{2k}\log_e\frac{\alpha+v}{\alpha-v} - \frac{v}{k}.$$

Prove that the locomotive will reach a speed which is one-half of its maximum speed in a distance $\alpha(\ln 3 - 1)/2k$, and then, if steam is shut off, come to rest in a further distance $\alpha/(2k)$.   (O.C.)

4. It is known theoretically that the velocity of a particle moving in a straight line is given by $v = kt/(a^2 + t^2)$, where t is the time and k and a are positive constants. Find the distance travelled by the particle from rest before it begins to decelerate.

In an experiment it is observed that, when $t = 0$, $v = 0$ and when $t = a$, $v = k/2a$. The distance travelled by this particle is then calculated on the incorrect assumption that it is uniformly accelerated. Find the error in this calculation, expressed as a percentage of the true distance, correct to three significant figures.   (O.C.)

5. The position vector $\mathbf{r}$ of a particle, with respect to an origin O, satisfies the equation $\ddot{\mathbf{r}} = -\omega^2\mathbf{r}$, where a dot denotes differentiation with respect to time t, and ω is a constant. By choosing the x-axis to pass through a point where r, the magnitude of $\mathbf{r}$, is a maximum, or otherwise, prove that the particle describes an ellipse, in general.

Prove that the speed at any point is equal to $\omega\sqrt{(c^2 - r^2)}$, where c is a constant.
                                                                     (O.C.)

6. A body attached to a parachute is released from an aeroplane which is moving horizontally with velocity V. The parachute exerts a drag opposing motion which is k times the weight of the body, k being a constant. Neglecting air resistance to the motion of the body, prove that, if v be its velocity when its path is inclined at an angle ψ to the horizontal,

$$v = \frac{V\sec\psi}{(\sec\psi + \tan\psi)^k}.$$

Prove that, if $k = 1$, the body cannot have a vertical component of velocity greater than $\frac{1}{2}V$.   (O.C.)

7. A particle moves in a plane in such a way that its tangential and normal components of acceleration are always constant. Prove that in general the particle describes a logarithmic spiral $s = Ae^{k\psi}$, where A and k are constants. Determine the loci for the particular cases in which one component vanishes.   (O.C.)

8. A body of mass m is continuously ejecting matter backwards with relative velocity u. Show that the forward thrust on the body is $-u\dfrac{dm}{dt}$.

Hence, or otherwise, show that the equation of motion of a rocket fired vertically upwards, air resistance being neglected, is

$$m\frac{dv}{dt} + u\frac{dm}{dt} + mg = 0,$$

where m is the mass and v the velocity of the rocket at time t and u is the relative backward velocity of the ejected matter.

A rocket ejects matter with constant relative velocity u. Show that, if m_0 is the initial mass and V the initial velocity, its velocity at time t, when its mass is m, is

$$v = V - gt + u \ln(m_0/m).$$

The rocket burns for time τ and its mass after burning for time $t(< \tau)$ is $m_0(1 - t/2\tau)$. Show that, if $u > 2g\tau$, the velocity increases throughout the burning period and that the greatest velocity is $V - g\tau + u \ln 2$.   (O.C.)

9. A spherical raindrop initially of radius a falls freely from rest under gravity. As it falls its volume increases continuously through condensation at a rate equal to k times its surface area at any instant, k being constant. Show that after a time t its radius r is equal to $a + kt$.

Given that the raindrop has velocity v at time t, use the principle that 'applied force equals rate of change of momentum' to prove that

$$\frac{dv}{dt} = g - 3k\frac{v}{r}.$$

Hence prove that

$$4kv = g\{a + kt - a^4(a + kt)^{-3}\}.$$ (O.C.)

10. A satellite of mass m is moving in a plane orbit about the earth. The equation of its path referred to polar coordinates with origin at the centre of the earth is

$$\frac{1}{r} = 1 + e \cos \theta,$$

where 1 and e are constants. By differentiating this equation prove that

$$\left(\frac{dr}{d\theta}\right)^2 = -r^2 + \frac{2r^3}{l} - \frac{(1 - e^2)r^4}{l^2}.$$

Assuming that the only force acting on the satellite is mgR^2/r^2 directed towards the earth's centre when distant r, R being the earth's radius, and that when $r = 2R$, $\dot{r} = 0$ and $r\dot{\theta} = V$, prove that

(i) $r^2\dot{\theta} = 2RV$,

(ii) $\quad \ddot{r} = \dfrac{4R^2V^2}{r^3} - \dfrac{gR^2}{r^2},$

(iii) $\quad \dot{r}^2 = -\dfrac{4R^2V^2}{r^2} + \dfrac{2gR^2}{r} + V^2 - gR.$

Deduce from these equations the value of $(dr/d\theta)^2$ and hence prove that $l = 4V^2/g$. (O.C.)

11. Assuming that the acceleration due to gravity at height y above the earth's surface is $gR^2/(R+y)^2$, where R is the earth's radius, show that the work done against gravity in raising a mass m from the earth to a height h is $mgRh/(R+h)$. A small satellite moves in a circle about the earth at a height h above its surface. Find its speed in orbit and its period of revolution. Find the speed with which the satellite must be projected from the earth's surface so as to move in this orbit, assuming all energy loss in transit to be due to the gravitational pull of the earth. (O.C.)

12. A particle is projected in a medium which offers a resistance to motion equal to kv per unit mass, k being a constant. Prove that in the subsequent motion

$$\frac{dv}{d\psi} = v\tan\psi + \frac{k}{g}v^2\sec\psi.$$

By means of the integrating factor $\sec\psi/v^2$, solve this differential equation to obtain the relation between v and ψ.

If the particle is projected with velocity $10\sqrt{3g}/k$ at an angle of elevation $60°$, prove that the velocity at the highest point of its path is $5\sqrt{3g}/16k$. (O.C.)

13. The greatest speed v at which a car can travel safely on a path with radius of curvature ρ is given by $v^2 = k\rho$ where k is a constant. The car travelling initially with speed V is braked with a constant deceleration f and at the same time is steered on a path with the smallest possible safe radius of curvature ρ. When it has been turning for a distance s, show that

$$k\frac{d\rho}{ds} = -2f.$$

Hence find an equation between s and ψ the angle its direction has been turned through. Prove that its speed then is $Ve^{-f\psi/k}$. (O.C.)

14. A particle of mass m slides without friction on the spoke of a horizontal wheel but is attached to the centre of the wheel by a spring of natural length a and modulus of elasticity λ. When the wheel is fixed the period of a small oscillation is $2\pi/n$. Prove that $\lambda = man^2$.

The wheel is made to rotate with a constant angular velocity ω ($< n$). Prove that the particle can remain at rest relative to the wheel at a distance $an^2/(n^2 - \omega^2)$ from the centre, provided that the wheel is sufficiently large. If the particle is disturbed slightly from this position, prove that it executes a simple harmonic motion relative to the spoke of the wheel with period $2\pi/\sqrt{(n^2 - \omega^2)}$. (O.C.)

15. A particle of unit mass moves in a plane under a force k times its speed acting in a direction $90°$ ahead of the direction of its velocity. Initially the particle is passing through the origin and the components of its velocity there are (u, v). Prove that the particle moves in the circle whose equation is

$$(kx+v)^2 + (ky-u)^2 = v^2 + u^2.$$ (O.C.)

PART V—STATISTICS

CHAPTER 22

STATISTICS

22.1 Introduction

In this chapter we consider statistical methods of arranging and classifying numerical results obtained from experiment or observation.

The method employed for the classification of the results is the same whether the results be the breaking strengths of steel bars, the heights of a number of individuals, the daily takings of a shop, marks obtained in an examination or any set of numbers derived from a common source.

The first, and most obvious, way of describing a set of numbers is to quote their average value. Thus we have the average number of runs scored by a cricketer, the average number of eggs produced daily by a poultry farm, the average life of an electric-light bulb, etc. In statistics the average of a set of numbers is called the *mean*, and the first step in analysing any set of numbers is to find their mean. In dynamics the mean is associated with the position of the centroid; thus the mean distance of the particles of a lamina from an axis in its plane is the distance of its centroid from the axis.

The second statistical parameter used to describe a set of numbers is called the *standard deviation*, and is usually denoted by the Greek letter sigma. This quantity σ is a measure of the spread of the set of numbers about the mean, and corresponds to the radius of gyration about an axis through the centroid in dynamics. It measures the compactness of a set of numbers. For example, if the average mark of a number of students in an examination was 50 per cent, the marks might be closely grouped around 50 per cent or they might be spread over values ranging from 0 to 100 per cent. In the former case the value of σ would be small, in the latter case it would be comparatively large.

22.2 The Mean, Standard Deviation and Variance

Let a set of n numbers be $x_1, x_2, \ldots x_n$. Then the mean $\bar{x}$ of the set of numbers is defined by the equation

$$\bar{x} = \frac{1}{n}(x_1 + x_2 + \ldots + x_n),$$

$$= \frac{1}{n}\sum_{r=1}^{n} x_r.$$

410

The standard deviation σ of the set of numbers is defined by the equation

$$\sigma^2 = \frac{1}{n}\{(x_1 - \bar{x})^2 + (x_2 - \bar{x})^2 + \ldots + (x_n - \bar{x})^2\},$$

$$= \frac{1}{n}\sum_{r=1}^{n}(x_r - \bar{x})^2.$$

The quantity σ^2, which is the square of the standard deviation, is called the *variance* of the set of numbers.

The quantity $x_r - \bar{x}$ is called the deviation of the number x_r from the mean. The sum of the deviations from the mean, $\sum_{r=1}^{n}(x_r - \bar{x})$, is zero, from the definition of the mean. The sum of the squared deviations, however, is not zero unless all the numbers of the set are equal, and the variance is the mean value of the squared deviations from the mean.

Example 1. *A light rod has particles of unit mass fixed at distances of 3, 7, 8, 12, 15 cm from one end of the rod. Find the distance of the centre of gravity of the system from the end of the rod and the radius of gyration about an axis through the centre of gravity perpendicular to the rod. Show that these lengths are equal to the mean and standard deviation of the set 3, 7, 8, 12, 15 in.*

The distance $\bar{x}$ of the centre of gravity from the end of the rod is given by

$$\bar{x} = \frac{1}{5}(3 + 7 + 8 + 12 + 15),$$

$$= 9 \text{ cm}.$$

The moment of inertia of the masses about the axis is given by

$$I = (3-9)^2 + (7-9)^2 + (8-9)^2 + (12-9)^2 + (15-9)^2,$$

$$= 36 + 4 + 1 + 9 + 36,$$

$$= 86.$$

Also $I = 5k^2$, where k is the radius of gyration,

$$k^2 = 17 \cdot 2,$$

$$k = 4 \cdot 15 \text{ cm}.$$

The values of $\bar{x}$ and k are obtained by the same methods as the mean and standard deviation of the numbers.

Hence, for this set of numbers

$$x = 9 \text{ cm},$$

$$\sigma = 4 \cdot 15 \text{ cm}.$$

22.3 Second Moment of a Set of Numbers

Just as in dynamics we may calculate the moment of inertia about an axis which does not pass through the centroid, so in statistics the second moment of a set of numbers $x_1, x_2, \ldots x_n$ about a value $x = a$ is denoted by $\mu_2(a)$ and defined by the equation

$$\mu_2(a) = \frac{1}{n}\{(x_1-a)^2+(x_2-a)^2+\ldots+(x_n-a)^2\},$$

$$= \frac{1}{n}\sum_{r=1}^{n}(x_r-a)^2.$$

The variance is, therefore, the second moment about the mean.

The second moment of the set of numbers 3, 7, 8, 12, 15 cm about the value zero is

$$\mu_2(0) = \frac{1}{5}\{3^2+7^2+8^2+12^2+15^2\},$$

$$= \frac{1}{5}\{9+49+64+144+225\},$$

$$= \frac{491}{5},$$

$$= 98 \cdot 2.$$

If the numbers are considered as the distances from the end of the rod at which particles of unit mass are fixed to the rod, it is easily seen that $\mu_2(0) = 98 \cdot 2$ is the square of the radius of gyration of the weighted rod about an axis perpendicular to the rod through its end.

Corresponding to the parallel axis theorem for moments of inertia we have an important relation between the second moment and the variance of a set of numbers, namely

$$\mu_2(a) = \sigma^2+(\bar{x}-a)^2. \tag{1}$$

We have

$$\mu_2(a) = \frac{1}{n}\sum_{r=1}^{n}(x_r-a)^2,$$

$$= \frac{1}{n}\sum_{r=1}^{n}x_r{}^2-\frac{2a}{n}\sum_{r=1}^{n}x_r+\frac{a^2}{n}\sum_{r=1}^{n}1,$$

$$= \frac{1}{n}\sum_{r=1}^{n}\bar{x}_r{}^2-2a\bar{x}+a^2.$$

Also,
$$\sigma^2 = \mu_2(\bar{x}),$$

$$= \frac{1}{n}\sum_{r=1}^{n}x_r{}^2-2\bar{x}^2+\bar{x}^2.$$

Therefore,
$$\mu_2(a)-\sigma^2 = \bar{x}^2-2a\bar{x}+a^2,$$

$$\mu_2(a) = \sigma^2+(\bar{x}-a)^2.$$

Thus for the set 3, 7, 8, 12, 15 cm, we found

$$\sigma^2 = 17\cdot2,$$
$$\mu_2(0) = 98\cdot2,$$
$$\mu_2(0) - \sigma^2 = 81,$$
$$= \bar{x}^2.$$

When calculating the mean and standard deviation of a set of numbers it may be found that the mean is not a whole number and thus each of the deviations $x_r - \bar{x}$ will contain fractions or decimals. In this case it is very much simpler to calculate the second moment about an integer value $x = a$, and deduce the value of the standard deviation from the equation (1). It should be noted that the variance is always less than the second moment about any other value of x.

22.4 Calculation of the Mean and Standard Deviation

The arithmetic of the calculation of the mean and standard deviation is simple, but to avoid errors it is essential that some of the elementary rules of computation should be observed. Thus, digits must be clearly formed and equally spaced, numbers which are to be added must always be arranged in columns and never in rows, and the digits to be added must also form a vertical column. No subsidiary calculation should be done on rough paper and the whole should be so arranged that every figure can be quickly checked by another computor.

In calculating the mean, the computation is often simplified if a rough approximation to the mean is taken and the difference between the mean and this approximation computed.

Thus, for a set of numbers $x_1, x_2, \ldots x_m$, let α be an approximate value of the mean.

Writing

$$x_r = \alpha + z_r,$$

we have a set of numbers z_r, and we have

$$\frac{1}{n} \sum_{r=1}^{n} x_r = \frac{1}{n} \sum_{r=1}^{n} \alpha + \frac{1}{n} \sum_{r=1}^{n} z_r.$$

That is

$$\bar{x} = a + \bar{z},$$

where $\bar{z}$ is the mean of the quantities $\bar{z}_r$. It is often convenient to calculate the second moment about the same approximation to the mean. Then we have

$$\mu_2(\alpha) = \frac{1}{n} \sum_{r=1}^{n} (x_r - \alpha)^2,$$

$$= \frac{1}{n} \sum_{r=1}^{n} z_r{}^2,$$

and

$$\sigma^2 = \mu_2(\alpha) - \bar{z}^2.$$

Example 2. *Calculate the mean and standard deviation of the breaking strengths of 16 steel bars in the following table:*

Breaking Strengths (N/m^2)

36·7	35·9	38·2	37·6
35·8	36·4	37·3	36·5
37·9	36·7	36·6	34·5
38·3	36·5	36·8	38·1

Let x_r be the breaking strength of rth bar; taking $\alpha = 34·5$ as a first approximation to the mean we write $x_r = 34·5 + z_r$, and tabulate the quantities z_r and z_r^2 so as to calculate $\bar{z}$ and $\mu_2(\alpha)$. The values of z_r^2 may be written down from a table of squares.

x	z	z^2
36·7	2·2	4·84
35·8	1·3	1·69
37·9	3·4	11·56
38·3	3·8	14·44
35·9	1·4	1·96
36·4	1·9	3·61
36·7	2·2	4·84
36·5	2·0	4·00
38·2	3·7	13·69
37·3	2·8	7·84
36·6	2·1	4·41
36·8	2·3	5·29
37·6	3·1	9·61
36·5	2·0	4·00
34·5	0	0
38·1	3·6	12·96
Total	37·8	104·74
Mean	2·3625	6·54625

Hence

$$\bar{z} = 2·3625,$$
$$\alpha = 34·5,$$
$$\bar{x} = 36·8625,$$
$$\mu_2(\alpha) = 6·54625,$$
$$\bar{z}^2 = 5·58141,$$
$$\sigma^2 = 0·96484,$$
$$\sigma = 0·982.$$

Since the original figures are given to one place of decimals only, we may write

$$\bar{x} = 36·86 \text{ N/m}^2,$$
$$\sigma = 0·98 \text{ N/m}^2.$$

EXERCISES 22 (a)

1. Find the mean and standard deviation of the natural numbers 1, 2, 3, 4, 5, 6, 7, 8, 9, 10.
2. Find the second moment about the value 2 of the natural numbers 1 to 10.

3. Twelve measurements of a length in cm are:

| 125 | 136 | 131 | 128 | 127 | 133 |
| 129 | 129 | 134 | 132 | 133 | 130 |

Find the mean and standard deviation of the measurements.

4. Ten rounds fired from a gun at the same elevation fall at the following distances in m from the gun:

| 9875 | 9842 | 9920 | 9894 | 9873 |
| 9901 | 9863 | 9876 | 9910 | 9859 |

Find to the nearest m the mean range and standard deviation.

5. Eight measurements of an angle are:

| 72° 25′ 32″ | 72° 25′ 49″ | 72° 25′ 45″ | 72° 25′ 30″ |
| 72° 25′ 28″ | 72° 25′ 37″ | 72° 25′ 40″ | 72° 25′ 35″ |

Find the mean and standard deviation.

6. The mean of a number of measurements is 25 m and their second moment about the value 20 m is 50 $(m)^2$. Find their standard deviation and their second moment about the value 28 m.

7. The breaking strengths of 16 steel specimens in N/m^2 are:

| 32·3 | 33·1 | 33·2 | 32·9 | 32·6 | 32·8 | 32·8 | 32·7 |
| 33·3 | 33·0 | 32·7 | 32·9 | 32·8 | 33·0 | 33·5 | 32·8 |

Find the mean breaking strength and the standard deviation.

8. The weights in lb of twelve individuals are:

| 140 | 162 | 175 | 144 | 164 | 182 |
| 150 | 164 | 192 | 152 | 161 | 194 |

Find the mean weight and the standard deviation.

9. The atmospheric pressure in millibars at Kew at noon on ten successive days was

$$995, 993, 989, 994, 994, 1014, 1016, 1015, 1015, 1016.$$

Find the mean pressure and its standard deviation.

10. Six measurements of the extension in centimetres of a steel bar under a load were:

$$0·241, 0·238, 0·244, 0·250, 0·240, 0·245.$$

Find the mean extension and the standard deviation.

11. The number of faulty articles produced by a machine in ten successive shifts were:

$$47, 32, 29, 48, 53, 65, 84, 41, 52, 45.$$

Find the mean number and the standard deviation.

12. The marks, out of 100, obtained by 18 students in an examination were

72	35	50	55	93	13
28	45	84	49	70	44
52	70	54	23	54	69

Find the mean mark and the variance.

13. A sample containing n_1 members has mean M_1 and standard deviation σ_1. A second sample of n_2 members has mean M_2 and standard deviation σ_2. Show that the common mean of the samples is $(n_1 M_1 + n_2 M_2)/(n_1 + n_2)$ and that their common variance about this mean is

$$\frac{n_1 \sigma_1{}^2 + n_2 \sigma_2{}^2}{n_1 + n_2} + \frac{n_1 n_2 (M_1 - M_2)^2}{(n_1 + n_2)^2}.$$

14. Ten numbers have mean 32 cm and standard deviation 2·5 cm. Twelve other numbers have mean 33 cm and standard deviation 3 cm. Find the mean and standard deviation of the twenty-two numbers taken together.

15. The table below gives the annual sunshine in hours, rounded to the nearest 10 hours, at a certain meteorological station. Find the mean annual sunshine in this 10-year period and the standard deviation.

Year	1940	1941	1942	1943	1944	1945	1946	1947	1948	1949
Sunshine	1470	1200	1300	1470	1190	1470	1300	1430	1360	1580

(L.U.)

16. Define the mean and standard deviation of a distribution. In a given distribution, M is the mean and σ the standard deviation. When a provisional mean M' is chosen, the corresponding provisional standard deviation is found to be σ_1. Prove that $\sigma_1{}^2 = \sigma^2 + (M - M')^2$. Explain briefly the advantage of this procedure in numerical work.

(L.U.)

22.5 Frequency Distributions

When a large number of values of a quantity are obtained it is often impracticable to calculate the mean and standard deviation of the set by the methods considered in the previous sections. For example, if there were 1000 values of the quantity, the computation would extend over several pages. A large set of this kind is dealt with by first of all reducing it to what is called a *frequency distribution*. The range of values of the quantity is divided into a certain number of intervals, the number of values falling in each interval is found, and this is called the frequency of the quantity in the interval. For example, let the heights of 50 individuals be given in the following table, where for convenience the heights are arranged in order of magnitude.

Heights of 50 individuals (in)

64·7	65·9	66·6	67·0	67·3	67·7	67·9	68·1	68·7	69·3
65·0	66·1	66·6	67·0	67·4	67·7	67·9	68·3	68·7	69·7
65·6	66·3	66·7	67·1	67·6	67·8	68·0	68·3	68·8	70·0
65·7	66·4	66·8	67·2	67·6	67·8	68·0	68·4	68·9	70·3
65·7	66·4	66·9	67·2	67·6	67·8	68·0	68·6	69·0	70·4

The range of variation is from 64·7 to 70·4 in, so we may take six intervals each of one in, that is the intervals are

64·5–65·5, 65·5–66·5, 66·5–67·5, 67·5–68·5, 68·5–69·5, 69·5–70·5.

The number of individuals whose heights fall in these intervals are respectively,

2, 8, 12, 17, 7, 4,

and these are the frequencies for the intervals. It is usual to specify each interval by its central value. Thus we have the set of 50 heights of individuals reduced to the following frequency distribution:

Centre of Interval (in)	65	66	67	68	69	70	Total
Frequency	2	8	12	17	7	4	50

The mean and standard deviation are then calculated by assuming that all the individuals in each interval have a value exactly equal to that of the centre of the interval.

The method of calculating the mean and standard deviation of a frequency distribution will be considered in §21.7.

In the formation of a frequency table the number of intervals which is required will usually depend on the nature of the observations which are recorded and their accuracy, but more than twenty intervals for a frequency distribution would be unusual. A difficulty arises when a number of the set falls exactly on the dividing line between two intervals, and this is sometimes counted as half a frequency for each of the intervals.

22.6 Graphs of Frequency Distributions

A frequency distribution can be represented graphically by plotting the intervals on a horizontal axis and drawing a line parallel to the axis above each interval at a height such that the area is proportional to the frequency in that interval. Such a diagram is called a *histogram*.

For example, let the frequency distribution be the following, which gives the breaking strength of 120 steel bars.

Centre of Interval (N/m²)	30·5	31·0	31·5	32·0	32·5	33·0	33·5	34·0	Total
Frequency	2	7	19	32	39	14	6	1	120

The intervals are 30·25 to 30·75, 30·75 to 31·25, etc. and the histogram is as shown in Fig. 273.

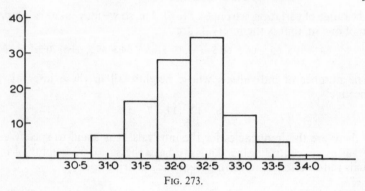

FIG. 273.

A frequency distribution may also be shown graphically by what is called a *frequency polygon*, by plotting a value equal to the frequency for the interval above the centre of each interval and joining the points by straight lines. Thus, the frequency polygon for the distribution of the breaking strength of steel bars is as shown in Fig. 274.

In a histogram the horizontal portions of lines which represent the frequencies are usually joined up to the axis by vertical lines, so that the diagram consists of a number of rectangles, and it is the areas of these rectangles which give to the eye a picture of the frequency distribution. The *relative frequency* for any interval is defined as the frequency for that interval divided by the total frequency, and for a histogram the scale to which the frequencies are plotted is not of great importance, since the picture presented to the eye is of the relative frequencies of the intervals.

When the total frequency is small, a histogram or a frequency polygon will usually be somewhat irregular in form, but with a larger total frequency the irregularity often disappears and the element of chance in the selection of the original observations will have less effect. We may thus arrive at a graph of regular shape, and a smooth curve may be drawn to fit the

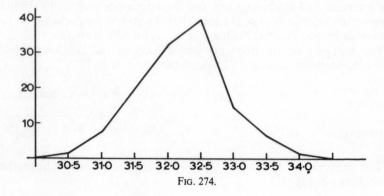

FIG. 274.

histogram or frequency polygon. The areas under the curve above each interval would then give a picture of the relative frequency for that interval. This curve might then be regarded as giving a picture, not only of the observations actually recorded, but of all possible observations of the quantity which is being measured. Thus, for example, from a curve which fitted the diagram of breaking strengths of 120 steel bars one would be able to deduce the distribution of the breaking strength of a large consignment of steel bars, of which the 120 tested were a sample.

22.7 Mean and Standard Deviation

In calculating the mean and standard deviation of a frequency distribution it is assumed in the first instance that each frequency is associated with the centre of its respective interval.

Let $x_1, x_2, \ldots x_n$ be the centres of the intervals, $f_1, f_2, \ldots f_n$, the corresponding frequencies and N the total frequency.

Then
$$N = f_1 + f_2 + \ldots + f_n,$$
$$= \sum_{r=1}^{n} f_r.$$

The mean $\bar{x}$ is defined by the equation

$$\bar{x} = \frac{1}{N} \sum_{r=1}^{n} f_r x_r.$$

The variance σ^2 is defined by the equation

$$\sigma^2 = \frac{1}{N} \sum_{r=1}^{n} f_r (x_r - \bar{x})^2.$$

The second moment of the distribution about a value α is defined by the equation

$$\mu_2(\alpha) = \frac{1}{N} \sum_{r=1}^{n} f_r (x_r - \alpha)^2.$$

We have also

$$\mu_2(\alpha) = \frac{1}{N} \sum_{r=1}^{n} f_r x_r^2 - \frac{2\alpha}{N} \sum_{r=1}^{n} f_r x_r + \frac{\alpha^2}{N} \sum_{r=1}^{n} f_r,$$

$$= \frac{1}{N} \sum_{r=1}^{n} f_r x_r^2 - 2\alpha \bar{x} + \alpha^2,$$

$$\sigma^2 = \frac{1}{N} \sum_{r=1}^{n} f_r x_r^2 - \frac{2\bar{x}}{N} \sum_{r=1}^{n} f_r x_r + \frac{\bar{x}^2}{N} \sum_{r=1}^{n} f_r,$$

$$= \frac{1}{N} \sum_{r=1}^{n} f_r x_r^2 - 2\bar{x}^2 + \bar{x}^2.$$

Hence,

$$\mu_2(\alpha) - \sigma^2 = \bar{x}^2 - 2\alpha\bar{x} + \alpha^2,$$

$$\mu_2(\alpha) = \sigma^2 + (\bar{x} - \alpha)^2.$$

This is the formula already obtained in § 21.3 which enables us to deduce the value of the variance from the value of the second moment about an arbitrary value.

22.8 Calculation of the Mean and Standard Deviation

Let $x_1, x_2, \ldots x_n$ be the centres of the intervals, $f_1, f_2, \ldots f_n$ the corresponding frequencies and N the total frequency.

Let α be a first estimate of the mean, and let

$$x_1 = \alpha + z_1,$$
$$x_2 = \alpha + z_2,$$
$$\cdots \cdots \cdots$$
$$x_n = \alpha + z_n.$$

Then
$$\bar{x} = \frac{1}{N} \sum_{r=1}^{n} f_r(\alpha + z_r),$$

$$= \alpha + \frac{1}{N} \sum_{r=1}^{n} f_r z_r,$$

$$= \alpha + \bar{z}, \text{ where } \bar{z} \text{ is the mean of the frequency}$$

distribution for z.

$$\mu_2(\alpha) = \frac{1}{N} \sum_{r=1}^{n} f_r(x_r - \alpha)^2,$$

$$= \frac{1}{N} \sum_{r=1}^{n} f_r z_r^2.$$

To calculate the values of $\bar{z}$ and $\mu_2(\alpha)$ we need to form the sums of the quantities fz and fz^2. This is done by drawing up a table in which successive columns are values of $x_r, f_r, z_r, f_r z_r, f_r z_r^2$. In this table the terms in the fourth column are products of terms in the second and third columns, and terms in the fifth column are products of terms in the third and fourth columns. The sum of the fourth column in $N\bar{z}$ and of the fifth column $N\mu_2(\alpha)$.

Example 3. *The weights of* 100 *adults are given in the following frequency table:*

Centre of Interval (kg)	50	55	60	65	70	75	80	85	Total
Frequency	2	12	12	25	27	10	9	3	100

Calculate the mean and standard deviation.

Centre of Interval, x	Frequency, f	$x - 65 = z$	fz	fz^2
50	2	-15	-30	450
55	12	-10	-120	1200
60	12	-5	-60	300
65	25	0	—	—
70	27	5	135	675
75	10	10	100	1000
80	9	15	135	2025
85	3	20	60	1200
Total . .	100		$-210 + 430$	6850
Mean . .			2·2	68·5

Hence

$$\bar{z} = 2\cdot2$$
$$\bar{x} = 67\cdot2,$$
$$\mu_2(\alpha) = 68\cdot5,$$
$$\bar{z}^2 = 4\cdot84,$$
$$\sigma^2 = 63\cdot66,$$
$$\sigma = 7\cdot98.$$

Thus the mean is 67·2 kg and the standard deviation 7·98 kg approximately.

22.9 Sheppard's Correction

The assumption that each frequency is associated with the centre of its interval causes a certain loss of accuracy in the calculation of both mean and variance. In the case of the mean this is negligible since, if the assumption causes overestimates of values of the set which are less than the mean it usually causes underestimates of values greater than the mean, and the errors tend to balance out.

In the case of the variance, the deviations from the mean are squared, and these deviations tend to be overestimated by assuming all frequencies to be related to the centres of their intervals. This is evident when the graph of the frequency distribution tapers away on each side of the mean. The overestimate of the deviations causes the variance as calculated to be too large, and an allowance is made for this by subtracting from the calculated variance the quantity $c^2/12$, where c is the magnitude of an interval of the distribution.

Denoting the corrected variance by σ_c^2, we have

$$\sigma_c^2 = \sigma^2 - \frac{c^2}{12}.$$

This is known as Sheppard's correction for grouping.

Example 4. *In the example of §22.8, we found*

$$\sigma^2 = 63 \cdot 66.$$

The class interval for the distribution is 5 kg and we have

$$\frac{c^2}{12} = \frac{25}{12},$$

$$= 2 \cdot 08.$$

Therefore $$\sigma_c{}^2 = 61 \cdot 58,$$

$$\sigma_c = 7 \cdot 85 \text{ kg}.$$

The corrected value of the standard deviation is therefore $7 \cdot 85$ kg.

EXERCISES 22 (b)

1. The heights of 50 individuals in inches are given in the following table to the nearest inch. Form a frequency distribution of the heights and draw a histogram of the results.

66	65	66	64	65	66	65	63	64	65
64	67	65	62	66	65	64	67	66	64
68	66	64	66	67	63	66	65	65	67
65	64	65	64	66	65	65	63	64	66
63	65	63	67	64	68	67	64	65	64

Calculate the mean of the distribution.

2. The crushing load in kN on 40 wooden cubes is given in the following table. Form a frequency distribution with intervals of 0·5 kN centred at 6 kN, 6·5 kN, etc. Draw a histogram and a frequency polygon of the distribution and calculate the mean.

7·76	8·51	8·96	6·66	6·92	7·02	7·40	8·69
6·48	7·50	8·84	7·62	7·53	7·59	8·07	7·28
8·05	7·16	9·35	6·14	8·42	7·96	6·98	8·31
8·39	9·12	7·94	9·22	8·16	6·30	7·72	8·20
9·56	7·32	6·87	7·99	8·56	7·12	7·24	7·82

3. The marks out of 10 obtained by 100 candidates in an examination are given in the following frequency table:

Mark	0	1	2	3	4	5	6	7	8	9	10	Total
Frequency	7	3	1	12	16	37	14	4	3	2	1	100

Draw a frequency polygon and calculate the mean and standard deviation.

4. Find the mean and standard deviation of the grouped distribution:

Centre of Interval (cm)	25	27	29	31	33	35	Total
Frequency	2	13	24	25	9	2	75

5. Twenty-five measurements of a length in centimetres are given in the following frequency table, the readings being grouped to the nearest centimetre:

Centre of Interval	275	276	277	278	279	280	281	282	Total
Frequency		1	2	3	4	8	4	2	1	25

Find the mean and standard deviation.

6. An article is being manufactured to a mass specification of 25 kg. Thirty finished articles are measured and their masses in grammes above or below 25 kg are given in a frequency table in which the interval is 1 g:

Centre of Interval	−4	−3	−2	−1	0	1	2	3	4	Total
Frequency	1	2	1	6	12	4	2	1	1	30

Find the mean weight and standard deviation.

7. The heights of 50 individuals are given in the following table, grouped in a frequency distribution with an interval of one inch:

Centre of Interval	62	63	64	65	66	67	68	Total
Frequency	1	5	12	14	10	6	2	50

Calculate the mean and standard deviation.

8. The following frequency table gives the crushing load in kN on 40 wooden cubes, grouped with an interval of 0·5 kN:

Centre of Interval	6·0	6·5	7·0	7·5	8·0	8·5	9·0	9·5	Total
Frequency	1	3	7	8	9	6	4	2	40

Calculate the mean and standard deviation.

9. Twenty observations of an angle are made. The following table gives the differences in seconds of the observations from 20° 32′ 25″ to the nearest second:

Centre of Interval	−4	−3	−2	−1	0	1	2	3	Total
Frequency	1	1	4	7	3	1	2	1	20

Find the mean value of the observations and their standard deviation.

10. The breaking strengths in kN/m^2 of 100 specimens are given in the following frequency table:

Centre of Interval	32·0	32·2	32·4	32·6	32·8	33·0	33·2	33·4	33·6	33·8	Total
Frequency	1	4	11	13	21	24	12	9	3	2	100

Find the mean and standard deviation.

11. The birthrate per thousand of the population in 60 towns is given in the following table, where the frequency is the number of towns whose birthrate lies in each interval:

Birthrate (centre of Interval)	8	9	10	11	12	13	14	15	16	Total
Frequency	2	4	5	10	15	9	8	5	2	60

Find the mean birthrate and the standard deviation.

12. From the records of accidents in a large factory a table is drawn up showing the number of shifts in which 0, 1, 2, etc. accidents occurred.

Accidents per shift	0	1	2	3	4	5	6	Total
Number of shifts	652	243	97	21	6	0	1	1020

Find the mean number of accidents per shift and the standard deviation.

13. The masses in pounds of 250 adults are given in the following frequency table with an interval of 10 lb:

Centre of Interval	120	130	140	150	160	170	180	190	200	210	220	Total
Frequency	4	12	25	30	37	41	35	32	25	7	2	250

Find the mean and standard deviation.

14. A hundred rounds are fired from a machine gun at a fixed elevation and their ranges in metres beyond a mark 2000 m from the gun are given in the following frequency table:

Centre of Interval	60	80	100	120	140	160	180	200	Total
Frequency	2	5	14	28	25	18	7	1	100

Find the mean range and the standard deviation.

15. The heights in inches of 2000 adults is given in the following frequency table:

Centre of Interval	59	60	61	62	63	64	65	66	67
Frequency	7	22	34	75	113	168	252	285	277

Centre of Interval	68	69	70	71	72	73	Total
Frequency	268	218	131	87	49	14	2000

Find the mean and standard deviation.

16. The frequency distribution of the numbers 0, 1, 2,...n, is such that the frequency of the number r is ^nC_r. Show that the total frequency is 2^n, the mean is $\dfrac{n}{2}$, and the variance is $\dfrac{n}{4}$.

17. A batch of 200 metal bars was made to a supposed length of 34 cm. On measurement the number n of bars of length l was found to be:

l	30	31	32	33	34	35	36	37	38	39
n	4	8	23	35	62	44	18	4	1	1

Draw a frequency diagram and calculate (i) the mean length, (ii) the standard deviation from the mean. (L.U.)

18. Define the mean and standard deviation of a set of observations. In the following table f is the frequency of an observation x.

x	2·7	2·9	3·1	3·3	3·5	3·7
f	2	7	15	21	12	3

Calculate the mean and standard deviation of x. (L.U.)

22.10 Parameters of a Frequency Distribution

The two chief parameters which are used to describe a set of values of a quantity are the mean and the standard deviation. In this section we consider some other numbers which are used to describe a set.

(a) *The median*

The median is defined as the middle number of a set when the numbers are arranged in order of magnitude, or as being such that there are the same numbers of values greater and less than it. If the number of values in the set is even, the median is taken as half-way between the two middlemost values. In a frequency distribution the median is calculated on the assumption that individuals grouped in each interval are spread uniformly over the interval.

Example 5. *Find the median of the distribution.*

Centre of Interval (cm)	25	27	29	31	33	35	Total
Frequency	2	13	24	25	9	2	75

The median will be the value corresponding to the 38th individual, that is, since there are 15 in the first two intervals, of the 23rd individual in the third interval. The interval is from 28 to 30 cm, and the 24 individuals are assumed to be spread over the interval, therefore the median

$$= 28 + \frac{23}{24} \times 2,$$

$$= 29 \cdot 92 \text{ cm}.$$

(b) *The quartiles*

The quartiles are values of a set which divide it into four equal sets. Thus the first quartile is such that if the numbers are arranged in order of magnitude 25 per cent of them are less than it and 75 per cent of tham are greater. The second quartile is identical with the median, the third quartile is such that 75 per cent of the numbers are less than it and 25 per cent greater. One half of the difference between the first and third quartiles is called the *semi-interquartile range*.

To obtain the quartiles of a frequency distribution of total frequency N we can consider the first quartile as being the value of the $\frac{N+1}{4}$th individual, the second quartile or median as the value of the $\frac{2(N+1)}{4}$th individual, and the third quartile as the value of the $\frac{3(N+1)}{4}$th individual. If these numbers are fractions the quartiles are fractions of the differences between individuals.

Example 6. *Find the first and third quartiles and the semi-interquartile range of the distribution:*

Centre of Interval (cm)	25	27	29	31	33	35	Total
Frequency	2	13	24	25	9	2	75

The first quartile is the value of the 19th individual and the third quartile the value of the 57th.

The 19th individual lies in the interval 28 to 30 cm and is the 4th in this interval. Therefore the first quartiles

$$= 28 + \frac{4}{24} \times 2,$$

$$= 28 \cdot 33 \text{ cm}.$$

The 57th individual lies in the interval 30 to 32 cm and is the 18th in this interval. Therefore the third quartile

$$= 30 + \frac{18}{25} \times 2,$$

$$= 31 \cdot 44 \text{ cm}.$$

The semi-interquartile range

$$= \frac{31 \cdot 44 - 28 \cdot 33}{2},$$

$$= 1 \cdot 55 \text{ cm}.$$

(c) *The mode*

The mode is defined as the value of a set corresponding to a maximum of a curve drawn to fit the frequency distribution. The mode is thus the value of greatest frequency. The mode can only be determined by finding the curve that fits the distribution, but it is sometimes taken as being the centre of the interval with the greatest frequency. This is not very satisfactory since it makes the value of the mode depend on the size of the interval.

When a distribution is symmetrical about the mean, the mean, median and mode coincide. When a distribution is slightly asymmetrical the mean, median and mode occur in this order (which is alphabetical order) or in this order reversed, that is, the median lies between the mean and the mode. An empirical relation for slightly asymmetrical distributions which gives surprisingly good results is

Mode − Mean = 3 (Median − Mean).

This gives a better estimate of the mode than the centre of the interval of greatest frequency.

When the magnitudes in a frequency distribution are not grouped and the frequencies relate to exact values, the median is the exact value to which the middle frequency belongs, and the mode may be taken as the value with the highest frequency.

Example 7.

For the distribution:

Centre of Interval (cm)	25	27	29	31	33	35	Total
Frequency	2	13	24	25	9	2	75

the mean is 29·85, and the median was found in §22.10 (a) to be 29·92 cm.

Therefore

$$\text{Median} - \text{Mean} = 0·07,$$

$$\text{Mode} - \text{Mean} = 0·21,$$

$$\text{Mode} = 30·06 \text{ cm}.$$

(d) *Skewness*

When the mode does not coincide with the mean the distribution is said to be skew, and a curve drawn to fit the distribution will tail off more rapidly on one side of the mean than on the other.

The skewness of a distribution is sometimes measured by a formula due to Pearson, namely,

$$\text{Skewness} = \frac{\text{Mean} - \text{Mode}}{\text{Standard deviation}}$$

Using the empirical relation between the mode and the median, this gives

$$\text{Skewness} = \frac{3(\text{Mean} - \text{Median})}{\text{Standard deviation}}.$$

This gives positive skewness if the mean has a greater value than the median and negative skewness if the mean is less than the median.

Example 8.

For the distribution:

Centre of Interval (cm)	25	27	29	31	33	35	Total
Frequency	2	13	24	25	9	2	75

$$\text{mean} = 29·85 \text{ cm},$$

$$\text{median} = 29·92 \text{ cm},$$

$$\text{standard deviation} = 2·07 \text{ cm},$$

$$\text{skewness} = -\frac{0·21}{2·07},$$

$$= -0·1 \text{ approximately}.$$

(e) *Coefficient of variation*

The standard deviation shows the variation of a set of quantities, and the standard deviation expressed as a percentage of the value of the mean gives a measure of variation independent of the units of the set. This is called the coefficient of variation, C, and we have

$$C = \frac{100\,\sigma}{\bar{x}}.$$

The coefficient of variation can be used to compare the variability of distributions whose units are different.

Example 9.

For the distribution given in §22.10 (d) we have

$$x = 29\cdot85 \text{ cm},$$
$$\sigma = 2\cdot07 \text{ cm},$$
$$C = \frac{207}{29\cdot85},$$
$$= 6\cdot9.$$

22.11 The Normal Distribution

The histograms or frequency polygons of a large number of distributions derived from experiment or from observation of natural phenomena are found to fit very closely to a curve, known as *the error curve*, whose equation is

$$y = \frac{1}{\sigma\sqrt{(2\pi)}}e^{-\frac{(x-m)^2}{2\sigma^2}},$$

where m is the mean of the distribution and σ its standard deviation. The shape of the error curve is that of a cocked hat, it is symmetrical about the value $x = m$, and is defined for values of x running from $-\infty$ to $+\infty$ although if x differs from the mean by more than about 3σ the value of y is negligible.

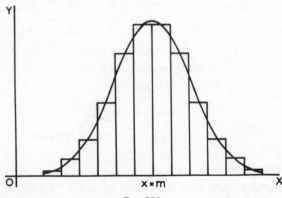

FIG. 275.

The diagram (Fig. 275) shows an error curve fitting closely the histogram of a distribution. If the fit is exact the distribution is said to be a *normal distribution* and as such has several important properties.

(1) The total area included between an error curve and the x-axis is 1, and a histogram fitting it would have the same area and would therefore show relative frequencies.

(2) The area under the curve between any two values of x corresponds to the relative frequency of the distribution between these two values of x. These values of x need not be the end points of intervals of the distribution.

(3) Almost the whole area (in fact 99·75 per cent of the area) under the error curve is comprised between the values $x = m - 3\sigma$ and $x = m + 3\sigma$, and therefore almost the whole frequency distribution will lie between these values of x.

(4) About 95·5 per cent of the total area lies between $x = m - 2\sigma$ and $x = m + 2\sigma$, 68·3 per cent between $x = m - \sigma$ and $x = m + \sigma$, and 50 per cent between $x = m - \frac{2}{3}\sigma$ and $x = m + \frac{2}{3}\sigma$.

(5) If we know that a distribution is normal and know its mean m and standard deviation σ, we can take $m - 3\sigma$ and $m + 3\sigma$ as limits outside which there is only a chance of 0·25 per cent, or 1 in 400, of an individual value of the quantity lying.

Similarly the chance of an individual value lying outside the limits $m - 2\sigma$ to $m + 2\sigma$ is 4·5 per cent, or about 1 in 22.

These results for a normal distribution can be proved from the equation of the error curve by methods of numerical integration which are outside the scope of this book.

22.12 Standard Error of the Mean

If we have a frequency distribution of n individual numbers we can determine the mean $\bar{x}$ and the standard deviation σ of the distribution. Now, distributions are of interest less for their own sake than as samples of a very much larger set of results. Thus we may test the strength of steel specimens to find out all we can about a large consignment of steel which we do not test. We therefore regard the mean $\bar{x}$ as the mean of a sample of n individuals and we wish to discover the magnitude of the true mean m of the larger unsampled set.

If we take repeated samples, each of n individuals, we will get a series of values for the mean which may be denoted by $\bar{x}_1$, $\bar{x}_2$, $\bar{x}_3$....These means will not usually be identical, and by taking a large number of samples we get a new frequency distribution of which each individual is the mean of a sample of n members. This distribution is called a *sampling distribution of the mean*.

An important theorem of statistics states that if a very large number of samples were taken, the sampling distribution of the mean would usually be very close to a normal distribution, whose mean m would be the true mean of the numbers as a whole and whose standard deviation would be $\dfrac{\sigma}{\sqrt{n}}$, where σ is the standard deviation of the numbers as a whole and n the number in the sample.

This quantity $\dfrac{\sigma}{\sqrt{n}}$ is called the *standard error of the mean.*

It follows that individual means of samples would be very unlikely to differ from the true mean by more than $3\dfrac{\sigma}{\sqrt{n}}$. This is the same as saying that the true mean would be very unlikely to differ from a sample mean by more than $3\dfrac{\sigma}{\sqrt{n}}$. If we take just one sample of n members with mean x and standard deviation σ, and we accept σ as being an estimate of the standard deviation of the numbers as a whole, we may say that the true mean m is very unlikely to lie outside the range,

$$\bar{x}-3\frac{\sigma}{\sqrt{n}} \text{ to } x+3\frac{\sigma}{\sqrt{n}}.$$

We thus have, by measuring the mean and standard deviation of a sample, a bracket for the true mean of the numbers as a whole. The larger the sample the smaller is the value of $\dfrac{\sigma}{\sqrt{n}}$ and the closer the determination of the true mean. We may use a smaller bracket for the true mean, namely

$$\bar{x}-2\frac{\sigma}{\sqrt{n}} \text{ to } \bar{x}+2\frac{\sigma}{\sqrt{n}},$$

and there is about one chance in twenty-two of the true mean lying outside this range.

In stating the mean of a set of observations it is usual to give also the standard error of the mean.

Thus if a sample of n has mean $\bar{x}$ and standard deviation σ, we write

$$\text{the mean} = \bar{x}\pm\frac{\sigma}{\sqrt{n}};$$

this is equivalent to stating that the mean is determined to within $3\dfrac{\sigma}{\sqrt{n}}$ either side of $\bar{x}$.

Example 10.

We found (§22.8), for 100 adults, that their mean mass was 67·2 kg with standard deviation 7·98 kg.

If we regard these 100 adults as being a fair sample from a much larger population and wish to determine the mean weight of the population as a whole, we have

$$\bar{x} = 67 \cdot 2 \text{ kg,}$$

$$\sigma = 7 \cdot 85 \text{ kg,}$$

$$\frac{\sigma}{\sqrt{100}} = 0 \cdot 785 \text{ kg,}$$

$$= 0 \cdot 80 \text{ kg approximately,}$$

$$\bar{x} \pm \frac{\sigma}{\sqrt{100}} = 67 \cdot 2 \pm 0 \cdot 80 \text{ kg.}$$

This is the form in which the mean would be stated, implying that the true mean of the population is very unlikely to differ from 67·2 kg by more than about $3 \times 0 \cdot 80 = 2 \cdot 4$ kg.

EXERCISES 22 (c)

1. Find the median and mode of the grouped distribution of 100 measurements in centimetres:

Centre of Interval	0	1	2	3	4	5	6	7	8	9	10	Total
Frequency	7	3	1	12	16	37	14	4	3	2	1	100

2. Find the quartiles of the crushing load in kN on 40 wooden cubes, given in the following table:

Centre of Interval	6·0	6·5	7·0	7·5	8·0	8·5	9·0	9·5	Total
Frequency	1	3	7	8	9	6	4	2	40

3. Find the mode of the distribution given in Exercise 2 and the skewness of the distribution.

4. Find the three quartiles of the distribution of the heights in inches of 2000 adults given in the following table:

Centre of Interval	59	60	61	62	63	64	65	66	67
Frequency	7	22	34	75	113	168	252	285	277

Centre of Interval	68	69	70	71	72	73	Total
Frequency	268	218	131	87	49	14	2000

5. Find the median, mode and skewness of the following distribution of the heights in inches of 50 individuals:

Centre of Interval	62	63	64	65	66	67	68	Total
Frequency	1	5	12	14	10	6	2	50

6. Twenty-five measurements of a length in centimetres are given in the following frequency table:

Centre of Interval	275	276	277	278	279	280	281	282	Total
Frequency		1	2	3	4	8	4	2	1	25

Calculate the skewness and the coefficient of variation.

7. For the distribution given in Exercise 4, find the skewness and the coefficient of variation.

8. Two thousand candidates were given a test, the marks for which were zero or one of the integers 1 to 20. The following table gives the number of candidates obtaining various marks:

Mark	0	1	2	3	4	5	6	7	8	9	10
Frequency	6	39	43	82	124	145	152	187	191	226	165

Mark	11	12	13	14	15	16	17	18	19	20
Frequency	187	145	89	84	63	38	14	10	6	4

Find the mean, mode and median of this distribution and plot a frequency polygon. The standard deviation of this distribution is 3·76; find the value of Pearson's measure of its skewness from the formula (Mean–Mode)/Standard Deviation.   (L.U.)

9. Assuming that the heights of 50 individuals given in Exercise 5 are a sample from a normally distributed population, find limits within which the heights of 99·75 per cent and 95·5 per cent respectively of the population should lie. Show that 50 per cent of the heights should lie between 64·19 and 65·93 inches.

10. Assuming that the distribution of crushing loads on wooden blocks given in Exercise 2 is a sample from a normally distributed set of crushing loads, find 99·75 per cent and 95·5 per cent limits for crushing loads.

11. Twenty observations of an angle are made and the following table gives the differences of the observations from $20° \ 32' \ 25''$, to the nearest sec:

Centre of Interval	−4	−3	−2	−1	0	1	2	3	Total
Frequency		1	1	4	7	3	1	2	1	20

Find the mean with its standard error.

12. The heights of 2000 individuals given in Exercise 4 have mean 66·62 in and standard deviation 2·67 in. Assuming that these heights are a sample from a large normal population, give limits (99·75 per cent limits) outside which it is unlikely that the mean height of the population will lie.

13. The masses in pounds of 250 adults are given in the following table with an interval of 10 lb:

Centre of Interval	120	130	140	150	160	170	180	190	200	210	220	Total
Frequency	4	12	25	30	37	41	35	32	25	7	2	250

Find the mean with its standard error.

14. Twenty steel bars from a large consignment are tested and their breaking strength in kN/m^2 is given in the following table:

Centre of Interval	30·0	30·4	30·8	31·2	31·6	32·0	32·4	Total
Frequency	1	1	3	5	4	4	2	20

Give limits outside which the mean breaking strength of the consignment is unlikely to lie. Give limits outside which the breaking strength of individual bars is unlikely to lie.

ANSWERS TO EXERCISES

EXERCISES 1 (a) (p. 11)

2. $13\{(5/13)i+(12/13)j\}$. 3. $3i-2j, \sqrt{(13)}$. 5. $1/2$.
7. $6\cdot5$. 13. $120°, 90°$. 14. $3\cdot6$ N, $29°\ 26'$.
15. $2AB$ at $60°$ to AB. 16. $4/5, 2/5$. 17. $2\mathbf{v}_1+\mathbf{v}_2$.

EXERCISES 1 (b) (p. 25)

1. $7\{(2/7)i+(6/7)j+(2/7)k\}$. 2. $\sqrt{65}(i+8j)/13$. 3. $\sqrt{(1766)}, (-5:30:-29)$.
4. $\sqrt{(105)}, (-2:1:10)$. 5. $9, (i+4j+8k)/9$.
6. $\sqrt{(55)}$ N; $\cos^{-1}5/\sqrt{(110)}, \cos^{-1}6/\sqrt{(110)}, \cos^{-1}7/\sqrt{(110)}$.
7. $7, (3i-2j-6k)/7$. 8. $-2/63, \frac{1}{2}\sqrt{(3965)}$. 11. $21i+46j+16k, \frac{1}{2}\sqrt{(2813)}$
12. $-(3i+6j+2k)/7$. 14. 40 newton metres.
15. $2\sqrt{(1+2t^2)}, 2\sqrt{2}, \cos^{-1}\{\sqrt{2}t/(1+2t^2)^{\frac{1}{2}}\}$.
18. $2i-j+3k$. 19. $\{\mathbf{r}-(i+2j+3k)\}.(26i+27j-5k) = 0$.
20. $i+j, \frac{1}{4}i+4j$.

EXERCISES 1 (c) (p. 26)

1. $97\cdot13$ km, $297°\ 50'$. 3. $\sqrt{(61)}$ m at $86°\ 18'$ to AC. 7. $\sqrt{7}$ N.
8. $14\cdot14$ km/h from N.W. 9. $377\cdot1$ N, N $47°\ 44'$ E. 11. $\frac{1}{2}\sqrt{(369)}$.
12. $(-3i+8j+5k)/7$. 13. $2\sqrt{(42)}$. 14. $10/3$.

EXERCISES 2 (a) (p. 33)

1. $18\cdot25$ N, $25°\ 17'$. 2. $10\cdot82$ N. 3. $68°\ 12', 27°\ 41'$.
4. $17\cdot32g$ N, $5\cdot18g$ N.

EXERCISES 2 (b) (p. 34)

1. $5P, 36°\ 52'$. 2. $11\cdot18$ N, N. $26°\ 34'$ E.
3. $9\cdot99$ N, $3\cdot16$ N. 4. $P\sqrt{2}, P$.

EXERCISES 2 (c) (p. 36)

1. $\sqrt{2}:1:1$. 2. $8g$ N, $6g$ N. 3. $10\sqrt{3}g, 20\sqrt{3}g$ N.
4. $5\cdot18g, 7\cdot32g$ N.

EXERCISES 2 (d) (p. 38)

1. $3\cdot6$ N, $29°\ 26'$. 2. 2 N, $60°$. 3. 13 N, 7 N.
4. $111\cdot8$ N, S. $18°\ 26'$ E., N. $5°\ 34'$ W. to N. $29°\ 52'$ W., $136\cdot8$ N.
5. 6 N at $60°$ to BA. 6. (1) same, (2) second method.
9. $120°, 90°$. 10. $cW/b, aW/b$.
13. $57\cdot2$ N, $49°\ 39'$ S. of E. 15. $10\cdot64g$ N, $26\cdot95g$ N, $32°\ 8'$.

EXERCISES 3 (a) (p. 43)

1. On median AD (i) at $\frac{2}{3}AD$, (ii) at $2AD$ from A. 2. $\frac{1}{2}k.CA$ parallel to CA.
3. 2 m, 1 m. 4. $20g$ N, 6 m.

EXERCISES 3 (b) (p. 46)

1. $BC:AC$.
2. 6 kg, $9\frac{1}{3}$ m.
3. 9 kg, 2 m.
4. (i) 280 kg, (ii) 28 kg.
5. 12·5 kg

EXERCISES 3 (c) (p. 50)

1. 9 m N.
2. $75g$ N, $45g$ N m.
3. $312\cdot5g$ N.
4. $1\cdot5\,Mg$ N.

EXERCISES 3 (d) (p. 50)

1. $22\sqrt{2}/7$, $6\sqrt{2}/7g$ N, $45°$ with AB.
2. 14, 26 kg.
3. $10\sqrt{5}$ N at 1·2 m from B in BC.
4. $2P$ at $2BC$ from B.
6. 10 kg, 50 cm.
7. 5 cm from AB, $\sqrt{68}g$ N.
8. $(p+q)$ kg.
10. $\sqrt{3}BC/4$ from BC, $2g$ N parallel to CB.
11. (i) 12, (ii) 4 kg.
12. 56 kg.
13. $1\cdot5\sqrt{3}a$.
14. $2\sqrt{5}g$ N, $\tan^{-1} 2$ with AB, $2g$ N m, 50 cm.
15. $\sin^{-1} G/Wa$ to vertical, vertical, W N.
16. 15 N, $\pi+\tan^{-1}\frac{3}{4}$ with OX, 10 m.
17. $2\sqrt{5}$ N, 2 m.
18. $5\sqrt{2}g$ N at $45°$ to AB, $0\cdot25g$ N m.
19. Moment of quantity weighed about C balances moment of P about M.
20. 25 cm.
21. $1112g$ N, $42°$ 17′.
22. 75, 45, 40, $40g$ N.

EXERCISES 4 (a) (p. 59)

1. $10\sqrt{2}$, $\tan^{-1}\frac{4}{3}$, $13\sqrt{2}AB/20$.
3. $10\sqrt{2}P$ at $45°$ to AB.
4. BA, BC, DC, DA.
5. $1\cdot5\sqrt{3}a$.
6. $\sqrt{5}$ N, $63°$ 26′ with BC, $0\cdot75\sqrt{3}a$.
7. $-P, \frac{1}{2}P, -\frac{1}{2}\sqrt{3}P$.
8. $2\frac{1}{3}$.
9. $\frac{1}{2}(\sqrt{6}-\sqrt{2})F, (3\sqrt{3}-5)F, (2\sqrt{6}-3\sqrt{2})F$.
10. $24\sqrt{2}$ N.
11. $\dfrac{96\sqrt{3}-34}{179}a$ from A.

12. $6F$, $\tan^{-1}\dfrac{5\sqrt{5}-9}{8}$ to AB, $4\cdot17\,AB$, $1\cdot14\,BC$.

13. 1·3 N, 3·93 N, $81°$ 6′ to AB, $16a$ from A.
14. $21a$.
16. $6i-3j$, $16/3$, $-26°$ 34′.

EXERCISES 4 (b) (p. 65)

1. $W/6$, $\sqrt{37}W/6$ at $\tan^{-1} 6$ to horizontal.
2. $1146g$ N, $737g$ N at $21°$ 15′ to horizontal.
4. $49°$ 7′, $\sqrt{3}W/3$, $2\sqrt{3}W/3$.
6. $4\cdot20g$ N, $10\cdot85g$ N, $67°$ 14′ to horizontal.
11. m, $6mg/\sqrt{33}$.
16. $18°$ 26′, 73·18 cm.

EXERCISES 4 (c) (p. 69)

1. $86\cdot6g$ N, $62\cdot5g$ N, $46°$ 6′ to horizontal.
2. $25\sqrt{2}g$ N, $5\sqrt{41}g$ N, $\tan^{-1}\frac{1}{20}$.
3. $365g$ N, $1040g$ N.
4. $66g$ N, $61g$ N, $\tan^{-1}\frac{25}{36}$ to horizontal.
5. $10\cdot5g$ N, $14g$ N vertically.
6. $15W$.
7. $2g$ N, $8\sqrt{3}g$ N, $150°$ to AB.
9. 11·5 kg.
12. $\tan^{-1}\frac{4}{3}$ to horizontal.
13. $\frac{1}{2}(W+W')\sec\alpha$, $\frac{1}{2}(W-W')\sec\alpha$, $W'\sec\alpha$, $W'\tan\alpha$.

EXERCISES 4 (d) (p. 73)

1. $2W$.
2. $4W$, $\sqrt{13}W/2$, $5W/2$.
3. $3W/4$.

4. aW/l.   5. W, W, W.   7. $\sqrt{7}W/2, \sqrt{19}W/2$.

8. $\frac{1}{4}W \sec 18°$ horizontally, $\frac{1}{4}W \csc 18° - \frac{1}{2}W$ vertically.

9. $\frac{ab(a+b)}{2(a^2+b^2)}w$, $\frac{a^3-b^3}{2(a^2+b^2)}w$ horizontally and vertically.   11. $11.75g$ N.

13. $\sqrt{19}W/2$, $\tan^{-1}\sqrt{3}/4$; $\sqrt{7}W/2$, $\tan^{-1}\sqrt{3}/2$ to vertical.

14. $W(2^{\frac{2}{3}}-1)^{\frac{1}{2}}$.   15. $2\sqrt{3}W/9$.

16. $22w \tan^{-1} 1.9$ to horizontal.   17. $W, W/2, 45°$.

18. $40/\sqrt{3}g, 40/\sqrt{3}g, 5g$ N.

EXERCISES 5 (a) (p. 80)

2. $\sqrt{2}/4g, 4\sqrt{2}-2\sqrt{3}g$ N.   3. $20+5\sqrt{3}g$ N.

4. $73.6g$ N.   6. $\dfrac{PW}{Q\sqrt{(P^2+W^2)}}$.

7. $52\frac{1}{2}°, 7\frac{1}{2}°, W/\sqrt{2}$ at $7\frac{1}{2}°$ to plane.   8. $19.6g$ N at $19°$ $17'$ to plane.

EXERCISES 5 (b) (p. 82)

2. (i) $\frac{1}{4}W(\cos\alpha \pm 2\frac{h}{a}\sin\alpha)$, (ii) $\frac{1}{4}W(\cos\alpha \mp 2\frac{h}{a}\sin\alpha)$.   7. $W/4$.

EXERCISES 5 (c) (p. 84)

1. $aW/h\mu'$ or $\mu W/\mu'$.   3. (i) by sliding, (ii) by toppling.

5. $\sqrt{2}W$.

EXERCISES 5 (d) (p. 87)

3. $\frac{30}{59}$, AB will slip.   6. $W_1(1-\mu\tan 2\theta) = W\mu\tan 2\theta$.

8. $(4-\sqrt{7})/3, (4-\sqrt{7})/9$.

EXERCISES 5 (e) (p. 88)

4. $3\sqrt{2}g$ N, $\sqrt{2}g$ N.   12. $\dfrac{\mu(1+\mu)Mg}{1+\mu+2\mu^2}$.   15. (ii) 2.5 kg.

17. $\tan 15°, \frac{1}{3}\tan 15°$.   19. 84.5 kg.   20. 2λ.

EXERCISES 6 (a) (p. 95)

1. 1.73 N perpendicular to BC; 30 cm.   2. 3.61 N at $73°$ $50'$ to BA; 40 cm.

3. 14.14 N at $45°$ to AB.   4. 29.3 cm from end.

5. $6.6g, 7.4g$ N.   6. $24.6g, 6.4g$ N.

EXERCISES 6 (b) (p. 99)

1. $4.71, 4.71, 3.73, 3.73, 6.67g$ kN.

2. Struts, $AD, 3.2$; $DE, 1.8$; $EF, 1.8$; $FC, 3.9$; $BD, 1.4$; $BF, 2.1g$ kN.
   Ties, $AB, 2.25$; $BC, 2.75$; $BE, 2.5g$ kN.

3. Struts, $AE, 8.7$; $DE, 7.3g$ kN.
   Ties, $AB, 7.5$; $BC, 4.6$; $CD, 6.35$; $BE, 5.8$; $CE, 3.5g$ kN.

4. $AB, 17.3$; $CD, 17.3$; $AD, 34.6$; $BC, 34.6$; $AC, 40$.

5. $35, 88, 173, 135g$ N, tension in AC.
   $153g$ N at A at $60°$ to AD.

6. $AE, 99$; $BC, 80$; $CD, 113$; $DE, 80$; $EF, 70$; $FA, 70$; $BF, 60$; $BE, 14$; $CE, 80 \times 100g$ N.

7. $AB, 40$; $BC, 70$; $CD, 30$; $AE, 57$; $EF, 80$; $FG, 60$; $GD, 42$; $EB, 57$; $BF, 14$; $FC,$ **14**;
   $CG, 42 \times 10^3 g$ N.

8. Struts, $AE, 21.7$; $ED, 13.0$; $CD, 30.3$; $BD, 4.3g$ N.
   Ties, $AB, 10.8$; $BC, 15.2$; $BE, 4.3g$ N.

9. $400, 200, 200g$ **N, all tensions.**

10. $1·15$, $1·53 \times 10^3 g$ N; Ties, AB, $1·73$; AD, 1; Struts, BC, 2; AC, $1·15$; DC, $2·31 \times 10^3 g$ N.

EXERCISES 6 (c) (p. 103)

1. $10(\sqrt{6}-\sqrt{2})$, $\dfrac{80}{\sqrt{3}}$, $\dfrac{20}{\sqrt{3}}$, $\dfrac{80}{\sqrt{3}} - 20g$ N.

2. BD, X; AB, $\dfrac{2}{\sqrt{5}}X$; CD, $\dfrac{2}{\sqrt{5}}X$; AD, $\dfrac{X}{\sqrt{5}}$; BC, $\dfrac{X}{\sqrt{5}}$.

3. Struts, CD, $8·48$; DE, 12; BE, $8·48$. Ties, AB, 18; BC, 6; BD, $8·48$. Reaction, $18·97$.

4. $6·25$, $6·25$, $6·25$, $6·25$, $7·5g$ N.

5. Struts, BD, $56·6$; CE, $72·1$; DE, 40. Ties, AB, 80; BC, 60; BE, $44·7$.

6. $2\sqrt{2}$, tie; 1, strut.

7. $32g$ N vertical; AB, 60; BC, 32; CD, 60; AC, $68g$ N.

8. AB, 30; BC, 30; AC, $30\sqrt{2}$; BD, $20\sqrt{2}$; CD, 20; CE, $10\sqrt{2}$; ED, $10g$ N.

9. AB, $5\sqrt{3}$; AC, $2·5\sqrt{3}$; BC, $\dfrac{5}{\sqrt{3}}$; BD, $\dfrac{10}{\sqrt{3}}g$ N.

10. AB, BE, EF, DE, CD, $10g$ N; AC, DF, $10\sqrt{2}g$ N, BC, BD, 0.

11. (i) At A, $85·6$; at C, $22·4g$ N.
    (ii) AE, EB, BD, ED, $55·8$; AB, $42·8$; BC, $13·0$; CD, $26g$ N; EB, BC ties.

12. AB, BC, AD, CD, $0·35W$; BD, $\frac{1}{2}W$.

13. $0·6$ at A, $0·72 \times 10^3 g$ at B.

14. $P = 2\sqrt{3}g$. Reaction $2\sqrt{7}g$,
    OA, $\dfrac{6}{\sqrt{3}}g$; OB, $\dfrac{4}{\sqrt{3}}g$; OC, $\dfrac{4}{\sqrt{3}}g$; OD, $\dfrac{10}{\sqrt{3}}g$; AB, $\sqrt{3}g$; BC, $\dfrac{2}{\sqrt{3}}g$; CD, $\dfrac{2}{\sqrt{3}}g$ N;
    AB, OC, BC, CD ties.

15. CE, $2g$; EF, 0; AD, $14g$; DC, $10g$; AE, $12·1g$; DE, $4g$; EB, $8·7g$; CF, $10g$; BF, $10g$ N.

16. AC, $4·2g$; AE, $14·3g$; ED, $15·7g$; CD, $11·8g$; BC, $16·0g$; CE, $3·5g$ kN.

EXERCISES 7 (b) (p. 113)

1. $10/3$, $25/6$, $15/2$ or $5/6$ cm. 2. $bc^2/(a^2 - 4c^2)$ from O on AD. 4. $103·8$ cm.

5. $16·5$ cm. 7. $5h/4$.

EXERCISES 7 (c) (p. 115)

1. 24 cm from C. 2. $\dfrac{6a^2 - x^2}{3(4a - x)}$, $\dfrac{12a^2 - ax}{6(4a - x)}$, $(3 - \sqrt{6})a$.

4. $\dfrac{a^3 - ax^2 + x^3/3}{2a^2 - x^2}$ from 2 faces. 6. 47 cm; $27°$. 7. $0·38$.

EXERCISES 7 (d) (p. 120)

1. $\dfrac{4\sqrt{2}a}{9\pi}$. 2. $\frac{1}{4}OB$ from O, $\dfrac{OB}{\pi}$ from AB. 5. $13r/14$.

EXERCISES 7 (e) (p. 121)

1. $60°$. 4. $195/8$, $15/8$ cm. 5. $\tan^{-1}\frac{42}{47}$.

6. $7\frac{2}{11}$ cm from A, $4·31$ cm. 7. $11h/56$. 9. $\frac{1}{18}$ of a side.

10. $\tan^{-1}\frac{16}{33}$. 11. $77·6°$. 13. $11·10$, $9·85$ cm.

14. $1·2$ m. 15. $a/(2\pi - 3\sqrt{3})$ from centre. 17. Yes.

19. $6·05$ cm.

EXERCISES 8 (a) (p. 128)

1. 1471 J. 2. (i) $0·375g$, (ii) $1·04g$ J.

3. 785 J. 4. $16g$ J.

EXERCISES 8 (b) (p. 134)

1. $8g$, $20g$ N.
2. $15.9g$ N.
3. $1\frac{1}{8}W$.
4. 129 kg; $129g$ N.
5. $\frac{1}{11}$.
6. $2aP = (b-c)W$.
7. $27.8g$ N.
8. 390 N.
9. The 24 cm side.
10. 65 per cent.
11. $5/2\pi$.
12. $4525g$ N.
13. $12\frac{1}{2}$ per cent.
14. $\dfrac{Wb}{4a}$, $\dfrac{b}{4an}$.
15. 16704 J, $P = 310 + 0.31W$.
16. (i) $45g$ N, (ii) $32g$ N.
17. $7.5g$ N, $18g$ N m.

EXERCISES 9 (p. 146)

1. -56, -88, -80.
2. $60g$, $150g$.
3. $5400g$.
4. $-498g$, $-777g$.
5. $-2363g$.
6. $-230g$.
7. $-13\,225g$
8. $532\frac{1}{8}g$.
9. $-267.36g$.
10. $-72.9g$.
12. $\frac{3}{8}Wl$, $\frac{1}{4}Wl$.
13. $-5400g$.
14. (i) $2188g$, (ii) $1230g$.
15. $6.3g$, $-56.35g$.
16. $4978g$ at $7\frac{2}{3}$ m from A.
17. $W(l-a)/4$.
18. 4 m from end.
19. $18g$ m kN at 12 m from A.
20. 17.5 cm from end, $20.5g$ cm N.
21. $800g$ at second support.
22. $0.2931l$ from end.
24. $\dfrac{W}{8}(l-4a)$, $\dfrac{W}{4l}(l-2a)^2$, $l(1-\frac{1}{2}\sqrt{2})$.

EXERCISES 10 (p. 159)

2. $Ma^2/2$.
3. $\frac{4}{3}M(a^2+b^2)$.
4. (i) Ma^2, (ii) $M\left(\dfrac{a^2}{2}+\dfrac{l^2}{12}\right)$.
5. $M\dfrac{3}{20}a^2+\dfrac{3}{5}h^2$.
6. $\frac{2}{3}Ma^2$.
8. $\frac{13}{8}M$, (ii) $\frac{49}{32}M$.
9. $\sqrt{\left(\dfrac{b^3(4a+b)}{3(a+b)^2}\right)}$, $\sqrt{\left(\dfrac{a^3(a+4b)}{3(a+b)^2}\right)}$.
10. (i) $\sqrt{\left(\dfrac{(a^3+4b^3)}{3(a+b)}\right)}$, (ii) $\sqrt{\left(\dfrac{a^3+4b^3}{3(a+b)}-\dfrac{b^4}{(a+b)^2}\right)}$.
11. $7.75M$.
12. (i) $M\left(\dfrac{a^2}{4}+\dfrac{h^2}{3}\right)$, (ii) $M\left(\dfrac{5}{4}a^2+\dfrac{h^2}{12}\right)$.
13. $10a^4/3$.
14. $\frac{11}{32}a^4$.
15. (i) $93\,Ma^2/70$, (ii) $M(\frac{93}{140}a^2+\frac{8}{35}h^2)$.
16. (i) $\sqrt{\frac{5}{12}}a$, (ii) $\sqrt{\frac{8}{3}}a$.
17. $\frac{23}{50}Ma^2$, $\frac{121}{100}Ma^2$.
19. $\frac{8}{3}Ma^2$, $\frac{43}{36}Ma^2$.
20. $62ma^2/3$.
21. (i) $\frac{7}{2}Ma^2$, (ii) $\frac{9}{4}Ma^2$.

EXERCISES 11 (a) (p. 165)

1. 36.7 m.
2. 1.86×10^7 N/m^2.
3. 4.9.
5. 0.68 cc.
6. 10^5 N/m^2.
7. 3.125, 5.21 cm.

EXERCISES 11 (b) (p. 171)

1. 21.0 cm, 30.0 cm, 2943 N/m^2.
2. 27.2 cc.
3. 2.12 m, 1.90 m.
4. 7.42 N.
5. 3653 N.
6. (i) $58\,270$ N, (ii) $63\,804$ N.
7. $4:5$.
8. 981, 3188 N.
19. 13.6 N.
10. 7.68 m.
11. 408, 611 kN.
12. 204, 1410 kN.
13. 160 kN.
14. 151 kN.
15. 88.3 kN.
16. Depths $\dfrac{a}{\sqrt{3}}$, $\dfrac{\sqrt{2}a}{\sqrt{3}}$.
17. $40:87:92$.

EXERCISES 11 (c) (p. 178)

1. $3:1$.

3. $3:2$.

5. $9a/28$.

6. $52\cdot4$ kN, $1\cdot25$ m.

7. $\left(\dfrac{a}{2}\sin^2\theta+\dfrac{1}{1+\sin^2\theta}\right)$.

8. $5a/4$.

10. $50a/69$.

11. $a/3$.

14. Ratio of thrusts $4:5$.

15. $8\cdot54$, $3\cdot07$ m.

16. $100g$ N, $325g$ N, $33\frac{1}{3}$ cm.

18. $5a/8$, $11a/32$.

19. $707g$ N, $471g$ N m.

20. $13\cdot1$ kN.

21. 1786 kg/m³.

EXERCISES 12 (a) (p. 185)

1. $2\cdot225$ cm.

2. (a) 280, (b) 321 g.

3. $0\cdot16$ cm.

4. 75 kg.

5. $0\cdot9$.

6. 1333 cc, $7\cdot5$ g/cc.

7. $\frac{1}{4}$.

8. $7\cdot79$ mm.

9. $19\cdot5$ cc.

10. 80 cm, $22\cdot3$ cm.

EXERCISES 12 (b) (p. 187)

1. $62\cdot7$ gm, $33\cdot3$ gm.

2. $7\cdot6$; $0\cdot9$.

3. 15 cc.

4. A, $3\cdot5$ cc; B, $2\cdot5$ cc.

5. 10 cm, $6\cdot6$ cc.

6. $2\frac{1}{4}$ cm.

7. 151 g.

8. $2\cdot78$, $1\cdot83$.

9. $1\cdot6$, 10 cc ; $3\cdot2$, 5 cc.

10. 60 g.

EXERCISES 12 (c) (p. 189)

2. $0\cdot8$; $6\cdot4$ gm.

4. $\frac{5}{9}$.

5. $\frac{3}{8}$.

6. $1\cdot58$, $0\cdot53$ N.

7. 950 kg, $23\cdot1$ kN.

8. $30°$ to horizontal.

EXERCISES 12 (d) (p. 192)

1. $1:2$.

2. $\frac{1}{3}\pi r^2 w\sqrt{9r^2+h^2}$.

3. $W\sin\theta$.

4. $2:1:\sqrt{13}$.

EXERCISES 12 (e) (p. 193)

2. $V(\rho_2-\rho_1)$; $\frac{8}{27}$.

3. $1-b(1-\sigma_1)/a$.

4. $32\cdot1$, $39\cdot2$ N, $35°$ $5'$ to horizontal.

5. $3W/8$.

6. 463, 654 kN/m.

7. $0\cdot52g$ N, $1°$ $47'$ to horizontal.

9. 106 cc.

11. 1147 m², $9\cdot2$ cm.

12. $1\cdot03$ cm.

13. $5\cdot8$ cm, 969 cc, $0\cdot09$ cm.

14. 70 tonnes, 10 tonnes, 67 cm down.

15. (a) $32\cdot5$ N, (b) $4\cdot77$ N, (c) $7\cdot84$ N.

EXERCISES 13 (a) (p. 201)

1. 23 m/sec to centre of octagon.

2. $10^{-3}\times1\cdot75$ rad/sec; $0\cdot175$ cm/sec.

4. 10 rad/sec; $8\cdot16$ m/sec; $\tan^{-1}\dfrac{1}{\sqrt{2}}$ to horizontal.

5. $16°$ $40'$, $43°$ $20'$ east of north.

EXERCISES 13 (b) (p. 204)

1. $0\cdot584$ m/sec².

2. $51\cdot4$ km/h, $31\cdot7$, $47\cdot6$ cm/sec².

3. $22\frac{2}{3}$ m/sec.

4. $5/6$, $25/32$ m/sec², $55\cdot5$ sec.

5. $14\cdot52$ km.

7. 27 sec, 729 m.

8. $0\cdot5$, $0\cdot25$ m/sec².

9. 1 min.

10. 225 m, 15 m/sec, $8\cdot46$ sec.

11. $19\cdot04$ m/sec.

12. $28\cdot8$ m.

13. $24\cdot14$ sec.

14. $29\cdot4$ m.

15. $0\cdot0094$ sec, $5\cdot68\times10^4$ m/sec².

EXERCISES 13 (c) (p. 212)

1. 2·65, 7·75, 13·5, 18·5, 23·5, 26·5, 26·5, 26·5 cm/sec.
2. 50 cm/sec², 16·7 sec.
3. 0·22 m/sec²; after 67·5 sec.
4. 275 m.
6. (i) 62·5 m, (ii) 0·13 m/sec².
7. 500 m.
8. 17·5 m/sec; $216\frac{1}{4}$ m.
9. 3·75 sec.
10. 9·7 m/sec.

EXERCISES 13 (d) (p. 213)

1. $10\sqrt{2}$ km/h at 45° to horizontal.
2. 4·7 sec.
3. 7 m/sec, 45 m.
4. 17·1 m, 5·5 sec.
5. $(u_1 - u_2)^2/2(f_1 - f_2)$.
6. 76 m.
7. $(bt_1^2 + at_2^2)/t_1 t_2 (t_1 + t_2)$.
8. 0·019 m/sec².
10. 15 sec.
11. $(3u + v)/4(u + v)$.
12. $\frac{6}{7}$.
13. 19 min 19 sec.
15. 25 m/sec.
16. 3 m/sec, 0·5 m/sec², 720 m.
17. 13 m/sec, 0·6 m/sec².
18. 51·6 sec.
19. 27·1 m.
21. 10/3 m/sec, 1/18 m/sec², 43·75 m.
22. 10 m/sec, 3 m/sec², $142\frac{2}{3}$ m.
23. (i) 14·4 m/sec, (ii) 20·2 cm/sec².
24. 24 m/sec, 4/15 m/sec², 10·5, 18, 22·5, 24, 8 m/sec.
25. 6·92 sec, 1·0 m/sec², 2·0 m/sec².

EXERCISES 14 (a) (p. 224)

1. 18 m/sec, 16·7 m/sec.
2. N. $12\frac{1}{4}°$ W., 119 km/h.
3. 26 km/h, 35° 15′ S. of E.
4. N. 41° 49′ E., 26·8 min.
5. 3·7 h.
6. 84° 24′ to current; 36·2 sec.
7. 93 min.
8. 7·81 sea miles.
9. 3·8 knots, N. 33° E.
10. (a) $2\frac{1}{2}$ min, (b) $3\frac{1}{8}$ min.
11. 29 : 27 : 28.
12. 15·38 sea miles, N. 47° E.
13. N. 12° 13′ E., 10·1 knots, N. 10° 11′ W., 9·69 knots.
15. 146·8, 95·8 sea miles.
16. 26° 10′ E. of N.
17. 0·13 km.
18. 20·6 knots, E. 31° 5′ N.
19. $11\frac{1}{3}$ km/h, N. 41° 31′ W., 0·71 km.
20. 10 km/h, $\tan^{-1} \frac{4}{3}$ with A's direction.
21. 56·35 km/h, 27° 28′ N. of E., $4\frac{1}{2}$ min.
22. 35 km/h, 202 m, 36·7 m.
23. 7·29 km, 1·68 min after 3 a.m.
24. $8\sqrt{2}$ km/h from N.E.
25. 1·6 km, 4·8 min.
26. 324 sec.
27. 85°.
28. (A) 163·2 km/h; (B) 246·1 km/h; 282·8 km/h.
29. 30·5 knots at N. 20° 20′ W., 10·4 sea-miles.
30. 10° 12′ E., 11·5 km N.E.
31. 0·4 m/sec, S. 48° 20′ W.
32. 90°, $7\frac{1}{2}$ min, 375 cm.
33. 500 km/h, N. 68° 8′ W., 56·6 km.
35. (i) Directly across, (ii) 60° with bank upstream.
36. (i) 10 cm/sec, (ii) 3 cm, (iii) 1·5 and 0·7 sec.
37. $10\sqrt{2}$ knots, S.E.
38. 8·72 km/h from N. 54° W.
39. $\sin OPQ/\sin OQP$, $-\cos OPQ/\cos OQP$.
40. 62 min.

EXERCISES 14 (b) (p. 238)

1. 47·5 cm, 0° 11′.
2. $ut, vt - \frac{1}{2}gt^2$.
3. (39·2, 39·2), (49, 24·5).
4. $\tan^{-1}(\frac{16}{33})$. 112 m/sec.
8. $\sqrt{2gb}, ag/\sqrt{2gb}$.
9. $\sqrt{2gb}, ag/2\sqrt{2gb}$.
11. Yes.
12. 9·8 m/sec, 1·41 sec, 13·8 m, E. 30° 9′ N.
13. $\tan^{-1}(\frac{4}{3})$, 63·9 m/sec, 10 sec.
14. 960 m.
15. 2·08 sec.
16. 61·3 m.
17. 40 m.
18. 5·28 m.
19. 31·32 m/sec, 4·51 sec.
20. 990 m/sec, 50 km.
23. 15·5 m/sec.
24. 37 m, 34·6 m.
27. After $\frac{1}{2}$ sec, 18 m from A, 6·3 m above A.
28. 1·5h.
29. $5v^2/8g$; $\tan^{-1}\frac{1}{2}$.
30. $\tan^{-1}(\frac{3}{2})$.
31. $\pi V^4/4g^2$.
33. 268 m.
36. 0·85, 1·55 sec.
37. 73° 57′.
38. 76° 43′, $-13°$ 17′; 9·80 sec, 2·32 sec.
39. 600 m.

EXERCISES 15 (a) (p. 250)

2. 14·3 m, 5·93 m/sec, 8·45 sec. 3. 36·4 km/h. 4. 0·26 m/sec².
5. 0·15g, 0·021g, 16·1 cm. 8. 28·3g N, 60 sec.
9. 1·32 × 10³ N. 10. 4390 N, 0·269 sec.
11. g/13. 12. 48·3 kN.
13. 5·89 m/sec, 8·83 m. 14. 1/6, 5/8 m/sec², 138 sec.

EXERCISES 15 (b) (p. 255)

2. $\frac{1}{2}g$. 3. $\frac{1}{5}g$, 16·8 cm. 5. (1) 2g N, (2) $\frac{12}{7}g$ N, (3) $\frac{4}{3}g$ N.
6. 3·14g N, 1·93 m/sec, 28·2 cm. 8. 2½ sec, 1·06 m.
9. 0·58. 10. g/16. 11. g/23.
12. 7g/17, 24mg/17. 15. 1·5 sec, 2093 mm. 16. g/9, 0·3 sec.

EXERCISES 15 (c) (p. 259)

2. 5·35 m/sec. 3. 1·57 m/sec. 4. 72·5 km/h. 5. 4·5 × 10⁴ N.

EXERCISES 15 (d) (p. 260)

1. (i) $\left\{\dfrac{5MS}{9(F-MR)}\right\}^{\frac{1}{2}}$, (ii) $\left\{\dfrac{15MS}{9F+73\cdot6M-9MR}\right\}^{\frac{1}{2}}$. 2. 1 : 1 : 2.
3. 393 m. 4. 6·05 sec. 5. 443 m. 7. 2 : 1.
8. (i) 96 sec, (ii) 19 sec, (iii) 59·1 sec. 9. 5/108 m/sec², 24 000.
12. $1\frac{1}{11}g$ N, 5g/11. 13. 98·1 cm/sec vertically upwards.
15. (i) 2·55 sec, (ii) 1·28 sec. 16. 19·5g N. 17. g/4.
18. 12 kg, 20g N. 20. 0·452 m/sec².

EXERCISES 16 (a) (p. 268)

1. 30·0 km/h. 2. 98·6 km/h. 3. 9·37 kW.
4. 363 kW, 47·5 km/h. 5. 444 N, 0·42 m/sec². 6. 0·12 m/sec², 50·5 km/h.
7. 14·26 kW, 0·3 m/sec². 8. 24·5 km/h. 9. 22·9 kW.
10. 0·031 m/sec². 11. 417 kW. 12. 0·0306.
13. 31·5 kW. 14. 455 kW. 15. 2·94 kW, 0·082 m/sec².
16. 45·2 km/h, 0·096 m/sec². 17. 0·9 m/sec². 18. 57·3 km/h, 0·095 m/sec²

EXERCISES 16 (b) (p. 272)

1. (i) 400 kW, (ii) 989 kW. 2. 2·27 kW. 3. 1·77 kW.
4. 20 kg, 4000 J, 5·0 kW. 5. 24·9 kW.
6. 2943 kW, 23·4 kW. 7. 176 kW. 8. 40·7 kW.
9. 784 kW. 10. 1·43 × 10⁵ J. 11. 31 125 N, 467 kW.
12. 1·832 × 10⁵ J. 13. 2 N, 200 J, 40 W.

EXERCISES 16 (c) (p. 279)

1. 14 126, 11 664 J; 25.8 kW. 3. $6\frac{6}{7}$ m.
6. 5° 6′. 7. 0·256 m/s².

EXERCISES 16 (d) (p. 282)

1. 13 820. 2. 981² × 10³.
3. ft pdl; multiplied by (a) 10³, (b) 10⁵, (c) 10⁴, (d) 10⁶.
5. 0·042 J, 0·28 N. 6. 72·32 pdl, 2·36 ft pdl.
7. (i) 14·06, (ii) 0·746. 8. (i) 0·46, (ii) 9·2.

EXERCISES 16 (e) (p. 283)

2. 37·3 m, 23·6 m. 3. 29·7 m. 4. 69·6, 23·2 W.
6. 1045 kW. 7. 66·4 W.
8. 4000 N, 508 kW, 0·018 m/sec². 9. 0·61 m/sec², 276 kW, 59 km/h.
10. 31·9 m. 11. 6·82 kW.
12. 55·7 km/h, 155 kW. 13. (i) 375 kW, (ii) 750 kW.
14. 7·19 kW. 15. (i) 66 km/h, (ii) 14·5 kW. 16. 2400 N, 5° 2'.
17. 600 kW, 10·2 km/h. 18. 72·5%.
20. 7·07 m/sec, 500 J, before. 21. 35·6 m, 26 W. 22. 1304, 0·039.

EXERCISES 17 (a) (p. 293)

1. (a) 1·53 sec, (b) 3·06 sec; (a) 7·59 m, (b) 30·6 m.
2. 23·2 J, 28 N. 3. $1·323 \times 10^3$ N·
4. $\frac{W}{g}(u^2+v^2-\sqrt{2}uv)^{\frac{1}{2}}, \frac{1}{T}(u^2+v^2-\sqrt{2}uv)^{\frac{1}{2}}$.
5. 5 m/sec, 2 m/sec, $1·5 \times 10^4$ J. 6. 1 m/sec, 4×10^4 J.
7. $mM(v-V)/(m+M)$. 9. $3·7 \times 10^5$ N.
10. 22·4 m/sec, 63° 26' to horizontal, 5·83 sec. 11. m/M, 5×10^6 N.
12. 0·4 m/sec, 3202 J. 13. 12 m/sec, 1836×10^3 J, 3·92 cm.
14. 133 N. 16. 560 m/sec. 17. 1508 kg, 125 N.
18. 562·5 N. 19. 290 kW. 21. 200 N, 141 N m.
22. $2·90 \times 10^5$ N, 0·059 sec, $5·9 \times 10^4$ J.
24. 3280 kg, $6·44 \times 10^4$ J.
26. 55 300 N sec. 27. 2·43 m/sec, 3333 N.
28. 30 m/sec, 3600, 3780 J, 19/201. 29. 4/7 m.
30. 7 kW, 167 N. 31. 9 km/h, 5·54, 14·20 km/h.
32. 975 m/sec. 33. 654 N. 34. 2·26, 1·81 m/sec.

EXERCISES 17 (b) (p. 301)

1. 0·91. 2. 6·4 m, 2·28 sec. 3. 0·52.
5. (i) $v = \sqrt{(\sin^2\alpha + e^2\cos^2\alpha)}$ at $\tan^{-1}(e\tan\alpha)$ to plane; (ii) $m(u-v)$;
(iii) $\frac{1}{2}mu^2\sin^2\alpha(1-e^2)$. 6. 2·3 cm. 7. $5·27 \times 10^{-2}$ J.
8. 0·4 m from corner at $\tan^{-1}\frac{3}{2}$. 9. 17·7 m. 10. $\frac{1}{2}$.
11. $\frac{1}{3}$, 8·41 m/sec. 12. 1·38 m. 16. 0·605 sec.

EXERCISES 17 (c) (p. 308)

2. $\frac{m_1a}{J}\left(1+\frac{1}{e}\right), \frac{J}{m_1+m_2}$. 6. $\frac{1}{2}(1+e)u, \frac{1}{2}(1-eu)$. 8. $\frac{1}{2}$.
11. $\frac{13}{64}u, \frac{15}{64}u, \frac{36}{64}u$. 12. $\frac{3}{7}u$. 13. $\frac{1}{2}$.
14. $(1-e)\tan\theta' = 2\tan\theta$. 15. $\frac{1}{2}u(1-e), \frac{1}{2}u\sqrt{(e^2+2e+5)}$.
16. $\sqrt{(52)}$ m/sec, 46° 6' to rod. 19. $\frac{v}{\sqrt{3}}; \frac{v}{\sqrt{3}}; 1$. 20. $\frac{1}{3}$.

EXERCISES 18 (a) (p. 321)

1. $\frac{\mu Mmg}{M+2m}$. 2. 4·43 m/sec. 3. 60·2. 4. $4\pi^2$ N.
5. $8\pi^2$ N. 9. 0·59 N, 159. 10. 34·4, 28 N.
11. $\frac{2}{3}ml\omega^2, \frac{1}{3}ml\omega^2$. 12. 73·6, 756 N; 2·35 m/sec. 15. 83·5.
18. $a/b = 0·224$. 20. 105.

EXERCISES 18 (b) (p. 329)

1. 73·5 km/h.
2. 13° 17′, 0·24.
3. 71·3 km/h.
5. 0·86.
6. 63·5 km/h, 46° 34′.
7. 57·2 km/h.
8. 1·83 cm, 3000 N.
9. 34 800 N, 4·2 cm.
10. 7° 16′, 0·13.
11. 12° 54′, 0·64 unbanked, 0·36 banked.
13. 5·8 cm.
14. 29, 82 km/h.
15. 43·7 km/h.

EXERCISES 18 (c) (p. 335)

1. $3·5mg$
2. 2·62 m/sec.
3. 1:7.
4. $2mg$.
6. 239 cm/sec^2, 1·24 gmf.
7. 7 m/sec, 1·11, 3·12 m/sec.
8. String is slack at height $\frac{2}{3}a$ above O.
9. $3mg$.
10. $(gl/3)^{\frac{1}{2}}$, $\cos^{-1}\frac{2}{3}$.
12. 11·77 N.
13. $2a/3$.
14. $\frac{1}{2}\sqrt{(ga)}$.

EXERCISES 19 (a) (p. 344)

1. 32·5 cm, 1·3 m/sec, 5·2 m/sec^2.
2. 5 m, $\pi/6$ sec.
3. 75 cm, π sec, 1·5 m/sec.
4. 15·9 cm, 4·41 cm/sec, 1·57 cm/sec^2.
5. 25 cm, 27·4 cm/sec^2, 20·9 cm/sec.
6. $1:\sqrt{2}$.
7. 4·5 sec, 14·75 m/sec.
8. 25 m, π sec.
9. 8 sec, 0·39 m.
10. π m/sec, $\frac{\pi\sqrt{3}}{2}$ m/sec.
14. (i) $2\pi n(a^2 - x^2)^{\frac{1}{2}}$, (ii) $2\pi na \sin 2\pi nt$.
17. $9·88 \times 10^{-3}$ cm, $50\sqrt{2}$ vibrations per sec.

EXERCISES 19 (b) (p. 350)

1. 2·30 cm.
2. 1·26 sec.
4. 0·4 sec, 0·27 m/sec; 2·45 m/sec^2.
5. (a) $5/\pi$ m, (b) $25\pi/2$ J/sec.
7. 0·71 sec, 4·42 m/sec.
8. 2·0 m/sec, 1 m, 0·94 m/sec.
9. (i) $2\pi\sqrt{(l/5g)}$, (ii) $\sqrt{(gl/5)}$.
10. 1·42 sec, 2·45 J.
11. 0·78 sec, $4·09 \times 10^4$ ergs.
13. $8\pi/3g$.
14. $2 - \cos\sqrt{(g/2)}t$, $\pi/\sqrt{490·5}$ sec.
15. 0·348 sec, 0·00163 J.

EXERCISES 19 (c) (p. 356)

1. $\frac{5}{216}$ per cent shortened.
2. 0·356 m; 4:9.
3. 9·762 m/sec^2.
5. Lengthened $\frac{5}{54}$ per cent.
7. Gains 148 sec.
8. Gains 270 sec.
9. 30·2 ft/sec^2.
10. Shortening 0·179 per cent.

EXERCISES 19 (d) (p. 361)

1. $-18\cos 3t$.
4. 38 m/sec, 33 m.
8. $8000 (1 - 1/e)$, $80/e$.
9. 348 m.
11. 182 m.
13. 162 m.

EXERCISES 20 (a) (p. 369)

1. $3g/4a$.
2. 109 r.p.m.
3. $\sqrt{g/2a}$.
5. 4·43 rad/sec.
7. $9·87 \times 10^4$ J, 628 N.
8. 2·14 kg m^2.
10. $\left\{\dfrac{2\sqrt{3}g}{3l}\right\}^{\frac{1}{2}}$.
11. $\left\{\dfrac{2mgx}{M+m}\right\}^{\frac{1}{2}}$.
13. $2·96 \times 10^5$ J, 472 N m, 4 min.
14. 2·44 N m.
15. $g/5$.
16. 699 r.p.m.
18. $g/6$.
19. 0·2 kgm^2, 333 N.
20. $(M-m)gr^2/\{(M+m)r^2 + I\}$.
21. 2·62 rad/sec.

EXERCISES 20 (b) (p. 378)

2. $2\pi\sqrt{\left(\dfrac{13l}{15g}\right)}$.

3. $11r/6$.

4. $4b/3$ from AB.

5. $\{6g(\sqrt{2}-1)/5a\}^{\frac{1}{2}}$, $(2\cdot2-0\cdot6\sqrt{2})Mg$.

6. 17·5 cm from centre of gravity.

8. 3·07 sec.

9. 2·17 sec.

12. 35 cm.

13. $2\pi\sqrt{\left(\dfrac{185a}{42g}\right)}$.

14. $0\cdot58a$, $0\cdot076a$ from centre.

15. $2\pi\sqrt{\left(\dfrac{b^2+3a^2}{2ag}\right)}$.

16. $2\pi\sqrt{(3a/2g)}$.

18. 2·36 sec.

19. 41′.

20. (a) 4·49 rad/sec, (b) 2·8 sec.

EXERCISES 20 (c) (p. 384)

1. 100 J.

2. 200 r.p.m.

3. $\cos^{-1}(\tfrac{11}{12})$.

4. 2·82 N sec.

5. 762 r.p.m., $3\cdot13\times10^5$ J.

6. 465 m/sec.

7. 8·09 m/sec, 2·48 sec.

8. 8·37 m/sec, 2·4 sec.

9. 7 m/sec, 2·86 sec.

10. $\dfrac{(M+nm+m')a^2g\sin\alpha}{2Ma^2+mn(4a^2+ab+b^2)/3+m'(a^2+b^2/2)}$.

11. 4·47 J, 559 N.

12. 2·5 cm/sec, 1·39 J.

13. 1000 J, 12·7 m.

14. 0·9 kg m^2, $g/7$.

15. $6\cdot53\times10^6$ J, 5 per cent.

16. 2 min 4 sec.

17. 0·687 rad/sec.

18. $16\tfrac{2}{3}$ revs, 1·03 m.

EXERCISES 21 (a) (p. 388)

1. $dx/dt = kx/100-n$, $(N-100n/k)e^{kt/100}+100n/k$.

2. $k = 7$; $k > 7$.

4. $x > 0$, $y > 0$, $x > y$, $xy \leqslant 40$. $y \geqslant 3$; $6\cdot15 < x \leqslant 10\cdot87$; $x = 13\cdot3$, $y = 3$.

5. $\alpha = ka/(k+k_1)-kb/(k+k_1)^2$, $\beta = kb/(k+k_1)$, $\mu = -(k+k_1)$; $k/(k+k_1)$.

6. $1/(2\pi)$ cm/sec.

7. $k = 13$, $a = 8$, $c = \tfrac{1}{2}\pi$, $n = \tfrac{1}{2}\pi$.

9. $\pi a^2 \tan\theta$.

11. $\tfrac{1}{2}\pi v^2 a$.

16. $F = \rho\omega^2 A/g$, $v = k\omega$, $v_{\max} = cl^{\frac{3}{4}}$.

17. $1-x/a = (1-t/T)^2$.

EXERCISES 21 (b) (p. 395)

2. $dx/dt = -\lambda x$, $dy/dt = -\mu y + \lambda x$.

4. $dT/dt = -k(T-T_0)$.

6. $-g/R$.

7. $p = p_0\{1-(\gamma-1)h/(\gamma v_0 p_0)\}^{\gamma/(\gamma-1)}$.

9. $dy/dt = kx - k'y$, $x = (1/40)\{1+e^{-(k+k')t}\}$.

12. $\exp(5ak_1 t) = (2a+x)/(2a-4x)$.

13. $x = ae^{-kt}$, $y = (a+b)-2ae^{-kt}+(a-b)e^{-2kt}$.

14. $c = c_0 q_0 t(2v_0+q_0 t)/(v_0+q_0 t)^2$.

15. $2(9-x) = 9(2-x)e^{14t}$.

EXERCISES 21 (c) (p. 401)

1. $-13\cdot5+6\sqrt{3}$ J, the same.

2. $\pi k a^4 \omega$.

3. $2n\pi(a+bn\pi)$.

5. $P\pi a$, $P\pi a/c$.

EXERCISES 21 (d) (p. 407)

1. $2n\pi\sqrt{(Pag/I)}$.

4. $\tfrac{1}{2}k\ln 2$, 30 per cent.

7. (i) straight line, (ii) circle.

10. $-r^2+\tfrac{1}{2}gr^3/V^2+(V^2-gR)r^4/4R^2V^2$.

11. $\{gR^2/(R+h)\}^{\frac{1}{2}}$, $2\pi\sqrt{\{(R+h)^3/gR^2\}}$, $\sqrt{\{gR(R+2h)/(R+h)\}}$.

12. $\sec\psi/v + k\tan\psi/g = $ constant.

13. $2fs = V^2(1-e^{-2f\psi/k})$.

EXERCISES 22 (a) (p. 414)

1. 5·5, 2·87.

2. 20·5.

3. 130·58 cm, 3·04 cm.

4. 9881 m, 23 m.

5. 72° 25′ 37″, $\sqrt{(47)}$ sec.

6. 5 m, 34 (m)^2.

7. 32·9 N/m^2, 0·28 N/m^2.

8. 165 lb, 16·95 lb.

9. 1004·1 mb, 11·2 mb.

10. 0·243 cm, 0·0039 cm.

11. 49·6, 15·1.

12. 53·3, 410.

14. 32·55 cm, 2·83 cm.

15. 1380 hr, 120 hr.

EXERCISES 22 (b) (p. 422)

1. $\dfrac{\begin{array}{ccccccc} 62 & 63 & 64 & 65 & 66 & 67 & 68 \end{array}}{\begin{array}{ccccccc} 1 & 5 & 12 & 14 & 10 & 6 & 2 \end{array}}$, 65·06 in.

2. $\dfrac{\begin{array}{ccccccccc} 6 & 6·5 & 7 & 7·5 & 8 & 8·5 & 9 & 9·5 \end{array}}{\begin{array}{ccccccccc} 1 & 3 & 7 & 8 & 9 & 6 & 4 & 2 \end{array}}$, 7·81 kN.

3. 4·54, 1·97.

4. 29·85 cm, 2·07 cm.
5. 278·64 cm, 1·62 cm.
6. 24·9999 kg; 1·614 g.

7. 65·06 in, 1·33 in.
8. 7·81 kN, 0·83 kN.
9. 20° 32′ 24″·3, 1·65 sec.

10. 32·89 kN/m², 0·36 kN/m².
11. 12·13, 1·87.

12. 0·520, 0·812.
13. 168·88 lb, 21·91 lb.
14. 2131·2 m, 27·4 m.

15. 66·62 in, 2·67 in.
17. (i) 33·9 cm, (ii) 1·48 cm.
18. 3·24, 0·224.

EXERCISES 22 (c) (p. 431)

1. 4·81 cm, 5·35 cm.
2. 7·20 kN, 7·83 kN, 8·48 kN.

3. 7·87 kN, −0·07.
4. 64·82 in, 66·66 in, 68·50 in.

5. 65·04 in, 65·00 in, 0·05.
6. −0·44, 0·57.

7. −0·045, 4·0.
8. 8·66, 9, 9, −0·09.

9. 61·06 to 69·06 in, 62·40 to 67·72 in.
10. 5·32 to 10·30 kN, 6·15 to 9·47 kN.

11. 20° 32′ 24″·3 ± 0″·37.
12. 66·44 in to 66·80 in.

13. 168·88 ± 1·39 lb.

14. 30·99 to 31·81 kN/m², 29·55 to 33·25 kN/m².

INDEX

(The numbers refer to pages)